DFG

Occupational Toxicants

Distribution:

VCH, P.O. Box 10 11 61, D-6940 Weinheim (Federal Republic of Germany)

Switzerland: VCH, P.O. Box, CH-4020 Basel (Switzerland)

United Kingdom and Ireland: VCH (UK) Ltd., 8 Wellington Court, Cambridge CB1 1HZ (England)

USA and Canada: VCH, Suite 909, 220 East 23rd Street, New York, NY 10010-4606 (USA)

ISBN 3-527-27019-1 (VCH, Weinheim)   ISBN 1-56081-115-3 (VCH, New York)

DFG Deutsche Forschungsgemeinschaft

Occupational Toxicants

Critical Data Evaluation for MAK Values and
Classification of Carcinogens

Volume 1

Commission for the Investigation of Health
Hazards of Chemical Compounds in the
Work Area
(Chairman: D. Henschler)

Prof. Dr. Dietrich Henschler
Senatskommission
zur Prüfung gesundheitsschädlicher Arbeitsstoffe
der Deutschen Forschungsgemeinschaft
Versbacher Straße 9
D-8700 Würzburg

Published jointly by
VCH Verlagsgesellschaft mbH, Weinheim (Federal Republic of Germany)
VCH Publishers. Inc., New York, NY (USA)

Translator: Dr. A. E. Dunlop

Library of Congress Card No. applied for.

British Library Cataloguing-in-Publication Data:
Occupational toxicants : critical data evaluation for
    MAK values and classification of carcinogens.
    Vol. 1.
    1. Man. Cancer. Pathogens : Industrial chemicals
    I. Henschler, D (Dietrich) III. Deutsche Forschungsgemeinschaft
    616.994071
    ISBN 3-527-27019-1

Deutsche Bibliothek Cataloguing-in-Publication Data:
CIP-Titelaufnahme der Deutschen Bibliothek
Occupational toxicants : critical data evaluation for MAK
values and classification of carcinogens/DFG, Deutsche
Forschungsgemeinschaft, Commission for the Investigation of
Health Hazards of Chemical Compounds in the Work Area.
(Chairman: D. Henschler). – Weinheim : VCH.
    Einheitssacht.: Gesundheitsschädliche Arbeitsstoffe ⟨engl.⟩
    ISBN 3-527-27019-1
NE: Henschler, Dietrich [Hrsg.]; Deutsche Forschungsgemeinschaft/
    Kommission zur Prüfung Gesundheitsschädlicher Arbeitsstoffe; EST
Vol. 1 (1991)
    ISBN 3-527-27021-3

© VCH Verlagsgesellschaft mbH, D-6940 Weinheim (Federal Republic of Germany), 1991

Printed on acid-free paper.

Composition, Printing and Bookbinding:
Konrad Triltsch, Graphischer Betrieb, D-8700 Würzburg.
Printed in the Federal Republic of Germany

Foreword

The Commission for the Investigation of Health Hazards of Chemical Compounds in the Work Area was called into being by the Deutsche Forschungsgemeinschaft in 1955. Its mandate was to continue the development begun by German toxicologists in the last century and to establish a scientific basis for the protection of workers from the adverse effects of toxic chemicals, making recommendations for the establishment of MAK values (maximum concentrations at the workplace) and the classification of carcinogenic substances. Since then the scope of the Commission's activities has been extended to include the establishment of Biological Tolerance Values for Working Materials (BAT values), the evaluation of embryotoxic and foetotoxic effects and of germ cell mutagens as well as the investigation and evaluation of analytical methods for monitoring exposure and adherence to threshold values.

The recommendations of the Commission are published annually in the form of the List of MAK and BAT Values* and as a series of critical reviews** of the available scientific data such as those in the present volume. With this series of evaluation documents it is the objective of the Commission to make clear which observations, experience and considerations determined the established MAK value; the Commission does not hesitate to indicate where the available data are inadequate or to express doubt as to the validity of particular published observations. At the same time in these critical reviews the Commission attempts to draw attention to those substances for which more toxicological studies or occupational medical data are required to support the established MAK value or to justify its revision.

The MAK value is defined as the maximum permissible concentration of a chemical compound present in the air within a working area (as gas, vapour, particulate matter) which, according to current knowledge, generally does not impair the health of the employee nor cause undue annoyance. Under these conditions, exposure for a daily period of eight hours and an average working week of 40 hours can be repeated and of long duration without having adverse effects on the exposed persons.

In the establishment of MAK values highest priority is given to well documented industrial data and results obtained in studies on man. For many substances, however, data on human toxicity are not available or are inadequate and the MAK value or classification of the substance is based on the results of animal studies and short term tests for genotoxicity. In all cases the quality of the database is made clear in the evaluation document.

---

* Available from the publisher, VCH Verlagsgesellschaft mbH, D-6940 Weinheim both in the original German edition and as an English translation

** Toxikologisch-arbeitsmedizinische Begründung von MAK-Werten, VCH Verlagsgesellschaft mbH, D-6940 Weinheim 1972, 1973, 1974, 1975, 1977, 1978, 1979, 1981, 1982, 1983, 1984, 1985, 1986, 1987, 1988, 1989, 1990

The present volume is to be the first in a series of English translations of the evaluation documents described above. The documents included in this first volume represent a selection from the Commission's work in the establishment of MAK values in the last two years. Future volumes will extend the scope of the documentation and include reappraisals of the substances and their classification when new data make this necessary.

D. Henschler

Chairman of the Commission
for the Investigation of Health Hazards
of Chemical Compounds in the Work Area

The German MAK List

In the present volume reference is frequently made to the various sections of the List of MAK and BAT Values (MAK List). They are therefore described here in brief.

Maximum Concentrations at the Workplace

I. Significance and Usage of MAK Values (Maximum Concentration Values in the Workplace)

The MAK value is defined as the maximum permissible concentration of a chemical compound present in the air within a working area (as gas, vapour, particulate matter) which, according to current knowledge, generally does not impair the health of the employee nor cause undue annoyance.

The MAK List begins with an explanatory preamble which defines the significance, limitations and application of MAK values and discusses monitoring of the workplace air and the limitation of exposure peaks. The Commission's position with respect to the application of MAK values during pregnancy and the classification of substances as germ cell mutagens is also presented in this section.

II. List of Compounds

a) **Substances with assigned MAK Values**
   Section IIa lists those substances to which MAK values have been assigned together with those in Section III (see below).
b) **Substances for which as yet no MAK Value can be established**
   Section IIb is a list of substances evaluated by the Commission but for which the database is still insufficient for the establishment of a MAK value.
c) **Substances with MAK Values which have been examined for their potential hazard during pregnancy but which could not be assigned to any of the pregnancy groups**

III. Carcinogenic Working Materials
   (unequivocally proven and justifiably suspect)

A **Working materials which have been unequivocally proven carcinogenic**

A1) Compounds capable of inducing malignant tumours as shown by experience with humans
A2) Compounds which in the Commission's opinion have proven so far to be unmistakably carcinogenic in animal experimentation only; namely under

conditions which are comparable to those for possible exposure of a human being at the workplace, or from which such comparability can be deduced

Compounds in Section III A for which currently available data indicate a distinct cancer risk for humans have no concentration value listed in Section IIa) since no values have been established for a safe concentration range.

B Compounds which are justifiably suspected of having carcinogenic potential

Section III B lists substances for which a suspected carcinogenic potential requires urgent clarification. Where MAK values already existed for these compounds at the time of their classification in this category, they have been retained provisionally. Carcinogenic medicines, passive smoking at work, the formation of carcinogenic nitrosamines by nitrosation of amines and carcinogenesis as a result of the metabolism of azo dyes are discussed in this section as well.

IV. Dusts and Fumes

Dusts and fumes and the general threshold limit for dusts are introduced in Section IV.

V. Special Working Materials

Organic peroxides, gasoline, turpentine, pyrolysis products of organic materials and metal-working fluids are discussed in Section V.

Biological Tolerance Values for Working Materials

VI. Significance and Usage of BAT Values

The BAT value is defined as the maximum permissible quantity of a chemical compound or its metabolites, or any deviation from the norm of biological parameters induced by these substances in exposed humans.

VII. List of Compounds

VIII. Carcinogenic Working Materials

Contents of Volume 1

Carcinogenic Medicines
(used for tumour therapy)

1 Toxic Effects and Modes of Action

Substances with carcinogenic potential or for which such potential must be expected because of their mode of action are used as medicines in the treatment of cancer. This group of drugs includes alkylating agents, antimetabolites, mitosis inhibitors and antibiotics. By interfering with metabolic processes or destruction of cell structures they affect the genetic machinery and inhibit the multiplication of tumour cells. Since the points of attack in the tumour cell are also present in normal cells, the latter are also affected by the therapy. Thus many of these substances are mutagenic, induce chromosomal changes and, in animal studies, tumours. In patients, tumours resulting from therapy have developed particularly after treatment with alkylating agents or antimetabolites. In nursing staff who handled cytostatic medicines, sister chromatid exchange (SCE) [1, 2] and achromatic lesions [2] in peripheral lymphocytes were increased. Falck et al. [3] found higher mutagenic activity in *Escherichia coli* and *Salmonella typhimurium* in the presence of S9 mix from rat liver in the urine of seven nurses who handled cytostatic drugs than in the urine of a control group. No mutagenicity in *S. typhimurium* was demonstrable with the urine of eight hospital pharmacists who prepared cytostatics under a fume hood [4]. For hospital nursing staff Stiller *et al.* [5] too found neither an increase in structural chromosome aberrations or SCE in peripheral lymphocytes nor an increase in SCE in isolated peripheral lymphocytes which had been mixed with urine from the donor. In these studies, however, unlike in those of Falck *et al.* [3], the urine was used without previous concentration.

The data available to date on the consequences of exposure of nursing staff to substances applied in cancer therapy are certainly inadequate. Since, however, cytostatics are genotoxic and produce tumours both in animals and, occasionally, in patients treated with these substances they must be classified as carcinogenic. Appropriate protective measures are therefore necessary.

2 List of substances

A large proportion of the substances used in cytostatic therapy has been evaluated by the International Agency for Research on Cancer (IARC) [6–9]. The evaluation of the material presented here was published largely in Volume *26* (1981) and in Supplement 4 (1982).

1. Alkylating agents react with cell components including DNA causing DNA damage and thus, depending on the concentration, mutation, cytotoxicity and cell death.

Name CAS number	IARC evaluation	References
Altretamine = Hexamethylmelamine 645-05-6	has not yet been evaluated	—
Aminoglutethimide 125-84-8	has not yet been evaluated	—
Bischloroethyl nitrosourea (BCNU) = Carmustine 154-93-8	produces point and chromosome mutations in experimental systems, is carcinogenic in animals, for practical purposes is considered to be carcinogenic for man	[8, 9]
Busulfan = Myleran 55-98-1	produces point and chromosome mutations; there is limited evidence of carcinogenicity in animals; there is sufficient evidence of carcinogenic potential in man	[9]
Carmustine 154-93-8	see Bischloroethyl nitrosourea (BCNU)	
Chlorambucil 305-03-3	produces point and chromosome mutations in experimental systems; there is sufficient evidence of carcinogenic potential in animals and man	[6, 8, 9]
1-(2-Chloroethyl)-3- cyclohexyl-1-nitrosourea (CCNU) 13010-47-4	produces point and chromosome mutations in experimental systems, is carcinogenic in animals, for practical purposes is considered to be carcinogenic in man	[8, 9]
Cyclophosphamide 6055-19-2	produces point and chromosome mutations in experimental systems; there is sufficient evidence of carcinogenic potential in animals and man	[6, 8, 9]
Estramustine 2998-57-4	has not yet been evaluated	—
Hexamethylmelamine 645-05-6	see Altretamine	
Isophosphamid = Ifosfamide 3778-73-2	produces point and chromosome mutations, is carcinogenic in animals; there is no information on effects in man	[8]

1. (continued)

Name CAS number	IARC evaluation	References
Melphalan 148-82-3	produces point and chromosome mutations in experimental systems; there is sufficient evidence of carcinogenic potential in animals and man	[6, 9]
Myleran 55-98-1	see Busulfan	
Nimustine 42471-28-3	has not yet been evaluated	—
Thiotepa 52-24-4	produces point and chromosome mutations in experimental systems, is carcinogenic in animals; there are no available data on carcinogenic potential in man	[6, 9]
Treosulfan 299-75-2	produces chromosome mutations in plants; there are no other data available on mutagenicity in vitro; has not not yet been tested for carcinogenic effect in animals; there is sufficient evidence of carcinogenic potential in man	[8, 9]
Tretamine 51-18-3	has not yet been evaluated	—
Trofosfamide 22089-22-1	has not yet been evaluated	—

2. Folic acid antagonists block the reduction of dihydrofolic acid to tetrahydrofolic acid and so interfere with C_1-metabolism, which is important for the synthesis of nucleic acid bases. From a theoretical standpoint, these substances are unlikely to be carcinogenic.

Name CAS number	IARC evaluation	References
Methotrexate 59-05-2	induces point and chromosome mutations, is a recombinogen in *Drosophila*; there is no evidence from animal studies, including some with inadequate methods, for carcinogenic effects nor from studies on man which are also not all satisfactory	[8–10]

4   *Carcinogenic Medicines*

3. Pyrimidine analogues inhibit thymidylate synthetase and thus DNA synthesis.

Name CAS number	IARC evaluation	References
5-Azacytidine 320-67-2	induces point and chromosome mutations in experimental systems; there are indications of a carcinogenic effect in mice; no adequate data are available for evaluation of carcinogenic potential in man	[8]
Cytarabine 147-94-4	has not yet been evaluated	–
5-Fluorouracil 51-21-8	induces chromosomal mutations in experimental systems; unsatisfactory animal studies produced no evidence of a carcinogenic effect; inadequate human data do not indicate a carcinogenic potential	[8, 9]
Mopidamol 13665-88-8	has not yet been evaluated	–
Tegafur 17902-23-7	has not yet been evaluated	–

4. Purine analogues inhibit various enzymes of purine biosynthesis or are incorporated into the DNA as purine analogues.

Name CAS number	IARC evaluation	References
Azathioprine 446-86-6	induces point and chromosome mutations in experimental systems; there are indications of a carcinogenic effect in animal studies and sufficient evidence of carcinogenic potential in man	[8, 9]
6-Mercaptopurine 50-44-2	induces point and chromosome mutations in experimental systems and chromosome mutations in man; no evidence for a carcinogenic effect was found in inadequate animal studies; reports of individual cases of cancer in man cannot be evaluated	[8, 9]
Thioguanine 154-42-7	has not yet been evaluated	–

5. Antibiotics intercalate in the DNA and so inhibit the DNA-dependent RNA polymerase.

Name CAS number	IARC evaluation	References
Aclarubicin 57576-44-0	has not yet been evaluated	—
Actinomycin D 50-76-0	see Dactinomycin	
Adriamycin = Doxorubicin 23214-92-8	induces point and chromosome mutations in experimental systems and chromosome mutations in man, is carcinogenic in animals; unsatisfactory human data provide no evidence for a carcinogenic potential	[7, 9]
Bleomycin 11056-06-7	induces point and chromosome mutations in experimental systems and chromosome mutations in man; animal studies on carcinogenic effects cannot be evaluated because reports are incomplete; unsatisfactory human data provide no evidence for carcinogenic potential	[8, 9]
Dactinomycin = Actinomycin D 50-76-0	has not yet been evaluated	—
Daunomycin = Daunorubicin hydrochloride 20830-81-3	carcinogenic in rats after a single i.v. injection and in mice after repeated s.c. injections; no human data available	[7]
Doxorubicin 23214-92-8	see Adriamycin	
Epirubicin 56420-45-2	has not yet been evaluated	—
Epirubicin hydrochloride 56390-09-1	has not yet been evaluated	—
Mithramycin = Plicamycin 18378-89-7	has not yet been evaluated	—
Mitomycin 50-07-7	is carcinogenic in animals	[7]
Mitoxantrone 65271-80-9	has not yet been evaluated	—
Plicamycin 18378-89-7	see Mithramycin	

6. Mitosis inhibitors inhibit cell division at metaphase and, at high concentrations, produce chromosome damage.

Name CAS number	IARC evaluation	References
Etoposide 33419-42-0	has not yet been evaluated	—
Teniposide 29767-20-2	has not yet been evaluated	—
Vinblastine sulfate 143-67-9	not mutagenic in bacteria or yeasts; the effects seen *in vitro* and *in vivo* in mammals are a result of inhibition of spindle formation and not of a mutagenic effect; inadequate animal studies and unsatisfactory human data are not to be seen as evidence for a carcinogenic potential	[8, 9]
Vincristine sulfate 2068-78-2	not mutagenic in bacteria or yeasts; the effects seen *in vitro* and *in vivo* in mammals are a result of inhibition of spindle formation and not of a mutagenic effect; inadequate animal studies and unsatisfactory human data are not to be seen as evidence for a carcinogenic potential	[8,9]
Vindesine 53643-48-4	has not yet been evaluated	—

7. Other substances with various mechanisms of action

Name CAS number	IARC evaluation	References
Cisplatin 15663-27-1	induces point and chromosome mutations in experimental systems; there are indications of carcinogenic potential in one study with mice; currently available human data do not permit evaluation	[8, 9]
Dacarbazine 4342-03-4	is mutagenic in insects and *in vitro* in mammalian cells, is carcinogenic in animals; unsatisfactory human data is not sufficient evidence of a carcinogenic potential	[8]
Flutamide 13311-84-7	has not yet been evaluated	—

7. (continued)

Name CAS number	IARC evaluation	References
Hydroxycarbamide = Hydroxyurea 127-07-1	has not yet been evaluated	–
Mitobronitol 488-41-5	has not yet been evaluated	–
Procarbazine 671-16-9	induces point and chromosome mutations in experimental systems and chromosome mutations in man, is carcinogenic in animals; inadequate human data provide no evidence for a carcinogenic potential but for practical purposes is considered to be carcinogenic for man	[8, 9]
Trimethylolmelamine 1017-56-7	has not yet been evaluated	–

References

1. Norppa, H., M. Sorsa, H. Vainio, P. Gröhn, E. Heinonen, L. Holsti, E. Norman: *Scand. J. Work Environm. Hlth 6*, 299 (1980)
2. Waksvik, H., O. Klepp, A. Brogger: *Cancer Treatm. Rep. 65*, 607 (1981)
3. Falck, K., P. Gröhn, M. Sorsa, H. Vainio, E. Heinonen, L.R. Holsti: *Lancet I*, 1250 (1979)
4. Stainio, H., J. F. Gallelli, R. H. Adamson, S. S. Thorgeirsson: *Lancet I*, 615 (1981)
5. Stiller, A., G. Obe, I. Boll, W. Pribilla: *Mutat. Res. 121*, 253 (1983)
6. International Agency for Research on Cancer (IARC): *IARC Monographs on the Evaluation of the Carcinogenic Risk of Chemicals to Man*, Vol. 9, Lyon, France, 1975
7. International Agency for Research on Cancer (IARC): *IARC Monographs on the Evaluation of the Carcinogenic Risk of Chemicals to Man*, Vol. 10, Lyon, France, 1976
8. International Agency for Research on Cancer (IARC): *IARC Monographs on the Evaluation of the Carcinogenic Risk of Chemicals to Humans*, Vol. 26, Lyon, France, 1981
9. International Agency for Research on Cancer (IARC): *IARC Monographs on the Evaluation of the Carcinogenic Risk of Chemicals to Humans*, Vol. 1–29, Suppl. 4, Lyon, France, 1982
10. Würgler, F. E., Z. Graf, H. Frei, H. Juon: *Mutat. Res. 122*, 321 (1983)

completed 26. 8. 1985

Germ Cell Mutagens

1 Introduction

The term "germ cell mutagen", as understood by the Commission, is applied to substances causing hereditary disorders in the progeny due to mutational damage in male and female germ cells. The term as it is used here, therefore, is limited specifically to genetic effects on male and female germ cells, as opposed to somatic cell genotoxicity which can contribute to initiation of cancer. Furthermore, substances are only designated as germ cell mutagens when the genetic damage that they cause in the germ cells results in hereditary disorders in the progeny. This limits the use of the term "germ cell mutagen" to substances for which a cause and effect relationship exists between exposure, alteration of the genetic information in germ cells and hereditary diseases in children.

The results of animal experiments indicate that biological mechanisms exist to eliminate damaged germ cells, e.g. during meiosis. This process is termed germinal selection. After fertilization has taken place, damaged genetic material can be eliminated by death of the embryo or foetus so that the child with a hereditary disease is never born. Thus the human genetic constitution is protected from adverse modification by natural elimination of defective genetic material. During the long process of evolution, the forces of mutation and selection together have produced the well-adapted, balanced gene pools of today's species, including man. In our industrialized world the equilibrium of these processes may be disturbed in two different ways. Firstly, it may be assumed that the mutation frequency can be increased by exposure to toxic agents or to ionizing radiation. Secondly, the pressure of natural selection may be decreased, e.g. by modern medical therapy. The reduced selection pressure promotes the spread of the genetic component of multifactorial diseases within the population. It may also be particularly these diseases with partly genetic origins which are increased in frequency by germ cell mutagens. However, such an effect cannot be demonstrated in population studies. Even for monogenic hereditary diseases, the epidemiological proof that their frequency is increased by exposure to ionizing radiation or to chemical mutagens is extremely difficult.

2 Limitations of epidemiological methods

It has not been possible to date to demonstrate the existence of a cause and effect relationship between exposure to a substance or to radiation and the occurrence of hereditary diseases in man. Epidemiological studies of the offspring of Japanese parents who had been exposed to ionizing radiation in Hiroshima and Nagasaki revealed no statistically significant increase in the frequency of the selected indicators of genetic damage. In the early studies, hereditary diseases of the offspring could not be assessed but indicators with varying genetic component were used, such as embryonal and neonatal mortality including congenital malformations, survival of children until the age of 17 and alteration of the sex ratio among the offspring [1, 2].

Later studies included more specific genetic endpoints, namely structural and nu-
merical chromosome anomalies (balanced translocations, inversions, trisomy 21 and
sex chromosome aneuploidy), mutations affecting protein charge or enzyme activity
and certain childhood cancers due to germ cell mutations [3–9]. The results of these
studies did not change the original conclusion that a significant increase in the
frequency of hereditary diseases after exposure to radiation could not be demonstrated. The reason does not lie in the ineffectiveness of ionizing radiation but in the
difficulties encountered in genetic epidemiological studies. The problems include the
determination of exposure levels (which had to be revised for the Japanese atomic
bomb explosion [10]), the size of the exposed population, an adequate control population as well as the choice of appropriate genetic endpoints. A critical discussion
of these problems has appeared recently [11]. Similarly, it was not possible to demonstrate an increased frequency of hereditary diseases among children of cancer patients successfully treated with cytostatics [12]. These results seem to be in conflict
with the fact that an increase in structural chromosome changes has been observed
in germ cells of men exposed to radiation [13, 14]. However, an effective elimination
process, mentioned above, operates on germ cells with damaged chromosomes.

There are two types of epidemiological studies. Cohort studies seek to demonstrate a more frequent occurrence of hereditary diseases due to new mutations which
can be causally associated with the exposure. It is difficult to recognize new mutations because the background level of hereditary diseases must be taken into account. Familial occurrence of hereditary diseases must be distinguished from spo-
radic events which can be considered to be new mutations. Then comparison of a
control group with an exposed group reveals whether a higher frequency of new
mutations occurred after a particular exposure. The latest edition of McKusick's
catalogue of human phenotypes with Mendelian inheritance lists 4651 entries [15].
Only a small number of these phenotypic features are suitable for epidemiological
studies, namely, dominant hereditary diseases which manifest themselves during
childhood. Although a doubling of the mutation rate may be considered to be a large
effect, one cannot expect to detect such rare events as new mutations with sample
populations of a few hundred to a few thousand individuals. For some years now,
a program has been in operation in Hungary to determine the mutation rate for 25
exemplary dominant hereditary diseases, the so-called "sentinel phenotypes" [16].
This study is only possible because Hungary has a register of hereditary diseases and
congenital malformations. The average mutation rate for 15 of these sentinel phenotypes is 3.7×10^{-5} mutations per gamete [17]. It is thus of the same order of magnitude as the frequency of dominant-cataract mutations in the mouse (4.4×10^{-5}) [18].
The Hungarian program will provide a suitable basis for future epidemiological
studies in Hungary. On the basis of these data it has been calculated that 47500
live-born children would have to be examined in order to detect a doubling of the
mutation rate with 95 % confidence [19]. Since data of this kind do not exist for other
countries or ethnic groups, control groups must always be studied in parallel. As a
rule these are too small to determine the mutation rate even approximately, even
when suitable genetic end-points are chosen.

The second kind of epidemiological study of exposure-related mutagenic effects in
humans is the case control study. By very detailed anamnesis of patients with hered-

itary diseases, one can attempt to establish a relationship with possible parental exposures. It has not yet been possible with this method either to demonstrate a cause and effect relationship between exposure and an increase in hereditary diseases of chromosomal origin [20, 21].

Genetic epidemiological studies are rendered even more difficult by the fact that exposure to a particular mutagen will not induce a specific and therefore conspicuous syndrome, such as the non-genetic malformations caused by thalidomide. The nature of the genetic code implies that DNA damage and the resulting mutational events are randomly distributed in the genome and thus can lead to a random variety of hereditary diseases. The exposure-induced genetic changes in somatic cells are also random and yet one finds characteristic cancers with organ or tissue specificity in certain exposed populations. This is due to the mode of exposure and/or the organ specificity of a certain genotoxic metabolite and of tumour-promoting factors. The organ specificity is irrelevant in exposure-related hereditary diseases because the genetic changes occur in the germ cells. There is also a decisive difference in the population size necessary to detect carcinogenicity and germ cell mutagenicity in epidemiological studies. The targets for mutational induction of cancer are the billions of exposed somatic cells of the individual being studied. Thus an increase in the frequency of cancer after a particular exposure can be recognized in a relatively small population. In contrast, in a genetic epidemiological study each individual studied represents only one single exposed cell or, at most, two cells if both parents were exposed.

It is concluded that the probability of producing epidemiological proof that a substance is a human germ cell mutagen is very low, even with an optimal population study.

3 Categories of germ cell mutagens

Germ cell mutagens are to be classified into three categories:

1. substances which have been demonstrated to be germ cell mutagens in humans
2. substances which have been demonstrated to be germ cell mutagens in experimental mammals
3. substances which have been demonstrated to cause genetic damage in mammalian (including human) germ cells without proof of transmission

4 Comments on the classification of germ cell mutagens

1. Substances which have been demonstrated to be germ cell mutagens in humans

In section 2 it was discussed in detail why epidemiological studies have still produced no evidence that exposure of a particular population has resulted in an increase in the frequency of hereditary diseases. This applies for exposures to ionizing radiation and to chemical mutagens. It is not to be expected that such evidence will be available within the foreseeable future, even with further improvements in epidemiological methods. Category 1 will most likely remain without any entries.

2. Substances which have been demonstrated to be germ cell mutagens in experimental mammals

In the absence of human data, the results of animal studies must be given particular attention. It may be assumed that germ cells of humans and experimental animals react to mutagenic substances in a comparable way. There are several grounds for this assumption and they have been discussed in detail in the literature [22]. Most important is the universality of the genetic code. Genetic changes in germ cells have largely the same consequences in man and in experimental animals. In addition, the biological and physiological processes of germ cell development are common to all mammals, that is, to the most frequently used experimental animals, rat, mouse and hamster, and man. Finally, an increasing number of mouse mutants are available as models for the study of the development and effects of human hereditary diseases [23, 24]. Our ever-increasing knowledge of the localization of genetic information on the chromosomes allows us to recognize chromosomal regions which are homologous in mouse and man [25].

Often, not the substance itself but an active metabolite is responsible for the mutagenic effect in mammals. It is then necessary to demonstrate for the respective category 2 substance that the metabolite relevant in the experimental mammal is also formed in man.

Substances are to be classified in category 2 when they cause an increase in the frequency of genetically altered, live progeny in animal experiments, e.g. in a test for specific locus mutations [18] or in a heritable translocation assay [26]. In addition, substances should be classified in category 2 if they cause an increase in embryonic death, e.g. in a dominant lethal test [27]. This is an assay for progeny which are not viable because of chromosomal damage. The viability of individuals with damaged chromosomes may be markedly different in man and experimental animals. Chromosomally unbalanced human foetuses may survive until birth and longer [28] in contrast to those of the mouse. Therefore an increase in dominant lethal mutations in animal experiments must be considered relevant for the classification of a substance in category 2.

3. Substances which have been demonstrated to cause genetic damage in mammalian (including human) germ cells without proof of transmission

For many substances experimental data allowing classification in category 2 are not available but they have been tested with methods which reveal damage to the genetic material of germ cells. These methods include studies of germ cells from exposed mammals for chromosomal aberrations [29], sister chromatid exchange [30], DNA strand breaks [31] and unscheduled DNA (repair) synthesis [32] or the demonstration of covalent binding to germ cell DNA. Results of cytogenetic studies on the sperm of exposed men are also relevant [33]. It is to be expected that more and especially molecular genetic methods will be developed.

A positive result in one of these tests is proof that the substance or a reactive metabolite reaches the germ cells where it is able to induce genetic damage. This is substantial but indirect evidence that the substance can be a germ cell mutagen as defined above. Therefore such substances are classified in category 3.

5 Concluding remarks

The large-scale literature study of the U.S. Environmental Protection Agency (EPA), known as the "Gene-Tox Program", has demonstrated that information permitting a classification in category 2 or 3 is still only available for very few substances [34]. The primary mechanisms of genotoxicity and germ cell mutagenicity are largely identical so that particularly the genotoxic substances of Section III of the MAK List, Carcinogenic Working Materials, must be expected to be germ cell mutagens as well. In fact there are still no experimental data which show that a germ cell mutagen is not also genotoxic in somatic cells [35]. However, examples are known of the reverse situation where some genotoxic substances do not affect germ cells [36]. The most plausible explanation of this phenomenon is that the active metabolite is formed in one particular organ, has a short life-time and does not reach the germ cells. The principle of protection from genotoxic substances in the absence of germ cell data is upheld, in any case, by the classification of such substances in Section III, Carcinogenic Working Materials.

6 References

1. Neel, J. V., H. Kato, W. J. Schull: *Genetics 76*, 311 (1974)
2. Schull, W. J., J. V. Neel, A. Hashizume: *Amer. J. hum. Genet. 18*, 328 (1966)
3. Awa, A. A.: *J. Radiat. Genet.*, Suppl. 16, 75 (1975)
4. Awa, A. A., T. Honda, S. Neriishi, T. Sufuni, H. Shimba, K. Ohtaki, M. Nakano, Y. Kodama, M. Itoh, B. Hamilton: in Obe, G., A. Basler (Eds.): *Cytogenetics: Basis and Applied Aspects*, p 166, Springer, Berlin, 1987
5. Neel, J. V., W. J. Schull, M. Otake: in Bora, K. C., G. R. Douglas, E. R. Nestmann (Eds.): *Progress in Mutation Research*, Vol. 3, p 39, Elsevier Biomedical, Amsterdam, 1982
6. Neel, J. V., C. Satoh, K. Goriki, J.-I. Asakawa, M. Fujita, N. Takahashi, T. Kageoka, R. Hazama: *Amer. J. hum. Genet. 42*, 663 (1988)
7. Schull, W. J., M. Otake, J. V. Neel: in Hook, E. B., I. H. Porter (Eds.): *Population and Biological Aspects of Human Mutation*, p 277, Academic Press, New York, 1981
8. Schull, W. J., M. Otake, J. V. Neel: *Science 213*, 1220 (1981)
9. Schull, W. J., J. V. Neel, M. Otake, A. Awa, C. Satoh, H. B. Hamilton: in Sugimura, T., S. Kondo (Eds.): *Environmental Mutagens and Carcinogens*, p 687, Alan R. Liss, New York, 1982
10. Roesch, W. C.: *U.S. Japan Joint Assessment of Atomic Bomb Radiation Dosimetry in Hiroshima and Nagasaki: Final Report*, Radiation Effects Research Foundation, Hiroshima, Japan, 1987
11. Sankaranarayanan, K.: *Amer. J. hum. Genet. 42*, 651 (1988)
12. Mulvihill, J. J., J. Byrne: *Semin. Oncol. Nurs. 5*, 29 (1989)
13. Brewen, J. G., R. J. Preston, N. Gengozian: *Nature (Lond.) 253*, 468 (1975)
14. Martin, R. H., K. Hildebrand, J. Yamamoto, A. Rademaker, M. Barnes, G. Douglas, K. Arthur, Th. Ringrose, I. S. Brown: *Mutat. Res. 174*, 219 (1986)
15. McKusick, V. A.: *Mendelian Inheritance in Man*, 8th ed., John Hopkins Univ. Press, Baltimore, USA, 1988

16. Mulvihill, J. J., A. Czeizel: *Mutat. Res. 123*, 345 (1983)
17. Czeizel, A.: *Mutat. Res. 212*, 3 (1989)
18. Ehling, U. H., D. J. Charles, J. Favor, J. Graw, J. Kratochvilova, A. Neuhäuser-Klaus, W. Pretsch: *Mutat. Res. 150*, 393 (1985)
19. Czeizel, A., A. Kis-Varga: *Mutat. Res. 186*, 73 (1987)
20. Hook, E. B.: in Obe, G., A. Basler (Eds.): *Cytogenetics: Basis and Applied Aspects*, p 141, Springer, Berlin, 1987
21. Hook, E. B., P. K. Cross: *Amer. J. hum. Genet. 42*, 482 (1988)
22. Favor, J.: *Genome 31*, 844, 1989
23. Erickson, R. P.: *Amer. J. hum. Genet. 43*, 582 (1988)
24. Pretsch, W., C. J. Charles, S. Merkle: *Biochem. Genet. 26*, 89 (1988)
25. Searle, A. G., J. Peters, M. F. Lyon, E. P. Evans, J. H. Edwards, V. J. Buckle: *Genomics 1*, 3 (1987)
26. Adler, I.-D.: *BGA-Schriften 3*, 291 (1984)
27. Ehling, U. H.: *Arch. Toxicol. 38*, 1 (1977)
28. Schinzel, A.: *Catalogue of Unbalanced Chromosomal Aberrations in Man*, W. de Gruyter Verlag, Berlin, 1984
29. Adler, I.-D.: in Venitt, S., J. M. Parry (Eds.): *Mutagenicity Testing. A Practical Approach*, p 275, IRL Press, Oxford, 1984
30. Allen, J. W., S. A. Latt: *Nature (Lond.) 260*, 449 (1976)
31. Sega, G. A., E. E. Generoso: *Mutat. Res. 197*, 93 (1988)
32. Sega, G. A., J. G. Owens, R. B. Cumming: *Mutat. Res. 36*, 193 (1976)
33. Martin, R. H.: *Cytogenet. Cell Genet. 53*, 253 (1983)
34. Russell, L. B., C. S. Aaron, F. J. de Serres, W. M. Generoso, K. L. Kannan, M. Shelby, J. Springer, P. Voytek: *Mutat. Res. 134*, 143 (1984)
35. Adler, I.-D., J. Ashby: *Mutat. Res. 212*, 55 (1989)
36. Holden, H. E.: *J. appl. Toxicol. 2*, 196 (1982)

completed 29. 5. 89

Limitation of exposure peaks

Limitation of exposure peaks and short-term exposures

Date of inclusion in the List of MAK Values: 1983

1 Introduction

In Section I of the List of MAK Values, "Significance and Usage of MAK Values" it is explained that MAK values are conceived as average concentrations and that therefore additional measures are required for dealing with short-term exposures * to higher concentrations. These measures must take the specific properties of the substance in question into account. The Commission for the Investigation of Health Hazards of Chemical Compounds in the Work Area in the Federal Republic of Germany has endeavoured to develop such a concept.

The basis for this concept was presented for discussion as early as 1975 and 1979 [1, 2]. Both the toxicological basis and the special aspects of analysis and measurement strategy were described. The next task was to bring these two together into a concept which would provide a scientifically tenable approach for use in practice.

2 Principles for the establishment of strategies for measuring concentrations in the work area

The necessity for a systems analytical approach arises from the complexity of the task of assessing the occupational hygienic situation, a complexity associated with the technicalities of analysis and conditioned by the interaction of the parameters, emission from the process into the room air, transmission within the plant and the resulting exposure of the employees. Emission, transmission and exposure are determined by the technology of the plant, the work process and the behaviour of the workers. The monitoring strategy has to take this into account by surveillance of the technical condition of the plant, the course of the process and the safety of the workers' behaviour.

In practice, the sum of all three parameters may be assessed by exposure monitoring. Strictly speaking, however, exposure cannot be measured. In all but a few exceptional situations such as when gas masks are worn, there is a direct correlation between exposure and the concentration of the substance in the breathing zone of the worker. This concentration can be measured at regular intervals and compared with the threshold limit values. Single measurements, however, cannot give a complete

---

* In the text which follows, according to internationally accepted terminology, exposure is considered to be equivalent to the concentration in the work area

picture of the concentrations in various parts of a room and thus of the actual exposure but can only provide temporally and spatially limited samples. The exposure estimation, therefore, is necessarily subject to statistical variation. To reduce the hazards for the employees as much as possible, this element of uncertainty must be limited as far as possible by intensive attention to hazard assessment. This requires investigation of the parameters affecting exposure, that is the measurement and evaluation of emission rates, process patterns, distribution patterns of the substance in the air as well as the movements of the workers and the exposure pattern expected to result from the combination of these parameters. This analysis of process parameters must take place before routine analytical measurements are started so that the measurement procedure can be fitted to the exposure pattern to ensure that the control measurements do actually cover all the critical phases of the process.

"Measurement procedure" in this context does not cover just the analytical method but the whole programme of measurements which register exposure during the whole shift to provide representative information on the hygienic situation. In some cases measurement of the average concentration for the whole shift can be sufficient or in others it may be necessary to take repeated shorter samples for this purpose, especially during process phases which make a significant contribution to the exposure.

Calculations performed with the values obtained in the course of the shift with this measurement programme yield a result which is compared with the MAK value. In the simplest case the measured value, e.g. the mean concentration for the shift, is the required result and may be compared directly. Where several measurements were made for shorter periods the required result is obtained by averaging and, if necessary, weighting of the individual values.

Determination of the required result can be analytically and arithmetically complex, particularly when the exposure duration is shorter than the shift length or when the process is such that there are marked fluctuations in exposure. Then analytical methods with shorter sampling periods are necessary to register the exposure fluctuations. On the other hand, when the exposure pattern is known and has been evaluated in the course of assessment of known process parameters, longer sampling periods may be used.

The establishment of the measurement procedures on the basis of known process parameters makes it possible to carry out routine control measurements according to a fixed scheme and, at the same time, to follow exposure fluctuations. The short-term exposure limits given below are intended as a guide for process parameter evaluation and should formally be taken into account in measurement procedures. The appropriate assessment of process parameters is thus the most important prerequisite for the use of short-term levels.

3 Short-term exposure limits

1. Short-term exposure limits are applied in the assessment and avoidance of risks from brief high level exposures. They supplement the MAK values in that they limit the size, duration and frequency of concentration excursions above the mean

level for the shift. The nature of the permitted excursions depends on the specific properties of the particular substance. It is therefore not possible to define short-term exposure limits in terms of a single parameter; a subdivision of substances into five categories has, however, proved to be adequate.

2. For each category the short-term exposure limit is defined as the maximal allowable level, duration and frequency per shift of the increased exposure. Depending on the mechanism of action of the substance, the maximal allowable level is either a momentary value or is averaged over the period of the short-term exposure.

3. Intervals between the periods of increased exposure should be at least three times as long as the allowed short-term exposure time.

4. The categories and short-term exposure limits are listed in Table 1.

5. The decisive parameter for the effect of local irritants (category I) and of substances with an intensive odour (category V) is the concentration. It is therefore necessary to limit exposure peaks to a ceiling concentration, a momentary value which may not be exceeded.

   A momentary value which may not be exceeded even for brief exposure periods cannot be monitored in practice because a sampling period is fundamental to all analytical methods and determines the resolving power of the procedure.

   The maximal momentary value is thus intended as a limit to be observed in work area technical planning. As long as the monitoring procedures during the assessment phase have ensured by analysis of the specific process conditions for the works in question and with the appropriate analytical methods that there is no reason to expect excursions above the ceiling value, then routine control can make use of standard analytical procedures to determine the average concentration for the period of increased exposure up to the maximal short-term exposure time.

6. Most systemically acting substances are to be found in category II. The Commission has carried out detailed case studies [3] for substances in this category and

Table 1. Categories and short-term exposure limits

Category	Short-term exposure level	duration	Frequency per shift
I local irritants	$2 \cdot$ MAK	5 min, momentary value	8
II substances with systemic effects onset of effect $\leq$ 2h			
II,1: half-life < 2h	$2 \cdot$ MAK	30 min, average value	4
II,2: half-life 2h to shift length	$5 \cdot$ MAK	30 min, average value	2
III substances with systemic effects onset of effect > 2h half-life > shift length (accumulate markedly)	$10 \cdot$ MAK	30 min, average value	1
IV substances eliciting very weak effects MAK > 500 ml/m³	$2 \cdot$ MAK	60 min, momentary value	3
V Substances having intensive odour	$2 \cdot$ MAK	10 min, momentary value	4

Table 2. Variation of the short-term exposure limit as a function of the exposure duration

Category II,1		Category II,2		Category III	
duration (h)	maximal level	duration (h)	maximal level	duration (h)	maximal level
0.5	2 · MAK	0.5	5 · MAK	0.5	10 · MAK
1	1.3 · MAK	1	3 · MAK	1	5 · MAK
2	1 · MAK	1.5	2 · MAK	2.5	2 · MAK
		4	1 · MAK	6	1 · MAK

good approximations of dose-effect relationships were obtained. Therefore the exposure limit may be in the form of an average value which should not be exceeded. The subdivision of the substances into those with half-lives of less than 2 hours (category II,1) and more than two hours (category II,2) has been shown to be adequate. The value should be averaged over the duration of the increased exposure up to the maximal short-term exposure time. The reduced maximal short-term levels for longer exposures may be taken from Table 2.

The data in the table were obtained with the transition function derived in Section 4 below. It is adequate to use a linear interpolation to derive values lying between those given in the table.

7. Category III contains substances which accumulate markedly and are eliminated only slowly from the organism. In practice this group includes particularly metals and polychlorinated organic compounds (mostly insecticides). The product of concentration and time determines the toxic effect of such substances and the short-term limit is therefore an average value. Fluctuations in levels during the shift have very little influence on the effect of the substance so that adherence to the mean value for the shift is of prime importance.

8. Category IV contains substances of very low toxicity for which the MAK values were not established on the basis of effects. For these substances in the absence of substance-specific stipulations the short-term limit is to be understood as a momentary value.

4 Transition function defining the variation of the short-term limit with the exposure duration

For the categories II and III the short-term limit is defined as an average value over the exposure duration as long as this does not exceed the duration given for the short-term exposure limit. In practice, however, it is also necessary to evaluate longer exposures. Since the effects of substances in these categories are primarily dependent on the product of concentration and time [3] a relationship between exposure duration and concentration can also be determined for periods longer than the duration given for the short-term exposure level.

The amount of substance or its metabolites in the body can be approximated by a simple equation which says that the change with time in the amount of a substance or its metabolites in the body is given by the difference between the uptake and elimination rates:

$$dm = \alpha \cdot C(t) \cdot dt - \varepsilon \cdot m(t) \cdot dt$$

where dm = change in the amount of substance or its metabolites per unit time
   α = uptake factor
   $C(t)$ = concentration as a function of time
   dt = unit of time
   ε = elimination factor
   $m(t)$ = amount of substance or its metabolites in the body as a function of time

From the above equation, which represents the balance of the substance or its metabolites in the body, may be derived the linear differential equation which is frequently used in inhalation and clearance calculations:

$$\frac{dm}{dt} = \alpha \cdot C(t) - \varepsilon \cdot m(t)$$

It provides a good approximation for integrals; for differentials the factors must be replaced with functions of C and m. Since we are concerned with an integral, the linear equation is sufficient for our purposes. The solution of the differential equation for the limiting condition, $m(0) = 0$ is given by

$$m(t) = \left[\alpha \cdot \int_0^t C(t) \cdot e^{\varepsilon \cdot t} \cdot dt \right] e^{-\varepsilon \cdot t}$$

If one makes the further approximation that the concentration is constant for the exposure duration T, then the amount of substance in the body at the end of the exposure is given by

$$m(T) = \frac{\alpha}{\varepsilon} \cdot C \cdot (1 - e^{-\varepsilon \cdot T})$$

Applied to the short-term limit and the corresponding duration, the maximal amount of substance in the body at the *end of the short-term exposure time* is given by

$$m(T_{STL}) = \frac{\alpha}{\varepsilon} \cdot C_{STL} \cdot (1 - e^{-\varepsilon \cdot T_{STL}})$$

Applied, on the other hand, to the MAK value and the shift length the maximum amount of substance in the body at the *end of the shift* is given by

$$m(T_{MAK}) = \frac{\alpha}{\varepsilon} \cdot C_{MAK} \cdot (1 - e^{-\varepsilon \cdot T_{MAK}})$$

If one now requires that the amount of the substance in the body after the brief increased exposure is not higher than it would be after exposure to the MAK value for the whole of the shift, that is, that

$$m(T_{STL}) = m(T_{MAK})$$

then

$$C_{STL} \cdot (1 - e^{-\varepsilon \cdot T_{STL}}) = C_{MAK} \cdot (1 - e^{-\varepsilon \cdot T_{MAK}})$$

or if we let $C_{STL} = H \cdot C_{MAK}$ and $T_{MAK} = N \cdot T_{STL}$

then

$$H \cdot (1 - e^{-\varepsilon \cdot T_{STL}}) = (1 - e^{-\varepsilon \cdot N \cdot T_{STL}})$$

This equation expresses the relationship between the level of the short-term exposure and the elimination factor. The value of ε for each of the categories can then be determined using the appropriate value for the short-term limit.

Now it is possible to establish the allowable exposure level when the exposure continues for periods longer than the duration given for the short-term exposure level. Given that

$$T = n \cdot T_{STL}   and   C = h \cdot C_{STL}$$

then

$$h(n \cdot T_{STL}) = H \, \frac{(1 - e^{-\varepsilon \cdot T_{STL}})}{(1 - e^{-\varepsilon \cdot n \cdot T_{STL}})}$$

This transition function, $h(n \cdot T_{STL})$, decreases rapidly with increasing exposure duration. The curves derived for the three categories are shown in the figures. The maximal allowable mean concentration which, according to this model, corresponds to the MAK value for the shift can be read from the curves for a given duration of increased exposure. If the duration of the increased exposure is less than the duration given for the short-term level then the short-term exposure level should be applied.

5 References

1. Breuer, W., D. Henschler: *Arbeitsmed. Sozialmed. Präventivmed. 10*, 165 (1975)
2. Henschler, D., Th. zur Mühlen, E. Drope: *Arbeitsmed. Sozialmed. Präventivmed. 14*, 191 (1979)
3. Bolt, H. M.: *Arbeitsmed. Sozialmed. Präventivmed. 19*, 21 (1984)

completed 8. 2. 1983

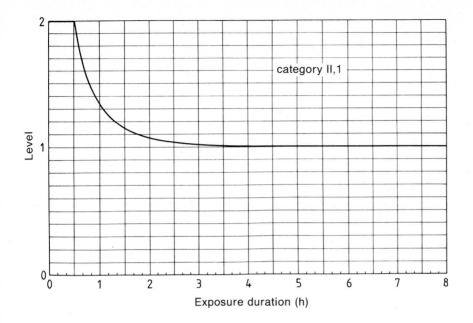

Exposure duration (h)

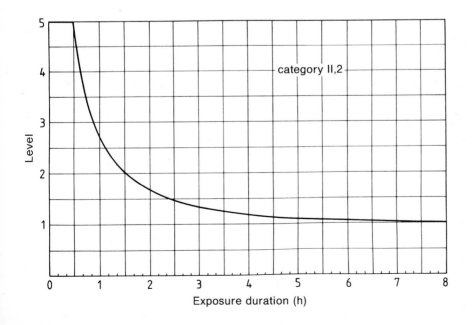

Exposure duration (h)

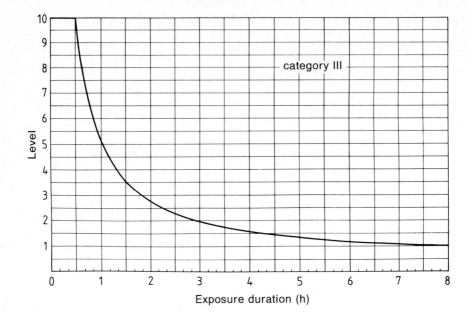

Nitrosation of volatile Amines at the Workplace

1 Introduction

Amines can be converted to nitrosamines by reaction with nitrosation agents. Such nitrosation reactions can take place even under conditions which are far from optimal and, with few exceptions, the nitrosamines produced have proved in animal studies to be very potent carcinogens. Of the about 300 different N-nitroso compounds which have been tested to date, 90 % have been shown to have carcinogenic activity in about 40 species of animals; no animal species is resistant. The doses required for tumour induction are extremely small. In chronic studies with rats, 0.1 mg/l N-nitrosodimethylamine or N-nitrosodiethylamine in the drinking water were clearly tumorigenic [1, 2]. 0.03 mg/l N-nitrosodimethylamine induced hyperplastic nodules in the rat liver after survival times of more than 900 days [2]. In a combined mutagenicity-carcinogenicity bioassay in mice, the mother animals were given 0.01 mg/l N-nitrosodimethylamine in the drinking water from 4 weeks before mating, during and after pregnancy and, together with the progeny, until week 22 after the birth. An increased frequency of lung tumours was found in the exposed progeny [3]. Although there are not yet any epidemiological data which demonstrate unambiguously that these substances also induce tumours in man, comparative metabolic studies make it seem very likely that man could react in the same way as the many animal species which have been studied to date.

2 Mechanism of the Nitrosation Reaction

N-Nitrosamines are formed in the nitrosation reaction from primary, secondary [4] and tertiary [5] amines. The end product of the nitrosation of aromatic primary amines is a diazonium salt; with primary alkyl amines a mixture of products [4] is obtained which can also contain small amounts of dialkyl nitrosamines [6]. In all these cases the first and rate-limiting step is an electrophilic attack by the nitrosating agent (NO · Y) on the free electron pair of the amine nitrogen. The amine is preferentially attacked in its unprotonated, basic form [7]. Most secondary amines react under acidic conditions according to equation I.

$$R_2\overset{..}{N}H \quad \longrightarrow \quad R_2\overset{\oplus}{N}\diagdown_{\substack{N=O \\ Y^{\ominus}}}^{H} \quad \longrightarrow \quad R_2N-N=O \qquad I$$
$$Y-N-O$$

Tertiary amines can be converted to nitrosamines by dealkylative nitrosation. This reaction proceeds via a methylene immonium ion intermediate which yields the nitrosamine after reaction with ionic nitrite and cleavage of the aldehyde group (see Scheme II). The reaction rates, however, are considerably less than in the nitrosation of secondary amines [8].

$$II$$

A reaction pathway involving methyl immonium intermediates has also been suggested for the formaldehyde catalyzed nitrosation of secondary amines [9] (see Scheme III).

$$III$$

Nitrosation of primary amines yields primary N-nitrosamines which are unstable at normal temperatures. They decompose according to the reaction:

$$RNH_2 \longrightarrow R-NH-NO \longrightarrow R-N=N-OH \longrightarrow R-\overset{\oplus}{N}_2$$

Primary aryl amines yield stable aryl diazonium ions. Alkyl diazonium ions, on the other hand, are not stable in aqueous solution and break down to yield nitrogen and alkyl carbonium ions [4, 10, 11] which can take part in a multitude of alkylation reactions. Secondary nitrosamines also arise in the reaction of primary amines with nitrosating agents although with very low yields. Thus, e.g., N-nitrosodibutylamine is formed with a yield of 0.01 % in the reaction between butylamine and sodium nitrite [12]. In the reaction of nitrite with methylamine, N-nitrosodimethylamine is formed according to the reactions shown in Scheme IV [6].

$$IV$$

Table 1. Nitrosation of secondary amines

Amine	pKa	Nitrosamine yield (%)	
		(1)	(2)
dipentylamine	11.18	0.22	—
dipropylamine	11.00	0.08	—
piperidine	10.82	—	4.6
diethylamine	10.76	—	2.9
dimethylamine	10.35	—	12
methylbenzylamine	9.54	2.8	71
morpholine	8.33	3.5	100
N-methylaniline	4.75	35	—
diphenylamine	0.79	85	—

(1) after 1 h at 37 °C and pH 2 with equimolar amounts of amine and $NaNO_2$ in HCl solution (concentrations not given) [13]
(2) after 6 h at 37 °C and pH 3 with 0.02 M amine and 0.04 M nitrite in citric acid/disodium hydrogen phosphate buffer [14]
— no data given

The yield of nitrosamine is higher at pH 5 than at pH 2. Heterocyclic N-nitrosamines can be formed from primary diamines and nitrite [12].

The nitrosation of amines is markedly pH-dependent. The reaction kinetics depends, among other things, on the concentration of unprotonated amine which decreases with decreasing pH. In nitrosation reactions at acid pH, the yield of nitrosamine is determined essentially by the basicity of the amine (see Table 1). Thus nitrosation takes place more readily if the amine is less basic.

The kinetics of the nitrosation reaction also depends on the nature of the nitrosation agent, NO · Y. The best known agent for nitrosation is nitrite, but nitrite as such cannot react with amines [11]. The actual nitrosation agent is formed in the reaction between undissociated nitrous acid and a nucleophilic catalyst, Y (see Scheme V).

$$NO_2^- \xrightleftharpoons{H_3O^+} HO-N=O \xrightleftharpoons{H_3O^+} \overset{+}{H_2O}-N=O \xrightarrow{Y^-} Y-N=O + H_2O$$

$$Y^- = NO_2^-, Cl^-, SCN^-, \text{ u.s.w.}$$

V

$$R_2NH_2^+ \underset{H_3O^+}{\rightleftharpoons} R_2NH + Y-NO \longrightarrow R_2N-NO + HY$$

In the absence of other nucleophiles nitrite can function as the catalyst. In this simplest case the nitrosating agent is N_2O_3. It may be seen from Scheme V that the reaction rate of the nitrosation of secondary amines with N_2O_3 depends on the square of the nitrite concentration. With primary amines the kinetics are like those for secondary amines; for tertiary amines the published data is still inconsistent [reviewed in 15].

In the presence of other ions other nitrosating agents are formed. $NO \cdot I$, $NO \cdot Br$, $NO \cdot Cl$ and $NO \cdot SCN$ are more electrophilic than N_2O_3 and so accelerate the nitrosation.

For secondary amines, the reaction rate of nitrosation with $NO \cdot$ halide or $NO \cdot SCN$ is proportional to the nitrite concentration and not to its square [4] as can also be seen from Scheme V.

Thus the marked pH-dependence of nitrosation reactions may be readily understood because the concentrations of both reaction partners is determined by the pH. If the concentration of free amine is adequate, the optimal pH for nitrosation with N_2O_3, $NO \cdot$ halide or $NO \cdot SCN$ is the pKa for nitrite. The pKa for nitrite is also affected by the ionic strength and composition of the reaction milieu. Values ranging from 2.89 [16] to 3.4 [17] have been published.

There are numerous other nitrosating agents, some of which have a quite different pH-dependence. Gaseous NOCl and the nitrogen oxides NO_2, N_2O_3 and NO are effective nitrosating agents, in aqueous solution even at alkaline pH [review in 15]. Nitrosation of amines can also take place with nitrite esters, in some cases even under alkaline conditions [18, 19], and with metal-nitrite complexes [20].

3 Nitrosation in the Gas Phase

The formation of nitrosamines in the gas phase under a variety of conditions has been studied by a number of authors [21–28]. Various amines were reacted with various mixtures of nitric oxide and nitrogen dioxide in the presence of traces of water to yield nitrosamines according to the reaction shown in Scheme VI.

$$NO + NO_2 + H_2O \longrightarrow 2\ HNO_2$$

VI

Secondary amines react readily in the dark to form nitrosamines; tertiary amines, however, are converted to nitrosamines more rapidly in sunlight. Practically no reaction is observed in a dry atmosphere. The nitrosation appears to take place

Table 2. Nitrosamine formation in the air [24]

	Initial concentration (ml/m³)			nitrosamine yield in the dark	after 1–2 h sunshine
	amine	NO	NO2		
diethylamine	0.50	0.08	0.17	14 µl/m³ (2.8%)	1.7 µl/m² (0.3%)
triethylamine	0.50	0.08	0.16	4.1 µl/m³ (0.8%)	9.1 µl/m³ (1.8%)
dimethylamine	0.50	0.08	0.16	~5 µl/m³ (1%)	–
trimethylamine	0.50	0.08	0.16	trace	trace

– no data given

preferentially on surfaces. In sunlight the nitrosamines formed are photolysed or photooxidized to nitramines (see Table 2).

4 Nitrosamine Formation at the Workplace

At places of work where persons are exposed to amines there are two ways in which nitrosamine formation can present a risk. On the one hand, if the ubiquitous nitrogen oxides react with amines in the workplace atmosphere, the nitrosamines formed can then be taken up by inhalation. The nitrosamine formation in this case has taken place outside the human body.

In addition to the intake of preformed nitrosamines, it is conceivable that nitrosamines are formed in the human body after intake (by inhalation or direct skin contact) of amines.

4.1 Nitrosamine formation outside the human body

The extent of nitrosamine formation in the workplace air depends on the amine concentration, the humidity, the room temperature and the concentration of nitrogen oxides. The nitrogen oxide concentration indoors depends on the concentration in the ambient air outdoors and so on the nitrogen oxide immission from the plant. The concentration of nitrogen oxides in the ambient air can vary between 0.05 and 1 ml/m^3. Combustion processes in the indoor working environment can, however, result in much higher levels. Motorized vehicles driven by gas or diesel engines and unvented gas heating systems, for example, can produce nitrogen oxides and cause the levels in the workplace air to rise into the ppm range [29].

A special case is nitrosamine formation during processing as a result of direct contact between products containing amines and nitrosating chemicals. At the high temperatures prevailing during the production of rubber products the vulcanization inhibitor, N-nitrosodiphenylamine, (retarder A) gives off NO$_x$ which can then react with the amines in the rubber mixture to form nitrosamines [30]. When vulcanization baths (salt bath curing) containing nitrite are used, direct contact with amine-containing rubber mixtures also results in nitrosamine formation. The nitrosamines formed in the vulcanization mixtures are volatile and concentrations up to 130 µg N-nitrosodimethylamine/m^3 can be measured in the workplace air in such areas [30]. Nitrosamine formation in liquids can also result in exposure by direct skin contact or by inhalation of vapours or aerosols. N-Nitrosodimethylamine, e.g., is regularly found as an impurity (0.65–17.3 mg/kg) in samples of liquid dimethylamine [31].

Nitrite is sometimes still added to metal-working fluids as a corrosion inhibitor, particularly for grinding operations. In metal-working fluids containing up to 45% triethanolamine, up to 3% N-nitrosodiethanolamine is found as an impurity [32]. Such metal-working fluids have pH values between 9 and 11 and often contain metal salts. Catalysis by metal-nitrite compounds could play a significant role here [20]. Nitrite is also added as an oxidation inhibitor to products in tins. N-nitrosodimethylamine was found in herbicides stored in tins in the form of the dimethylamine salt [33].

It is not only liquid nitrosamines which may occur at the workplace but also nitrosamine-containing particles. Thus, e.g., nitrosation of a pesticide which can be inhaled as dust produces another possible source of exposure at work. Janowski *et al.* [34] have shown that the herbicides Atrazine, Simazine and Carbaryl can be nitrosated both as dry powder as well as in aqueous solution below pH 5 by reaction with nitrogen oxides from the air. It is well known that exposure to asbestos increases the carcinogenicity of tobacco smoke [review in 35]. Tobacco smoke contains considerable amounts of secondary amines, e.g., nicotine, as well as NO_x which can be adsorbed on to the surface of the chrysotile fibres where a stable adsorbed N-nitroso compound is formed [36].

During drying of fish meal, N-nitrosodimethylamine can be formed in quantities which are toxic for farm animals [37–39]. Koppang [40] suggests that nitrogen oxides from the oil burner of the rotary dryer serve as nitrosating agents for the amines which are present in fish in large quantities.

Studies of the occurrence of nitrosamines in industry have been carried out in particular at those places where people are known to handle amines or their derivatives. The studies which have been carried out to date are summarized in Table 3. The highest exposures were found in the metal-working industry, in tanneries, in the rubber industry and in the production of rocket fuels. The highest levels in the air were about 0.4 mg N-nitrosodimethylamine/m^3. The occurrence of nitrosamines in these workplaces could always be accounted for by the presence of the corresponding amines or their derivatives.

4.2 In vivo nitrosamine formation

In the literature, it has frequently been suggested that nitrosamines may be formed in the human body after intake of amines. Stomach, urinary bladder, intestine and mouth have been mentioned as sites where amines are likely to encounter and react with nitrosating agents.

The fate of absorbed amines in the body depends on the route of absorption and on their chemical structure. Inhaled amines, e.g., are absorbed directly into the blood from the lungs or transferred to the digestive tract by the lung clearance mechanisms. Even chemically very similar amines have different metabolic breakdown pathways. 98% of absorbed methylamine but only 68% of ethylamine is metabolized in the body [49]. Dimethylamine and diethylamine [49] as well as morpholine [50] are excreted unchanged in the urine. Trimethylamine is excreted largely in the form of the oxide [51]. This means that dimethylamine, diethylamine, morpholine and trimethylamine oxide, e.g., could take part in nitrosation reactions in the bladder, but methylamine could not.

Nitrite, formed in human saliva after ingestion of nitrate, could serve as a source of nitrosating agents *in vivo* [52, 53]. In studies in which measured amounts of nitrate were ingested in food (vegetables) levels of nitrite in saliva up to 900 mg/l were found.

Inhaled nitrogen oxides could also provide a source of nitrosating agents. On being absorbed into the bloodstream from the respiratory passages, they are converted to nitrate and nitrite.

Table 3. Nitrosamine intake at work

Branch of industry/workplace	Nitrosamine	Uptake[a]	Ref.
metal working industry (turning, grinding, rolling)	NDElA	***	[41–43]
	NMOR	unknown	
tanneries	NDMA	***	[44]
rubber and tyre industry	NDMA	***	[30, 41, 45, 46]
	NDEA	***	
	NDBA	**	
	NMOR	***	
	NMPhA	***	
chemical industry:			
rocket fuel production	NDMA	***	[47]
dyestuff production	NDMA	*	[41]
	NDEA	*	
production of soaps, detergents and surfactants	NDMA	*	[41]
production of amines and pesticides	various	unknown	[29]
use of hydraulic fluids (esp. in mines)	NDBA	unknown	[29]
foundries (production of moulds)	NDMA	**	[41, 48]
	NDEA	**	
fish factories (production of fish meal)	NDMA	*	[41]
storage and sales (esp. rubber products)	NDMA	**	[30]

[a] uptake: *** > 50 µg nitrosamine/day
          ** > 5 µg nitrosamine/day
           * < 5 µg nitrosamine/day
The uptake was calculated on the basis of the highest measured air concentration at the workplace and assuming that 12 m^3 of air is inhaled per shift.
  NDElA: N-nitrosodiethanolamine
  NMOR: N-nitrosomorpholine
  NDMA: N-nitrosodimethylamine
  NDEA: N-nitrosodiethylamine
  NDBA: N-nitrosodi-*n*-butylamine
NMPhA: N-nitrosomethylphenylamine

Nitrite has also been detected in human ileostomy fluids (350–1510 µmol/kg) [54]. This suggests that nitrosating agents could also exist in the intestine. It has been demonstrated that nitrate and probably also nitrite are synthesized in human metabolism from more highly reduced nitrogen compounds [55–58]. The metabolic pathways are not known.

High nitrate intake correlates with high urinary nitrate levels [59]. During bladder infections, nitrate-reducing bacteria are present in human urine and could play a role in the production of nitrosating agents.

Nitrosamine formation in human urine, stomach juices or saliva has been described by a number of authors. Recent studies have demonstrated, however, that the nitrosamine levels in such biological materials have often been overestimated because the analytical methods used produced artefacts. One such artefact may be

Table 4. *In vivo* studies with dimethylamine hydrochloride and nitrite administered *per os* to rats or mice

Dose of amine	Dose of nitrite	Species (number)	Number of doses	Duration of experiment	Measured parameters and results	Ref.
50 ng	250 ng	mouse (∼10)	1	100 min	N-nitrosodimethylamine in the whole mouse ∼15 ng NDMA (18%) synthesized in ∼5 min	[72]
250 μg	250 μg	mouse (∼12)	1	15 min	N-nitrosodimethylamine in the whole mouse max. yield 70 ng/mouse (mean value) after 3 min	[73]
2 mg	NO$_2$ gas 44.5 ml/m^3	mouse (4)	1	4 h	N-nitrosodimethylamine in the whole mouse yield 60–70 ng/mouse (0.0034%) NDMA synthesis inhibited by ascorbic acid and sulfamic acid	[77]
					liver necroses: died:	
500 mg/kg	100 mg/kg	mouse (30)	1	3 d	none none	[78]
1000 mg/kg	100 mg/kg	mouse (30)	1		57% none	
2000 mg/kg	100 mg/kg	mouse (30)	1		93% 5%	
500 mg/kg	150 mg/kg	mouse (70)	1		57% none	
1000 mg/kg	150 mg/kg	mouse (70)	1		91% 19%	
2000 mg/kg	150 mg/kg	mouse (70)	1		91% 70%	
2500 mg/kg	100 mg/kg	mouse (17)	1	3 d	3/17 died within 24 h 9/14 survivors had liver necroses	[79]
15 mg	35 mg	rat (4)	3	5 d	no liver changes	[80]
5.9 g/kg diet (∼40 mg/d)	1 g/l drinking water (∼6.4 mg/d)	mouse	1	16 weeks	no lung adenomas	[81]
360 mg/kg	110 mg/kg	rat (6)	2	3 d	SGPT increased; increase prevented by giving 70 mg/kg ascorbic acid	[82]
1000 mg/kg	125 mg/kg	rat (10)	1	48 h	liver necroses 24× higher SGOT 19× higher SGPT 4× higher SOCT	[83]

Table 4 (continued)

Dose of amine	Dose of nitrite	Species (number)	Number of doses	Duration of experiment	Measured parameters and results	Ref.
1500 mg/kg	125 mg/kg	rat (13)	1	48 h	liver necroses 38 × higher SGPT 44 × higher SGOT NDMA yield ~40 mg/kg (3% DMA nitrosated) administration of 360 mg/kg ascorbic acid reduced NDMA yield to ~10 mg/kg	[84]
2000 mg/kg	150 mg/kg	mouse (12)	1	18 h	62% inhibition of liver RNA synthesis after 6 h; 62% inhibition of liver protein synthesis after 2 h	[85]
2000 mg/kg	150 mg/kg	mouse (4)	1	3.5 h	65% inhibition of testes DNA synthesis	[86]
1000 mg/kg	150 mg/kg	mouse (4)	1	3.5 h	64% inhibition of testes DNA synthesis	
2000 mg/kg	100 mg/kg	mouse (4)	1	3.5 h	59% inhibition of testes DNA synthesis	
1000 mg/kg	100 mg/kg	mouse (4)	1	3.5 h	57% inhibition of testes DNA synthesis	
1.47 µmol/ kg (~0.1 mg/kg)	1.74 µmol/ kg (~0.1 mg/kg)	mouse + rat	1	2 h	intrahepatic *S. typhimurium* 1.1 ± 0.4 revertants/ 10^7 survivors i.e. yield NDMA ~1.5 µmol/kg i.e. ~0.1% DMA nitrosated	[87]
0.89 µmol/ kg	0.12 µmol/ kg	mouse	1	5 h	intrasanguinous test with the yeast *Schizosaccharomyces pombe*: positive	[88]
1.5 mg/kg	50 mg/kg	rat (2)	1	6 h	increased radioactivity in liver DNA	[89]

DMA: dimethylamine
NDMA: N-nitrosodimethylamine
SGPT: serum glutamate pyruvate transaminase
SGOT: serum glutamate oxaloacetate transaminase
SOCT: serum ornithine carbamoyl transferase

seen in the study by Yamamoto *et al.* [60]. These authors demonstrated that the yield of the nitrosation reaction between diethylamine and nitrite in the presence of ethanol, glucose or sucrose is greater when the reaction is "stopped" by the addition of NaOH than with sulfamic acid. Their results and those of other groups [18, 19] may be explained by the fact that alcohols can react with nitrite and the nitrite esters produced are very effective nitrosating agents, especially at high pH. The extensively used practice of stopping nitrosation reactions by increasing the pH must then lead to increased and irreproducible background values in studies of biological material. Since this is certainly not the only possible source of error in the analysis of ni-trosamines in biological material, analytical controls are absolutely essential but frequently not carried out. Nitrosamine concentrations up to 780 µg/l, e.g., have been determined in human urine which was infected with bacteria. The samples were made alkaline, however, before analysis so that the possibility cannot be excluded that the nitrosamine measured was actually formed during the analysis [61 – 63].

Interference with the analysis is certainly not the only role of nitrite esters. They could also occur *in vivo* [15] as potential nitrosating agents at neutral and basic pH values in urine, in the intestine and mouth. Nitrosation reactions in the presence of bacteria [64], in sterile filtered bacterial supernatants [65] and in human saliva [66] can also possibly be explained by the formation of nitrite esters. Metal-nitrite com-plexes could also be involved in such nitrosation reactions [20].

There are no direct measurements of *in vivo* nitrosamine formation in man and the available indirect evidence does not come from the occupational sphere. Correla-tions between use of nitrate fertilizer and gastric carcinoma in Chile [67], nitrate levels in drinking water and gastric carcinomas in a city in England [68] as well as in a Departement in Columbia [59, 69] are explained by the authors in terms of increased *in vivo* nitrosamine formation. Urothelial tumours are directly correlated with previous chronic bladder infection [70]. Other authors [63, 71] also account for such correlations in terms of reduction of nitrate to nitrite by bacteria in the infected urine and subsequent nitrosation of the amines in the urine.

Animal studies show that oral administration of amine with nitrite can lead to nitrosamine formation [72, 73] and to induction of tumours [74, 75]. Other effects of orally administered nitrosamines are also imitated by the administration of amine-nitrite mixtures. The serum levels of glutamate-oxaloacetate transaminase, gluta-mate-pyruvate transaminase and ornithine-carbamoyl transaminase may be in-creased either by oral administration of N-nitrosodimethylamine or of the combination, dimethylamine with nitrite. The inhibition of DNA, RNA and protein synthesis which, like DNA alkylation, is caused by N-nitrosodimethylamine [76] is also brought about by the combined administration of amine and nitrite (see Table 4).

It is clear from the available literature that amines like dimethylamine and diethyl-amine which are not readily nitrosated *in vitro* after oral administration do not give rise to large yields of nitrosamine *in vivo* either. The results of experiments in which dimethylamine was administered per os to rats or mice together with nitrite are assembled in Table 4.

When diethylamine.HCl (0.5% in the diet) was administered to rats together with nitrite (0.5% in the diet) for 76 days and the animals observed for a total of 380 days, no organ damage was observed [90]. 0.3 % diethylamine in the diet with 0.5 % nitrite for 6 months [13] and 0.5 % diethylamine in the diet with 0.1 % $NaNO_2$ in the drinking water lifelong from the age of 30 days [91] were tolerated by rats without pathological changes. Fed for one year with nitrite (0.5 %), triethylamine (0.5 % in the diet) was also ineffective [92]. When, however, the same amount of less basic amines such as, e.g., morpholine (pKa 8.33) or N-methylbenzylamine (pKa 9.54) was added to the diet with 0.5 % nitrite, the rats developed liver or oesophagus tumours, respectively, which were lethal in all animals within 234 days [74]. Piperazine (pKa 5.6) and morpholine, each 0.6 % in the diet, and 1 g/l $NaNO_2$ in the drinking water induced lung adenomas in the mouse [75]. Under the same conditions dimethylamine (pKa 10.92) induced no adenomas [81].

In feeding studies, highly basic amines and nitrite added to the diet were never effective in producing tumours. Under these conditions less readily nitrosatable amines seem not to yield adequate amounts of nitrosamine because of the dilution effect or competition for the nitrite in reactions with other dietary constituents [74]. After oral administration of dimethylamine and nitrite to fasting animals, however, *in vivo* N-nitrosodimethylamine formation could be demonstrated (see Table 4). Likewise, nitrosamine formation was found when 50 mg/kg diethylamine was administered to the rat by gastric intubation with 50 mg/kg $NaNO_2$. Half an hour after administration of the amine, the stomach homogenate contained 210 µg N-nitrosodiethylamine/kg [93]. When, however, 20 mg/kg N-methylbenzylamine with 20 mg/kg nitrite was administered under the same conditions the yield of nitrosamine was 1500 µg/kg.

One of the substances which is said to be able to inactivate nitrite in the stomach is ascorbic acid [94]. The induction of lung adenomas by piperazine or morpholine is inhibited by ascorbic acid in a dose-dependent manner [75]. *In vivo* synthesis of N-nitrosodimethylamine is also inhibited by ascorbic acid (see Table 4). The substance must be in the stomach simultaneously with the nitrite in order to inhibit the amine-nitrite induction of hepatotoxicity. It has no effect on the hepatotoxicity of preformed nitrosamines [82].

In studies in which the amine and the nitrite are administered separately (e.g., amine in the diet and nitrite in the drinking water) it is probable that the reaction partners do not often appear simultaneously in the stomach. Epstein [95] has demonstrated that the hepatotoxicity is much less if the mouse is given the nitrite by gavage half an hour before the amine whereas if the amine is given half an hour before the nitrite, the toxic effect is still marked. The amine must be available for reaction in the rat stomach for much longer than the nitrite [96].

Fong *et al.* [97] have investigated further the effect of bladder infection on tumour induction. Rats were given aminopyrine (0.5 g/l) and $NaNO_3$ (0.5 g/l) in the drinking water, 5 days weekly for 80 weeks. Without induced bladder infection, there was no organ damage. Tumours developed in animals with chronic bladder infection whether or not they had been given the amine-nitrate mixture. In two from the group of 50 infected animals which had been given no amine or nitrate in the drinking water, malignant lymphomas were found in the mesenteric lymph nodes. In the 100 infected animals which had been given amine and nitrate in the drinking water there were four malignant mesenteric lymphomas, one gastric adenocarcinoma, one carcinoma of the seminal vesicle and one bronchial carcinoma. These data demonstrate unambiguously the connection between bladder infection and tumour development. A relationship between amine-nitrate in the drinking water and tumour development was not revealed, probably because of the presence of sufficient amine and nitrate in the normal diet.

There is no longer any doubt that nitrosamine formation can occur *in vivo* if amine and nitrite are present simultaneously. Whether tumour development is the result seems to depend on the extent of the nitrosamine formation. If highly basic amines which yield very little nitrosamine are added to the diet, no tumours develop. Tumour production under the same conditions, but with readily nitrosatable amines, has been described repeatedly.

In vivo production of nitrosamines is also conceivable after simultaneous inhalation of amine and nitrogen oxides or on inhalation of nitrogen oxides after previous exposure to amines. A study in which rats inhaled dimethylamine and NO_2 did reveal a slight increase in tumours but the increase was not statistically significant [98]. Combined inhalation of dimethylamine (0.05 mg/m^3), NO_2 (0.3 mg/m^3) and N-nitrosodimethylamine (0.08 mg/m^3) produced markedly higher tumour frequencies in male animals than were found in the control group which inhaled N-nitrosodimethylamine (0.08 mg/m^3) alone. Epstein *et al.* [99] describe the formation of N-nitrosomorpholine after oral administration of morpholine (2 mg) and subsequent NO_2 inhalation (2–50 ml/m^3). The formation of N-nitrosodimethylamine was observed by Uozumi *et al.* [100] after oral or i.v. administration of very readily nitrosated aminopyrine (17–100 mg) with subsequent NO_2 inhalation (25–100 ml/m^3).

5 Mutagenic Products of Nitrosation Reactions

The simultaneous administration of dimethylamine and nitrite to *Drosophila melanogaster* caused an increase in sex-linked recessive lethal mutations above that produced by the administration of dimethylamine alone [101].

Salmonella typhimurium was injected i.v. into mice and rats. Ten minutes later the animals were given dimethylamine hydrochloride solution by gavage. Two hours later the animals were killed and dilutions of the liver homogenate plated out for the determination of revertants and surviving bacteria. Dimethylamine was only mutagenic in this test when nitrite was also administered to the animals immediately after the amine and also by gavage [87]. In a similar test with *Schizosaccharomyces pombe* injected i.v. into mice dimethylamine and nitrite administered together were also mutagenic [88].

Combined with nitrite, the primary amines, methylamine and ethylamine, are mutagenic in *Escherichia coli* without metabolic activation. Isopropylamine with nitrite is not mutagenic [102]. Methylamine combined with nitrite methylates DNA *in vitro* [103]. It has been suggested that these results may be accounted for by the direct production of an alkylation agent in the reaction between the primary amine and nitrite.

6 Manifesto

Model experiments demonstrate that the reaction between amines and nitrogen oxides in the air can yield N-nitroso compounds. Numerous measurements at places of work prove that exposure to nitrosamines takes place where amines or amine-containing products are manufactured or processed. The details of the kinetics of nitrosation in the atmosphere have not yet been studied under realistic conditions.

At present it is not possible to say whether or not there is an additional risk associated with *in vivo* formation of nitrosamines in persons exposed to amines.

The nitrosation reaction, *in vivo* and *in vitro*, is influenced by numerous catalysts and inhibitors and can take place under a very wide range of conditions. It is at present not possible to predict whether or how much nitrosamine formation is to be expected for a given amine intake. In animal studies the yields of nitrosamine are mostly markedly larger than would be predicted from simple kinetics [72, 104, 105] but the difficulties of analysis in biological materials allow us to draw the logical conclusions from these results only with reservations.

For man the risk of *in vivo* nitrosamine formation seems to be higher when he is exposed to high concentrations of nitrate and simultaneously suffers from a bladder infection [59, 68, 70]. The extent of nitrosation of absorbed amines also seems to be higher when the nitrite concentration in saliva is high and the stomach is empty. There are no studies of nitrosamine formation in persons inhaling amines or absorbing them through the skin.

7 References

1. Peto, R.: *Nitrosamines and Human Cancer*, paper given at Banbury Meeting, based on the BIBRA study, 1982
2. Crampton, R. F: *Oncology 37*, 251 (1980)
3. Anderson, L. M., L. J. Priest, J. M. Budinger: *J. nat. Cancer Inst. 62*, 1553 (1979)
4. Ridd, J. H.: *Quart. Rev. chem. Soc. 15*, 418 (1961)
5. Hein, G. E.: *J. chem. Educ. 40*, 181 (1963)
6. Obiedzinski, M. W., J. S. Wishnok, S. R. Tannenbaum: *Food Cosmet. Toxicol. 18*, 585 (1980)
7. Hughes, E. D., C. K. Ingold, J. H. Ridd: *J. chem. Soc.* 58 (1958)
8. Smith, P. A. S., R. N. Loeppky: *J. Amer. chem. Soc. 89*, 1147 (1967)
9. Keefer, L. K., P. P. Roller: *Science 181*, 1245 (1973)
10. Austin, A. T.: *Nature (Lond.) 188*, 1086 (1960)
11. Austin, A. T.: *Sci. Progr. 49*, 619 (1961)
12. Warthesen, J. J., R. A. Scanlan, D. D. Bills, L. M. Libby: *J. Agric. Food Chem. 23*, 898 (1975)
13. Sander, J., F. Schweinsberg, H.-P. Menz: *Hoppe-Seylers Z. physiol. Chem. 349*, 1691 (1968)
14. Ziebarth, D.: *Arch. Geschwulstforsch. 43*, 42 (1974)
15. Challis, B. C., J. A. Challis: in Patai, S. (Ed.): *The Chemistry of Amino, Nitroso and Nitro Compounds and Their Derivatives*, p 1151, Interscience, John Wiley & Sons, New York, USA, 1982
16. Cachaza, J. M., J. Casado, A. Castro, M. A. L. Quintela: *Z. Krebsforsch. 91*, 279 (1978)
17. Mirvish, S. S.: *J. nat. Cancer Inst. 44*, 633 (1970)
18. Challis, B. C., D. E. G. Shuker: *J. chem. Soc. Chem. Commun.* 315 (1979)
19. Challis, B. C., J. R. Outram, D. E. G. Shuker: *IARC Sci. Publ. No. 31*, 43 (1980)
20. Croisy, A. F., J. C. Fanning, L. K. Keefer, B. W. Slavin, S.-J. Uhm: *IARC Sci. Publ. No. 31*, 83 (1980)

21. Hanst, P. L., J. W. Spence, M. Miller: *Environm. Sci. Technol. 11*, 403 (1977)
22. Gehlert, P., W. Rolle: *Experientia (Basel) 33*, 579 (1977)
23. Tuazon, E. C., A. M. Winer, R. A. Graham, J. P. Schmid, J. N. Pitts: *Environm. Sci. Technol. 12*, 954 (1978)
24. Pitts, J. N., D. Grosjean, K. van Cauwenberghe, J. P. Schmid, D. R. Fitz: *Environm. Sci. Technol. 12*, 946 (1978)
25. Glasson, W. A.: *Environm. Sci. Technol. 13*, 1145 (1979)
26. Pitts, J. N. (Jr.): *Phil. Trans. A 290*, 551 (1979)
27. Crosby, D. G., J. R. Humphrey, K. W. Moilanen: *Chemosphere 9*, 51 (1980)
28. Geiger, G., J. R. Huber: *Helv. chim. Acta 64*, 989 (1981)
29. Spiegelhalder, B.: in Deutsche Forschungsgemeinschaft (DFG): *Das Nitrosamin-Problem*, p 27, Verlag Chemie GmbH, D-6940 Weinheim, 1983
30. Spiegelhalder, B., R. Preussmann: *Carcinogenesis 4*, 1147 (1983)
31. Spiegelhalder, B., G. Eisenbrand, R. Preussmann: *Angew. Chem. 90*, 379 (1978)
32. Fan, T. Y., J. Morrison, D. P. Rounbehler, R. Ross, D. H. Fine, W. Miles, N. P. Sen: *Science 196*, 70 (1977)
33. Ross, R. D., J. Morrison, D. P. Rounbehler, S. Fan, D. H. Fine: *J. agric. Food Chem. 25*, 1416 (1977)
34. Janzowski, C., R. Klein, R. Preussmann: *IARC Sci. Publ. No. 31*, 329 (1981)
35. Deutsche Forschungsgemeinschaft (DFG): „Asbest-Feinstaub und asbesthaltiger Feinstaub (Nachtrag)", in Henschler, D. (Ed.): *Gesundheitsschädliche Arbeitsstoffe. Toxikologisch-arbeitsmedizinische Begründung von MAK-Werten*, 6th issue, Verlag Chemie GmbH, D-6940 Weinheim, 1978
36. Mouvier, G., J. P. Contour, I. Guérin: *Proc. 1st Europ. Symp. Phys.-chem. Behav. Atmos. Pollut.*, 1979, Commun. Europ. Communities, Rep. ISS EUR 6621, p 210, 1980
37. Koppang, N.: *Nord. Vet.-Med. 16*, 305 (1964)
38. Juszkiewicz, T., B. Kowalski: *IARC Sci. Publ. No. 14*, 375 (1976)
39. Mirna, A., K. Harada, U. Rapp, H. Kaufmann: *Fleischwirtschaft 56*, 1014 (1976)
40. Koppang, N.: *Amer. J. Path. 74*, 95 (1974)
41. Rounbehler, D. P., J. M. Fajen: *Report NIOSH Contract No. 210-77-0100*, Cincinnati, Ohio 45226, USA, 1982
42. Loeppky, R.: in Deutsche Forschungsgemeinschaft (DFG): *Das Nitrosamin-Problem*, p 305, Verlag Chemie GmbH, D-6940 Weinheim, 1983
43. Spiegelhalder, B., M. Hartung, R. Preussmann: *IARC Sci. Publ. No. 57*, 943 (1984)
44. Rounbehler, D. P., I. S. Krull, U. E. Goff, K. M. Mills, J. Morrison, G. S. Edwards, D. H. Fine, J. M. Fajen, G. A. Carson, V. Rheinhold: *Food Cosmet. Toxicol. 17*, 487 (1979)
45. Fajen J. M., G. A. Carson, D. P. Rounbehler, T. Y. Fan, R. Vita, U. E. Goff, M. H. Wolf, G. S. Edwards, D. H. Fine, V. Rheinhold, K. Biemann: *Science 205*, 1262 (1979)
46. Nutt, A.: *Scand. J. Work Environm. Hlth 9, Suppl. 2*, 49 (1983)
47. Fine, D. H., D. P. Rounbehler, E. D. Pellizari, J. E. Bunch, R. W. Berkley, J. McCrae, J. T. Bursey, E. Sawicki, K. Krost, G. A. DeMarrais: *Bull. environm. Contam. Toxicol. 15*, 739 (1976)
48. Spiegelhalder, B.: *Scand. J. Work Environm. Hlth 9, Suppl. 2*, 15 (1983)
49. Rechenberger, J.: *Hoppe-Seylers Z. physiol. Chem. 265*, 275 (1940)
50. Maller, R. K., C. Heidelberger: *Cancer Res. 17*, 296 (1957)
51. Benoit, C. J., E. R. Norris: *J. biol. Chem. 158*, 433 (1945)
52. Spiegelhalder, B., G. Eisenbrand, R. Preussmann: *Food Cosmet. Toxicol. 14*, 545 (1976)
53. Tannenbaum, S. R., M. Weisman, D. Fett: *Food Cosmet. Toxicol. 14*, 549 (1976)
54. Tannenbaum, S. R., D. Fett, V. R. Young, P. D. Land, W. R. Bruce: *Science 200*, 1487 (1978)
55. Green, L. C., S. R. Tannenbaum, P. Goldman: *Science 212*, 56 (1981)
56. Green, L. C., K. Ruiz de Luzuriaga, D. A. Wagner, W. Rand, N. Istfan, V. R. Young, S. R. Tannenbaum: *Proc. nat. Acad. Sci. (Wash.) 78*, 7764 (1981)
57. Wagner, D. A., V. R. Young, S. R. Tannenbaum: *Proc. nat. Acad. Sci. (Wash.) 80*, 4518 (1983)
58. Wagner, D. A., D. S. Schultz, W. M. Deen, V. R. Young, S. R. Tannenbaum: *Cancer Res. 43*, 1921 (1983)
59. Hawksworth, G., M. J. Hill, G. Gordillo, C. Cuello: *IARC Sci. Publ. No. 9*, 229 (1975)

60. Yamamoto, M., T. Yamada, A. Tanimura: *J. Food Hyg. Soc. Jap. 20*, 15 (1979)
61. Brooks, J. B., W. B. Cherry, L. Thacker, C. C. Alley: *J. infect. Dis. 126*, 143 (1972)
62. Eisenbrand, G., E. von Rappardt, R. Zappe, R. Preussmann: *IARC Sci. Publ. No. 14*, 65 (1976)
63. Hicks, R. M., T. A. Gough, C. L. Walters: *IARC Sci. Publ. No. 19*, 465 (1978)
64. Sander, J.: *Hoppe-Seylers Z. physiol. Chem. 349*, 429 (1968)
65. Collins-Thompson, D. L., N. P. Sen, B. Aris, L. Schwinghamer: *Canad. J. Microbiol. 18*, 1968 (1972)
66. Tannenbaum, S. R., M. C. Archer, J. S. Wishnok, W. W. Bishop: *J. nat. Cancer Inst. 60*, 251 (1978)
67. Zaldivar, R.: *Experientia (Basel) 33*, 264 (1977)
68. Hill, M. J., G. Hawksworth, G. Tattersall: *Brit. J. Cancer 28*, 562 (1973)
69. Cuello, C., P. Correa, W. Haenszel, G. Cordillo, C. Brown, M. Archer, S. Tannenbaum: *J. nat. Cancer Inst. 57*, 1015 (1976)
70. Schöll, H., P. Narath: *Z. Urol. 69*, 123 (1976)
71. Hill, M. J., G. Hawksworth: *IARC Sci. Publ. No. 3*, 116 (1972)
72. Rounbehler, D. P., R. Ross, D. H. Fine, Z. M. Iqbal, S. S. Epstein: *Science 197*, 917 (1977)
73. Iqbal, Z. M., S. S. Epstein, I. S. Krull, U. Goff, K. Mills, D. H. Fine: *IARC Sci. Publ. No. 31*, 169 (1980)
74. Sander, J., G. Bürkle: *Z. Krebsforsch. 73*, 54 (1969)
75. Mirvish, S. S., A. Cardesa, L. Wallcave, P. Shubik: *Proc. Amer. Ass. Cancer Res. 14*, 102 (1973)
76. Villa-Trevino, S.: *Biochem. J. 105*, 625 (1967)
77. Iqbal, Z. M., K. Dahl, S. S. Epstein: *J. nat. Cancer Inst. 67*, 137 (1981)
78. Asahina, S., M. A. Friedman, E. Arnold, G. N. Millar, M. Mishkin, Y. Bishop, S. S. Epstein: *Cancer Res. 31*, 1201 (1971)
79. Pollard, M., N. Sharon, C. F. Chang: *Proc. Soc. exp. Biol. (N.Y.) 140*, 1073 (1972)
80. Lijinsky, W., M. Greenblatt: *Nature new Biol. 236*, 177 (1972)
81. Greenblatt, M., S. Mirvish, B. T. So: *J. nat. Cancer Inst. 46*, 1029 (1971)
82. Kamm, J. J., T. Dashman, A. H. Conney, J. J. Burns: *IARC Sci. Publ. No. 9*, 200 (1975)
83. Astill, B. D., L. T. Mulligan: *Food Cosmet. Toxicol. 15*, 167 (1977)
84. Cardesa, A., S. S. Mirvish, G. T. Haven, P. Shubik: *Proc. Soc. exp. Biol. (N.Y.) 145*, 124 (1974)
85. Friedman, M. A., G. Millar, M. Sengupta, S. Epstein: *Experientia (Basel) 28*, 21 (1972)
86. Friedman, M. A., J. Staub: *Mutat. Res. 37*, 67 (1976)
87. Whong, W.-Z., N. D. Speciner, G. S. Edwards: *Environm. Mutag. 1*, 277 (1979)
88. Barale, R., D. Zucconi, N. Loprieno: *Mutat. Res. 85*, 57 (1981)
89. Meier-Bratschi, A., C. Schlatter: *Mitt. Lebensmittel Hyg. 72*, 71 (1981)
90. Sander, J., F. Schweinsberg: *Zbl. Bakt., I. Abt. Orig. B 156*, 321 (1972)
91. Druckrey, H., D. Steinhoff, H. Beuthner, H. Schneider, P. Klärner: *Arzneimittel-Forsch. 13*, 320 (1963)
92. Schweinsberg, F., J. Sander: *Hoppe-Seylers Z. physiol. Chem. 353*, 1671 (1972)
93. Schweinsberg, F.: *IARC Sci. Publ. No. 9*, 80 (1974)
94. Bunton, C. A., H. Dahn, L. Loewe: *Nature (Lond.) 183*, 163 (1959)
95. Epstein, S. S.: *IARC Sci. Publ. No. 3*, 109 (1972)
96. Mirvish, S. S., K. Patil, P. Ghadirian, V. R. G. Kommineni: *J. nat. Cancer Inst. 54*, 869 (1975)
97. Fong, L. Y. Y., F. W. T. Wong, W. C. Chan: *IARC Sci. Publ. No. 31*, 693 (1980)
98. Benemansky, V. V., V. M. Prusakov, M. E. Leshchenko: *Vop. Onkol. 27*, 56 (1981)
99. Epstein, S. S., Z. M. Iqbal, M. D. Johnson: *IARC Sci. Publ. No. 31*, 195 (1980)
100. Uozumi, M., T. Kusumoto, T. Kimura, A. Nakamura, T. Nakajima: *IARC Sci. Publ. No. 41*, 425 (1982)
101. Blijleven, W. G. H.: *Mutat. Res. 64*, 128 (1979)
102. Hussain, S., L. Ehrenberg: *Mutat. Res. 26*, 419 (1974)
103. Kriek, E., P. Emmelot: *Biochim. biophys. Acta 91*, 59 (1964)
104. Mirvish, S. S.: *Toxicol. appl. Pharmacol. 31*, 325 (1975)
105. Mysliwy, T. S., E. L. Wick, M. C. Archer, R. C. Shank, P. M. Newberne: Brit. J. Cancer *30*, 279 (1974)

completed 19. 3. 1984

Passive Smoking at Work

1 Introductory Remarks

In 1985 the List of Maximum Concentrations at the Workplace (MAK list) [1] itemized 132 substances or mixtures with unequivocally proven or justifiably suspect carcinogenic effects. The carcinogenic effectiveness of these substances varies markedly, ranging from that of substances like aniline, bitumen and hydrazine which have very weak carcinogenic effects, only demonstrable with very high doses in animal studies, to that of, e.g., bis-chloromethyl ether, which has been shown to be extremely carcinogenic for man as well. There is also an extraordinarily wide range of effectiveness among the many products of pyrolysis of organic material, discussed in their own section in the MAK list. Since our ability to estimate the cancer risk for man from the results of animal studies is still very limited, the Commission for the Investigation of Health Hazards of Chemical Compounds in the Work Area of the Federal Republic of Germany has included in the list of carcinogenic working materials, on principle, also those substances and mixtures which have probably only very weak effects in man.

The marked carcinogenic effect of actively inhaled cigarette smoke has been known for many years. Extensive prospective epidemiological studies have produced reliable quantitative data on the risks for active smokers of cigarettes, pipes and cigars. Several epidemiological studies have suggested that involuntary inhalation of tobacco smoke, particularly cigarette smoke, by non-smokers ("passive smoking") is associated with a cancer risk. Since people smoke in many work environments and non-smokers too are exposed to sometimes excessive amounts of tobacco smoke, the Commission has examined in detail the significance of the epidemiological findings for the cancer risk at work. This was necessary in particular because the carcinogenic effect of tobacco smoke adds to, and probably even potentiates the effect of other occupational carcinogens, as has been shown, for example, for the combination asbestos and actively inhaled tobacco smoke (reviewed in [2]). The following report is a state of the art review drawn up by members of the Commission. It discusses exposure conditions and the currently available epidemiological studies, in particular the controversy as to the validity and significance of the findings. The third section goes into the available analytical data and the carcinogenic effectiveness of known components of tobacco smoke in animals. Finally the considerations behind the Commission's brief comment in the MAK list on "Passive Smoking at the Workplace" are presented.

2 Exposure conditions

2.1 The most important toxic principles and their occurrence in mainstream and sidestream tobacco smoke

Passively inhaled tobacco smoke is not like the usual substances handled in industrial processes but is a mixture present in the air of work environments where people smoke. The compounds it contains are mostly derived from so-called sidestream smoke which is emitted into the air by burning cigarettes, cigars or pipes during the puff intervals. Mainstream smoke, on the other hand, is that which is actively inhaled by the smoker. The smoke components which are not absorbed or retained in the respiratory passages of the active smoker are breathed out into the air where they mix with the diluted sidestream smoke (passive smoke). Individual differences in smoking technique determine how much of the toxic mixture in the mainstream smoke is retained by the smoker. During the puff intervals the active smoker too inhales diluted sidestream smoke. In this context it should be noted that burning tobacco, e.g. a cigarette, produces during the puff intervals a volume of sidestream smoke which is four times the volume inhaled by the active smoker with the mainstream [3].

Of the numerous and incompletely known constituents of tobacco smoke, only few have been determined quantitatively in mainstream and sidestream smoke. The principle toxic substances known to date and their quantities in mainstream and sidestream smoke are shown in Tables 1 and 2 [3]. They differ quantitatively but not qualitatively, a fact which is reflected in the data for the distribution of substances between mainstream and sidestream smoke and which is important in the evaluation of adverse effects on health. In sidestream smoke volatile components, e.g., are present in up to 100 times higher concentrations than in mainstream smoke so that a passive smoker – even after the smoke has been extensively diluted in the air – inhales the volatile substances in amounts not really different from those inhaled by

Table 1. Amounts of the principal non-carcinogenic substances in the mainstream and sidestream smoke of one cigarette (from [3])

Boiling point (°C)		Mainstream smoke	Sidestream smoke	$\dfrac{\text{Sidestream}}{\text{Mainstream}}$	Ref.
−192	CO	13–22 mg	46–61 mg	2.5–4.7	[4]
~246	nicotine	1.33–1.83 mg	3.87–4.31 mg	2.11–3.24	[5]
−152	NO	n.s	2–3 mg	4–10	[6]
		n.s	2.7 mg	n.s.	[7]
	nitrogen oxides	14 µg	51 µg	3.6	[8]
~−33	NH$_3$	0.16 mg	7.4 mg	46	[8]
		0.0794–0.131 mg	5.14–5.77 mg	44–73	[9]
		0.055 mg	5.781 mg	105	[10]
		0.050 mg	5.3–8.5 mg	106–170	[4]

Table 2. Amounts of the principal carcinogens, proven or highly suspect, in the mainstream and sidestream smoke of one cigarette (from [3])

Boiling point (°C)	Amount per cigarette in mainstream smoke	in sidestream smoke	Sidestream / Mainstream	Ref.	Section of MAK list [1]
dry condensate	31.0–33.3 mg	43.1–58.0 mg	1.29–1.87	[5]	–
	31.4 mg	52.0 mg	1.66	[11]	
52 acrolein	70 µg	925 µg	~12	[7, 12]	IIa
	(25–140) µg				
−19 formaldehyde	30 µg	1526 µg	~51	[7, 13]	III B
	(20–90) µg				
– N-nitrosonornicotine	0.24–3.70 µg	0.15–6.1 µg	0.48–7.1	[14]	–
184 aniline	0.364 µg	10.8 µg	29.7	[15]	III B
765 cadmium	0.10–0.12 µg	0.43–0.72 µg	3.6–7.2	[16]	III B, III A2)
2800 nickel	0.02–0.08 µg	0.62–1.03 µg	12.9–31.0	[16]	III A1)
475 benzo[a]pyrene	38 ng	131 ng	3.5	[11]	Vd
	12 ng	25 ng	2.1	[17–19]	
113 hydrazine	32 ng	n.s.	3	[20]	III A2)
435 benz[a]anthracene	30 ng	81 ng	2.7	[17–19]	–
	2.6–51.7 ng	204–612 ng		[23]	
214 N-nitrosopyrrolidine	3.1–30.3 ng	296–700 ng	n.s.	[21]	III A2)
	1.5–29 ng	2.8–150 ng	2.6–52.7	[22]	
151 N-dimethylnitrosamine	0.1–27 ng	143–415 ng	11.5–437.5	[22]	III A2)
	1.8–13.8 ng	213–558 ng	n.s	[21]	
	1.7–97 ng	680–1040 ng	n.s.?	[23]	
177 N-diethylnitrosamine	1.1–3.8 ng	8.2–73 ng	2.2–78.8	[23]	III A2)
163 N-ethyl-N-methylnitrosamine	0.1–2.5 ng	5–27 ng	4.5–11.5	[22]	III A2)
	0.1–9.1 ng	9–75 ng	n.s.	[23]	
~ −14 vinyl chloride	5.6–15.8 ng	n.s.		[24]	III A1)

n.s: not specified

the active smoker in the mainstream smoke. The very low level of particles in sidestream smoke is reduced even more by rapid sedimentation and absorption on surfaces so that the passive smoke contains much less of the non-volatile substances than does the actively inhaled smoke.

In model studies in which smokers smoked a given number of cigarettes in closed rooms under standardized conditions, concentrations of the principal toxic substances, CO and nicotine, hydrocyanic acid and nitrogen oxides [25] as well as of polycyclic aromatic hydrocarbons (PAH) [26, 27] in the air were measured and expressed in terms of the number of cigarettes smoked and the room size. The level of volatile substances in the air is proportional to the number of cigarettes smoked and dependent on the ventilation. In contrast, the level of particles in the air fluctuates markedly because the sedimentation rates are determined by the structure and the furnishing of the room as well as by the number of people in it. These data demonstrate the quantitatively very different compositions of actively and passively inhaled tobacco smoke.

2.2 Exposure of passive smokers at work to the toxic substances contained in passively inhaled cigarette smoke

Only recently have the concentrations of various smoke constituents been measured in the air of offices, restaurants and workshops under normal conditions and taking ventilation into account [28]. Only these data are of relevance for the evaluation of the exposure of passive smokers at work and they form the basis of the following assessment of the possible adverse effects of passive smoking on health.

The main toxic constituents of tobacco smoke which have been measured in the air of particular work environments with sufficient accuracy for our purposes are listed in Table 3. The MAK values and the concentrations outdoors are given for comparison. From these data the amounts of toxic and carcinogenic substances inhaled by the passive smoker at work can be calculated. It is assumed that for work done sitting down or other light work and a respiratory minute volume of 8 to 10 litres per minute, 500 to 600 litres of air are inhaled per hour. A comparison with the amount of the substance inhaled with the mainstream while smoking a cigarette is also indicated. It must be remembered here that the active smoker also inhales passive smoke and that his toxic burden results from the combined inhalation.

The amount of a toxic tobacco smoke constituent inhaled by a passive smoker per hour or per working day may be expressed in terms of the equivalent number of cigarettes (Table 3). These data express the number of cigarettes or fractions of a cigarette which contain the same amount of the substance in the mainstream smoke as is inhaled by the passive smoker in an hour or a working day at a certain concentration of the substance in the air. The data demonstrate that passive smokers are exposed to only very low concentrations of the particulate, non-volatile components of tobacco smoke. The amount of smoke particles and of nicotine inhaled during a whole working day are equivalent at most to the amounts contained in the mainstream smoke of one tenth of a cigarette. Benzo[a]pyrene is likewise present in passive smoke at only low levels. Much higher are the amounts of volatile substances to which the passive smoker is exposed, whereby the exposure to CO may be considered as moderate and that to formaldehyde (Table 2) and dimethylnitrosamine, in contrast, as comparatively high. The amount of nitrogen oxides inhaled by the passive smoker is also noteworthy. The same is true for acrolein. Similar behaviour is also to be expected from other volatile substances which are not listed, such as ammonia, aniline and also volatile nitrosamines, e.g., N-nitrosopyrrolidine, which have not yet been determined precisely in air (Tables 1 and 2).

Table 3. Measured concentrations of toxic substances in the outdoor air, and indoors at places of work, in offices and restaurants (from [28, 29]) and the calculated amounts inhaled by passive smokers compared with active smokers

| | Particulate fraction | | Volatile substances | | | Particulate benzo[a]pyrene ng/m³ | Volatile N,N-dimethyl-nitrosamine ng/m³ |
	smoke particles mg/m³	nicotine mg/m³	CO mg/m³	NO$_x$ mg/m³	acrolein mg/m³		
MAK	–	0.5	33	NO$_2$:9	0.25	Vd	III A2)
outdoor air	0.02–0.06	–	1–5	0.02–0.2	–	0.5–100	< 3
office/restaurant	0.1–0.7	0.01–0.05	1–12	0.01–0.2	0.02–0.12	0.25–22	10–100
	mg	mg	mg	mg	mg	ng	ng
calculated amount inhaled per hour with passive smoke	0.05–0.3	0.05–0.025	0.5–6	0.005–0.1	0.01–0.06	0.125–11	5–50
amount inhaled per cigarette from mainstream smoke	~10	1–2	~18	0.03–0.3	~0.1	10–50	2–14 (with filter)
cigarette equivalents inhaled passively							
per 1 hour	0.005–0.03	0.01–0.025	0.03–0.3	~1	0.1–0.5	~0.1	1–10
per 8 hours	0.040–0.24	0.08–0.2	0.24–2.4	~8	0.8–4.0	~0.8	8–80

Incomplete absorption of volatile substances inhaled by the active smoker causes a corresponding increase in exposure of the passive smoker to the volatile compounds. Analysis shows (Tables 1 and 2) that, even when he smokes several cigarettes per hour, a smoker inhales only twice as much formaldehyde, nitrogen oxides and dimethylnitrosamine as the passive smoker under realistic conditions in a work environment contaminated with tobacco smoke. In general it may be stated that the passive smoker is exposed to almost the same amounts of volatile cigarette smoke constituents as the active smoker.

2.3 The determination of nicotine and cotinine in body fluids

The exposure level estimates for passive smokers have been confirmed by analysis of tobacco toxins in their body fluids. In a large London hospital nicotine concentrations were measured in saliva and urine from 82 smokers and 56 non-smokers at the end of their morning's work [30]. The exposure of the passive smokers could only be estimated by questioning. The non-smokers who claimed exposure to passive smoke had significantly higher nicotine values than those who were not exposed. The values were very scattered. The results, however, permitted the important conclusion that the amounts of nicotine found in some individual passively exposed non-smokers attained values which were characteristic for smokers after two or three cigarettes. Working conditions involving close contact with smokers but also enormous differences in the times between exposure and saliva collection may have contributed to the unusually marked overlap of the values from active and passive smokers.

Nicotine determinations in the blood of American stewardesses who were occupied for prolonged periods in the smoking or non-smoking compartments during a flight from Tokyo to San Francisco confirmed the results of the above study [31]. The non-smokers from the smoking compartment had twice as much nicotine in their blood as did those from the non-smoking compartment. The investigators also measured the urine nicotine levels and, on the basis of the known pharmacokinetics of nicotine, attempted to estimate the total nicotine burden for the stewardesses. They concluded that during the flight the passive smokers absorbed 0.12 to 0.25 mg nicotine, one tenth of the amount in one cigarette. As much as 0.4 mg was absorbed by the stewardesses who were most exposed to passive smoke.

A Japanese study made use of cotinine to indicate exposure of passive smokers [32]. An oxidative metabolite of nicotine with a half-life of 30 hours, cotinine is excreted much more slowly than its precursor and so attains much higher urine concentrations which can be determined more reliably. The values were dependent on the number of cigarette smokers with whom the passive smoker lived or worked. Another London study produced similar results [33]. The authors even reported a highly significant dependence of the cotinine excretion on the estimated occupational exposure. Even though the exposure details are unknown because there are no data as to airborne nicotine concentrations, the studies indicate that the passive smoker not only inhales the constituents of the tobacco smoke but also actually absorbs them. Thus nicotine, together with other toxins, can serve as a measure of the toxic burden.

3 Epidemiological Studies

The currently available epidemiological data come for the most part from 3 prospective [34–36] and 7 retrospective [37–47] studies as well as from one prospective study on the relationship between passive smoking and coronary heart disease.

3.1 Prospective (cohort) studies

3.1.1 T. Hirayama [34], Japan (1981)

In a study of the health effects of factors such as cigarette smoking, alcohol, occupation, and family status, 265 118 people (122 261 men and 142 857 women) aged 40 years or more, 91–99% of the census population, were interviewed in autumn 1965 in 29 health centre districts and 6 prefectures in Japan and, with the help of a record link system, were observed for the next 14 years (1966–1979). The observed direct effects of cigarette smoking were reported by Hirayama elsewhere. The publication which interests us here discusses the question of the risk of bronchial carcinoma in non-smoking wives of smokers (91 540 women).

The mortality data, standardized according to age and occupation of the husband (farming: "yes" or "no"), were calculated for classes defined by the smoking habits of the husband. The principle results are assembled in Table 4. The last two columns in the table reveal a marked (statistically significant) dose-frequency relationship. No explicit statement is made about the residual group of 33 951 women. In a letter to the editor [48] Hirayama explains that these are unmarried non-smoking women

Table 4. Results from the publication by Hirayama [34] (Japan): deaths from bronchial carcinoma and their dependence on the class of "active" or "passive" smokers.

Smoking habits	Number of women	Number of bronchial carcinoma[a] deaths	Standardized bronchial carcinoma mortality[b]	Ratios of bronchial carcinoma mortality
non-smoking wives				
husband: non-smoker	21 895	32	8.7	1.00
husband ex-smoker or 1–19 cigs/d	44 184	86	14.0	1.61
husband: 20 and more cigs/d	25 461	56	18.1	2.08
all non-smoking wives	91 540	174	n.s.	n.s.
actively smoking women	17 366	106	32.8	3.77
residual women[c]	33 951	66	n.s.	n.s.
all women	142 857	346	n.s.	n.s.

n.s.: not specified

[a] in a period of 14 years (1966-1979)

[b] standardized according to age and occupation of the husband (pp 183 and 184 of Hirayama's publication [34])

[c] unmarried, non-smoking women of whom 66 died of bronchial carcinoma: 85% widows, 9% divorced, 6% single (Hirayama [48]

of whom 66 died of bronchial carcinoma. This group makes up 24% of the women in the study.

It may also be seen from this publication that the risk was particularly high in families of farmers who were between 40 and 59 years old at the beginning of the study. The smoking habits of the husband, on the other hand, were not correlated statistically with the risk of the wife dying for other reasons, such as cancer of the stomach, collum carcinoma or ischaemic heart disease, with the exception of mammary carcinoma and suicide [49]. The risk of emphysema and asthma in non-smoking wives of heavy smokers was increased relative to that in non-smoking wives of non-smokers, but the difference was not statistically significant.

No association could be demonstrated between the drinking habits of the husband and the cause of his wife's death, including bronchial carcinoma.

Evaluation: The study population is the whole population of several regions of Japan. The collective is not representative in the statistical sense [50–52] but is typical for Japan. Many epidemiological studies are not statistically representative. Nevertheless, statistical associations between factors and illnesses can be studied reliably using such data. The groups being compared were standardized according to age and occupation of the husband but not according to the region. Hirayama [53] states that the age of the husband is closely correlated with that of his wife. Since the husband being a smoker is a property of the man, the data were standardized according to the husband's age, but, in addition, also according to the age of the wife (according to Hirayama at the Symposium "Passivrauchen aus medizinischer Sicht" (Passive Smoking from a medical Viewpoint), 9–12.4.84 in Vienna).

It may be presumed that an apparent association between passive smoking and bronchial carcinoma has not been produced by the standardization procedure [54, 55]. The level of passive smoking was registered in terms of the indicator, cigarette consumption by the husband, the period of passive smoking in terms of his age. This has been criticized [56, 57].

The life style of Japanese wives, especially in rural districts, makes this parameter a better indicator that it would be in western countries. Distortion of the data could arise if the frequency of women who did not admit to smoking were higher in the groups where the husbands were smokers than non-smokers. This is, however, unlikely because in married couples a smoking wife of a smoker should admit to her smoking more readily than the smoking wife of a non-smoker. If such distortion did occur, however, it would reduce the significance of the association.

Hammond and Selikoff [58] consider that the imprecision in the index of exposure estimation is more likely to conceal a trend than to produce artificially one of the kind demonstrated by Hirayama.

The frequency of bronchial carcinoma is also very high in the "null group" (non-smoking wives of non-smokers) [50]. Standardized according to age and occupation of the husband, it is 8.7/100 000 (see Table 4). From Figure 2 of Hirayama's publication it may be seen that in 1978 the age adjusted mortality for lung cancer in Japan was about 4/100 000 women.

Heller [59] explains this discrepancy with the fact that the population in Hirayama's study consisted of women *over* 40 years old whereas the lung cancer mortality rate for Japan includes women *under* 40 as well.

Mantel [60] suggested that an arithmetical error was the basis for the significance of Hirayama's results. According to Lee [54, 61], however, Mantel had overlooked the necessity for standardization of the data.

The differences published by Hirayama [34] between the mortality data for non-smoking wives of non-smokers and for non-smoking wives of smokers (and, in analogy, for the results communicated by Hirayama in a letter [62] for non-smoking husbands of smokers) are statistically significant [54, 55, 61, 63, 64].

The absence of significant differences between the frequency of bronchial carcinoma in the groups of various intensity of passive smoking at some of the levels examined does not contradict the overall result: marked, mostly statistically significant dose-frequency relationships at all levels studied. These dose-frequency relationships are demonstrable in spite of unavoidable imprecision of the exposure estimation and the causes of death (mostly death certificates). The associations could possibly be more distinct had the exposure and causes of death been registered more accurately. It is noteworthy in this context that no dose-frequency relationship between the drinking habits of the husband and the cause of his wife's death is found in the same data material using the same methods.

In this study the causes of death, including bronchial carcinoma, were mostly taken from the death certificates. There is no reason to believe that the information on the death certificate as to the cause of death would be distorted by the smoking habits of the husband; random errors tend, however, to conceal a trend and not to produce a fictitious one.

In 23 cases which were examined histologically the diagnosis, adenocarcinoma, arises more frequently than would be expected from studies of active smoking [48]. This result has been criticized [57, 65].

Hirayama expresses the opinion that the constant carcinogenic stimulus of passively inhaled smoke could result in a predominance of adenocarcinomas. Stock [66] points out that although passive smokers inhale the smoke mostly through the nose, there is no nasal filtering of the gaseous fraction of the tobacco smoke nor of the particles smaller than 1 µm and that particles more frequently aggregate during passage through the nose and so probably are deposited in the bronchi to a greater extent than are those of the mainstream smoke. Thus a different mechanism of action is to be expected. This supports Hirayama's hypothesis.

To date there is little information available as to the frequency of adenocarcinomas in passive smokers. It is known that adenocarcinomas are more frequent in women than in men. The possibility that frequent passive smoking makes a contribution to this effect can at present not be excluded. The high frequency of adenocarcinomas among the 23 cases for which autopsies were carried out (23/174 patients with bronchial carcinoma) in Hirayama's collective is no reason to doubt the validity of the demonstrated association. It is, however, difficult to interpret the data by a simple extrapolation of information gained in studies of active smoking to possible effects of passive smoking.

Hirayama's comparison between the effects of passive and active smoking comes to the surprising conclusion that passive smoking has about half to one third the effect of active smoking on the women. In a letter to the editor [53] Hirayama points out that according to a study in Aichi prefecture, which lies within the study area, wives of heavy smokers (30 and more cigarettes per day) inhale about 14 cigarettes passively, seen from the epidemiological standpoint.

With all the weaknesses associated with this kind of secondary evaluation of large amounts of data, there remains a statistical association between passive smoking and bronchial carcinoma which must be taken seriously in the present context.

3.1.2 L. Garfinkel [35], USA (1981)

Garfinkel evaluated the data from the prospective study of the American Cancer Society for the question of passive smoking and the risk of bronchial carcinoma.

In a study of 375 000 female non-smokers, 176 739 (45 %) non-smoking wives were classified according to the smoking habits of their husbands:

a) men who had never smoked,
b) men who smoked on a regular basis but less than 20 cigarettes per day,
c) men who smoked 20 cigarettes and more each day

Most men had smoked for 20 years or more before the start of the study. 28 % of the husbands of non-smoking wives were non-smokers compared with 21 % in the total study population. The expected mortality values were based on lung cancer rates during a twelve year period (1960–1972) for 5 year age classes of non-smoking wives of non-smokers. No attempt was made to eliminate further confounding factors.

The relative risks were found to be 1.00, 1.27 and 1.10 for the three groups defined by the smoking habits of the husbands.

In addition the data was evaluated by the method of matched pairs. Women from the group of non-smoking wives of non-smokers (null group) were matched on the one hand with non-smoking wives of moderate smokers and on the other with non-smoking wives of heavy smokers with respect to age, race, educational status of the husband or wife, town/country and occupational exposure of the man to dust, smoke or gases. The author compared the women from the null group first with those from the group whose husbands were moderate smokers and then with the group whose husbands were heavy smokers. The relative risks were 1.00 and 1.37 for the former comparison and 1.00 and 1.04 for the latter.

The differences are not significant.

Evaluation: In an interview with the Münchner Medizinische Wochenschrift [56] Garfinkel was asked for his explanation of the fact that he had found an only slightly increased risk for women whose husbands smoke but no dose-frequency relationship. He answered: he did not know whether the American social structure can be compared with that of Japan. On the other hand, he did know that in his study 13 % of the women who died from lung cancer had been married more than once. It is unclear whether these women should really be classified according to the smoking habits of the last husband, as was the case, or according to those of the earlier husband. Neither does one know whether the women were exposed to passive smoke elsewhere or whether they avoided their husband's smoke.

Hirayama [49] is not surprised by the difference between the studies in Japan and America because the methods of recruiting the collectives differ. Hirayama's study is based on a census population with a 95% response rate among the interviewed men and women. Garfinkel's collective was comprised of volunteers willing to be interviewed. There the smoking history of the husbands was known for only 27% of the women non-smokers with lung cancer (153 of 564) whereas in Hirayama's collective it was 72% (174 of 240). As other possible reasons for differences between the studies Hirayama [49] suggests: a) higher percentage of office workers among women in the USA, b) higher divorce rate (see above), c) smaller rooms in Japan, d) less consideration for non-smokers in Japan, e) different confounding factors. Thus the two studies demonstrate the same trend.

3.1.3 C.R. Gillis *et al.* [36], Scotland (1984)

Between 1972 and 1976, 16171 persons aged between 45 and 64 years (80% of the target population) were registered in a cardiorespiratory screening programme in the Scottish towns, Renfrew and Paisley. Information as to smoking habits and respiratory or cardiovascular symptoms was obtained on a questionnaire that the persons filled in themselves and that was carefully checked when they visited the screening centre. Using a record linkage to the official statistics, mortalities in the cohort were registered up to 31.12.1982. The cause of death "cancer" was checked by the West of Scotland Cancer Register. Since more than one person per household attended the screening centre, it was possible to identify 8128 persons as smokers and non-smokers living as partners of smokers or non-smokers. The 8128 persons were classified in the categories "control persons", "passive smokers", "active smokers without passive smoking" and "active smokers with passive smoking". The definitions are given in the footnote to Table 5.

The prevalence of self-reported symptoms "frequent phlegm", "respiratory difficulties" and "hypersecretion" (not defined in the publication) in the group of passive smokers is significantly different (p < 0.01) from that in the group of control persons. The frequency of anginal symptoms and ECG anomalies in women was slightly higher for passive smokers than for the control group.

The mortality data are shown in Table 5. The relative age-standardized mortality from bronchial carcinoma in men was 1:3.25:5.50:6.25 and, in contrast, in women 1:1:1.75:1.50; that is, no effect of passive smoking alone can be seen here. The situation is reversed for cancer excluding bronchial carcinoma, and for heart failure and total mortality: for women the dose-frequency trends for the indicators of passive and active smoking are more marked than for men.

Evaluation: This is a cohort study of a geographically defined population aged between 45 and 64 years at the time of registration. According to the author, the men and women belong to a single social class and are of the same ethnic origins. All information as to passive smoking was obtained from the questionnaire which the persons filled in themselves, an attempt to avoid interviewer bias (systematic errors from the questioning). It is unclear how often the diagnosis of bronchial carcinoma was confirmed histologically. Hirayama's study [34] covered a period of 14 years, the present study 6 or 10 years. That is, the observation period is relatively short. The number of deaths from bronchial carcinoma in the groups "control persons" and "passive smokers" is small (2 and 4 cases in men, 2 and 6 cases in women). Never-

Table 5. Results from the publication by Gillis *et al.* [36] (Scotland)

Groups		Number of persons	Number of bronchial carcinoma mortalities	Annual[6] age-stan-dardised bronchial carcinoma mortalities	Relative age-standardized mortality			
					bronchial carcinoma	cancer without bronchial carcinoma	heart attack	all causes of death
Men	controls[1]	517	2	40	1.00	1.00	1.00	1.00
	passive smokers[2]	310	4	130	3.25	0.50	1.45	0.99
	active smokers[3] without passive smoking	1395	30	220	5.50	2.00	1.94	1.71
	active smokers[4] with passive smoking	1845	44	250	6.25	1.83	1.48	1.71
	total (men)	4067	80	n.s.	n.s.	n.s.	n.s.	n.s.
Women	controls[1]	523	2	40	1.00	1.00	1.00	1.00
	passive smokers[2]	1394	6	40	1.00	1.26	3.00	1.45
	active smokers[3] without passive smoking	310	2	70	1.75	1.37	4.75	2.18
	active smokers[4] with passive smoking	1834	11	60	1.50	1.16	5.25	1.93
	total (women)	4061	21	n.s.	n.s.	n.s.	n.s.	n.s.
	total (men and women)	8128	101	n.s.	n.s.	n.s.	n.s.	n.s.
	remainder[5]	8043	n.s.	n.s.	n.s.	n.s.	n.s.	n.s.
	all registered persons	16171						

1　non-smokers with the same address as another non-smoker
2　non-smokers with the same address as smoker
3　smokers with the same address as a non-smoker
4　smokers with the same address as another smoker
5　persons not within the age range 45–64 years and/or ex-smokers and/or who lived alone or with a person not within the age range 45–64 years
6　annual mortality per 100000, given in the original per 10000

97.6% of the pairs were male/female partners

theless the annual mortality (per 100000, in the original publication per 10000) is considerably higher than that described by Hirayama (twice to five times as high). The authors state that the study was carried out in an area with the highest national incidence of bronchial carcinoma. Internationally, Scotland is known to have one of the highest bronchial carcinoma mortality rates for women [67]. The method of data standardization is not described. Gillis *et al.* [36] do not quote the results of significance tests for the mortality data. The confidence interval for men and women in Figure 1 was calculated from the data in [36] according to the method of Miettinen [68] but, because of lack of appropriate data in the publication, standardization for age could not be carried out.

The study results are not consistent and are considered by the authors to be preliminary (observation period too short). For death from myocardial infarction in women a dose-frequency relationship is recognizable. This is in agreement with the statistically significant results of Garland *et al.* [69]. Seen as a whole, the results show the same trend as the associations found in most of the other studies.

3.2 Retrospective studies (case-control studies)

The main data and results of the available case-control studies are assembled in Table 6.

Evaluation: in general in these studies an interviewer bias can not be excluded. The situation during an interview with a cancer patient is quite different from that with control persons who are healthy or not seriously ill.

3.2.1 D. Trichopoulos *et al.* [37, 38], Greece (1981, 1983)

Several aspects of the comparability of the cases with bronchial carcinoma and the controls are questionable, in particular the period of matrimony. The main objection to the study is the fact that only *one* control group was obtained and that from another hospital. The association could therefore be an effect of differences between the hospitals of the "cases" and the "controls".

The exposure estimation was as good as it can be in a retrospective study of this kind. In Greece – as in Japan – the smoking habits of the husband could well be a relatively good indicator of the level of passive smoking of his non-smoking wife.

The study was continued. In 1983 in a letter to the editor [38] Trichopoulos *et al.* reported data from 77 cases and 225 controls. In the table of results the odds ratios from the previous publication were used. The correct odds ratios, calculated on the basis of the quoted case numbers, (and thus the RR = relative risk values) are smaller but still significant (p < 0.01) (see footnote to Table 6).

3.2.2 P. Correa *et al.* [39], USA (1981)

Like the investigation by Trichopoulos *et al.* [37, 38] , this is a hospital case-control study and not a population-based study. Although the results of such studies are not representative in a statistical sense, they are still in principle suitable for the demon-

Table 6.* Retrospective (case-control) studies on passive smoking

Authors	Cases	Controls	Indicators of passive smoking	Results
Trichopoulos *et al.* (1981) [37]	40 non-smoking married woman from 51 cases of bronchial carcinoma in women in an Athens hospital: Confirmation of diagonsis: 14 histolog., 19 cytolog.. 18 clin. & X-ray; 8 adenocarcinomas and alveolar carcinomas not incl.	149 non-smoking married women without bronchial carcinoma, with bone or joint disorders from among 163 possible controls in an orthopaedic hospital in the same area of Athens	smoking habits of the husband: non-smoker, ex-smoker, moderate smoker (1–20 cigarettes/d), heavy smoker (≥21 cigarettes/d)	RR estimated from odds ratios: 1:1.8:2.4:3.4 $p < 0.02$
Trichopoulos *et al.* (1983) [38] continuation of study	77 cases of bronchial carcinoma (like the 40 cases described above)	225 control cases (see above)	as above	results confirmed 1:1.9:.95:2.5 $p < 0.01$
Correa *et al.* (1983) [39]	8 men and 22 women who were non-smokers and married, selected from 1338 cases of bronchial carcinoma registered in all larger hospitals in 21 counties in Louisiana Diagonsis confirmed from hospital notes (97% histol. confirmation) Bronchoalveolar carcinomas not included	180 men and 130 women with heart, circulation and gastro-intestinal disorders without bronchial carcinoma, nonsmokers, married from 1393 possible control cases; matched pairs according to race, sex, age and hospital	smoking habits of spouse: non-smokers, 1–40 pack-years, > 40 pack-years (1 pack-year, e.g.: 1 pack/d × 1 year or 0.5 pack/d × 2 years)	RR estimated from odds ratios: 1:1.48:3.11 $p < 0.05$

Sandler et al. a) (1985) [40]	518 patients with cancer at various sites (not only bronchial carcinoma) non-smokers and smokers from hospital cancer register for North Carolina Memorial Hospital, Chapel Hill	209 friends or acquaintances of the patients, 209 persons found by telephone sampling matched with respect to race, sex, age; also similar occupation and smoking habits	spouse a smoker	RR for cancer estimated from odds ratios: 1:1.6 p < 0.01 increased risk of cancer of the lung (1.9), mamma (2.2), cervix (2.0), endocrine organs (2.5); for bronchial carcinoma not sign. (few cases n = 22) (not standardized)
Sandler et al. b) (1985) [41]	from collective (a) those persons who had lived with their natural parents for most of the first 10 years of their lives (369 patients and 409 controls)		number of smokers in the home until the age of 10 years and/or smoking by the study person or their spouse	RR for cancer estimated from odds ratios according to no. of smokers in the home: 0 1 2 3+ / 1.0 1.4 2.3 2.6 / p < 0.01
Chan & Fung (1982) [42]	84 non-smoking, married women from 189 cases of bronchial carcinoma in women	139 non-smoking, married women from 189 patients of the same age group as the "cases" from the orthopaedic ward of the same hospital	spouse a smoker	RR for bronchial carcinoma estimated from odds ratios
Chan & Colbourne (1979) [43]	15 squamous epithelial carcinomas 38 adenocarcinomas 31 without histological identification			1:0.75

Table 6 (continued)

Authors	Cases	Controls	Indicators of passive smoking	Results
Koo et al. (1984) [44, 45]	88 married female patients with bronchial carcinoma	137 married women without bronchial carcinoma	husband a smoker	RR for bronchial carcinoma estimated from odds ratios 1 : 1.48
Kabat & Wynder (1984) [46]	134 "validated" non-smokers from 2668 patients with bronchial carcinoma. Of these 25 men and 53 women were questioned about passive smoking. The 234 cases were classified histolog. according to Kreyberg	matched pairs formed according to age, sex, race, hospital, interview date and non-smoker status (25 men and 53 women)	a) current exposure to smoke at home b) current exposure to smoke at work c) current and previous smoking by the spouse	RR for bronchial carcinoma estimated from odds ratios 　　　 men　women a) 1.26　0.92 b) 3.27　0.88 　　(p < 0.05) c) 1.00　0.78
Miller (1984) [47] Miller (1981) [70]	123 non-smokers who died of cancer from a group of 4130 women who died during the 20 months following the end of 1974 in Erie County (PA). Those younger than 30 years, dying in accidents or without relatives in Erie County not included. Cause of death according to statement of relatives. Only 5 deaths from bronchial carcinoma, not considered separately	from the group of 4130 women, 414 who died from causes other than cancer (see "cases"), i.e. those younger than 30 years, dead in accidents or without relatives in Erie County not included	husband a smoker according to statement of relatives (smoker: more than 20 packets of cigarettes during his lifetime)	RR for cancer estimated from odds ratios 1 : 1.40 all women 1 : 1.94 housewives (p < 0.05, n = 448) 1 : 0.80 working women (n = 89) **mean age at death** (years) husband a smoker 　　　 yes　no cancer　 71　68 control　83　75

* Relative risks (RR) can be estimated in case-control studies using so-called odds ratios (Cornfield [71])

stration of associations between factors and illnesses. For maximal comparability of cases and controls, statistical pairs were matched on the basis of race, sex, age and hospital.

In contrast to the study by Trichopoulos *et al.* [37, 38], here the control persons are not drawn from a single hospital but from many hospitals in 29 counties in Louisiana. The exact number of clinics involved is, however, not given. In 97% of cases the diagnosis was confirmed histologically; information as to the frequency of particular types of carcinoma is not given. It is stated merely that initially 32 bronchoalveolar carcinomas were not taken into account but that they were included later in the data evaluation. This must refer to the total number of 1338 bronchial carcinoma patients.

Passive smoking studies of this kind usually have very small case numbers because it is very difficult to find a sufficiently large number of non-smokers with bronchial carcinoma. In spite of this small number of cases, the association between passive smoking and bronchial carcinoma is statistically significant. In principle we agree with the authors when they consider their results to be confirmation of the findings of Trichopoulos *et al.* [37]. In addition, associations with the smoking habits of parents were studied and a statistically significant relationship between the risk of bronchial carcinoma and the mother's smoking habits was demonstrated. This result is plausible because during childhood contact with the mother is usually closer than that with the father.

3.2.3 D.P. Sandler *et al.* [40, 41], USA (1983)

The exceptional feature of this case-control study is that the authors have studied cancer at various sites and passive smoking in both smokers and non-smokers using statistical pairs (healthy persons) matched according to age, sex, race and occupation. Although the authors claim that neither patients, control persons nor interviewers knew the precise objective of the study, the reservations stated above as to the questioning of cancer patients and control persons still apply, especially as the population of tobacco-producing North Carolina where the study was carried out ought to know that cancer has something to do with smoking. Other sources of distortion could lie in the questioning methods and the choice and comparability of patients and control persons. The case numbers are not all consistent. It is therefore difficult to evaluate the results. The increased risk of mammary carcinoma is of interest because Hirayama [49] also found an increase in death from mammary carcinoma in wives exposed to passive smoke and this was taken by Lehnert [50] and Gostomzyk [72] as an indication that something was wrong with Hirayama's data. Now Sandler *et al.* [40, 41] also describe an increased risk of mammary carcinoma in passive smokers. These authors also describe associations with passive smoking for cancers at other sites and for cancer in general. The results of two studies from Hong Kong [42–45] and one from USA [46] are inconsistent. It is noteworthy that Kabat and Wynder [46] estimated using odds ratios for men exposed to passive smoke at work a relative risk of 3.27 (statistically significant) which, however, must be seen in the context of a series of non-significant results in other subgroups. In Kabat and Wynder's study systematic errors were avoided with great care. The relative risk for women was less than 1 and reference is made to the discussion of Garfinkel's results [56] with American women as compared to Japanese. The studies by Miller [47, 70] show that an effect of passive smoking on cancer in general (not only bronchial carcinoma) is demonstrable for housewives in the USA whereas the inclusion of women who go out to work seems to result in a contamination of the control group. In this study, however, the cause of death "cancer" was based only on information provided by the relatives.

3.3 Synopsis and Evaluation

It must be emphasized that Hirayama has also published, in a letter to the editor [62], a correlation with passive smoking for *non-smoking men* which corresponds essentially with that for the women. In epidemiological studies it is of fundamental importance to differentiate between random and systematic error. Random error may be estimated from the 95 % confidence limits shown in Figure 1. In this diagram the confidence limits for the results of Hirayama [34, 62], Garfinkel [35] and Sandler *et al.* [40] are those given by the authors; the remainder were calculated using Miettinen's method [68] and the data quoted in the publications, whereby the effect of age could not be taken into account for the results of Gillis *et al.* [36] because the necessary details were lacking. With two exceptions the relative risk was higher than 1.0 and sometimes the lower 95 % confidence limit was as well, which indicates that the result is statistically significant. Systematic errors arising in the selection of study persons and questioning bias in case-control studies cannot be excluded.

   Thus, each of the discussed publications has defects. Imprecision, e.g., of exposure determination and recording of cause of death in cohort studies would, however, be more unlikely to mask possible associations than to simulate a non-existing one. Most of the established associations have the same sign. The result is supported by the fact that Hirayama [49], Sandler *et al.* [40] and Miller [47] all found relationships with cancers other than bronchial carcinoma, e.g., with mammary carcinoma and cancer in general, Sandler *et al.* [40, 41] and Gillis *et al.* [36] established quantitative effects of both the combination with active smoking and additionally for passive smoking alone (in terms of an indicator) and Garland *et al.* [69] and Gillis *et al.* [36] demonstrated associations between passive smoking and coronary heart disease in prospective studies.

4 Mutagenic and Carcinogenic Effects of Tobacco Smoke and its Constituents

4.1 Mutagenic substances in urine

Mutagenic substances are formed in the organism in active and passive smokers. They have been demonstrated in urine without previous identification using the so-called Ames test. Tested in particular strains of bacteria, urine from smokers was 10 times more mutagenic than that from non-smokers. Compared with the latter, the

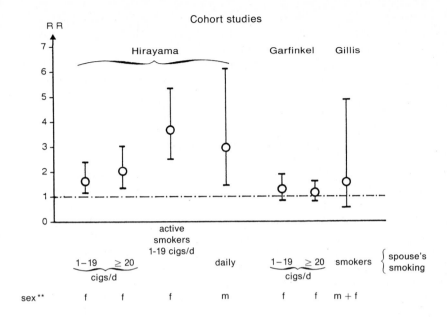

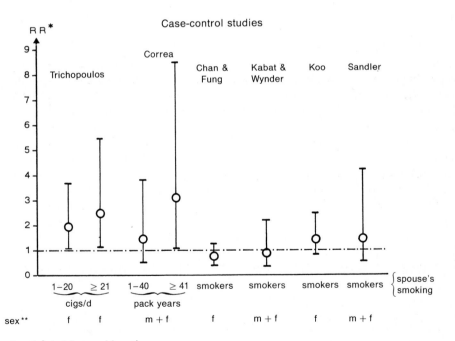

*   estimated from odds ratios
** f = female, m = male

Figure 1. Relative risk (RR) and 95% confidence limits from the studies on passive smoking and bronchial carcinoma

urine from passive smokers revealed about a 50% higher mutagenic activity. This is a further indicator for the genotoxic properties of passively inhaled tobacco smoke [73]. Studies on rats which were forced to inhale tobacco smoke confirmed in animals the mutagenic properties of the urine [74].

4.2 Carcinogenic substances in passively inhaled tobacco smoke

Tobacco smoke is qualitatively not comparable with the smoke which is produced on burning of wood, coal or oil. All these do have in common the sometimes carcinogenic products of incomplete combustion, the polycylic aromatic hydrocarbons which are produced in amounts which vary depending on the temperature and other factors. In addition, because of its high levels of N-containing bases and nitrogen oxides, tobacco smoke contains nitrosamines. The high protein levels mean we can also expect other additional pyrolysis products. These additional active constituents require particular consideration.

In mainstream smoke there are numerous substances which are carcinogenic or which promote or inhibit tumour growth in animals. In other concentrations the same substances occur in sidestream smoke where the volatile substances predominate (Table 2). Their carcinogenic potency during exposure to passive smoke is described below.

4.2.1 Polycyclic aromatic hydrocarbons (PAH)

During incomplete combustion of organic material (pyrolysis), among many other substances about 500 different PAH can be emitted [75]. Thus PAH are ubiquitous airborne toxins. Numerous PAH have been shown to be carcinogenic in animals [76]. The most studied member of this group is benzo[a]pyrene; it is considered to be a powerful carcinogen (see also [77]). Benzo[a]pyrene itself accounts for only a small fraction of the total carcinogenic potential of the volatile products of pyrolysis. Benzo[a]pyrene is often used as an indicator of the presence and level of PAH but it cannot be taken as a measure of the total carcinogenic potential when very different PAH-containing mixtures are being compared. The marked divergence between the inhaled amount of benzo[a]pyrene and the carcinogenic effect may be illustrated in the comparison of the epidemiological results for active smokers and workers in cokes plants. A rough estimation indicates that the inhalation of benzo[a]pyrene with traditional cigarette smoke is about 30–40 times as effective as the same calculated amount with coke oven emissions [78]. Although the size of this factor may change depending on the source of the data, the difference remains considerable.

Even the high benzo[a]pyrene levels discharged into the atmosphere in earlier years represent a far lesser carcinogenic potential than the same amount of benzo[a]pyrene with tobacco smoke. This discrepancy must be given particular attention when considering the dependence of the lung cancer risk from passive smoking on the benzo[a]pyrene level, particularly, e.g., when the tobacco smoke has contributed only a small part of the air contamination and the greater part comes from burning coal.

To what extent these differences are due to gaseous constituents and to what extent to others cannot be decided at present. Both seem to play a role. In terms of its benzo[*a*]pyrene level, cigarette smoke condensate had a 2–10 times greater tumorigenic effect on mouse skin and after subcutaneous application than did other pyrolysis products [79–84]. About half of the carcinogenic effect of cigarette smoke condensate on mouse skin may be accounted for by the PAH fraction [79].

4.2.2 Nitrosamines

Nitrosamines are powerful carcinogens in animals. Dimethylnitrosamine is the prototype which has been studied in most detail [85]. In all tested species it induces tumour development, not always in the same organs. Even *single* doses can lead after months or years to the development of cancer. Other nitrosamines which have been detected to date in passive smoke have similar but, in some cases, weaker effects. Epidemiological studies are not expected to produce results for nitrosamines because these substances are ubiquitous in our environment [86]. The amount of nitrosamine ingested daily with food is estimated to be about 1 to 2 µg [86]. In active and passive smokers about ten times this amount of nitrosamines is taken up (see Tables 2 and 3) [87]. It is, however, still unclear which role they play in the development of lung tumours since much larger amounts of nitrosamines than are present in tobacco smoke can be formed constantly in the organism from the reaction of nitrite with endogenous or exogenous secondary or tertiary amine bases [87]. The limiting factor is the amount of nitrite which is produced by bacterial reduction of nitrate in the intestine and oral cavity. The conditions for nitrosamine formation and the mechanisms involved are discussed in "The Nitrosation of volatile Amines at the Workplace" (this volume). Nitrite can, however, be substituted by the NO_x present in mainstream and sidestream smoke. Nitrosamines are formed from nicotine, nornicotine and other related bases during the fermentation of tobacco and during the burning process as well. The nitrosamine production then continues in the organism [88].

The studies by Bartsch [87] indicate that endogenous production of nitrosamines is about twice as high in smokers as in non-smokers. It is not yet clear, however, to what extent the total nitrosamine burden of passive smokers is increased by endogenous production.

Nitrosamines can probably not be given the whole responsibility for lung tumours in passive smokers because they occur in the air at up to 100 times higher concentrations during certain processes in the rubber industry and in leather processing [89] than in restaurants, bars and discotheques. In rooms filled with smoke under experimental conditions 0.02–0.15 ng/l dimethylnitrosamine was measured and in bars and restaurants the level ranged from under the detection limit to 0.07 ng/l [12] and 0.24 ng/l [90]. The few and incomplete epidemiological studies which are available for the above-mentioned industries, however, do provide indications of an increased cancer risk for the employees.

4.2.3 Protein pyrolysis products

An extract of tobacco smoke condensate which was tested for mutagenicity to bacteria in the Ames test possessed a mutagenic activity which was 10000 to 20000 times that of the benzo[*a*]pyrene that it contained [91].

Even when the mutagenic effects of all polyaromatics and nitrosamines in the condensate were considered, they did not account for the unusually high activity. Improved analytical methods disclosed the presence of a number of highly mutagenic [92] and carcinogenic [93] nitrogen-containing aromatics in tobacco smoke condensate as well as in the fumes from roast meat and fish. They are formed during the heating or burning of protein-containing material of plant or animal origin.

4.2.4 Formaldehyde

Formaldehyde must be given particular attention in an evaluation of the carcinogenic substances in passive smoke. Together with acrolein it has marked irritant effects. Because it is highly volatile and present at high levels in sidestream smoke, passive smokers are exposed to the same amounts as are active smokers. The severe irritation that it produces contributes to its tumour promoting activity. It has been shown to increase the carcinogenic effect of diethylnitrosamine in animals [94]. The development of nasal tumours in rats which have inhaled high concentrations of formaldehyde has been verified. In these cases the tumour development is accompanied by chronic inflammation [95].

4.3 Passive smoking in animal studies

Numerous inhalation studies have been carried out with tobacco smoke using high doses of mainstream smoke for short periods and exposing the animals at the maximum tolerated carbon monoxide levels.

Under these conditions tumours are produced mostly in the upper respiratory passages [96]. These studies demonstrate only that tobacco smoke has a carcinogenic effect, a fact which has also been unambiguously demonstrated for man in epidemiological studies. The results of these inhalation studies can contribute little to the solution of the specific questions of passive smoking. Where the cancer risk for the relatively low level exposure of passive smokers cannot be determined quantitatively from studies of this group of persons, extrapolation from studies of smokers should be more reliable than from the results of these animal studies.

5 Manifesto

Tobacco smoke passively inhaled at work is considered to be harmful to health. If the employee (non-smoker) inhaling passive smoke is exposed to tobacco smoke involuntarily, the passively inhaled smoke is no different from other harmful substances, including carcinogenic substances and mixtures, encountered in the work environment. In particular, it must be taken into account that a very large number of workers is exposed passively to tobacco smoke; there is probably no other harmful substance or mixture of substances which is so widely distributed.

The ten epidemiological studies published to date on the cancer risk associated with passively inhaled tobacco smoke have produced results with a clear trend (Figure 1). Non-smokers exposed by passive inhalation have more tumours of the mucous membranes of the respiratory tract, particularly bronchial carcinomas, than non-exposed persons. In implementation and applicability, the above-mentioned studies are not all equally satisfactory. Only three reveal markedly significant differences. Nonetheless, the essentially similar trend of the results of all studies gives weight to the suggested association. However, even examination of all the studies available to date does not prove the association beyond doubt. It is emphasized that it will certainly be very difficult to recruit a collective large enough to provide a statistically valid answer to the question because the biological effect is expected to be very small and the variability of life style and behaviour of modern populations is large.

However, tobacco smoke does without doubt contain a large number of carcinogenic substances. Some of these are also present in sidestream smoke, to which the passive smoker is particularly exposed, in higher concentrations than in mainstream smoke. In very smoky rooms the quantitative exposure of the passive smoker to the volatile substances is without doubt of the same magnitude as the exposure of the active smoker. For this reason a cancer risk for the passive smoker must be assumed. At present it is not possible to estimate the size of this risk. The scanty results from animal exposures to passive smoke do not permit a quantitative statement.

For this reason the Commission for the Investigation of Health Hazards of Chemical Compounds in the Work Area has formulated the following statement for inclusion in the List of MAK Values:

"That bronchial cancer may be caused by inhalative cigarette smoking was suspected more than five decades ago. Then, 30 years ago, epidemiologists confirmed the association unequivocally and documented it quantitatively; a number of other kinds of cancer are also associated with tobacco smoking, although to a markedly lesser extent. Lately, the risk of cancer associated with passive smoking has also come under discussion. Epidemiological studies demonstrate that this association is statistically significant for non-smoking wives of smokers. This results in a hypothesis which must be given serious consideration. The causality of the relationship, however, is at present a matter of controversy.

Tobacco smoke contains a multitude of carcinogenic substances, some of which are also known as carcinogenic working materials. Their carcinogenicity, like that of tobacco smoke, may be demonstrated unequivocally in appropriate animal experiments. In sidestream smoke, which is proportionately more important in passive smoking than in active, some carcinogenic principles are present in higher concentrations than in mainstream smoke. Therefore, a certain risk of cancer is to expected at some workplaces. It is at present not possible to estimate reliably the extent of the risk, a situation which applies for most other carcinogenic substances occurring at the workplace. An additive, possibly potentiating effect of passive smoking with known carcinogenic working materials must also be considered. Under these circumstances, the Commission recommends the institution of appropriate preventive measures in workplaces strongly contaminated with tobacco smoke."

6 References

1. Deutsche Forschungsgemeinschaft (DFG): *Maximum Concentrations at the Workplace and Biological Tolerance Values for Working Materials*, Report No. XXI of The Commission for the Investigation of Health Hazards of Chemical Compounds in the Work Area, VCH Verlagsgesellschaft mbH, D-6940 Weinheim, 1985
2. Deutsche Forschungsgemeinschaft (DFG): „Asbest" In: Henschler, D. (Ed.) *Gesundheitsschädliche Arbeitsstoffe, toxikologisch-arbeitsmedizinische Begründung von MAK-Werten.* Verlag Chemie, Weinheim, 1973, 1978 and 1981.
3. Klus, H., H. Kuhn: *Beitr. Tabakforsch. 11*, 229 (1982)
4. Johnson, W. R., R. W. Hale, J. W. Nedlock, H. J. Grubbs, D. H. Powell: *Tobacco Sci. 17*, 141 (1973); cited in [2]
5. Neurath, G., H. Ehmke, H. Horstmann: *Beitr. Tabakforsch. 2*, 361 (1964); cited in [2]
6. Adams, J. D., K. D. Brunnemann, D. Hoffmann: *Determination of nitric oxide in unaged smoke by GSC-TEA*, Communicated at the 32nd Tobacco Chemists' Research Conference, Montreal, Canada, 1978; cited in [2]
7. Jermini, C., A. Weber, E. Grandjean: *Int. Arch. occup. environm. Hlth 36*, 169 (1976)
8. Scassellati-Sforzolini, G., A. Savino: *Riv. ital. Igiene 28*, 1 (1968); cited in [2]
9. Brunnemann, K. D., D. Hoffmann: *J. chromat. Sci. 13*, 159 (1975); cited in [2]
10. Williams, J. F., G. F. Hunt: *Ammonia in mainstream and sidestream smoke*, communicated at the 21st Tobacco Chemists' Research Conference, Durham, NC, USA, 1967; cited in [2]
11. Neurath, G., H. Ehmke: *Beitr. Tabakforsch. 2*, 117 (1964); cited in [2]
12. Stehlik, G., O. Richter, H. Altmann: *Ecotoxicol. environm. Safety 6*, 495 (1982)
13. Wahl, R., O. Heil: „Die Entwicklung einer neuen Rauchapparatur unter besonderer Berücksichtigung der Strömungsverhältnisse": in: *Sonderheft anläßlich des 25jährigen Bestehens der Bundesanstalt für Tabakforschung in Forchheim*, p 16, 1953; cited in [2]
14. Hoffmann, D., J. D. Adams, K. D. Brunnemann, S. S. Hecht: *Cancer Res. 39*, 2505 (1979)
15. Patrianakos, C., D. Hoffmann: *J. analyt. Toxicol. 3*, 150 (1979); cited in [2]
16. Menden, E. E., V. J. Elia, L. W. Michael, H. G. Petering: *Environm. Sci. Technol. 6*, 830 (1972); cited in [2]
17. Pyriki, C.: *Mitt.-Bl. GDCh-Fachgr. Lebensmittelchem. gerichtl. Chem. 14*(2), 27 (1960); cited in [2]
18. Pyriki, C., R. Müller, W. Moldenhauer: *Ber. Inst. Tabakforsch. (Dresden) 7*, 81 (1960); cited in [2]
19. Pyriki, C.: *Nahrung 7*, 439 (1963); cited in [2]
20. Brunnemann, K. D., J. D. Adams, D. P. S. Ho, D. Hoffmann: *The influence of tobacco smoke on indoor atmospheres, II. Volatile and tobacco specific nitrosamines in mainstream and sidestream smoke and their contribution to indoor pollution*, Proc. 4th Jt Conf. on Sensing of Environm. Pollut., New Orleans, LA, USA, 1977, in Amer. chem. Soc. J , 876 (1978); cited in [2]
21. Rühl, Ch., J. D. Adams, D. Hoffmann: *J. analyt. Toxicol. 4*, 255 (1980); cited in [2]
22. Brunnemann, K. D., W. Fink, F. Moser: *Oncology 37*, 217 (1980)
23. Brunnemann, K. D., L. Yu, D. Hoffmann: *Cancer Res. 37*, 3218 (1977)
24. International Agency for Research on Cancer (IARC): *IARC Monographs on the Evaluation of the Carcinogenic Risk of Chemicals to Humans*, Vol. 19, p 383, Lyon, France, 1979
25. Valentin, H., H.-P. Bost, E. Wawra: *Zbl. Bakt., I. Abt. Orig. B 167*, 405 (1978)
26. International Agency for Research on Cancer (IARC): *IARC Monographs on the Evaluation of the Carcinogenic Risk of Chemicals to Man*, Vol. 3, p 91, Lyon, France, 1973
27. Grimmer, G., H. Böhnke, H.-P. Harke: *Int. Arch. occup. environm. Hlth 40*, 93 (1977)
28. Repace, J. L., A. H. Lowry: *Science 208*, 464 (1980)
29. Sterling, T. D., H. Dimich, D. Kobayashi: *J. Air Pollut. Control Ass. 32*, 250 (1982)
30. Feyerabend, C., T. Higenbottam, M. A. H. Russell: *Brit. med. J. 284*, 1002 (1982)

31. Foliart, D., N. L. Benowitz, C. E. Becker: *New Engl. J. Med. 308*, 1105 (1983)
32. Matsukura, S., T. Taminato, N. Kitano, Y. Seino, H. Hamada, M. Uchihashi, N. Nakajima, Y. Hirata: *New Engl. J. Med. 311*, 828 (1984)
33. Wald, N. J., J. Boreham, A. Bailey, C. Ritchie, J. E. Haddow, G. Knight: *Lancet I*, 230 (1984)
34. Hirayama, T.: *Brit. med. J. 282*, 183 (1981)
35. Garfinkel, L.: *J. nat. Cancer Inst. 66*, 1061 (1981)
36. Gillis, C. R., D. J. Hole, V. M. Hawthorne, P. Boyle: *Europ. J. resp. Dis. 65, Suppl. 133*, 121 (1984)
37. Trichopoulos, D., A. Kalandidi, L. Sparros, B. MacMahon: *Int. J. Cancer 27*, 1 (1981)
38. Trichopoulos, D., A. Kalandidi, L. Sparros: *Lancet II*, 677 (1983)
39. Correa, P., L. W. Pickle, E. Fontham, Y. Lin, W. Haenszel: *Lancet II*, 595 (1983)
40. Sandler, D. P., R. Everson, A. J. Wilcox: *Amer. J. Epidem. 121*, 37 (1985)
41. Sandler, D. P., A. J. Wilcox, R. Everson: *Lancet I*, 312 (1985)
42. Chan, W. C., S. C. Fung: "Lung cancer in non-smokers in Hong Kong", in Grundmann, E. (Ed.): *Cancer Campaign*, 6th ed., p 199, Gustav Fischer Verlag, D-7000 Stuttgart, 1982
43. Chan, W. C., M. J. Colbourne, S. C. Fung, H. C. Ho: *Brit. J. Cancer 39*, 182 (1979)
44. Koo, L. C., J. H. C. Ho, N. Lee: *Int. J. Cancer 35*, 149 (1985)
45. Koo, L. C., J. H. C. Ho, D. Saw: *J. exp. clin. Cancer Res. 3*, 277 (1984)
46. Kabat, G. C., E. L. Wynder: *Cancer 53*, 1214 (1984)
47. Miller, G. H.: *West. J. Med. 140*, 632 (1984)
48. Hirayama, T.: *Brit. med. J. 282*, 1393 (1981)
49. Hirayama, T.: *Münch. med. Wschr. 123*, 1489 (1981)
50. Lehnert, G.: *Münch. med. Wschr. 123*, 1485 (1981)
51. MacDonald, E. J.: *Brit. med. J. 283*, 915 (1981)
52. MacDonald, E. J.: *Brit. med. J. 283*, 1465 (1981)
53. Hirayama, T.: *Brit. med. J. 283*, 916 (1981)
54. Lee, P. N.: *Food chem. Toxicol. 20*, 223 (1982)
55. Harris, J. E., W. H. Dumouchel: *Brit. med. J. 283*, 915 (1981)
56. Garfinkel, L.: *Münch. med. Wschr. 123*, 1496 (1981)
57. Wynder, E., M. T. Goodman: *Epidem. Rev. 5*, 177 (1983)
58. Hammond, E. C., I. J. Selikoff: *Environm. Res. 24*, 444 (1981)
59. Heller, W. D.: *Münch. med. Wschr. 124*, 12 (1982)
60. Mantel, T.: *Brit. med. J. 283*, 914 (1981)
61. Lee, P. N.: *Brit. med. J. 283*, 1465 (1981)
62. Hirayama, T.: *Brit. med. J. 283*, 1466 (1981)
63. Rutsch, M.: *Münch. med. Wschr. 124*, 15 (1982)
64. US Department of Health and Human Services: *The Health Consequences of Smoking: Cancer, Part IV. Involuntary Smoking and Lung Cancer*, Report of the Surgeon General, Public Health Service, Office on Smoking and Health, Rockville, MD 20857, USA, 1982
65. Rose, G. A.: *Dtsch. Ärztebl. 79*, 30 (1981)
66. Stock, S. L.: *Lancet I*, 1014 (1982)
67. Becker, N., R. Frentzel-Beyme, G. Wagner: *Krebsatlas der Bundesrepublik Deutschland*, 2nd ed., Springer Verlag, Berlin, Heidelberg, New York, Tokyo, 1984
68. Miettinen, O.: *Amer. J. Epidem. 103*, 226 (1976)
69. Garland, C., E. Barrett-Connor, L. Suarez, M. H. Criqui, D. L. Wingard: *Amer. J. Epidem. 121*, 645 (1985)
70. Miller, G. H.: *Brit. med. J. 282*, 985 (1981)
71. Cornfield, J.: *J. nat. Cancer Inst. 11*, 1269 (1951)
72. Gostomzyk, J. G.: *Münchn. med. Wschr. 124*, 11 (1981)
73. Bos, R. P., J. L. G. Theuws, P. Th. Henderson: *Cancer Lett. 19*, 85 (1983)
74. Mohtashamipur, E., K. Norpoth, M. Heger: *J. Cancer Res. clin. Oncol. 108*, 296 (1984)
75. Herlan, A.: *Zbl. Bakt., Abt. Orig. B 165*, 174 (1977)
76. International Agency for Research on Cancer (IARC): *IARC Monographs on the Evaluation of the Carcinogenic Risk of Chemicals to Humans*, Vol. 32, p 211, Lyon, France, 1983
77. Deutsche Forschungsgemeinschaft (DFG): „Polycyclische aromatische Kohlenwasserstoffe (PAH)", in Henschler, D. (Ed.): *Gesundheitsschädliche Arbeitsstoffe. Toxikologisch-arbeitsmedi-*

zinische Begründung von MAK-Werten, 10th issue, Verlag Chemie GmbH, D-6940 Weinheim, 1984

78. Pott, F.: *Staub-Reinhalt. Luft 47*, 369 (1985)
79. Dontenwill, W., H.-J. Chevalier, H.-P. Harke, H.-J. Klimisch, H. Brune, B. Fleischmann, W. Keller: *Z. Krebsforsch. 85*, 155 (1976)
80. Misfeld, J., K. H. Weber: *Planta med. (Stuttg.) 22*, 281 (1972)
81. Grimmer, G., H. Brune, R. Deutsch-Wenzel, K.-W. Naujack, J. Misfeld, J. Timm: *Cancer Lett. 21*, 105 (1983)
82. Brune, H., R. Deutsch-Wenzel: *Untersuchungen zur carcinogenen Wirkung von Rauchgaskondensat aus Steinkohlebrikett-Heizung und seiner Fraktionen im chronischen Epikutanversuch an weiblichen CFLP-Mäusen*, Final report of the Committee for „Untersuchungen über die carcinogene Belastung des Menschen durch Luftverunreinigung", Umweltbundesamt, D-1000 Berlin, 1983
83. Deutsch-Wenzel, R., H. Brune, G. Grimmer, G. Dettbarn, J. Misfeld, J. Timm: *Cancer Lett. 25*, 103 (1984)
84. Pott, F., W. Stöber: *Environm. Hlth Perspect. 47*, 293 (1983)
85. International Agency for Research on Cancer (IARC): *IARC Monographs on the Evaluation of the Carcinogenic Risk of Chemicals to Humans*, Vol. 17, Lyon, France, 1983
86. Preussmann, R.: „Biologische Wirkungen, Metabolismus, Dosis- Wirkungs-Beziehungen und Risikobetrachtungen", in Deutsche Forschungsgemeinschaft (DFG): *Das Nitrosamin-Problem*, p 256, Verlag Chemie GmbH, D-6940 Weinheim, 1983
87. Bartsch, H., R. Montesano: *Carcinogenesis 5*, 1381 (1984)
88. Hoffmann, D., K. D. Brunnemann: *Cancer Res. 43*, 5570 (1983)
89. International Agency for Research on Cancer (IARC): *IARC Monographs on the Evaluation of the Carcinogenic Risk of Chemicals to Humans*, Vol. 28, Lyon, France, 1982
90. Brunnemann, K. D., D. Hoffmann: *IARC Sci. Publ. No. 19*, 343 (1978)
91. Sugimura, T., M. Nagao, T. Kawachi, M. Honda, T. Yahagi, Y. Seino, S. Sato, N. Matsukura, T. Matsushima, A. Shirai, M. Sawamura, H. Matsumoto: "Mutagen-carcinogens in food, with special reference to highly mutagenic pyrolytic products in broiled foods", in Hiatt, H. H., J. D. Watson, J. A. Winsten (Eds.): *Origins of Human Cancer*, Book C, p 1561, Cold Spring Harbor Laboratory, USA, 1977
92. Yoshida, D., T. Matsumoto: *Cancer Lett. 10*, 141 (1980)
93. Sugimura, T., S. Sato: *Cancer Res. 43*, 2415s (1983)
94. Dalbey, W. E.: *Toxicology 24*, 9 (1982)
95. Uehleke, H.: „Wo liegen Sicherheit und Gefahren von Formaldehyd?", in Brenner, W., H.-J. Florian, E. Stollenz, H. Valentin (Eds.): *Arbeitsmedizin aktuell*, p 27, Fischer Verlag, D-7000 Stuttgart, 1984
96. Pepelko, W. E.: *Environm. Res. 33*, 144 (1984)

completed 30. 10. 85

1-Chloro-1,1-difluoroethane

Classification/MAK value	**1000 ml/m³ (ppm)**
	4170 mg/m³
Classification/MAK value dates from:	**1989**
Synonyms:	R 142b
	FC 142b
	CFC 142b
	difluoromonochloroethane
	chlorodifluoroethane
	chloroethylidene fluoride
Chemical name (CAS):	1-chloro-1,1-difluoroethane
CAS number:	75-68-3

Structural formula:

$$Cl-\underset{\underset{F}{|}}{\overset{\overset{F}{|}}{C}}-\underset{\underset{H}{|}}{\overset{\overset{H}{|}}{C}}-H$$

Molecular formula:	$C_2H_3ClF_2$
Molecular weight:	100.5
Melting point:	not specified
Boiling point:	$-9.5\,°C$

1 ml/m³ (ppm) ≈ 4.17 mg/m³ **1 mg/m³ ≈ 0.240 ml/m³ (ppm)**

1 Toxic Effects and Modes of Action

1-Chloro-1,1-difluoroethane is considered to be a chlorofluorocarbon of very low toxicity [1–3]. The LC_{50} for the rat (6 hours inhalation) is more than 400 000 ml/m³ (40% v/v) [4].

2 Effects in Man

There are no reports available on industrial experience with 1-chloro-1,1-difluoroethane nor on specific human exposures to the substance.

3 Effects on Animals

The typical effects of chlorofluorocarbons have been repeatedly studied, the anaesthetic effect in the rat and mouse [3, 5, 6] and myocardial sensitization to adrenaline in the rat, dog and monkey [7–11]. They are found with 1-chloro-1,1-difluoroethane only after inhalation of concentrations of 50000 ml/m^3 or more.

Rats and dogs were exposed for 90 days to atmospheres containing 10000 ml 1-chloro-1,1-difluoroethane/m^3. No pathological lesions were found [12].

4 Mutagenicity and Carcinogenicity

A (weak) positive result was obtained in the Ames test with *Salmonella typhimurium* TA1535 and TA100 (without metabolic activation) [13]. A cell transformation test with BALB/3T3 cells produced negative results [14], another cell transformation test with BHK21 cells ("Styles test") was (weakly) positive [13].

Since the results of these short-term tests raised the question of a carcinogenic potential of 1-chloro-1,1-difluoroethane, a long-term inhalation study was carried out with groups of 110 male and female Sprague-Dawley-derived CD rats [14]. The animals inhaled concentrations of 0 (controls), 1000, 10000 or 20000 ml 1-chloro-1,1-difluoroethane/m^3, 6 hours per day, 5 days per week for 104 weeks. No effects on behaviour, clinical findings, body weight gain, clinical laboratory or morphological parameters were observed in the exposed groups. A carcinogenic effect of the substance was not demonstrated.

In addition, male rats of the same strain were exposed in groups of ten for 13 weeks to the same concentrations of the substance. The results of the subsequent cytogenetic investigation of bone marrow cells were considered to be negative [14]. A dominant lethal test was carried out on another set of groups of 10 male animals which had been exposed for 15 weeks, again under the same conditions. Triethylene melamine (0.5 mg/kg) was used in the positive control. With the exception of a single anomalous result caused by two animals in one group (mated after 7 weeks), no statistically significant accumulation of dead implants occurred in the experiments with animals given 1-chloro-1,1-difluoroethane. The results of the dominant lethal test were considered to be negative [14].

5 Manifesto (classification/MAK value)

A long-term inhalation study with 1-chloro-1,1-difluoroethane at concentrations up to 20000 ml/m^3 produced no indications of a carcinogenic effect. Weak positive results in the Ames test and in one cell transformation test are in contraposition to those of a negative cell transformation test, a negative cytogenetic study and a negative dominant lethal test. These data provide no evidence for a carcinogenic potential of the substance.

Both the long-term study and the various studies of acute toxicity demonstrate that the substance is only very slightly toxic. The MAK value is set at 1000 ml/m^3, not for toxicological reasons but for formal ones (upper limit of MAK values); the substance is therefore classified in category IV for the limitation of exposure peaks.

Studies on the reproductive toxicology of 1-chloro-1,1-difluoroethane are not available.

6 References

1. Carpenter, C. P., J. F. Smyth, U. Pozzoni: *J. industr. Hyg. 31*, 343 (1949)
2. Karpov, B. C.: *Trans. Lensing. Sanit. Gig. Med. Inst. 75*, 128 (1963)
3. Lester, D., L. A. Greenberg: *Arch. industr. Hyg. 2*, 335 (1955)
4. Litton Bionetics, Inc., 1978, unpublished data; cited in [14]
5. Davies, R. H., P. D. Bagnell, W. G. M. Jones: *Int. J. Quantum Chem.: Quantum Biol. Symp. 1*, 201 (1974)
6. Robbins, B. H.: *J. Pharmacol. exp. Ther. 86*, 197 (1946)
7. Aviado, D. M., M. A. Belej: *Toxicology 2*, 31 (1974)
8. Aviado, D. M., D. G. Smith: *Toxicology 3*, 241 (1975)
9. Belej, M. A., D. M. Aviado: *J. clin. Pharmacol. 15*, 105 (1975)
10. Belej, M. A., D. G. Smith, D. M. Aviado: *Toxicology 2*, 381 (1974)
11. Reinhardt, C. F., A. Azar, M. E. Maxfield, P. E. Smith, L. S. Mullin: *Arch. environm. Hlth 22*, 265 (1971)
12. Trochimowicz, H. T., J. P. Lyon, D. P. Kelly, T. Chin: *Toxicol. appl. Pharmacol. 41*, 200 (1977)
13. Longstaff, E., M. Robinson, C. Bradbook, J. A. Styles, I. F. H. Purchase: *Toxicol. appl. Pharmacol. 72*, 15 (1984)
14. Seckar, J. A., H. J. Trochimowicz, G. K. Hogan: *Food chem. Toxicol. 24*, 237 (1986)

completed 13. 12. 88

Chlorotrifluoromethane

Classification/MAK value	**1000 ml/m³ (ppm)**
	4330 mg/m³
Classification/MAK value dates from:	**1989**
Synonyms:	R 13
	FC 13
	CFC 13
	monochlorotrifluoromethane
	trifluorochloromethane
	trifluoromethyl chloride
	trifluoromonochlorocarbon
Chemical name (CAS):	chlorotrifluoromethane
CAS number:	75-72-9
Structural formula:	

$$F-\underset{\underset{F}{|}}{\overset{\overset{F}{|}}{C}}-Cl$$

Molecular formula:	$CCIF_3$
Molecular weight:	104.47
Melting point:	$-181\,°C$
Boiling point:	$-81\,°C$
Vapour pressure at 20 °C:	22.620 hPa

1 ml/m³ (ppm) ≈ 4.33 mg/m³   **1 mg/m³ ≈ 0.230 ml/m³ (ppm)**

1 Effects in Man

For chlorotrifluoromethane there are no reports of effects observed in man.

2 Effects on Animals

The narcotic effect of chlorotrifluoromethane was investigated in guinea pigs in comparison with other chlorocarbons and chlorofluorocarbons [1]. The narcotic potency was similar to that of methane and markedly less than that of chloromethane, dichlorofluoromethane, trichlorofluoromethane and chlorodifluoromethane. Loss of the righting reflex was seen in guinea pigs only after exposure to atmospheres containing 70 % v/v or more chlorotrifluoromethane and after exposure times of at least 90 minutes.

At concentrations of about 80% v/v or more chlorotrifluoromethane in the inhaled air (15 minute inhalation), myocardial sensitization to adrenaline was observed in the dog [2]. After brief exposure (10 minutes) of rats to concentrations up to 80% v/v, no effects on the CNS and no mortality were recorded. In these investigations chlorotrifluoromethane was shown to be by far the least toxic compound in a series of chlorofluorocarbons.

3 Genotoxicity

The mutagenicity of chlorotrifluoromethane with and without metabolic activation (liver microsomes) was studied in *Salmonella typhimurium* TA1535 and TA1538. The results were negative [3].

4 Manifesto (classification/MAK value)

Comparing typical features of this class of substances (effects on the central nervous system, cardiac effects) reveals that chlorotrifluoromethane is a chlorofluorocarbon of very low toxicity.

Accordingly, the MAK value is set at 1000 ml/m³ for formal rather than for toxicological reasons (upper limit of MAK values) and the substance is classified in category IV for the limitation of peak values.

There are no studies available on the reproductive toxicology of chlorotrifluoromethane.

5 References

1. Dittmann, E. Ch., E. Etschenberg: *Europ. J. Pharmacol. 24*, 389 (1973)
2. Clark, D. G., D. J. Tinston: *Hum. Toxicol. 1*, 239 (1982)
3. Longstaff, E., M. Robinson, C. Bradbook, J. A. Styles, I. F. M. Purchase: *Toxicol. appl. Pharmacol. 72*, 15 (1984)

completed 13. 12. 1988

1,2-Dichlorobenzene   H

Classification/MAK value:	**50 ml/m^3 (ppm)**
	300 mg/m^3
Classification/MAK value dates from:	**1958**
Synonyms:	o-dichlorobenzene
	1,2-DCB
Chemical name (CAS):	1,2-dichlorobenzene
CAS number:	95-50-1
Structural formula:	

Molecular formula:	$C_6H_4Cl_2$
Molecular weight:	147
Melting point:	$-17\,^\circ$C
Boiling point:	$180.5\,^\circ$C
Vapour pressure at 20 °C:	1.33 hPa

1 ml/m^3 (ppm) = 6.12 mg/m^3   **1 mg/m^3 = 0.164 ml/m^3 (ppm)**

1 Toxic Effects and Modes of Action

1,2-Dichlorobenzene (1,2-DCB) may be absorbed through the lungs, the gastrointestinal tract and the skin. It is metabolized oxidatively to dichlorophenol derivatives and excreted mostly in urine in the conjugated form. Brief exposures to 1,2-DCB in the air result in irritation of mucous membranes, hyperactivity, cyanosis and weight loss as well as damage to the liver (centrilobular necrosis) and kidneys (swelling of the tubular epithelium).

1,2-DCB, unlike 1,4-DCB, does not increase the production of hyaline droplets in the kidneys of male rats even on prolonged exposure.

1,2-DCB induces acquired porphyria. Repeated oral administration to rats results in the typical symptoms of porphyria and increases liver and kidney weights. Chronic administration to male rats and mice increases renal tubular regeneration; tumour formation has not been observed.

1,2-DCB is not genotoxic and has neither foetotoxic nor teratogenic effects.

In man after exposure to airborne 1,2-DCB, mucous membrane lesions and, very occasionally, adverse effects on the haematopoietic system have been described. There is also one report of a single case of sensitization.

1.1 Pharmacokinetics

Relatively soluble in lipids, 1,2-DCB readily penetrates membranes and can therefore be taken up through the lungs, the gastrointestinal tract and the skin. Together with the other two DCB-isomers, 1,2-DCB has been identified in the blood of residents of the city of New Orleans (USA) [1].

Male albino rats were given in their diet a mixture of chlorocarbons containing tetrachloroethene, hexachloro-1,3-butadiene, γ-hexachlorocyclohexane, 1,2-DCB, 1,3,5-trichlorobenzene, 1,2,3,4-tetrachlorobenzene and hexachlorobenzene. Groups of seven animals received daily doses of 2 or 4 mg/kg body weight of each component of the mixture for 4, 8 or 12 weeks. At the end of treatment the animals were killed and the chlorocarbon levels in adipose tissue were measured. In the animals of both dosage groups the 1,2-DCB level measured after 4 weeks on the diet was 20 mg/kg adipose tissue; after 12 weeks it was ca. 60 mg/kg. In animals who were not killed at the end of the treatment period, the 1,2-DCB level in the adipose tissue was unchanged after 1 week without any chlorocarbons in the diet and after 3 weeks 1,2-DCB could no longer be detected [2].

After oral administration of 500 mg 1,2-DCB/kg body weight, the following metabolites were detected in the urine of rabbits: 2,3-dichlorophenol (8.9%), 3,4-dichlorophenol (30%), catechols (3.90%), glucuronides (48%), ethereal sulfates (21%) and mercapturic acids (5.0%). The excretion rate was relatively slow; excretion of the metabolites was completed 5–6 days after 1,2-DCB administration [3].

Rats were given a single i.p. injection of 7.35 mg ^{14}C-1,2-DCB/kg body weight and were killed 6 or 24 hours later. The 1,2-DCB level in the liver sank from 10.4 µg/g liver to 2.4 µg/g, and the covalent binding to liver protein from 34 ng/mg to 20 ng/mg protein. 17% and 42% of the dose was excreted in the urine. Pretreatment of the animals with phenobarbital alone accelerated the excretion and increased the covalent binding to liver protein (45 ng/mg) whereas combined pretreatment with phenobarbital and SKF 525-A reduced the excretion rate markedly and reduced the binding to liver protein (27.3 ng/mg). It is concluded from these results and from data obtained for other halogenated benzene derivatives that there is a causal relationship between covalent binding to liver proteins and hepatotoxicity of 1,2-DCB [4].

In metabolism studies with rats, one of the exhaled metabolites of 1,2,4-trichlorobenzene was identified as 1,2-DCB, evidently produced by reductive dechlorination in intestinal bacteria [5, 6].

1.2 Other Effects

Incubation of isolated rat liver mitochondria with 1,2-DCB (35 µg/ml) decoupled oxidative phosphorylation and caused release of potassium ions [50].

2 Effects in Man

A case of sensitization to 1,2-DCB was reported in 1939 [7]. A worker who handled windows treated with 1,2-DCB developed severe erythema on the exposed skin areas and finally blisters. Later a brown skin pigmentation developed and persisted for 3 months.

Sewerage workers who inhaled fumes from the effluent of a dry cleaning establishment suffered from irritation of the eyes and respiratory tract as well as nausea [8]. A woman ironer in a dry cleaning business who was continually exposed to fumes containing 95% 1,2-DCB and 5% 1,4-DCB developed haemolytic anaemia with leukocytosis and polynucleosis [9]. Another report [10] describes 3 cases of leukemia after chronic exposure to mixtures containing 2%, 37% or 80% 1,2-DCB and one case of anaemia; a causal relationship with the 1,2-DCB exposure was not proved. In contrast, no indication of organ damage or damage to the haematopoietic system was found in workers who had been exposed for many years to 1,2-DCB levels of 6–264 mg/m^3 air (average level 90 mg/m^3) [11].

Applied for 1 hour to the anterior surface of the forearm in volunteers 1,2-DCB produced after about 15 minutes a severe burning sensation which disappeared when the 1,2-DCB was removed. A diffuse erythema developed initially at the application site which after 24 hours became dark red and covered with blisters. Later a brownish pigmentation appeared and was still visible after 3 months [12].

An analytical study investigated 1,2-DCB levels in human adipose tissue and in mothers' milk and found 9 µg/kg milk or 230 µg/kg milk fat and 13 µg/kg fat in adipose tissue [13].

3 Effects on Animals

3.1 Acute toxicity

The data available on the acute toxicity of 1,2-DCB are shown in Table 1.

The symptoms of toxicity during a 6 hour inhalative exposure of rats to 1,2-DCB levels between ca. 6000 and 18 000 mg/m^3 were hypotonia, somnolence and lacrimation. Deaths occurred mainly during the exposure and the subsequent 24 hours.

Table 1. Acute toxicity of 1,2-dichlorobenzene

Species	Application route	LD$_{50}$/LC$_{50}$	Ref.
rat	oral	500 mg/kg bw	[14]
rabbit	oral	500 mg/kg bw	[15]
guinea pig	oral	800–2000 mg/kg bw	[16]
rat	inhalation (6 h)	9192 mg/m^3	[17]
mouse	inhalation (6 h)	7416 mg/m^3	[17]
rat	i.p.	840 mg/kg bw	[18]
mouse (NMRI)	i.p.	1228 mg/kg bw	[19]

bw: body weight

Body weight gain of the survivors was still delayed at the last examination after 14 days. Autopsy of the survivors revealed no macroscopic lesions of the lungs, liver or kidneys [17]. In the other studies of acute toxicity the symptoms were not described in detail.

Subcutaneous injection of 0.5 ml 1,2-DCB/kg body weight produced macroscopically visible liver lesions in rabbits; occasionally these effects were obtained with a dose of only 0.0056 ml/kg body weight [20].

Rabbits died within 24 hours of an i.v. injection of 330–660 mg 1,2-DCB/kg body weight and within 20 seconds of an i.v. dose of 1310 mg 1,2-DCB/kg body weight [20].

A single exposure of rats, mice and guinea pigs to 1,2-DCB concentrations of 0.005% to 0.08% in air for various periods induced liver necroses in most animals and sometimes renal damage as well. Irritation of eyes and nose was observed during the exposure and some animals died after a protracted period in a comatose state [20].

Groups of 6 male Swiss OF1 mice were exposed briefly (ca. 5 minutes) to one of four concentrations of 1,2-DCB in the range from ca. 420 to 1200 mg/m^3 air and the RD50 value according to Alarie (irritant response in the airways) was determined as 1092 mg/m^3 [21].

In an earlier study a dog (Alsatian) was exposed for 1 hour to an atmosphere into which 2 ml 1,2-DCB/m^3 had been sprayed at a room temperature of 26 °C. When the experiment was repeated using twice the concentration (4 ml/m^3) the dog became somnolent [12].

In further inhalation studies mice, rats and guinea pigs were exposed for 1 hour to 2 ml 1,2-DCB/m^3. Agitation, which was immediately apparent in the mice, regressed in about 20 minutes. At the end of exposure the animals were severely cyanotic and they died within 24 hours. In the rats and guinea pigs, agitation was also observed but the animals recovered within a few hours [12].

Male rats were exposed to various concentrations of 1,2-DCB (3234–5862 mg/m^3 air) for 1–10 hours. During the exposure the animals were seen to suffer from agitation, irritation of the mucous membranes and respiratory difficulties. Transient weight loss was seen in the survivors. Deaths occurred within three days [16]. Organ damage was studied in 4 dosage groups each with 20 male rats — 5862 mg/m^3/1 hour, 5862 mg/m^3/0.5 hour, 3234 mg/m^3/6.5 hours and 3234 mg/m^3/3 hours. Half of the animals in each group were killed one day after the exposure. No lesions were found in the animals from the 5862 mg/m^3/0.5 hour group. In the other groups the liver and kidney weights were increased, there was marked centrilobular necrosis in the liver and swelling of the renal tubular epithelium [16].

Fasting male Holtzman rats were given a single i.p. injection of 735 mg 1,2-DCB/kg body weight. 24 hours after the injection, the bile duct/pancreas secretion was increased by about a factor of ten and the protein level of the bile was reduced to about 25% of the control value [22].

Inhalation hazard tests were carried out at various temperatures (exposure of the whole animal to a saturated atmosphere produced by active evaporation). The results are shown in Table 2. Abnormal behaviour, respiratory difficulties, agitation, sedation and irritation of the mucous membranes were observed [23].

Table 2. Acute inhalation studies with rats exposed to air saturated with 1,2-dichlorobenzene

Sex	Temperature °C	Exposure time in h	Result*
♂	20	3	0/5/5
♂/♀	20	7	3/10/10
♂/♀	30	3	0/10/10
♂	30	7	3/5/5
♀	30	7	0/5/5
♂/♀	95	0.5	0/10/10
♂/♀	95	1	5/10/10
♂	95	3	5/5/5
♀	95	3	4/5/5
♀	95	7	5/5/5

* mortalities/animals with symptoms/initial number of animals

24 hours after male F344 rats had received a single i.p. injection of 397 mg 1,2-DCB/kg body weight, an increase in plasma alanine aminotransferase activity was observed. Simultaneous injection of 154 mg CCl_4/kg body weight prevented this increase and, at the same time, reduced the excretion of 1,2-DCB metabolites in the urine and faeces. Exhaled 1,2-DCB was increased. The results indicate that CCl_4 inhibits 1,2-DCB metabolism [24].

In male Sprague-Dawley rats who were exposed for 4 hours to 1,2-DCB concentrations of 1830, 2556, 3654 or 4644 mg/m^3 in air, increased activities of the serum enzymes glutamate dehydrogenase, aspartate aminotransferase, alanine aminotransferase and sorbitol dehydrogenase were found 24 hours after the exposure. A four hour exposure to 1224 mg 1,2-DCB/m^3 air had no effect [25].

Male Sprague-Dawley rats were exposed for 4 hours to 1,2-DCB levels of 1476, 2214, 3660 or 4434 mg/m^3 air. At concentrations of 2214 mg/m^3 or more, the activities of serum glutamate dehydrogenase and serum sorbitol dehydrogenase were increased and liver glucose-6-phosphatase was decreased [26].

Male Sprague-Dawley rats which had been pretreated with sodium chloride or phenobarbital were given an i.p. injection of 0.03 ml 1,2-DCB. There were indications of glycogen loss from the liver. Histological investigation revealed an increased frequency of centrilobular necrosis in the liver of animals pretreated with phenobarbital [27].

A single oral dose of 500 mg 1,2-DCB/kg body weight did not induce a detectable increase in arylhydrocarbon hydroxylase activity in the livers or intestines of rats [28].

A single oral dose of 120 or 300 mg 1,2-DCB/kg body weight caused no increase in formation of hyaline droplets in the renal cortex of rats of either sex. A slight, reversible ^{14}C-labelling of $\alpha_{2\mu}$-globulin was detected after oral administration of 500 mg ^{14}C-1,2-DCB/kg body weight [29].

3.2 Effects on skin and mucous membranes, percutaneous absorption

1,2-DCB is a mild irritant on intact rabbit skin (exposed for 24 hours) and is weakly irritating in the rabbit eye [23]. Two drops of 1,2-DCB in the rabbit eye produced mild conjunctivitis. The inflammation regressed within 7 days [16].

1,2-DCB was applied dermally to rats by painting the shaved abdominal skin (ca. 10 cm^2) twice daily. The animals did not tolerate the treatment at all well. One rat died with signs of severe systemic effects after 5 applications. Macroscopic examination of another animal which died after nine applications revealed a pale mottled liver and kidney changes. The skin of the application site was unaffected [12].

Female rabbits were treated dermally with 0.1 ml undiluted 1,2-DCB applied to the inner surface of the ear on each of 5 consecutive days and were then killed 12 days after the last application. 1,2-DCB did not have an acnegenic effect, nor were signs of systemic toxicity observed [30].

3.3 Subacute and subchronic toxicity

It has been demonstrated in several studies that 1,2-DCB can induce acquired porphyria in rats. Male albino rats were given daily doses of 455 mg 1,2-DCB/kg body weight by gastric intubation for 15 days and then a 24 hour urine sample was collected and the porphyrin content determined. 1,2-DCB caused a 10 times increase in the urine levels of coproporphyrin, uroporphyrin and porphobilinogen and a decrease in urine δ-aminolaevulinic acid. At the end of 15 days treatment with 450 mg 1,2-DCB/kg body weight/day the liver porphyrin levels were also increased – by a factor of about 1.5 for coproporphyrin, 2.5 for protoporphyrin and 10 for uroporphyrin. The 1,2-DCB treatment decreased the catalase activity in the liver by about 50 % [31].

In another study rats were given an oral dose of 250 mg 1,2-DCB/kg body weight on each of three consecutive days and then were killed 24 hours after the last dose. The relative liver weights, the microsomal protein levels and the activities of aminopyrine-N-demethylase and δ-aminolaevulinate synthetase were increased as a result of the 1,2-DCB treatment [32]. Female Wistar rats were given daily subcutaneous injections of 100 mg phenobarbital/kg body weight and daily doses of 500 mg 1,2-DCB/kg body weight by gastric intubation for 1–5 days. 24 hours after the last dose, the Harderian gland was removed to determine the levels of porphyrins and the activity of aminolaevulinate synthetase and aminolaevulinate dehydratase. On the first day after the first 1,2-DCB administration the porphyrin level was increased but on day 5 after 5 daily applications it had returned to normal whereas the enzyme activities remained unchanged. The relative liver weights increased after 1,2-DCB treatment [33]. Female rats received a total of 138 daily doses of 18.8, 188 or 376 mg 1,2-DCB/kg body weight by oral intubation on 5 days each week during a period of 192 days. Weight gain and mortality of the animals were normal. In the medium and high dose groups the organ weights of liver and kidney were increased; the spleen weight was decreased only in the 376 mg/kg group. The low dose (18.8 mg/kg) was tolerated without symptoms [16].

Oral administration of 1,2-DCB to female Wistar rats for 60 or 120 days caused an increase in triglyceride levels in comparison with the controls. The liver ATP levels were reduced in the treated animals [34].

After repeated whole animal exposure of male rats to 1854 mg 1,2-DCB/m^3 air (6 hours/day, 2 or 4 days) increased glutamate dehydrogenase (only after two exposures) and sorbitol dehydrogenase activities were found. The effect, however, was markedly less than that of a single 4 hour exposure [26].

No symptoms of toxicity were seen in a dog (Alsatian) which was exposed to a 1,2-DCB level of 2 ml/m^3, 2 hours daily for 16 days [12].

F344/N rats of both sexes received daily oral doses of 0, 60, 125, 200 (females only), 250 (males only), 500 or 1000 mg 1,2-DCB/kg body weight for 14 days by gavage. All animals in the 1000 mg/kg group died during the study. There was a dose-dependent reduction in body weight gain in all animals [35].

In a 13 week study [35] F344/N rats of both sexes received daily oral doses (gavage) of 0, 30, 60, 125, 250 or 500 mg 1,2-DCB/kg body weight on 5 days a week for 13 weeks. In the highest dose group the mortality of the females was increased, centrilobular necrosis and hepatocellular degeneration developed in the liver and lymphocyte deficiency in the thymus and spleen. In addition, there was a slight decrease in haemoglobin and haematocrit and, only in the males from this group, degeneration of the renal tubuli and reduction in erythrocyte count. In the animals from the 250 mg/kg group, necrosis of individual hepatocytes could be seen. In the 125 mg/kg group slight hepatocellular necrosis developed in just a few animals.

B6C3F$_1$ mice of both sexes were given daily doses of 0, 250, 500, 1000, 2000 or 4000 mg 1,2-DCB/kg body weight by gavage on 14 consecutive days. Most animals died after the 1,2-DCB treatment. Liver necrosis was found at doses of 250 mg/kg body weight or more. Because of the high mortality, the study was repeated using lower doses – 0, 30, 60, 125, 250 or 500 mg/kg body weight and day. One male from the 500 mg/kg group and one female from the 125 mg/kg group died. At the end of the study no macroscopically visible pathological changes were found in the survivors [35].

In another 13 week study with B6C3F$_1$ mice of both sexes, the animals were given daily oral (gavage) doses of 0, 30, 60, 125, 250 or 500 mg 1,2-DCB/kg body weight on 5 days per week. Many animals from the 500 mg/kg group died with centrilobular necrosis in the liver, hepatocellular degeneration, lymphocyte deficiency in the thymus and spleen as well as multifocal mineralization of the myocardial fibres and the skeletal muscles. Necrosis of individual hepatocytes developed in males from the 250 mg/kg group. No liver changes were found after 125 mg/kg body weight [35].

Male Wistar rats received daily doses of 500 mg 1,2-DCB/kg body weight for 7 days by gavage. No hyaline droplet formation was observed in the kidneys [36].

3.4 Chronic toxicity and carcinogenicity

Rats received daily oral doses of 0.001, 0.01 or 0.1 mg 1,2-DCB/kg body weight for 9 months. No symptoms developed in the animals of the 0.001 mg/kg group; in the other two groups there were changes in the conditioned reflexes, reduction in haematopoiesis and liver changes [37].

Rats, mice and guinea pigs were exposed to 1,2-DCB concentrations of 294 or 558 mg/m^3 air 7 hours daily on 5 days per week for 6–7 months. In addition 2 female monkeys were exposed to 558 mg 1,2-DCB/m^3. No symptoms of toxicity developed [16].

One carcinogenicity study with rats and mice has been published [35]. Groups of 50 male and 50 female F344/N rats received daily doses of 0, 60 or 120 mg/kg body weight on 5 days per week for 103 weeks by gavage. Survival was reduced in the males from the 120 mg/kg group . Body weight gain was unaffected even at the highest dose. The 120 mg/kg dose caused frequent renal tubular regeneration in the males. The spectrum of tumours obtained for the treated animals gave no evidence for a carcinogenic effect of 1,2-DCB. Thus 1,2-DCB was classified according to the NTP criteria as not carcinogenic in F344/N rats of either sex at doses of 60 or 120 mg/kg body weight and day.

Groups of 50 male and 50 female B6C3F$_1$ mice received daily doses of 0, 60 or 120 mg 1,2-DCB/kg body weight on 5 days per week for 103 weeks by gavage. There were no differences between control and treated animals with respect to body weight gain and mortality. A treatment-related increase in renal tubular regeneration was seen in the male mice of both dosage groups. The spectrum of tumours obtained for the treated animals yielded no evidence for a carcinogenic effect of 1,2-DCB in mice. Thus 1,2-DCB was classified according to the NTP criteria as not carcinogenic in B6C3F$_1$ mice of either sex at doses of 60 or 120 mg/kg body weight and day [35].

1,2-DCB was also tested for tumour-promoting effects in a rat liver foci bioassay. 18–24 hours after a 2/3 partial hepatectomy, rats of both sexes were given a single oral dose of 51 mg diethylnitrosamine/kg body weight followed by an i.p. injection of 147 mg 1,2-DCB/kg body weight after 1 and 5 weeks. The animals were killed two weeks after the second 1,2-DCB injection. 1,2-DCB did not cause an increase in γ-glutamyltranspeptidase positive foci in the rat livers after induction with diethylnitrosamine [38].

4 Genotoxicity

1,2-DCB was not mutagenic in numerous Ames tests, with or without S9 mix [39–44]. 1,2-DCB was also not mutagenic in the point mutation assay with *Escherichia coli* WP2 [42] or *Aspergillus nidulans* [45]. A test for 1,2-DCB-induced DNA damage in a polymerase I deficient strain of *E. coli* gave positive results; a similar test with a recombination deficient strain of *Bacillus subtilis* was negative [42]. 1,2-DCB was inactive in an assay for DNA damage in the eukaryote, *Saccharomyces cerevisiae* D3 [42].

With human lymphocytes in cell culture, in the absence of S9 mix and in the concentration range 1.47–147 µg/ml, 1,2-DCB produced a marked reduction in the rate of ^{3}H-thymidine incorporation into DNA and at 147 µg/ml cell survival was 15%. In the presence of S9 mix the ^{3}H-thymidine incorporation rate was not decreased and cell survival at 147 µg 1,2-DCB/ml was about 50% [46].

HeLa cells were incubated for 30 minutes with 350 µg 1,2-DCB/ml and the incorporation of ^{3}H-uridine into RNA and of ^{14}C-labelled amino acids into protein was measured. 1,2-DCB inhibited both synthetic processes almost completely [47].

In a micronucleus test, male NMRI mice received two i.p. injections 24 hours apart with 93.5, 187.5, 281 or 375 mg 1,2-DCB/kg body weight and were killed 30 hours after the first injection. A dose-dependent increase in the number of micronuclei was found [19].

5 Reproductive and Developmental Toxicity

In a teratology study [48] pregnant rats and rabbits were exposed to 1,2-DCB concentrations of 600, 1200 or 2400 mg/m^3 air for 6 hours per day from day 6 to day 15 (rats) or day 6 to day 18 (rabbits) of gestation. In rats of all dose groups maternal toxicity was evident in reduced body weight gain and, in the highest dose group, in increased liver weights. In rabbits only the highest concentration, 2400 mg/m^3, produced a transitory reduction in body weight gain. In spite of the high concentrations, no indications of embryotoxic, foetotoxic or teratogenic effects were found in either rats or rabbits.

In another study [49] rats were given daily doses of 50, 100 or 300 mg 1,2-DCB/kg body weight from day 6 to day 15 of gestation by gavage. No teratogenic effects were seen (no other details were given in the abstract).

6 Manifesto (MAK value, classification)

In most studies on the toxicity of 1,2-dichlorobenzene, the substance was administered orally. High doses have been shown to cause necrosis of the liver and kidney and haematotoxic effects. Appropriate inhalation studies are not available. Thus a MAK value must be derived indirectly.

Several assays for point mutations and DNA damaging effects gave negative results with 1,2-dichlorobenzene which, however, proved to be clastogenic when administered by i.p. injection in a micronucleus test. In long-term studies with rats and mice there was no evidence for a carcinogenic potential even at high doses. Inhaled or orally administered, 1,2-dichlorobenzene was neither foetotoxic nor teratogenic.

The long-established MAK value for 1,2-dichlorobenzene, 50 ml/m^3 (300 mg/m^3), will be retained for the present since there is no evidence of adverse effects at this concentration. However, there is no appropriate documentation available of industrial experience with persons exposed to the substance or of animal studies which would allow the direct deduction of a MAK value. Such studies are necessary to substantiate or discredit the current MAK value.

1,2-Dichlorobenzene is classified in the peak limitation category II,1 because of its pharmacokinetics and because systemic toxicity is the critical parameter in the range of the MAK value. Since it is readily absorbed through intact skin it receives the designation H.

Since the studies of reproductive toxicology in rats and rabbits produced no indication of embryotoxic or foetotoxic effects even at 2400 mg/m³ (400 ml/m³) and because no reports of adverse effects in man are known, the substance is classified in group C.

7 References

1. Dowty, B., D. Carlisle, J. L. Laseter: *Science 187*, 75 (1975)
2. Jacobs, A., M. Blangetti, E. Hellmund: *Vom Wasser 43*, 259 (1974)
3. Azouz, W. M., D. V. Parke, R. T. Williams: *Biochem. J. 59*, 410 (1955)
4. Reid, W. D., G. Krishna: *Exp. molec. Path. 18*, 80 (1973)
5. Tanaka, A., M. Sato, T. Tsuchiya, T. Adachi, T. Niimura, T. Yamaha: *Arch. Toxicol. 59*, 82 (1986)
6. Tsuchiya, T., T. Yamaha: *Agric. Biol. Chem. 47*, 1163 (1983)
7. Downing, J. G.: *J. Amer. med. Ass. 112*, 1457 (1939)
8. Dupont, R.: *Arch. Mal. prof. 1*, 312 (1938)
9. Gadrat, J., J. Monnier, A. Ribet, R. Bourse: *Arch. Mal. prof. 23*, 710 (1962)
10. Girard, R., F. Tolot, P. Martin, J. Bouret: *J. Méd. Lyon 50*, 771 (1969)
11. Hallowell, M.: *Arch. Dis. Childh. 34*, 74 (1959)
12. Riedel, H.: *Arch. Gewerbepath. Gewerbehyg. 10*, 546 (1941)
13. Jan, J.: *Bull. environm. Contam. Toxicol. 30*, 595 (1983)
14. Jones, K. H., D. M. Sanderson, D. N. Noakes: *Wld Rev. Pest. Control 7*, 135 (1968)
15. Thomson, W. T. (Ed.): *Agricultural Chemicals*, Book III, p 33, Thomson Publications, Fresno, CA, USA, 1978–79
16. Hollingsworth, R. L., V. K. Rowe, F. Oyen, T. R. Torkelson, E. M. Adams: *Arch. industr. Hlth 17*, 180 (1958)
17. Bonnet, P., Y. Morele, G. Raoult, D. Zissu, D. Gradiski: *Arch. Mal. prof. 43*, 261 (1982)
18. NIOSH: *Registry of Toxic Effects of Chemical Substances (RTECS)*, Supplement 1983–84, Vol. 1, p 405, 1985
19. Mohtashamipur, E., R. Triebel, H. Straeter, K. Norpoth: *Mutagenesis 2*, 111 (1987)
20. Cameron, G. R., J. C. Thomas, S. A. Ashmore, J. L. Buchan, E. H. Warren, A. W. McKenney Hughes: *J. Path. Bact. 44*, 281 (1937)
21. De Ceaurriz, J. C., J. C. Micillino, P. Bonnet, J. P. Guenier: *Toxicol. Lett. 9*, 137 (1981)
22. Yang, K. H., R. E. Peterson, J. M. Fujimoto: *Toxicol. appl. Pharmacol. 47*, 505 (1979)
23. Thyssen, J.: Unpublished report, Bericht Nr. 8556, Bayer AG, D-5600 Wuppertal-Elberfeld, 7.8.1979
24. Stine, E. R., J. Barr, I. G. Sipes: *Pharmacologist 28*, 181 (1986)
25. Brondeau, M. T., P. Bonnet, J. P. Guenier, J. De Ceaurriz: *Toxicol. Lett. 19*, 139 (1983)
26. Brondeau, M. T., M. Ban, P. Bonnet, J. P. Guenier, J. De Ceaurriz: *Toxicol. Lett. 31*, 159 (1986)
27. Brodie, B. B., W. D. Reid, A. K. Cho, G. Sipes, G. Krishna, J. R. Gillette: *Proc. nat. Acad. Sci. (Wash.) 68*, 160 (1971)
28. Manis, J., G. Kim: *Life Sci. 26*, 1431 (1980)
29. Charbonneau, M., J. Strasser, E. A. Lock, J. A. Swenberg: *3rd Int. Symp. on Nephrotoxicity*, Abstract Y8, Surrey, England, August 1987
30. Morse, D. L., E. L. Baker (Jr.), R. D. Kimbrough, C. L. Wisseman: *Clin. Toxicol. 15*, 13 (1979)
31. Rimington, C., G. Ziegler: *Biochem. Pharmacol. 12*, 1387 (1963)
32. Ariyoshi, T., K. Ideguchi, K. Iwasaki, M. Arakaki: *Chem. pharm. Bull. 23*, 824 (1975)
33. Eida, K., F. Hasumi, N. Nishimura, M. Kikutani: *Chem. pharm. Bull. 25*, 1209 (1977)
34. Mori, T.: *Okayama Igakkai Zasshi 94*, 967 (1983); cited in *Chem. Abstr. 99*, 17696 y (1983)
35. National Toxicology Program (NTP), Techn. Rep. No. 255, US Dept. of Health and Human Services, Research Triangle Park, N.C. 27709, USA, 1985
36. Bomhard, E., G. Luckhaus: *3rd Int. Symp. on Nephrotoxicity*, Abstract, Surrey, England, August 1987

37. Varshavskaya, S. P.: *Nauch. Tr. Aspir. Ordinatorov. 1-i, Mosk. Med. Inst.* 1967, 175–177; cited in US-EPA, Draft Criteria Document, Washington DC, USA, 1984
38. Herren-Freund, S. L., M. A. Pereira: *Environm. Hlth Perspect. 69*, 59 (1986)
39. Connor, T. H., J. C. Theiss, H. A. Hanna, D. K. Monteith, T. S. Matney: *Toxicol. Lett. 25*, 33 (1985)
40. Haworth, S., T. Lawlor, K. Mortelmans, W. Speck, E. Zeiger: *Environm. Mutag. 5, Suppl. 1*, 3 (1983)
41. Shimizu, M., Y. Yasui, N. Matsumoto: *Mutat. Res. 116*, 217 (1983)
42. Waters, M. D., S. S. Sandhu, V. F. Simmon, K. E. Mortelmans, A. D. Mitchell, T. A. Jorgenson, D. C. L. Jones, R. Valencia, N. E. Garrett: *Basic Life Sci. 21*, 275 (1982)
43. Andersen, K. J., E. B. Leighty, M. T. Takahashi: *J. agric. Food Chem. 20*, 649 (1972)
44. Tennant, R. W., S. Stasiewicz, J. W. Spalding: *Environm. Mutag. 8*, 205 (1986)
45. Prasad, J.: *Canad. J. Microbiol. 16*, 369 (1970)
46. Perocco, P., S. Bolognesi, W. Alberghini: *Toxicol. Lett. 16*, 69 (1983)
47. Myhr, B. C.: *J. agric. Food Chem. 21*, 362 (1973)
48. Hayes, W. C., T. R. Hanley (Jr.), T. S. Gushow, K. A. Johnson, J. A. John: *Fundam. appl. Toxicol. 5*, 190 (1985)
49. Ruddick, J. A., W. D. Black, D. C. Villeneuve, V. E. Valli: *Teratology 27*, 73 A (1983)
50. Ogata, M., T. Hasegawa, T. Mori, T. Meguro: *Industr. Hlth 19*, 31 (1981)

completed 19. 5. 1988

1,3-Dichlorobenzene

Classification/MAK value:	**not yet established** **see Section IIb)** **MAK list 1988**
Synonyms:	*m*-dichlorobenzene 1,3-DCB
Chemical name (CAS):	1,3-dichlorobenzene
CAS number:	541-73-1
Structural formula:	

Molecular formula:	$C_6H_4Cl_2$
Molecular weight:	147
Melting point:	$-26.3\,°C$
Boiling point:	$173\,°C$
Vapour pressure at 20 °C:	2 hPa

1 ml/m³ (ppm) = 6.12 mg/m³   **1 mg/m³ = 0.164 ml/m³ (ppm)**

1 Toxic Effects and Modes of Action

1,3-Dichlorobenzene (1,3-DCB) is a highly lipophilic substance and so is readily taken up by the usual routes and subjected to active oxidative metabolism. It is moderately irritating to mucous membranes and, after being assimilated in high doses, causes damage to parenchymatous organs, especially liver and kidney. It also has a depressive effect on the central nervous system. In contrast to 1,4-DCB, it does not cause an increase in hyaline droplets in the renal epithelia of the male rat.

1,3-DCB causes the induction of various enzymes in the liver, especially δ-amino-laevulinate synthetase. This is, however, probably not an effect of 1,3-DCB itself but of its metabolites 3,5-dichlorophenylmethylsulfoxide and 3,5-dichlorophenyl-methylsulfone.

Studies of the genotoxic effects of 1,3-DCB have not produced a consistent picture. Negative results have been obtained with bacteria and some positive ones with yeasts and in assays for DNA repair; clastogenic effects (micronucleus test) have also been reported. Carcinogenicity studies have not been carried out. No evidence for promoting activity of 1,3-DCB was obtained in an initiation-promotion study.

Reproductive toxicological studies produced no evidence of embryotoxic or teratogenic effects of 1,3-DCB.

1.1 Pharmacokinetics

The maximal blood concentration of 1,3-DCB was attained 30 minutes after oral administration of a dose of 200 mg/kg body weight to rats. Within the next 12 hours the decrease in the concentration of 1,3-DCB in blood was biphasic and exponential, with a half-life of 4.4 hours. The blood levels of the sulfoxide metabolites reached a maximum after 12 hours and then fell rapidly. The maximal blood levels of the sulfone metabolites were found 24–48 hours after administration of 1,3-DCB, and even after 120 hours the levels of 3,5-dichlorophenylmethylsulfone were still relatively high. The sulfoxide was mostly excreted within 48 hours in faeces and urine, the sulfone within 120 hours [1].

The metabolites, 2,4-dichlorophenylmethylsulfoxide and 3,5-dichlorophenylmethylsulfoxide, could no longer be detected in blood or liver 48 hours after oral administration of 200 mg 1,3-DCB/kg body weight to rats. 1,3-DCB itself was no longer detectable in blood or liver 12 hours after administration [2].

In rabbits the excretion of metabolites was complete 5 days after oral administration of 500 mg 1,3-DCB/kg body weight [3]. An increase in the excretion of sulfur-containing compounds in urine was observed after oral administration of 1,3-DCB doses of 1300 to 2940 mg/kg body weight to dogs [4].

In the urine of rabbits given 500 mg 1,3-DCB/kg body weight orally, 54% of the metabolites were in the conjugated form, mostly as glucuronides (36%), mercapturic acids (11%), ether soluble sulfates (7%) and also 3,5-dichlorophenol (3.6%) and dichlorocatechol (2.6%) [3]. In another study too, after oral dosing of rabbits, glucuronides (31%), sulfates (11%), mercapturic acids (9%) and catechols (4%) were found as well as 2,4-dichlorophenylmercapturic acid and 3,5-dichlorocatechol [5].

When mice were treated with various chlorinated benzenes (monochlorobenzene to tetrachlorobenzene) methylsulfonate metabolites were found in the urine [6]. After intraperitoneal injection of 1,3-DCB in mice the urine contained the metabolites mercaptoacetate, mercaptolactate, mercaptopyruvate, cystamine, N-acetylcysteine, cysteinylglycine and thiol dimers [7].

After oral administration of 200 mg 1,3-DCB/kg body weight to rats, the main metabolites in blood and urine were 2,4-dichlorophenylmethylsulfone and 3,5-dichlorophenylmethylsulfone together with the corresponding sulfoxides. Cysteine conjugates were not detected in urine [1]. After intraperitoneal injection of a dose of 200 mg 1,3-DCB/kg body weight into rats whose bile duct had been cannulated, no dichlorophenylmethylsulfone or only very little could be detected in blood, liver, kidneys, adipose tissue or bile. Pretreatment of the animals with antibiotics also led to a decrease in these metabolites in blood and the three tissues. No 1,3-DCB was detected in the bile. It may therefore be concluded that the precursors of the methylsulfonyl metabolites are excreted into the intestinal tract with the bile and then converted into sulfones by the action of intestinal bacteria [8].

Oral administration of 1,3-DCB produced marked depletion of liver glutathione. The glutathione content of the kidneys was not changed. In animals pretreated with diethyl maleate, the 1,3-DCB treatment did not lead to further glutathione depletion but to a marked reduction in the urine levels of sulfone and sulfoxide metabolites. The mercapturic acid levels in urine were unchanged so that the mechanism for production of sulfones and sulfoxides is probably different from that for mercapturic acids [1].

In vitro, liver microsomes form glutathione adducts with 1,3-DCB [9].

1.2 Enzyme induction

There is evidence that the alterations in liver parameters observed after administration of 1,3-DCB are caused by metabolites. After intraperitoneal injection of 50 µmoles 3,5-dichlorophenylmethylsulfoxide/kg body weight into rats, the activities of aniline hydroxylase and aminopyrine-N-demethylase were seen to increase; there was also an increase in the level of cytochrome P450 and a slight increase in cytochrome b5 in the liver. Similar results were obtained when 3,5-dichlorophenylmethylsulfone or 3,5-dichlorophenylmethylsulfoxide was administered [10].

The involvement of these metabolites is also indicated by the fact that after oral administration of 1,3-DCB the changes in microsomal aminopyrine-N-demethylase activity and cytochrome P450 levels in the liver parallel the hepatic levels of 3,5-dichlorophenylmethylsulfone. The authors, however, do not exclude the possibility that 1,3-DCB itself has inducing activity [2].

In rats with a cannulated bile duct and in animals pretreated with antibiotics (which causes a reduction in the metabolic production of the sulfones), in contrast to normal animals, no increase of aminopyrine-N-demethylase activity and no increase in cytochrome levels were observed after intraperitoneal injection of 1,3-DCB. Administration of 2,4-dichlorophenylmethylsulfone or 3,5-dichlorophenylmethylsulfone led to enzyme induction in both normal and pretreated rats. Thus the enzyme induction is very likely not an effect of 1,3-DCB itself but of the 2,4-dichlorophenylmethylsulfone or 3,5-dichlorophenylmethylsulfone produced in intermediary metabolism [8].

2 Effects in Man

In an analytical study [11], traces of 1,3-DCB were detected in mothers' milk (< 5 µg/kg milk) but not in adipose tissue.

Traces of 1,3-DCB as well as of the other two DCB-isomers were detected in blood plasma from residents of the city of New Orleans [12]. In residents of the cities of Bayonne and Elizabeth, concentrations of 1,3-DCB (including 1,4-dichlorobenzene) of 8.1 µg/m^3 were measured in exhaled air [13].

3 Effects on Animals

3.1 Acute toxicity

3.1.1 Oral administration

For female rats the LD_{50} was determined as about 2300 mg/kg body weight (95% confidence interval 2052–2591). In preliminary experiments there were no differences between the sexes. Macroscopic findings included pale brown discoloration of the liver with distinct lobule markings and brownish discoloration of the adrenals [14].

A single oral dose of 500 mg 1,3-DCB/kg body weight and day (by gastric intubation) led to increased porphyrin levels in the Harderian gland 24 hours after the administration. The level then returned to normal. The δ-aminolaevulinate synthetase activity in the liver was higher than the control values by a factor of 2–3; in the Harderian gland the effect on the δ-aminolaevulinate synthetase activity was marginal, maximal activity being attained 12 hours after 1,3-DCB administration [15].

3.1.2 Inhalation

In the inhalation hazard test (7 hours inhalation of an air stream saturated with 1,3-DCB at 20 °C) all animals survived the exposure. Hyperactivity, increased respiration rate, irregular respiration, hyporeflexia, trembling and balance disorders were observed as well as unspecific symptoms. Autopsy of the animals at the end of the study revealed nothing unusual [16].

3.1.3 Intraperitoneal administration

The mean lethal dose for male NMRI mice after intraperitoneal injection was 1062 mg 1,3-DCB/kg body weight [17].

Low-grade liver necrosis was observed in rats who had been given 0.03 ml 1,3-DCB by intraperitoneal injection. If the animals had been pretreated with phenobarbital then glycogen loss and massive necrosis was found [9].

48 hours after intraperitoneal injection of 200 mg 1,3-DCB/kg body weight into rats, the aminopyrine-N-demethylase activity and cytochrome P450 level in the liver were significantly increased. Aniline hydroxylase activity and cytochrome b5 levels were unchanged. The hexobarbital sleeping time and sleeping intensity were reduced [2].

3.1.4 Toxicity to skin and mucous membranes

Marked irritation of rabbit skin was evident after 24 hour occlusive exposure to 0.5 ml 1,3-DCB. 0.1 ml 1,3-DCB in the rabbit eye for 24 hours caused mild to marked swelling of the conjunctiva and slight clouding of the cornea [18].

3.1.5 In vitro studies

After incubation of rat liver fractions with 1,3-DCB in concentrations ranging from 0.147 to 1.470 mg/ml, decarboxylation of uroporphyrinogen and synthesis of coproporphyrinogen were unaffected or only very slightly reduced [19].

Incubated with rat liver mitochondria for 1 min, 35 µg 1,3-DCB/ml decoupled oxidative phosphorylation and caused release of K^+ ions by damaging the mitochondrial membrane [20].

3.2 Subacute and subchronic toxicity

After oral administration of 1,3-DCB to rats at a dose of 250 mg/kg/day for three days, relative liver weights were increased, as were the levels of microsomal inorganic phosphorus and protein. Aminopyrine-N-demethylase, aniline hydroxylase and δ-aminolaevulinate synthetase activities were increased. Microsomal cytochrome P450, glycogen and triglyceride levels in the liver were unchanged [21].

Oral administration of 1,3-DCB (800 mg/kg body weight and day for 1, 3 or 5 days) to rats caused a 3-fold to 4-fold increase in δ-aminolaevulinate synthetase activity, marked reduction in the hexobarbital sleeping time and increased degradation of bishydroxycoumarin. The blood levels of 1,3-DCB on day 3 were higher than on day 5 so that 1,3-DCB probably induces its own degradation. Minimal vacuolization of the liver was established microscopically. Oral administration of 1,3-DCB (800 mg/kg body weight and day) for 9 days induced an increase in coproporphyrin III excretion in urine which reached its maximum after 3 days. Uroporphyrinuria was not demonstrated. Higher doses (900–1000 mg/kg body weight) caused severe coproporphyrinuria and measurable uroporphyrinuria [22].

Rats were given oral doses of 500 mg 1,3-DCB/kg body weight and day for 1, 3 or 5 days and were killed 24 hours after their last dose. An increase in relative liver weights (relative to body weight) was found [15].

No evidence of an increased accumulation of hyaline droplets in the kidney was found in 5 male Wistar rats which had received daily oral doses of 500 mg 1,3-DCB/kg body weight for 7 days [23].

3.3 Chronic toxicity

There are no data available on the chronic toxicity of 1,3-DCB.

4 Reproductive and Developmental Toxicity

Groups of pregnant rats received daily oral doses of 50, 100 or 200 mg 1,3-DCB/kg body weight from day 6 to day 15 of gestation. Body weight gain and clinical chemical as well as histopathological parameters were used to assess maternal toxicity; for embryotoxicity litter size and foetal weights were determined and viscera and skeletons were examined. There was no evidence of an embryotoxic or teratogenic potential of 1,3-DCB (more details are not available from this study, published only as an abstract) [31].

5 Genotoxicity

5.1 Point mutations

In tests with the *Salmonella typhimurium* strains TA98, TA100, TA1535, TA1537 and TA1538 with and without an added metabolizing system (S9 mix from livers of rats or hamsters), 1,3-DCB was not mutagenic [25–28]. Similarly, in the *S. typhimurium* strains UTH8414 and UTH8413, whose DNA repair capacity is intact, no increase in the number of revertants was obtained with 1,3-DCB [28]. With *Escherichia coli* WP2 uvrA there was also no evidence of a mutagenic effect [25]. In the yeast strain *Saccharomyces cerevisiae* D3, 1,3-DCB induced mitotic recombination [25]. In *Aspergillus nidulans* 1,3-DCB caused an increased back mutation rate [29].

5.2 DNA damage

1,3-DCB yielded positive results in an assay for DNA repair with *E. coli* polA$^+$ and polA$^-$, with *Bacillus subtilis* rec$^+$ and rec$^-$ the result was negative [25].

After incubation of human lymphocytes with 1,3-DCB (1.47–147 mg/ml) a reduction in ^{3}H-thymidine incorporation in the cells was found. This effect was not detectable in the presence of S9 mix [30].

5.3 Chromosome damage

In a micronucleus test [17] NMRI mice were given two i.p. injections with 87.5, 175, 262.5 or 350 mg 1,3-DCB/kg body weight 24 hours apart and killed 30 hours after the first injection. 1,3-DCB induced a dose-dependent increase in the number of micronuclei.

6 Carcinogenicity

The tumour promoting activity of 1,3-DCB was studied in a rat liver foci bioassay. As initiator, the animals were given 51 mg diethylnitrosamine/kg body weight by gastric intubation, followed 1 and 5 weeks after the diethylnitrosamine by two i.p. injections of 147 mg 1,3-DCB/kg body weight. There was no evidence that 1,3-DCB has promoting activity [24].

7 Manifesto (MAK value, classification)

The data available on the toxicity of 1,3-DCB are limited to results from studies of acute exposures, enzyme induction and metabolism.

1,3-Dichlorobenzene was not mutagenic in the Ames test but had clastogenic effects after intraperitoneal injection in the micronucleus test. The results from other test systems (DNA repair) are contradictory. No embryotoxic nor teratogenic effects were observed in animal studies.

For 1,3-dichlorobenzene there are no systematic studies of persons exposed occupationally nor is data appropriate for the derivation of a MAK value available from animal studies. Thus a MAK value cannot be established. It is recommended that occupational-medical and animal studies be initiated so that a MAK value can be determined.

1,3-Dichlorobenzene is therefore added to Section IIb of the List of MAK Values.

8 References

1. Kimura, R., H. Sano, K. Itagaki, T. Kongure, M. Sato, T. Murata: *J. Pharmacobiodyn. 7*, 234 (1984)
2. Kimura, R., M. Kawai, Y. Kata, M. Sato, T. Aimoto, T. Murata: *Toxicol. appl. Pharmacol. 78*, 300 (1985)
3. Parke, D. V., R. T. Williams: *Biochem. J. 59*, 415 (1955)
4. Callow, E. H., T. S. Hele: *Biochem. J. 20*, 598 (1926)
5. Menzie, C. M.: *U. S., Fish Wildl. Serv., Spec. Sci. Rep.: Wildl. 212*, 381 pp, Washington DC, USA, 1978
6. Kitamura, S., K. Sumino, T. Mio: *Jap. J. Hyg. 32*, 200 (1977)
7. Mio, T., K. Sumino: *Environm. Hlth Perspect. 59*, 129 (1985)
8. Kato, Y., T. Kogure, M. Sato, T. Murata, R. Kimura: *Toxicol. appl. Pharmacol. 82*, 505 (1986)
9. Brodie, B. B., W. D. Reid, A. K. Cho, G. Sipes, G. Krishna, J. R. Gillette: *Proc. nat. Acad. Sci. (Wash.) 68*, 160 (1971)
10. Kimura, R., M. Kawai, M. Sato, T. Aimoto, T. Murata: *Toxicol. appl. Pharmacol. 67*, 338 (1983)
11. Jan, J.: *Bull. environm. Contam. Toxicol. 30*, 595 (1983)
12. Dowty, B., D. Carlisle, J. L. Laseter, J. Storer: *Science 187*, 75 (1975)
13. Wallace, L., E. Pellizzari, T. Hartwell, H. Zelon, C. Sparacino, R. Perritt, R. Whitmore: *J. occup. Med. 28*, 603 (1986)
14. Leist, K. H., W. Weigand: unpublished report, GT-Bericht 79.0207, Hoechst AG, D-6230 Frankfurt, 1979
15. Eida, K., F. Hasumi, N. Nishimura, M. Kikutani: *Chem. pharm. Bull. 25*, 1209 (1977)
16. Hollander, H., W. Weigand: unpublished report, GT-Bericht 79.0241, Hoechst AG, D-6230 Frankfurt, 1979
17. Mohtashamipur, E., R. Triebel, H. Straeter, K. Norpoth: *Mutagenesis 2*, 111 (1987)
18. Leist, K. H., W. Weigand: unpublished report, GT-Bericht 79.0208, Hoechst AG, D-6230 Frankfurt, 1979
19. Rios de Molina, M. D. C., W. de Calmanovici, L. C. San Marin de Viale: *Int. J. Biochem. 12*, 1027 (1980)
20. Ogata, M., T. Hasegawa, T. Mori, T. Meguro: *Industr. Hlth 19*, 31 (1981)
21. Ariyoshi, T., K. Ideguchi, M. Iwasaki, M. Arakaki: *Chem. pharm. Bull. 23*, 824 (1975)
22. Poland, A., J. Goldstein, P. Hickman, V. W. Burse: *Biochem. Pharmacol. 20*, 1281 (1971)
23. Bomhard, E., G. Luckhaus, M. Marsmann, A. Zywietz: unpublished report, Bayer AG, D-5600 Wuppertal-Elberfeld, 1987
24. Herren-Freund, S. L., M. A. Pereira: *Environm. Hlth Perspect. 69*, 59 (1986)
25. Waters, H. D., S. S. Sandhu, V. F. Simmon, K. E. Mortelmans, A. D. Mitchell, T. A. Jorgenson, D. C. L. Jones, R. Valencia, N. E. Garrett: in Fleck, R. A., A. Hollaender (Eds.): *Genetic Toxicology*, p 275, Plenum, New York, 1982
26. Haworth, S., T. Lawlor, K. Mortelmans, W. Speck, E. Zeiger: *Environm. Mutag. 5 (Suppl. 1)*, 3 (1983)
27. Shimizu, M., Y. Yasui, M. Matsumoto: *Mutat. Res. 116*, 217 (1983)
28. Connor, T. H., J. C. Theiss, H. A. Hanna, D. K. Monteith, T. S. Matney: *Toxicol. Lett. 25*, 33 (1985)
29. Prasad, I.: *Canad. J. Microbiol. 16*, 369 (1970)
30. Perocco, P., S. Bolognesi, W. Alberghini: *Toxicol. Lett. 16*, 69 (1983)
31. Ruddick, J. A., W. D. Black, D. C. Villeneuve, V. E. Valli: *Teratology 27*, 73 A (1983)

completed 19. 5. 1988

1,2-Dichloromethoxyethane   H

Classification/MAK value:	**see Section III B** **MAK List 1988**
Classification/MAK value dates from:	**1988**
Synonyms:	α,β-dichloroethylmethyl ether 1,2-dichloroethylmethyl ether
Chemical name (CAS):	1,2-dichloro-1-methoxyethane
CAS number:	41683-62-9
Structural formula:	$H_2CCl-CHCl-OCH_3$
Molecular formula:	$C_3H_6Cl_2O$
Molecular weight:	129
Melting point:	not specified
Boiling point (range):	127-132 °C
Vapour pressure at 20 °C:	not specified

1 ml/m³ (ppm) = 5.35 mg/m³   **1 mg/m³ = 0.186 ml/m³ (ppm)**

1 Toxic Effects and Modes of Action

1,2-Dichloromethoxyethane is strongly irritating and corrosive to skin and mucous membranes. It has alkylating potential and is mutagenic *in vitro*. These properties and the structural analogy with other α-halogenated ethers are indicative of a carcinogenic potential.

2 Effects in Man

There are no publications available on effects of 1,2-dichloromethoxyethane in man.

3 Effects on Animals

3.1 Acute toxicity and irritant potential

LD$_{50}$ rat, oral:	~ 300-900 µl/kg	[1]
LD$_{50}$ mouse, oral:	~ 830 µl/kg	[2]

LD_{50} mouse, i.p.: $\sim 20-70$ µl/kg   [2]
LD_{50} rabbit, dermal: < 200 mg/kg   [1]

The principal symptoms were apathy and dyspnoea.

Inhalation of an atmosphere enriched with 1,2-dichloromethoxyethane vapour (Inhalation Hazard Test) was lethal for all exposed rats within 3 minutes [1].

In the rabbit eye, corneal opacity developed after inhalation of the vapour and direct contact led to additional corrosion [1].

The undiluted substance had a corrosive effect within one minute on the dorsal skin of the rabbit [1].

3.2 Subacute toxicity

In a 4 week gavage study [3] the substance dissolved in polyethylene glycol 400 was administered in doses of 75, 150, 300 and 600 µl/kg body weight on 5 days per week to groups of 20 male and 20 female rats. In the highest dose group there were deaths (17/40 animals) and also unspecific symptoms of toxicity such as reduced appetite and reduced body weight gain in the males, dyspnoea, abdominal position, ruffled fur and expressions of pain in both sexes. Increased glucose and a shift to the left in the differential blood count were seen in clinical laboratory tests. Autopsy revealed increased relative weights of kidney and liver and, in the histological picture of both organs, increased fat deposition and hepatosis or nephrosis. After 300 µg 1,2-dichloromethoxyethane/kg body weight only the relative liver weights were increased; this finding was not reversible within the subsequent 14 day observation period. 150 and 75 µl/kg were tolerated without adverse effects.

4 Genotoxicity

In bone marrow cells from Chinese hamster chromosome analysis was carried out 24, 48 and 72 hours after oral administration of 300 µl/kg [4] or 6, 24 and 48 hours after oral administration of 500 µl/kg [5]. The number of aberrant metaphases (gaps and isogaps) was marginally increased above control values. In addition, occasional chromosome breaks were found in treated animals (as compared with untreated animals). 4 male and 4 female animals were used per treatment group (3 time intervals) and 50 metaphases were analysed per animal.

In the rat (Sprague-Dawley) after repeated administration of 75, 150, 300 or 600 µl/kg body weight and day for 4 weeks (20 administered doses, 5 animals per dose group and sex) no chromosome aberrations were observed in the bone marrow cells [6]. In the 600 µl/kg group 3 animals died; the other doses were tolerated without clinically visible symptoms of toxicity.

In the Ames test 1,2-dichloromethoxyethane was shown to be mutagenic in the *Salmonella typhimurium* strains TA100 and TA1535 (base pair) with and without metabolic activation. Revertants were increased by a factor of $1.7-3$ [7]. No mutagenic effects were seen in TA98, TA1537 or TA1538. The dose range used in the test was $4-2500$ µg/plate. From $100-500$ µg/plate toxic effects were seen which were reduced by the addition of S9 mix.

In the cell transformation test with 3T3 mouse cells positive results (transformation) were obtained with 1,2-dichloromethoxyethane [8]. The concentrations tested were 5×10^{-3} to 5×10^{-2} µl/ml in the presence of S9 mix and 2×10^{-5} to 2×10^{-4} µl/ml without S9 mix.

5 Manifesto (MAK value, classification)

1,2-Dichloromethoxyethane is an α-haloether and so is clearly an alkylating agent. Accordingly, the substance is a direct mutagen in various test systems. There are no data available from carcinogenicity studies. 1,2-Dichloromethoxyethane is therefore classified in Section III B of the List of MAK Values. A MAK value cannot be established.

Since it has been demonstrated that toxic amounts can be absorbed through the skin, the substance is designated with an "H".

6 References

1. Gelbke, H.-P., H. Th. Hofmann: *Prüfung der akuten Toxizität und des Reiz-/Ätzpotentials von α,β-Dichlorethylmethylether*, personal communication of unpublished results, BASF Aktiengesellschaft, D-6700 Ludwigshafen, 1963, 1975

2. Gelbke, H.-P., H. Th. Hofmann: *Bericht über die Prüfung der akuten, oralen und intraperitonealen Toxizität von α,β-Dichlorethylmethylether an der Maus*, personal communication of unpublished results, BASF Aktiengesellschaft, D-6700 Ludwigshafen, 1975

3. Gelbke, H.-P., H. Th. Hofmann: *Bericht über die toxikologische Prüfung von α,β-Dichlorethylmethylether im 4-Wochen-Sondierungsversuch an der Ratte*, personal communication of unpublished results, BASF Aktiengesellschaft, D-6700 Ludwigshafen, 1977

4. Gelbke, H.-P., H. Th. Hofmann: *Bericht über die Prüfung von α,β-Dichlorethylmethylether auf mutagene Wirkung am Chinesischen Hamster nach einmaliger oraler Applikation. – Chromosomenuntersuchungen*, personal communication of unpublished results, BASF Aktiengesellschaft, D-6700 Ludwigshafen, 1976

5. Gelbke, H.-P., H. Th. Hofmann: *Bericht über die Prüfung von α,β-Dichlorethylmethylether auf mutagene Wirkung am Chinesischen Hamster nach einmaliger oraler Applikation. – Chromosomenuntersuchungen*, personal communication of unpublished results, BASF Aktiengesellschaft, D-6700 Ludwigshafen, 1975

6. Gelbke, H.-P., H. Th. Hofmann: *Bericht über die Prüfung von α,β-Dichlorethylmethylether auf mutagene Wirkung an Sprague-Dawley-Ratten nach 4wöchiger Sondierung*, personal communication of unpublished results, BASF Aktiengesellschaft, D-6700 Ludwigshafen, 1975

7. Gelbke, H. P., H. Th. Hofmann: *Bericht über die Prüfung von α,β-Dichlorethylmethylether im Ames-Test*, personal communication of unpublished results, BASF Aktiengesellschaft, D-6700 Ludwigshafen, 1980

8. Gelbke, H.-P., H. Th. Hofmann: *Activity of T 1632 in the in vitro mammalian cell transformation assay in the presence and absence of exogenous metabolic activation*, personal communication of unpublished results, BASF Aktiengesellschaft, D-6700 Ludwigshafen, 1981

completed 11.4.1988

1,3-Dichloro-2-propanol

Classification/MAK value:	**see Section III A 2)** **MAK List 1989**
Classification/MAK value dates from:	**1989**
Synonyms:	dichloropropanol dichlorohydrin α-dichlorohydrin glycerol-α,γ-dichlorohydrin *sym*-glycerol dichlorohydrin *sym*-dichloroisopropyl alcohol
Chemical name (CAS):	1,3-dichloro-2-propanol
CAS number:	96-23-1
Structural formula:	$ClH_2C-CHOH-CH_2Cl$
Molecular formula:	$C_3H_6OCl_2$
Molecular weight:	129
Melting point:	$-4\,°C$
Boiling point:	$174.3\,°C$
Vapour pressure at 20 °C:	not specified

1 ml/m³ (ppm) = 5.35 mg/m³   **1 mg/m³ = 0.186 ml/m³ (ppm)**

1 Toxic Effects and Modes of Action

1,3-Dichloro-2-propanol is a direct mutagen and has genotoxic effects in mammalian cells *in vitro*. After oral administration of 1,3-dichloro-2-propanol to rats in the drinking water in a long-term study, increased incidence of tumours was found not only at the site of administration (tongue, oral cavity) but also in other organs (liver, kidney, thyroid). The metabolism of 1,3-dichloro-2-propanol has not yet been studied in detail.

1.1 Pharmacokinetics

There is one study of the metabolism of 1,3-dichloro-2-propanol in the rat in which, after administration of a single oral dose of 1,3-dichloro-2-propanol (50 mg/kg body weight), 3-chloro-2-hydroxypropionic acid (ca. 5% of the applied dose) and N-acetyl-S-(2,3-dihydroxypropyl)cysteine and S,S'-(1,3-bis-cysteinyl)propan-2-ol (ca.

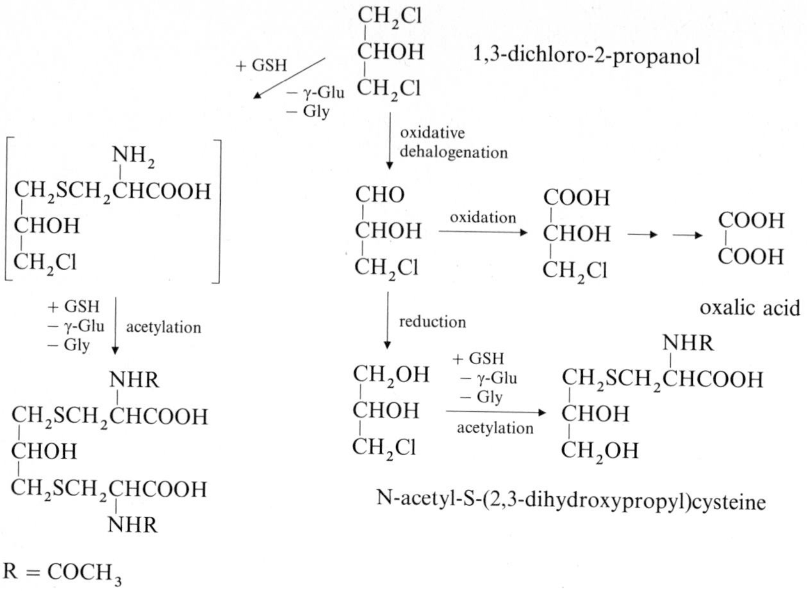

$$
\begin{array}{l}
CH_2Cl \\
CHOH \quad\quad \text{1,3-dichloro-2-propanol} \\
CH_2Cl
\end{array}
$$

+ GSH
− γ-Glu
− Gly

oxidative dehalogenation

$$
\left[
\begin{array}{l}
\quad\quad NH_2 \\
CH_2SCH_2CHCOOH \\
CHOH \\
CH_2Cl
\end{array}
\right]
$$

$$
\begin{array}{l}
CHO \\
CHOH \\
CH_2Cl
\end{array}
\xrightarrow{\text{oxidation}}
\begin{array}{l}
COOH \\
CHOH \\
CH_2Cl
\end{array}
\rightarrow \rightarrow
\begin{array}{l}
COOH \\
COOH
\end{array}
$$

oxalic acid

+ GSH
− γ-Glu
− Gly | acetylation

reduction

$$
\begin{array}{l}
\quad\quad NHR \\
CH_2SCH_2CHCOOH \\
CHOH \\
CH_2SCH_2CHCOOH \\
\quad\quad NHR
\end{array}
$$

$$
\begin{array}{l}
CH_2OH \\
CHOH \\
CH_2Cl
\end{array}
\xrightarrow[\text{acetylation}]{\substack{+ \text{GSH} \\ - \gamma\text{-Glu} \\ - \text{Gly}}}
\begin{array}{l}
\quad\quad NHR \\
CH_2SCH_2CHCOOH \\
CHOH \\
CH_2OH
\end{array}
$$

N-acetyl-S-(2,3-dihydroxypropyl)cysteine

R = COCH$_3$

Figure 1. Metabolism of 1,3-dichloro-2-propanol (hypothetical, based on the data of [1])

1 % of the applied dose) were detected in the urine [1]. The authors concluded from their studies of 1,3-dichloro-2-propanol and other dihalopropanols that, on elimination of HCl in the organism, 1,3-dichloro-2-propanol is first converted to epichlorohydrin which is either conjugated with glutathione or hydrolyzed to 3-chloropropanediol. In their metabolic scheme these authors postulate that HCl elimination yields other epoxide intermediates whose existence can, however, not be deduced conclusively from the available analytical data. Furthermore, it is known that epoxides are only formed from α-chlorohydrins under alkaline conditions and not at physiological pH. Therefore a scheme is proposed for the metabolism of 1,3-dichloro-2-propanol in which 1,3-dichloro-2-propanol is initially either converted to 3-chloro-2-hydroxy-propanal by oxidative dehalogenation or is metabolized by glutathione conjugation (spontaneous and/or enzymatic) (see Figure 1). Other authors [2] suggest that the chlorinated glutathione conjugates which are produced could have alkylating and mutagenic properties.

It is known from studies on the metabolism of tris(1,3-dichloropropyl) phosphate after i.v. injection in the rat that 1,3-dichloro-2-propanol is excreted as a metabolite in the urine [3].

2 Effects in Man

There is no information available as to effects of 1,3-dichloro-2-propanol on man.

3 Effects on Animals

3.1 Acute toxicity

The acute toxicity of 1,3-dichloro-2-propanol has been studied in the rat and the rabbit. The oral LD_{50} of 1,3-dichloro-2-propanol in the rat is given as 0.11 ml/kg body weight, the dermal LD_{50} for the rabbit as 0.8 ml/kg body weight. Rats (6 animals/group) all survived a 30 minute exposure to air saturated with 1,3-dichloro-2-propanol. The 4 hour LC_{50} for rats is about 125 ml/m^3. 1,3-Dichloro-2-propanol is mildly irritating on shaved rabbit skin and has a strong irritant effect in the rabbit eye [4].

3.2 Chronic toxicity

In a long-term study, male and female Wistar rats received daily 1,3-dichloro-2-propanol doses of 2.1, 6.25 or 19.3 mg/kg body weight (males) and 3.4, 9.6 or

Table 1. Neoplastic changes after administration of 1,3-dichloro-2-propanol to male and female Wistar rats for 104 weeks in the drinking water [5]

	Males				Females			
	Dose in mg/kg bw and day				Dose in mg/kg bw and day			
	0	2.1	6.25	19.3	0	3.4	9.6	29.8
liver								
hepatocellular adenomas	1/50	—	—	—	1/50	1/50	1/50	5/50
hepatocellular carcinomas	—	—	2/50	8/50	—	—	1/50	36/50
haemangiosarcomas	—	—	—	1/50	—	—	—	1/50
lungs								
carcinomas (metastases)	1/50	—	1/50	—	—	—	—	8/50
sarcomas (metastases)	—	—	1/50	—	—	—	—	2/50
kidneys								
tubular adenomas	—	—	3/50	9/50	—	—	—	1/49
tubular carcinomas	—	—	—	1/50	—	—	—	—
thyroid								
follicular adenomas	—	—	2/50	3/48	1/50	—	3/50	3/49
follicular carcinomas	—	—	2/50	1/48	—	—	—	2/49
C-cell adenomas	1/50	3/50	6/50	3/48	3/50	3/50	4/50	—
C-cell carcinomas	—	—	—	2/48	—	—	—	—
tongue								
papillomas	—	1/50	—	6/50	—	—	—	7/49
carcinomas	—	—	—	6/50	—	1/50	1/50	4/49
oral cavity								
carcinomas	—	—	—	2/3	—	—	1/2	—

—: incidence 0; oral cavity was not examined systematically
bw: body weight

29.8 mg/kg body weight (females) in the drinking water for 104 weeks. In both male and female animals from the two higher dose groups an increased incidence of tumours of the liver (hepatocellular adenomas and carcinomas, haemangiosarcomas), of the kidney (tubular adenomas and carcinomas), the epithelium of the oral cavity (not systematically examined) or the tongue (papillomas and carcinomas) and the thyroid (follicular adenomas and carcinomas) were registered [5] (see Table 1). Apart from a dose-related sinusoidal peliosis in the treated animals, lipid metabolism disorders in the livers of male animals from the two higher dose groups and significantly reduced body weight gain in male and female animals from the highest dose groups, no significant treatment-related toxic effects were seen.

4 Reproductive and Developmental Toxicity

Studies on male rats in which the animals were given daily oral doses of 30 mg/kg body weight 1,3-dichloro-2-propanol for 8 days revealed no effects on fertility [6].

5 Genotoxicity

1,3-Dichloro-2-propanol is mutagenic in the Ames test with the *Salmonella typhimurium* strains TA100 and TA1535, both with and without the addition of a metabolizing system (S9 mix from the livers of rats pretreated with Aroclor or Kanechlor) [7–9]. The numbers of revertants observed with and without the addition of the metabolizing system were similar in each system; in one case the addition of S9 mix reduced the number of revertants [7], in the two others it led to an increase.

1,3-Dichloro-2-propanol increased the frequency of sister chromatid exchange in hamster V79 cells *in vitro* both with and without the addition of a metabolizing enzyme system (S9 mix from the livers of rats pretreated with Aroclor). The SCE frequency was reduced by the addition of S9 mix [10]. 1,3-Dichloro-2-propanol also inhibits DNA synthesis in HeLa cells *in vitro* [11].

6 Manifesto (MAK value, classification)

1,3-Dichloro-2-propanol is a direct mutagen in the Ames test with *S. typhimurium* and has genotoxic effects (SCE, inhibition of DNA synthesis) in mammalian cell systems *in vitro*. In a long-term study with oral administration to rats in the drinking water, increased frequencies of tumours were observed at the application site (tongue, oral cavity) and in other organs (liver, kidney, thyroid). For these reasons 1,3-dichloro-2-propanol is classified in Category A 2) of Section III of the List of MAK Values.

7 References

1. Jones, A. R., G. Fakhouri: *Xenobiotica 9*, 595 (1979)
2. Gold, M. D., A. Blum, B. N. Ames: *Science 200*, 785 (1978)
3. Lynn, R. K., K. Wong, C. Garvie-Gould, J. M. Kennish: *Drug Metab. Dispos. 9*, 434 (1981)
4. Smyth, H. F., C. P. Carpenter, C. S. Weil, U. C. Pozzani, J. A. Striegel: *Amer. industr. Hyg. Ass. J. 23*, 95 (1962)
5. Research and Consulting Company AG (RCC): *104-week chronic toxicity and oncogenicity study with 1,3-dichlorpropan-2-ol in the rat*, Project 017820, Itingen, Switzerland, February 24, 1986
6. Ericsson, R. J., G. A. Youngdale: *J. Reprod. Fertil. 21*, 263 (1970)
7. Stolzenberg, S. J., C. H. Hine: *Environm. Mutag. 2*, 59 (1980)
8. Nakamura, A., N. Tateno, S. Kojima, M. Kaniwa, T. Kawamura: *Mutat. Res. 66*, 373 (1979)
9. Silhankova, L., F. Smid, M. Cerna, J. Davidek, J. Velisek: *Mutat. Res. 103*, 77 (1982)
10. Von der Hude, W., M. Scheutwinkel, U. Gramlich, B. Fißler, A. Basler: *Environm. Mutag. 9*, 401 (1987)
11. Painter, R. B.: in Stich, H. F., R. H. C. San (Eds.): *Short-term tests for chemical carcinogens*, p 59, Berlin, Springer, 1981

completed 30. 6. 1989

Diesel Engine Emissions

Classification/MAK value:	**see Section III A 2)**
	MAK List 1987
Classification/MAK value dates from:	**1987**

1 Effects in Man

The literature reviewed included 22 epidemiological studies of persons exposed at work to increased levels of diesel engine emissions. The following account is based mainly on one review article [1] and two commentaries [2, 3].

1.1 Lorry drivers

In the USA 14 studies have been carried out on the question of the occurrence of lung cancer in lorry drivers [1]. Of these, 9 revealed significantly increased relative risks (RR). Some were estimated using standardized mortality data (SMR), some with odds ratios from case-control studies. The authors of 3 studies on deceased persons quoted standardized proportional mortality rates. The value for these figures was below 1.0 in only one study, a case-control study [4] with short latency periods and a low probability of revealing any existing association between diesel engine emissions and lung cancer. The excess risk of developing lung cancer is mostly of the order of 20% to 50% for lorry drivers; in one case it was 82%. Lorry drivers are exposed to higher levels of diesel motor emissions than the general population, on the one hand, because of the higher background levels of diesel engine emissions on the roads and, on the other, because of the position of the exhaust pipe in older lorries, directly under the driver's cab. Most studies do not take the factor "smoking" into account. It should, however, be noted that the three larger studies [5–7], which did compensate for smoking by standardization or other methods, also found increased lung cancer risks (statistically significant in two of the three). In one case-control study [8], it was suggested that smoking and occupational exposure act synergistically in lorry drivers. In non-smoking drivers aged 70 years or more there is an increased lung cancer risk which is considered to be of occupational origin.

1.2 Employees of London bus companies

For this group of persons there are 3 studies on the question of diesel engine emissions and lung cancer [9–11]; the third study [11] examines maintenance men in bus garages (not bus drivers). The standardized mortality rates were not increased in these studies. In another study [12] 3 exposure groups were distinguished: (1) mechanics in bus garages, (2) bus drivers and conductors, (3) watchmen, etc. For the period 1961–1974 gradations could be seen between these groups in the SMR, the value of which was less than 1.0; for the period 1950–1960, however, the gradations were less clear. Deaths taking place after the persons had left the firms could not be included but this probably had no effect on the comparison of the three exposure groups [2]. A detailed analysis of the results was intended to answer the question of how high a lung cancer risk for the exposed workers could be without it being detected. For the model calculations [2] assumptions had to be made on the following points because of lack of information or because of other uncertainties:

1. differences in the smoking habits in the three categories
2. different concentrations of diesel engine emissions for the garage mechanics
3. concentration of diesel engine emissions for bus drivers and conductors
4. changes in the exposure with time
5. random fluctuation of lung cancer incidence
6. adequacy of the mathematical model used

The estimated ambient air concentrations were subtracted from the estimated occupational exposure levels. The formula used yields the maximal 95% confidence limits for a possible lung cancer risk. The authors come to the conclusion that the lung cancer risk is increased by a factor of about 0.05% of the lung cancer incidence per unit of life-long accumulated exposure, measured in $\mu g/m^3$ times years [2].

1.3 Railway workers

Three cohort studies which did not take smoking into account have been carried out in this sector. Division of the collective into three groups according to occupation at the time the person became disabled revealed a dose-effect relationship and an overall increase in the standardized mortality rate [13]. Another author also described increased mortality [14]. The third study found no increase in the SMR [15]; in this case, however, the latency period was too short.

1.4 Heavy construction equipment operators

A mortality study on 32 000 heavy construction equipment operators who had been exposed to diesel engine emissions for at least one year between 1964 and 1978 revealed no over-all increase in lung cancer mortality but a trend for increasing lung cancer with increasing latency period and with increasing period of employment [16]. In addition there was a significant increase in mortality from lung cancer in retired individuals (SMR = 164%, $p < 0.01$). Analysis according to occupation revealed no increase in lung cancer mortality in the groups expected to have higher exposure to diesel engine emissions. Since most persons involved had worked outdoors, the workplace concentrations must have been relatively low.

1.5 Case-control studies for occupations involving exposure to diesel engine emissions

500 patients with lung cancer and 500 other comparable hospital cases were compared [17]. After correction for smoking, an increased risk could not be demonstrat-

ed for the persons exposed occupationally to diesel engine emissions. A drawback of the study is the rather approximate division into occupational groups. Interviews were only carried out with 64% of the persons intended for the study. The overall power of the study to reveal an increased risk for specific occupations was relatively low.

1.6 Studies in progress

There are preliminary reports of a large cohort study with 60 000 railway workers [18] and of an analysis of proportional mortality of lorry drivers using ca. 10 000 death certificates [1]. A smoking anamnesis was obtained by questioning the relatives of a random sample of 2000 of the deceased.

Preliminary results of a case-control study of deceased US railway workers were presented in a poster session [19]. Data were available from 1256 cases of bronchial carcinoma and 2385 controls selected using the matched pair procedure according to age and date of death. The evaluation used multiple logistic regression analysis with the independent variables "diesel years", "asbestos (yes/no)" and three categories of smokers. The regression model was fitted both for the group up to 64 years old and for the age group 65 years old and more. As well as for the known association between smoking and lung cancer, in the former age group there was also a significant coefficient for "diesel years" ($p < 5\%$). This group had higher exposure to diesel engine emissions because in the older group many people had retired before 1959, i.e. shortly before or after the introduction of diesel locomotives. In this collective, however, the coefficients for cigarette smoking are higher than in the younger group.

1.7 Evaluation

The detection of carcinogenic substances on the surface of soot particles in diesel engine emissions provoked the first epidemiological studies. Seen as a whole, the results are inconclusive with respect to lung cancer frequencies among persons occupationally exposed to diesel engine emissions [1]. Many of the studies suffer from the usual drawbacks of case-control studies or historical cohort studies. Some of the latency periods were relatively short because diesel engines were introduced only recently in some industries. It is emphasized that there are considerable difficulties not only in the estimation of past exposures to diesel engine emissions but also in accurate exposure estimation today [1].

It must be added that such inaccuracies in the exposure determination lead on the one hand to "dilution effects" in the exposed or more markedly exposed groups and, on the other, to "contamination effects" in the control groups. These effects produce a reduction in the significance of any association which might be present. Nevertheless, the majority of studies revealed an increased risk as indication of an association between diesel engine emissions and lung cancer. The short latency periods in some studies also have the effect of reducing or concealing any possible association. In spite of these difficulties, an increased lung cancer risk was found in many studies.

A more important objection is the presence of confounding factors particularly in the form of "tobacco smoking". This confounding factor was not compensated in most of the studies. In 3 large surveys of lorry drivers, however, increased lung cancer risks (statistically significant in 2 studies) were still found when the results had been adjusted to compensate for smoking. Lorry drivers appear to smoke more than comparable persons in other occupations [8]. There are still questions to be answered with respect to the increased risk revealed by these studies. Must we assume that exposure to diesel engine emissions is always associated with heavy smoking? Were the mathematical methods used to compensate the confounding factor "smoking" in the three studies mentioned above so inadequate that the effects found were actually effects of smoking?

Other confounding factors could also play a role. For these, however, the same considerations apply as for smoking.

In summary, it may be concluded that some of the currently available epidemiological studies do reveal an increased risk of lung cancer but that, taken together, they provide no conclusive proof that diesel engine emissions induce lung cancer in man. Further studies in which smoking and other confounding factors are compensated are required. On the other hand, it is not surprising that no proof has been obtained to date; it could be that future studies also demonstrate merely that the inadequacies of the epidemiological method are insurmountable.

1.8 Estimation of the number of cases necessary for an epidemiological study

A calculation based on data from inhalation studies with animals serves to exemplify one of the difficulties of epidemiological methodology. It assumes that man and experimental rat are similarly sensitive to the effects of diesel engine emissions and makes use of the results of a study in which the weekly exposure time was comparable with that of a man's working week [20]. The rats inhaled diesel engine emissions with a particle concentration of $3.5 \, mg/m^3$ for 35 hours weekly. The exposure began when the animals were 16–17 weeks old and lasted for 2 years, after which the animals were observed until they died naturally. In the exposed group the tumour incidence was 4.6%, in the control group 1.4%. Thus diesel engine emissions caused an increase of 3.2%. Simplified, one can say that exposure to $3.5 \, mg/m^3$ by inhalation for 40 hours per week caused a tumour frequency of 3.5%. Therefore, assuming a linear relationship between exposure concentration and tumour frequency, a concentration of $1 \, mg/m^3$ inhaled for 40 hours weekly (by the rat) causes a 1% increase in tumour frequency relative to the control group. To date there is no adequate information as to the average concentrations of diesel engine emissions which prevail at workplaces over longer periods. Let us consider, for example, that a level of $2 \, mg/m^3$ could be reached. If $2 \, mg/m^3$ had been used in the experiment with the rats, assuming a linear dose-effect relationship, an increase of 2% in lung tumours would be expected. In man the proportion of deaths from lung cancer for males aged 45 years or more in the Federal Republic of Germany is 7%. If one uses this value as the value for "spontaneous" deaths from lung cancer, one is making the assumption that the proportional mortality from lung cancer will not change for the men living now and aged 45 or more, until the last member of this population group is dead. The life-long risk of dying from lung cancer for men more than 45 years old is, at 7%, much higher than that for the rat; the main reason for this is considered to be tobacco smoking. An increase of 2% caused by exposure at work to 2 mg/m^3 diesel engine exhaust particles would then result in a relative risk (RR) of 9%/7%, i.e. 1.3.

Having estimated the order of magnitude of the RR, it is possible to calculate the minimal cohort size necessary to demonstrate a statistically significant difference in lung cancer frequency in an epidemiological study. In order to prove statistically with a power of 90% in a 5 year study that the relative risk (RR) for the age group 45 years old and more is 1.3, one would need about 11 300 persons exposed to 2 mg/m^3. To demonstrate a relative risk of 1.5 for exposure to 3.5 mg/m^3 4500 cases would be required. If the long-term occupational exposure level were only 1.4 mg/m^3 the lung cancer frequency would be increased from 7% to 8.4% (RR = 1.2). To demonstrate the statistical significance of such an increase with 90% power it would be necessary to study about 24 500 exposed persons who inhaled this concentration for long periods. (The long-term average concentration of soot from diesel engine exhaust fumes, however, is probably below 500 μg/m^3 even in unfavourable work environments.) Table 1 shows the results of this estimation of the necessary numbers of cases. The assumptions on which these calculations are based are summarized below.

1. mortality of men aged 45 years and more (ICD 162) in the
   Federal Republic of Germany in 1984 [21]   0.2%
2. assumed annual increase (according to a model calculation by
   Abel [22], the mortality from lung cancer will remain constant
   for men in the FRG)   0
3. assumed annual frequency of cases lost to the study   2 %
4. level of significance (one-sided because a protective effect of
   diesel engine emissions may be excluded)   5 %
5. observation period in years   5
6. good comparability of the collectives (e.g., with respect to smoking)

The results of the model calculation shown in Table 1 make it clear that the number of cases in a cohort study must be very high in order to prove the statistical significance of an increase in lung cancer frequency caused by long-term exposure to diesel engine emissions containing less than 1 mg particles/m^3. Only if man is considerably more sensitive to the effects of diesel engine emissions than the rat is there a real chance of demonstrating such an effect with epidemiological methods.

Since measurements of particle concentrations from diesel engine emissions in various occupational environments have not yet been carried out and there are no details available of the numbers of exposed persons, it is currently not possible to predict whether a cohort study could be carried out nor whether it would have adequate power, quite apart from the ethical implications of such a prospective

Table 1. Estimation of case numbers[1] (= occupationally exposed men) necessary in a cohort study to demonstrate a statistically significant increase in lung cancer frequency caused by diesel engine emissions, assuming that the long-term exposure of man causes the same additional lung cancer risk as it does in the rat at the levels chosen for this calculation.

RR[2]	power[3]			diesel engine emissions particle concentration (mg/m^3)
	50%	80%	90%	
1.1	28 500	> 65 000	> 95 000	0.7
1.2	7 111	17 317	24 430	1.4
1.3	3 161	7 924	11 270	2.0
1.5	1 454	3 011	4 345	3.5

[1] Program "Power, Design 5: Cohort study: external controls" from the "Epilog" system by EPICENTER Software, P.O. Box 90073, Pasadena CA 91 109
[2] risk for the exposed persons relative to that for the general population
[3] power (i.e. probability of demonstrating that an actually existing factor-illness association is statistically significant)

study. It is also unknown how man's sensitivity to lung cancer induction by diesel engine emissions compares with that of the rat.

2 Effects on Animals

2.1 Inhalation studies

Recently a number of reports have appeared describing carcinogenicity studies in which rats, mice and golden Syrian hamsters inhaled diesel engine emissions for long periods. A statistically significant increase in lung tumour frequency was seen in all studies in which rats were exposed to concentrations of diesel particles above 2 mg/m^3 for more than 2 years [20, 23–26]. The gaseous phase of diesel engine emissions, free of particles, induced no tumours in rats [23, 24, 26]. A summary of the experimental data and results is shown in Table 2. No carcinogenic effects were observed in three other experiments in which low concentrations (up to 2 mg diesel particles per m^3) were inhaled by rats [25, 27, 28]. A fourth study of this kind was discontinued after 23 months [29]; here there were signs of a positive effect – 5 of 90 exposed rats had lung tumours.

A study with female NMRI mice revealed a statistically significant increase in tumour frequency compared with that of a control group (32% and 31% compared with 13%) both after inhalation of whole diesel engine emissions and of the gaseous phase alone [24]. In both exposed groups the proportion of malignant tumours was particularly increased (17% and 19% compared with 2.4%). The exposure to 4.2 mg particles/m^3 for 95 hours per week corresponded to that in the experiment carried out by the same authors with rats.

Table 2. Long-term inhalation studies with diesel engine emissions

Species strain	Number	Exposure concentration (particles)	Exposure duration	Observation period	Lung tumours	p (%)	Ref.
rat F344	72 ♀	6.6 mg/m³			39 = 54% ⎫		[23]
	71 ♂	6.6 mg/m³			16 = 23% ⎭ 38.5%	< 0.1	
	72 ♀	2.2 mg/m³			11 = 15% ⎫		
	72 ♂	2.2 mg/m³			3 = 4% ⎭ 9.7%	< 0.1	
	72 ♀	0.7 mg/m³	16 h/d,		0% ⎫		
	72 ♂	0.7 mg/m³	5 d/week for 24 months	30 months	1 = 1% ⎭ 0.7%		
	♀	gwp			*		
	♂	gwp			*		
	142 ♀	clean air			1 = 1% ⎫		
	140 ♂	clean air			3 = 2% ⎭ 1.4%		
rat Wistar	95 ♀	4.2 mg/m³	19 h/d 5 d/week	until	15 = 16%	< 0.1	[24]
	92 ♀	gwp	for 30 months	natural death	0%		
	96 ♀	clean air			0%		
rat F344/Jcl	60 ♀	4 mg/m³			3 = 5% ⎫		[25]
	64 ♂	4 mg/m³			5 = 8% ⎭ 6.5%	1.8	
	59 ♀	2 mg/m³			1 = 2% ⎫		
	64 ♂	2 mg/m³	16 h/d 6 d/week	30 months	3 = 5% ⎭ 3.3%		
	61 ♀	1 mg/m³	for 30 months		0% ⎫		
	64 ♂	1 mg/m³			0% ⎭ 0%		
	59 ♀	0.4 mg/m³			1 = 2% ⎫		
	64 ♂	0.4 mg/m³			0% ⎭ 0.8%		
	59 ♀	clean air			1 = 2% ⎫		
	64 ♂	clean air			0% ⎭ 0.8%		
rat F344	19 ♀	4.9 mg/m³		24 months	4		[26]
	5 ♀	4.9 mg/m³	8 h/d 7 d/week	30 months	4		
			for 24 months		─────		
					8 = 33%	1.1	
	24 ♀	gwp		24 months	0 = 0%		
	17 ♀	clean air		24 months	0		
	7 ♀	clean air		30 months	1		
					─────		
					1 = 4%		

Table 2 (continued)

Species strain	Number	Exposure concentration (particles)	Exposure duration	Observation period	Lung tumours		p (%)	Ref.
rat F344/N	69 ♀	7.1 mg/m³			13 = 19%	} 16.1%	< 0.1	[20]
	74 ♂	7.1 mg/m³	7 h/d,		10 = 14%		1.7	
	68 ♀	3.5 mg/m³	5 d/week		2 = 3%	} 4.6%		
	63 ♂	3.5 mg/m³	for 30 months	until natural death	4 = 6%			
	68 ♀	0.35 mg/m³			0%	} 0.7%		
	70 ♂	0.35 mg/m³			1 = 1%			
	68 ♀	clean air			0%	} 1.4%		
	73 ♂	clean air			2 = 3%			

* no statistical difference from control; no other details specified

gwp : gaseous phase without particles

 p%: probability of this difference arising by chance alone according to Fisher's exact test (one-sided)

In another study [30] male and female C 57 BL/6N mice were exposed to 2–4 mg particles/m³ for 4 × 4 hours each week. No lung tumours were found among the 76 animals killed during the first 12 months. In the total of 150 exposed mice which died or were killed between months 13 and 28, 12 adenomas and 5 adenocarcinomas were diagnosed, 1 adenoma was found in the 51 control animals. The authors describe this difference as statistically not significant. If one includes in the calculation the animals from the first year of the study, none of which had any tumours, then the difference between the two groups has a 4.4% probability of occurring by chance alone. If one considers only the animals which died or were killed during the months 13–28 the difference is statistically significant with a 3.1% probability of arising by chance alone (Fisher's exact test, one-sided).

In hamsters no tumours were observed in the respiratory tract [23, 24, 31].

The concentrations of a number of the constituents of diesel engine emissions are assembled in Table 3; the MAK values for these substances are shown for comparison.

The question as to whether inhalation of diesel engine emissions changes the frequency of respiratory tract tumours induced by known carcinogens has also been studied. In combination with diethylnitrosamine, diesel engine emissions were shown to have an amplifying effect on tumour development in the larynx-trachea area. The effect was seen not only with the whole diesel engine exhaust but also with the gaseous phase obtained by filtering the exhaust fumes [31]. In an experiment in which a known carcinogen was administered to groups of rats by injection or intratracheal instillation, some of the animals also inhaled either whole diesel engine emissions or the gaseous phase. Differences were observed which are difficult to interpret and which require further study [24]. In another experiment with rats and

Table 3. Mean concentrations of some of the constituents of diesel engine emissions diluted about 1 : 17 for use in the inhalation cages [24] and, for comparison, the corresponding MAK values

Substance	Concentration*	MAK value
CO	12.5 ml/m^3	30 ml/m^3
CO$_2$	0.38% v/v	5000 ml/m^3
SO$_2$	1.12 ml/m^3	2 ml/m^3
NO$_x$	11.4 ml/m^3	–
NO	10.0 ml/m^3	–
NO$_2$	1.5 ml/m^3	5 ml/m^3

* The exposure did not follow the MAK concept but was for a maximum of 19 h/d, 5 d/week.

relatively short exposure times (4 × 4 h/week, 2–4 mg diesel particles/m^3) the exhaust fumes induced no lung tumours but they did increase the frequency of lung tumours induced by di-isopropanolnitrosamine [30].

Gasoline engine emissions have also been tested for tumour-inducing effects in long-term inhalation studies. Dilutions of the exhaust gases of 1 : 27 to about 1 : 85 in air were ineffective [23, 24]. Diesel engine emissions could be administered at a dilution of 1 : 10 because of their lower CO content and induced statistically significant increases in tumour frequency down to a dilution of 1 : 36. The histological findings in the lungs of animals exposed in these experiments [24] have been described in detail [32]. Half of the lung tumours found in rats after inhalation of diesel engine emissions were squamous epithelial growths which were very largely classified as benign. They could be distinguished from squamous epithelial carcinomas by their cystic expansive organization and excessive keratin production. The keratin production originated in a seam of well-differentiated tumour cells which formed an outer layer around the growth. Bronchio-alveolar adenomas were also found. Other authors too have described benign tumours together with adenocarcinomas and squamous epithelial carcinomas [20, 25, 26]. The differentiation criteria were not uniform. The benign tumours are seen as the precursors of the malignant; they have the same histogenetic origins. Therefore in the present case the benign and malignant squamous epithelial tumours are counted together.

In addition, in almost all rats exposed to diesel engine emissions, bronchio-alveolar hyperplasia was found together with thickened septa and aggregations of crystalline cholesterol. Two thirds of the rats also had squamous epithelial metaplasia within the hyperplastic tissue lesion. Such changes occurred only very occasionally in control animals. The macroscopically conspicuous blackening of the lungs of animals which had inhaled whole diesel engine emissions was conspicuous in the microscopic picture too; both in the alveoli and in the interstitial tissues there were large aggregations of soot particles which had mostly been phagocytosed by macrophages. Moderate fibrotic changes were also observed, especially in lung areas overloaded with particles and in the vicinity of squamous epithelial metaplasias [32].

In a number of the carcinogenicity studies reviewed here [20, 23, 24] the general state of health of the animals was also examined. Whereas the survival times of the exposed rats were not different from those of the controls, the body weights were reduced in the higher dose groups in two studies [23, 24]. In the third study it is stated that inhalation of diesel engine emissions did not cause any obvious signs of toxicity in this experiment; the highest concentration used was 7.1 mg particles/m^3 for 35 hours per week. The body weights were unchanged for both male and female animals. Some blood parameters were changed after inhalation of diesel engine emissions [23] and some lung function parameters deviated markedly from the control values after inhalation of the high concentrations [24, 33].

In the long-term experiment with rats [20] the lung clearance and accumulation of diesel soot in the lungs was investigated after various exposure times and concentrations [34]. Short-term clearance was unaffected. Long-term clearance, however, was markedly slower at the medium and high concentrations. 2 years after the start of the study, particle accumulation in the lungs of animals from the medium and high concentration groups (3.5 mg/m^3 and 7.1 mg/m^3) was about twice as high as would have been expected if the lung clearance had been unaffected; on average 11.5 mg and 20.5 mg particles, respectively, were found per lung, in the lowest dose group (0.35 mg/m^3) 0.6 mg.

2.2 Other animal studies

The first positive carcinogenicity test with extracts of particles from diesel engine emissions applied to mouse skin was published in 1955 [35], the equivalent test with an extract of gasoline engine emissions in 1954 [36]. Only later after the strongly mutagenic effects of condensates from diesel engine emissions had been described [37] were large series of experiments carried out with 5 doses applied to the skin of groups of about 40 female and 40 male Sencar mice [38–40]. The authors tested extracts of tar, coke oven emissions as well as exhaust condensates from various diesel engines at least in a tumour initiation test, and some in a tumour promotion test and for their effectiveness as complete carcinogens. Four of the five extracts of condensates of diesel engine emissions from various engines initiated papillomas; carcinomas were initiated by only one of the five. The organic extract of coke oven emissions proved to be more effective.

It may be concluded from the results of these studies [39, 40] that the skin tumour initiating effect of extracts of particles from diesel engine emissions is, on average, weak in comparison to that of extracts of tar or coke oven emissions but that there can be enormous differences between the extracts from different diesel engines. It is possible that these differences in effectiveness could be explained plausibly if we knew the chemical composition of the extracts; this is, however, not known. Therefore it is not possible to make a precise comparison of the doses of known carcinogens administered or to correlate the doses with the effects.

Organic extracts of tar from the exhaust of a diesel lorry were tested for tumorigenic potential in several tests [41]. Papillomas were found in 4 of 50 animals after initiation on mouse skin with 45 mg extract and subsequent promoter treatment (controls: no tumours). In the subcutaneous test only the highest of 6 doses (5 × 500 mg/kg body weight) had a statistically significant effect; nicotine-free cigarette smoke condensate produced the same tumour frequency, about 20%, with a dose of only 5 × 10 mg/kg body weight although a 20 times higher dose produced a tumour frequency of only 43%. In the intratracheal test in Syrian hamsters, 15 doses of 1 mg extract of "diesel tar" had no tumorigenic effects.

Carcinomas developed after implantation of the hydrophobic fraction of condensate extract in rat lung, and also after implantation of that fraction of polycyclic aromatic hydrocarbons (PAH) containing only PAH with 4–7 rings [42]. Two years after the start of the study no carcinogenic effects were evident with the PAH fraction with 2–3 rings, the transcoron and the nitro-PAH fractions. Lung tumours were also observed after intratracheal instillation of particles from diesel engine emissions into female SPF F344 rats [43]. The ten instillations of 1 mg particles in 0.2 ml liquid (phosphate buffered saline with 0.05% Tween 80) were given to the animals at weekly intervals. 42 of the initial 59 rats still survived after 18 months; at least 1 lung tumour was found in 31 of these (in total 37 lung tumours, 11 benign and 26 malignant). It is noteworthy that a lung tumour was found in 11 of 23 animals (4 benign and 7 malignant) which survived for 18 months after 10 instillations of 1 mg activated charcoal; this experimental group consisted initially of 27 rats. 1 lung tumour developed in the group treated only with the suspension medium (27 animals initially, 23 examined) and none among the 50 or so untreated rats which were examined.

2.3 Discussion of the animal studies

The inhalation experiments carried out in four countries with diesel engine emissions from different engines all revealed dose-dependent lung tumour induction in rats after exposure to 2.2 to 7.1 mg/m^3 particulate fraction from diesel engine emissions for 35 to 96 hours per week for 2 years.

In essence, the carcinogenic effect can be attributed to the particulate phase of the emissions; an involvement of the gaseous phase cannot, however, be excluded, especially in view of the tumour induction in mice after inhalation of the gaseous phase alone [24]. The results of the two inhalation studies with diesel engine emissions and mice are, however, not equally conclusive. On the other hand, studies with the organic extracts of the particulate fraction of the emissions yielded unambiguously positive results after skin painting and subcutaneous injection in the mouse as well as in the lung implantation test in the rat. Taken together, this data base partially fulfills the requirements for the classification of diesel engine emissions in Section III A 2) of the List of MAK values.

No increase in lung tumour frequency was found in the inhalation experiments with gasoline engine emissions although diesel and gasoline engine emissions have about the same content of PAH [44]. Gasoline engine emissions, however, could be used in the animal experiments only at high dilutions (at least 1:27) because of the high CO concentration, whereas diesel engine emissions at dilutions between 1:10 and 1:36 caused a statistically significant increase in lung tumour frequency. In addition, PAH are more strongly adsorbed onto diesel soot than onto the particles from gasoline engine emissions so that we may expect a certain depot effect with better bioavailability in the case of diesel engine emissions. This would favour tumour induction by diesel particles. It has also been suggested (see below) that the larger surface area of the particles in diesel engine emissions increases tumour pro-

duction by means of unspecific irritant effects, effects which would be much less –
if they arose at all – with particles from gasoline engine emissions. To what extent
these various parameters play a role in the effects of diesel and gasoline engine
emissions cannot currently be decided.

The same is true for the emissions from fuel oil. They come from the same fuel as
diesel engine emissions but the differences in the burning process, in particular the
temperature, and possibly differences in the constituents of fossil fuels influence the
composition of the exhaust gases markedly, possibly even decisively. In both kinds
of emission, however, it is the effects of the genotoxic components which are of most
interest in the evaluation.

Under these conditions it is necessary to discuss from a theoretical standpoint the
nature and influence of possible modifying factors. It is also necessary to discuss our
current understanding of species specific differences in sensitivity to the effects of
inhalation of exhaust fumes.

Firstly it has been suggested that the tumorigenic effect could be an unspecific
reaction to the large mass of particles deposited in the lungs, to which the rat could
be particularly predisposed. This hypothesis is mainly supported by two arguments.
First, no respiratory tract tumours were found in the hamster in three inhalation
experiments with exposure conditions like those which had produced tumours in the
rat. Second, it was not expected that a tumorigenic effect would be demonstrable for
diesel engine emissions because of the relatively low PAH content of the particulate
fraction where the benzo[a]pyrene concentration in the inhalation experiment was
less than $50 \, ng/m^3$, significantly below the ambient air concentrations found until the
1970s in cities where buildings were heated with coal fires. In another inhalation
experiment the emissions from pyrolysed pitch, which are rich in PAH but poor in
particles, induced tumours in only 18% of the rats; the emissions contained about
$90 \, \mu g$ benzo[a]pyrene/m^3; the animals were exposed to this high concentration in the
second year of life [45, 46].

The very large difference between the PAH concentrations in the two inhalation
experiments which produced the same tumour frequencies can be accounted for, at
least in part, by the very different residence times of the PAH in the lungs, times
which depend on the reversibility of the PAH adsorption onto particles. Polycyclic
aromatic compounds are soluble in most organic solvents and in lipid; they may also
be relatively readily extracted from the soot particles produced in the burning of coal
but only with difficulty from the soot particles of diesel engine emissions. This large
difference has also been demonstrated for benzo[a]pyrene and 1-nitropyrene in animal studies. Whereas 99% of a radioactively labelled benzo[a]pyrene aerosol was
eliminated from the lung within one day of inhalation, only 50% of benzo[a]pyrene
adsorbed onto diesel particles was eliminated in this time [47]. The long-term clearance was significantly slower in both cases and from day 2 took 13 days for the free
benzo[a]pyrene and 26 days for the benzo[a]pyrene bound to diesel particles. It has
long been known that there is an increase in tumour frequency after intratracheal
instillation of benzo[a]pyrene which is not adsorbed onto carcinogenic particles [48,
49]. The above-mentioned amplifying effect is then to be expected particularly for
carcinogens which are strongly adsorbed onto diesel particles, and especially for the
polycyclic aromatic compounds (PAC). (PAC include not only the pure PAH but also

heterocyclic and substituted polycyclic aromatics). The large amounts of PAH in the inhalation experiment with pitch pyrolysis emissions or which enter the lungs of workers in cokes plants are very likely not metabolized to the actual carcinogenic substances in the lung but first absorbed and then broken down in the liver. The possibility must also be mentioned that among the many hundred organic constituents of engine emissions may be substances which have a much higher carcinogenic potency than, e.g., benzo[*a*]pyrene and which, accordingly, may play an essential role in tumour induction in the rat in inhalation experiments.

In contrast to the rat, the Syrian hamster developed no tumours of the respiratory tract after inhalation of diesel engine emissions in three experiments. However, unlike the rat, the Syrian hamster did not develop lung tumours after inhalation of cigarette smoke or of pitch pyrolysis emissions rich in PAH [50, 51]. In the hamster, tumours developed in the larynx and trachea after inhalation of cigarette smoke [52] and these tumours may most likely be accounted for by the action of the nitrosamines in cigarette smoke, in view of the known sensitivity of this species to nitrosamines. For man, however, the lung cancer inducing effects of cigarette smoke and coke oven emissions rich in PAH are evident. The greater similarity seems to be between rat and man. Neither is it possible to distinguish between the situation in rat and in man by means of the tumours which develop in the rat after inhalation of quartz. The quartz concentration in the inhalation experiment, 12 mg/m^3, was much higher than the levels to which man is exposed [53]. An increased lung cancer frequency caused by quartz, even after many years of exposures markedly exceeding the MAK value of 0.15 mg/m^3, would be practically undetectable with epidemiological methods unless man reacted much more sensitively to the tumorigenic effects of quartz than the rat. The same is true for the lung tumours found in the rat after inhalation of shale dusts containing about 10% quartz [54]. There are some suggestions that quartz is carcinogenic in man too [53].

Two other inhalation experiments are also cited in support of the hypothesis of an unspecific particle effect to which the rat is supposed to be particularly sensitive. After exposure to levels of coal dust (200 mg/m^3) and titanium dioxide (250 mg/m^3) of which only about 25% was inspirable, lung tumours were found in 4 of 36 and in 36 of 151 rats respectively [55, 56]. The hypothesis, maintained in particular by [57], cannot be disproved scientifically so that the possible involvement in the tumour induction by diesel engine emissions of an unspecific inflammatory reaction caused by overloading of the lung with very small particles (diameter < 0.3 µm) cannot be excluded.

This possibility requires scientific investigation for other fine dusts or fumes as well. The diesel particle concentrations of those emissions which had a statistically significant carcinogenic effect were, in fact, close to the MAK value for fine dust. This effect suggests a relatively marked toxicity of the soot particles or of their large surface area. Therefore the question must also be asked whether the so-called "unspecific" reaction is not actually a specific reaction to certain surface properties like that already demonstrated for mineral dusts *in vitro* [58]. This effect could be more marked in man than in the rat because of the longer persistence in the terminal respiratory passages in man, and in rat and man be relatively less after overloading of the lung than when the particles are evenly distributed over the lung surface so that the greater part of the particle surface can make contact with the biological milieu. These proposals are supported by the findings of a single experiment [43] in which activated charcoal had tumorigenic effects after intratracheal instillation. The specific surface area of the particles from diesel engine emissions is said to be similar to that of particles of activated charcoal [44].

3 Genotoxicity

3.1 in vitro studies

In 1978 it was demonstrated for the first time that extracts of soot particles from diesel engine emissions are mutagenic in bacteria [37, 59]. Since then this finding has been repeatedly confirmed and the results reviewed [60, 62–67]. Recent studies show that the gaseous phase of diesel engine emissions is also mutagenic in bacteria [61].

Extracts of soot particles from diesel engine emissions have a different mutagenic potency in different strains of bacteria. For example, the *Salmonella typhimurium* strains TA98 (base pair substitution) and TA100 (frameshift) are particularly sensitive whereas the strain TA1535 (base pair substitution) reacts only very little [62]. The mutagenicity of the extracts is markedly reduced in nitroreductase deficient strains [62, 63]. The mutagenicity depends on the kind and age of the engine, the kind of fuel and the operating conditions [62, 64–67]. Thus comparative tests with exhaust samples from various diesel engines produced results ranging from negative to highly positive.

The sample collection conditions also affect the mutagenicity of the soot particles. When the collection periods lasted for several hours artefacts were observed such as the formation of PAH nitro derivatives which can contribute to the mutagenicity of the soot particles [68]. With short sampling times ($\leq$ 45 min) such as have been used (e.g., by [62]) for detailed studies in various *in vitro* mutagenicity test systems (see Table 4), significant formation of artefactual nitro aromatics is not to be expected [69].

As a rule, the organic extracts of the soot particles are mutagenic without the addition of an activation system. In the presence of an activation system the mutagenicity of the extracts is often reduced [62] or completely suppressed [66].

In contrast to the clearly mutagenic effects of the components of diesel engine emissions in bacteria, in yeast only very weak genotoxic effects are seen (Table 4) [70]. This is very likely because of the absence of nitroreductase activity in these organisms [79].

A large number of different test systems have been used to study the genotoxic effects of organic extracts of soot particles from diesel engine emissions in mammalian cells (Table 4). The end points include primary DNA lesions, point mutations, chromosome aberrations and sister chromatid exchange. The spectrum of cell types used stretches from freshly isolated cells and organ cultures to permanent cell lines from various tissues and species including man. In most test systems a dose-dependent genotoxic effect of the organic extracts from soot particles was found. Not

Table 4. *In vitro* short-term tests with soot particles from diesel engine emissions and their extracts[a]

Test organism	Test/end point	Particle	Extract	Ref.
Bacteria				
Salmonella typhimurium	point mutation (his)[b]	+[c]	+	[37]
Salmonella typhimurium	point mutation (his)	+[c]	+	[60]
Escherichia coli	point mutation (trp)		+	[62]
Yeasts				
Saccharomyces cerevisiae D3	mitotic recombination		(+)	[70]
Saccharomyces cerevisiae D4	mitotic gene conversion		−	
Saccharomyces cerevisiae D7	mitotic crossing over		(+)	
Saccharomyces cerevisiae D7	back mutation		−	
Saccharomyces cerevisiae D7	gene conversion		−	
Mammalian cells				
L5178Y cells, mouse lymphoma	point mutation (TK)		+	[62]
			+	[70]
CHO cells, Chinese hamster ovary	point mutation (HGPRT)	+		[71]
			(+)	[72]
			(+)	[73]
TK6 cells, human lymphoblast cell line	point mutation (TK)		+	[74]
V79 cells, Chinese hamster lung	point mutation (HGPRT, ATPase)		+	[66]
human XP fibroblasts	point mutation (HGPRT)	+	+	[75]
Balb/c3T3, mouse fibroblasts	point mutation (ATPase)		(+)	[76]
human XP fibroblasts	DNA damage	+	+	[75]
SHE cells, Syrian hamster embryo	DNA strand breaks (alkaline elution)		−	[72]
WI38 cells, human fibroblasts	DNA repair (UDS)		+	[77]
hepatocytes, rat, primary culture	DNA repair (UDS)		+	[62]
hamster trachea, organ culture	DNA repair (UDS)		+	[78]
rat trachea, organ culture	DNA repair (UDS)		+	[43]
CHO cells	chromosome aberrations		+	[62]
human lymphocytes	chromosome aberrations		+	[62]
human lymphocytes	sister chromatid exchange		+	[66]
human lymphoblastoid cells (inherited defect with tendency to cancer)[d]	sister chromatid exchange		+	[66]
CHO cells	sister chromatid exchange		+	[62]
Balb/c3T3 fibroblasts	cell transformation		(+)	[76]

[a] particle: particulate fraction of diesel engine emissions, not extracted   extract: material extracted from the particulate fraction of diesel engine emissions with organic solvents

[b] abbreviations: his: mutation indicated by no requirement for histidine   trp: mutation indicated by no requirement for tryptophan   HGPRT: hypoxanthine-guanine-phosphoribosyltransferase (8-azaguanine or 6-thioguanine resistance)   TK: thymidine kinase (bromodesoxyuridine or trifluorothymidine resistance)   ATPase: Na^+/K^+-ATPase (ouabain resistance)   UDS: unscheduled DNA synthesis   XP: xeroderma pigmentosum

[c] no entry in the table means that no test was carried out
+: positive   (+): very weak positive   −: negative

[d] EB virus transformed cell lines from patients with Bloom syndrome, Fanconi syndrome, ataxia telangiectasia or xeroderma pigmentosum

only the extracts but also the particles themselves had DNA damaging or mutagenic effects in mammalian cells, i.e. in human fibroblasts [75] and CHO cells [71].

The effective concentrations of the extracts in most mammalian test systems was between 10 and 100 µg/ml and, in line with the multiplicity of cell systems and end points, differed markedly from one system to the next. For example, with one extract and the same end point – chromosome aberrations – the effective concentration in human lymphocytes was 0.1 µg/ml and in CHO cells 20 µg/ml [62]. The low sensitivity of the CHO cells is possibly caused by the absence of the nitroreductase required for activation of nitro aromatics [80]. There are as yet no data available as to nitroreductase activity in human lymphocytes. In the test for DNA strand breaks in Syrian hamster embryo cells which was carried out in parallel to the above tests, even 250 µg/ml of the organic extract produced no effect [72]. It must be taken into account here that the procedure used, which involves a shift in the sedimentation profile of DNA after alkaline elution [81], was shown in a comparative study to be the least sensitive of a number of tests for genotoxicity [64]. As in the bacterial systems, with mammalian cells an external metabolic activation system is not necessary for demonstration of the genotoxic effect of the organic extract of soot particles. This is also the case with cell lines such as V79, CHO or L5178Y which are unable to activate promutagens oxidatively. The external metabolizing cell fractions tended to reduce the mutagenicity of the extracts in the mammalian cell systems [66]. The situation is different for the fraction of diesel engine emissions which contains primarily PAH [74]. This fraction also proved to be mutagenic in human lymphoblastoid cells but its effect was dependent on the presence of a metabolic activation system.

Organic extracts of the particles from gasoline engine emissions have genotoxic effects in bacteria and mammalian cell systems which are similar to those of the extracts from diesel engine emissions [65, 82]. Unlike most of the mutagenic fractions from diesel engine emissions, they are markedly more effective in the presence of a metabolic activation system than in its absence. At present the data base is inadequate for a meaningful comparison of the genotoxic potential of emissions from diesel and gasoline engines. If one only considered the fact that gasoline engine emissions contain very many fewer particles than do diesel engine emissions, then one would conclude that the gasoline engine emissions have a lesser mutagenic potential. However, since the mutagenic substances in the two extracts are activated differently in the *in vitro* test systems and since the components of the gasoline engine emissions which are not bound to particles have been only inadequately investigated to date, it is clear that a statement as to the relative mutagenic potential of the two emissions can currently not be made.

3.2 in vivo studies

Diesel engine emissions have been tested with the usual *in vivo* procedures for their potential genotoxic effects in somatic cells and germ cells (Table 5). With one exception, the results were negative. In the one study with positive findings, the frequency of sister chromatid exchange in the lung cells of Syrian hamsters was doubled after the animals had inhaled diesel engine emissions (12 mg particles/m^3) for several

Table 5. *In vitro* genotoxicity of diesel engine emissions

Test organism	Test/end point	Whole emissions	Particle	Extract	Ref.
somatic cells					
mouse	micronucleus, bone marrow	−	−	+	[84]
mouse	micronucleus, bone marrow	−			[66]
Chinese hamster	micronucleus, bone marrow	−	−	(+)	[84]
mouse	sister chromatid exchange, bone marrow	−	+	+	[84]
rat	sister chromatid exchange, bone marrow	−			[66]
Syrian hamster	sister chromatid exchange, lung cells	+	+	+	[83]
Syrian hamster	mutation (HGPRT), transplacental	−	−	+	[66]
mouse	mutation *S. typhimurium* (host mediated assay)	−			[66]
germ cells					
mouse	dominant lethal test (chromosome damage)	−			[85]
mouse	heritable translocation (chromosome damage)	−			[85]
mouse	specific locus test (point mutation)	−			[85]

for explanations see Table 4

months [83]. The effect was also found after intratracheal instillation of the soot particles (130 mg/kg) from the exhaust fumes. In addition, soot particles (300 mg/kg) induced sister chromatid exchange in the bone marrow of mice [84] but even 640 mg/kg did not cause a significant increase in micronuclei in either mice or hamsters [84].

The organic extracts of diesel soot particles produced clearly genotoxic effects in several studies (Table 5). The frequency of sister chromatid exchange in lung cells was 10-fold higher after intratracheal instillation of the extracts (13 mg/kg) than after intratracheal administration of the soot particles [83]. In the bone marrow of mice (and Syrian hamsters) a dose of 1000 mg/kg now caused an increase in micronuclei [84]. After single intraperitoneal injection of 2000–4000 mg/kg extract of soot particles into pregnant Syrian hamsters on day 11 of pregnancy, numerous 8-azaguanine resistant mutants (HGPRT$^-$) were found in explanted embryo cells [66].

The genotoxic effects of diesel engine emissions have also been studied in insects and plants. Whereas no genotoxicity was observed in *Drosophila melanogaster* (sex-linked recessive lethal mutations) [86], in *Tradescantia* both mutations [87] and micronuclei [88] were found.

3.3 Activation of the components of diesel engine emissions in vitro and in vivo

The finding that diesel engine emissions and their organic extracts were also genotoxic in *in vitro* tests without the addition of a metabolizing system such as the post mitochondrial supernatant from liver homogenate suggests that in these test systems oxidation by cytochrome P450 dependent monooxygenases is not necessary for activation. This in turn suggests that the PAH and thioarenes which require activation by these enzymes [89, 90] have little significance for the genotoxic effect of the condensates of diesel engine emissions *in vitro*.

Nitroarenes were identified in a series of studies as being mainly responsible for the *in vitro* genotoxicity of organic extracts from the condensate of diesel engine emissions (reviews in [91, 92]). Although our understanding of the metabolic activation of nitroarenes is still incomplete, the main reactions which lead to the production of reactive breakdown products in bacteria and in mammalian cells have been recognized, at least for the highly mutagenic dinitropyrenes. Dinitropyrenes are reduced via nitroso and hydroxylamine intermediates to the corresponding amines [94, 95]. Hydroxylamines can bind to DNA either directly or after esterification [96–98] and can cause the observed genotoxic effects. These reactions apparently do not only take place in bacteria and mammalian cells *in vitro* but also in the mammalian animal. For example, after administration of 1,8-dinitropyrene to rats the faeces was shown to contain various reduction products including the diamine and diacetyldiamine which are also formed in *in vitro* test systems [99]. The formation of DNA adducts was also observed in the organs examined in this study, in liver, urinary bladder and mammary gland. The main DNA adduct was identified as desoxyguanosin-8-yl-1-amino-8-nitropyrene. Dinitropyrenes are also reductively metabolized by intestinal bacteria to products which can damage DNA [100, 101]. Metabolism by the intestinal microflora, however, does not seem to be essential for the production of DNA damage by dinitropyrene metabolites *in vivo* because the above mentioned desoxyguanosin-8-yl-1-amino-8-nitropyrene adducts were also found in germ free rats [99].

As for 1,8-dinitropyrene, there are indications that 1-nitropyrene is metabolized *in vivo* to DNA-binding products [98]. CD rats were administered 100 μmol 1-nitropyrene on the day of birth and once a week for the subsequent 7 weeks. 24 hours after the last injection, the liver was shown to contain the same desoxyguanosin-8-yl-1-aminopyrene adducts as are found in bacteria and mammalian cells *in vitro* [98]. The adducts were found only in female animals, not in males. The reason for the sex difference is not clear.

Studies in which rats were exposed to exhaust fumes (7.1 mg/m^3) for 600 days suggest that diesel engine emissions themselves can also cause the production of DNA adducts *in vivo* [93]. Under these conditions significant amounts of DNA adducts were detected in the lungs of some animals by means of the ^{32}P-postlabelling method.

3.4 Conclusions

Soot particles from diesel engine emissions and their organic extracts cause point mutations, chromosome aberrations, DNA damage and sister chromatid exchange *in vitro* in bacteria and mammalian cells. Numerous nitroarenes which are present in the condensate have proved to be particularly genotoxic. Components of diesel engine emissions are also genotoxic *in vivo* so that application of the particles from the exhaust fumes or of their organic extracts to various species leads to micronucleus formation, increased sister chromatid exchange and somatic mutations. *In vivo* metabolites and DNA adducts which are formed from diesel engine emissions and the nitroarenes that they contain are similar to those formed in bacteria and mammalian cells *in vitro*.

4 Risk estimation for diesel and gasoline engine emissions

Some groups of components of diesel and gasoline engine emissions are analytically well characterized. Total balance sheets, however, as with tobacco smoke, are not available because, on the one hand, the mixtures are very complex and the separation and identification of the individual components is consequently difficult and, on the other, the interests of the analysts involved are mostly restricted to specific aspects. The available data, which cannot be presented here in detail, do make it clear which groups of substances are important for a discussion of the toxic effects. These are aliphatic hydrocarbons, aromatic hydrocarbons, oxidation products of aliphatic hydrocarbons and polycyclic aromatic hydrocarbons including some of their nitro derivatives. Thus it is possible to make a rough comparison, sufficient for our purposes, of the mean levels or emission concentrations.

The initial comparison ignores the reduction in emissions which may be achieved with a catalyst although the substantial improvement made possible with this technology is beyond doubt. The available data indicate that the four relevant substance groups mentioned above are present in both diesel and gasoline engine emissions at levels of the same order of magnitude. This refers only to average values from a multitude of analytical data. The content of individual components can vary within extremely wide limits in both types of emissions, including extreme values for individual components of toxicological significance. These deviations from the mean can be decisive for the evaluation of individual cases. For approximate estimation of total exposure, however, we must make use of the mean values.

This rough stock-taking does not permit a reliable evaluation of the differential risk. Although the mutagenicity studies – as described above – indicate that there is no substantial difference between the genotoxic potential of diesel and gasoline engine emissions, it cannot be claimed that this would be confirmed under realistic conditions of inhalative exposure, as the particles which carry the genotoxic potential are very different in the two types of emissions. The binding of genotoxic substances is expected to be higher on the particles from the diesel engine emissions. This is the basis for the hypothesis (described in more detail above) that more potency is to be expected from diesel engine emissions because of the depot effect. This hypothesis is based only on studies of PAH which do not account for the whole genotoxic potential. Rather we are concerned with very complex mixtures whose components can influence not only adsorption and desorption of the others but also their genotoxic effects. The currently available hypotheses are insufficient for a reliable risk estimation. The question could be decided if diesel engine emissions and gasoline engine emissions could be tested at the same concentrations in an inhalation study. As explained above in detail, this possibility is limited by the carbon monoxide which would be the most toxic component in the gasoline engine emissions.

In summary, it is still unclear whether the carcinogenic risk associated with gasoline engine emissions is the same as that of diesel engine emissions, or whether it may be considered to be lower or even higher.

5 Manifesto (MAK value, classification)

The positive results of a series of inhalation studies in experimental animals fulfill the criteria for the classification of diesel engine emissions in Section III A 2) of the List of MAK Values. The concentrations used are higher than those at the workplaces in question but systematic concentration measurements in relevant occupational environments have not (yet) been made available to the Commission. When one, however, considers the peak values to be expected under unfavourable conditions (closed, poorly ventilated rooms, cold season of the year), the test concentrations used in the animal studies come close to the maximal conceivable workplace levels. The actual difference cannot be estimated at present because the necessary data is not available.

No quantitative risk estimation is (currently) possible from the epidemiological data. The studies which have been carried out demonstrate neither a statistical association nor one which could be considered to be causal; nor are they able to exclude such an association.

With the classification of diesel engine emissions in Section III A 2) the Commission wishes to draw attention to the fact that gasoline engine emissions, which must also be considered in principle to have carcinogenic potential, cannot – for other reasons (technical experimental difficulties) – be evaluated as extensively as diesel engine emissions. Regulations for the protection of workers should take this fact into account and not consider only one aspect of the problem. Further studies on the carcinogenic effects of gasoline engine emissions are urgently required.

6 References

1. Steenland, K.: *Amer. J. industr. Med. 10*, 177 (1986)
2. Harris, J. E.: *Potential risk of lung cancer from diesel engine emissions*, p 62, National Academy Press, Washington DC, USA, 1981
3. Cuddihy, R. C., W. C. Griffith, R. O. McClellan: *Environm. Sci. Technol. 18*, 14A (1984)
4. DeCoufle, P., K. Stanislawczyck, L. Houten: *A retrospective survey of cancer in relation to occupation*, NIOSH report No. 77–178 (1977); cited in [1]
5. Walrath, J., E. Rogot, J. Murray, A. Blair: *Mortality patterns among US veterans by occupation and smoking status*, NIH Publication No. 85–2756, U.S. Government Printing Office, Washington DC, USA, 1985; cited in [1]
6. Dubrow, R., D. Wegmann: *Occupational characteristics of cancer victims in Massachusetts, 1971–1973*, NIOSH Publication No. 84–109, 1984; cited in [1]
7. Williams, R., N. Stegens, J. Goldsmith: *J. nat. Cancer Inst. 59*, 1147 (1977)
8. Damber, L., L. Larsson: *Brit. J. industr. Med. 42*, 246 (1985)
9. Raffle, P.: *Brit. J. industr. Med. 14*, 73 (1957)
10. Waller, R. E.: in Pepelko, W. E., R. M. Danner, N. A. Clarke (Eds.): *Health effects of diesel engine emissions*, Proceedings of an internat. Symposium, Vol. II, p 1085, EPA publication No. EPA-600/9-80-057b, Govt. Printing Office, Washington DC, USA, 1980; cited in [1].

11. Rushton, L., M. Alderson, C. Nagarajah: *Brit. J. industr. Med. 40*, 340 (1983)
12. Waller, R., L. Hampton, P. Lawther: *Brit. J. industr. Med. 42*, 824 (1985)
13. Howe, G., D. Fraser, J. Lindsay, B. Presnal, Shun Zhang Yu: *J. nat. Cancer Inst. 70*, 1015 (1983)
14. Hueper, W.: *A quest into environmental causes of carcinoma of the lung*, Public Health Monograph, No. 36, U.S. Dept. HEW, PHS; cited in [1]
15. Kaplan, I.: J. Amer. med. Ass. *171*, 2039 (1959); cited in [1]
16. Wong, O., R. W. Morgan, L. Kheifets, S. R. Larson, M. D. Whorton: *Brit. J. industr. Med. 42*, 435 (1985)
17. Hall, N., E. Wynder: *Environm. Res. 34*, 77 (1984)
18. Schenker, M., T. Smith, A. Munoz, S. Woskie, F. E. Speizer: *Brit. J. industr. Med. 41*, 320 (1984)
19. Garshick, E., M. B. Schenker, A. Munoz, T. J. Smith, S. Woskie, K. Hammond, F. E. Speizer: *Diesel exhaust exposure and lung cancer in US railroad workers*, poster presentation at the 4th Health Effects Institute Annual Conference, Seabrook Island S.C., February 8–12, 1987 data from a case-control study of lung cancer and diesel exhaust exposure in railroad workers (EPA grant report R-807 515) and F.E. Speizer, T. Smith, W. Thilly: *Health effects of exposure to diesel exhaust*, (EPA grant report R-807 515)
20. Mauderly, J. L., R. K. Jones, R. O. McClellan, R. F. Henderson, W. C. Griffith: in Ishinishi, N., A. Koizumi, R. O. McClellan, W. Stöber (Eds.): *Carcinogenic and mutagenic effects of diesel engine exhaust*, p 397, Elsevier Sci. Publ., Amsterdam, New York, Oxford, 1986
21. *Statistisches Jahrbuch für die Bundesrepublik Deutschland 1986*. Ed. Statistisches Bundesamt, Wiesbaden, Kohlhammer, Stuttgart, D-6500 Mainz, 1986
22. Abel, U.: *Epidemiologie des Krebses. Aspekte der Aussagekraft und Anwendbarkeit von Krebsinzidenz- und -mortalitätsraten*, Profil Verlag, D-8000 München, 1986
23. Brightwell, J., X. Fouillet, A.-L. Cassano-Zoppi, R. Gatz, F. Duchosal: in Ishinishi, N., A. Koizumi, R. O. McClellan, W. Stöber (Eds.): *Carcinogenic and mutagenic effects of diesel engine exhaust*, p 471, Elsevier Sci. Publ., Amsterdam, New York, Oxford 1986
24. Heinrich, U., H. Muhle, S. Takenaka, H. Ernst, R. Fuhst, U. Mohr, F. Pott, W. Stöber: *J. appl. Toxicol. 6*, 383 (1986)
25. Ishinishi, N., N. Kuwabara, S. Nagase, T. Suzuki, S. Ishiwata, T. Kohno: in Ishinishi, N., A. Koizumi, R. O. McClellan, W. Stöber (Eds.): *Carcinogenic and mutagenic effects of diesel engine exhaust*, p 329, Elsevier Sci. Publ., Amsterdam, New York, Oxford, 1986
26. Iwai, K., T. Udagawa, M. Yamagishi, H. Yamada: in Ishinishi, N., A. Koizumi, R. O. McClellan, W. Stöber (Eds.): *Carcinogenic and mutagenic effects of diesel engine exhaust*, p 349, Elsevier Sci. Publ., Amsterdam, New York, Oxford, 1986
27. Kaplan, H. L., K. J. Springer, W. F. MacKenzie: *Studies of potential health effects of long-term exposure to diesel exhaust emissions*. Final Report No. 01-0750-103 (SWRI) and No. 1239 (SFRE), Southwest Research Institute, San Antonio, TX, USA, June 1983
28. Lewis, T. R., F. H. Y. Green, W. J. Moorman, J. A. R. Burg, D. W. Lynch: in Ishinishi, N., A. Koizumi, R. O. McClellan, W. Stöber (Eds.): *Carcinogenic and mutagenic effects of diesel engine exhaust*, p 361, Elsevier Sci. Publ., Amsterdam, New York, Oxford, 1986
29. White, H. J., J. Vostal, H. Kaplan, W. Mackenzie: *J. appl. Toxicol. 3*, 332 (1983)
30. Takemoto, K., H. Yoshimura, H. Katayama: in Ishinishi, N., A. Koizumi, R. O. McClellan, W. Stöber (Eds.): *Carcinogenic and mutagenic effects of diesel engine exhaust*, p 311, Elsevier Sci. Publ., Amsterdam, New York, Oxford, 1986
31. Heinrich U., L. Peters, W. Funcke, F. Pott, U. Mohr, W. Stöber: in Lewtas, J. (Ed.): *Toxicological effects of emissions from diesel engines*, p 225, Elsevier Sci. Publ. Co. Inc., New York, 1982
32. Mohr, U., S. Takenaka, D. L. Dungworth: in Ishinishi, N., A. Koizumi, R. O. McClellan, W. Stöber (Eds.): *Carcinogenic and mutagenic effects of diesel engine exhaust*, p 459, Elsevier Sci. Publ., Amsterdam, New York, Oxford, 1986
33. Mauderly, J. L., N. A. Gillett, R. F. Henderson, R. K. Jones, R. O. McClellan: *Ann. occup. Hyg. 22*, 659, Supplement 1 (1988)
34. Wolff, R. K., R. F. Henderson, M. B. Snipes, J. D. Sun, J. A. Bond, Ch. E. Mitchell, J. L. Mauderly, R. O. McClellan: in Ishinishi, N., A. Koizumi, R. O. McClellan, W. Stöber (Eds.): *Carcinogenic and mutagenic effects of diesel engine exhaust*, p 199, Elsevier Sci. Publ., Amsterdam, New York, Oxford, 1986

35. Kotin, P., H. L. Falk, M. Thomas: *Arch. industr. Hlth 11*, 113 (1955)
36. Kotin, P., H. L. Falk, M. Thomas: *Arch. industr. Hyg. 9*, 164 (1954)
37. Huisingh, J. Lewtas, R. Bradow, R. Jungers, L. Claxton, R. Zweidinger, S. Tejada, J. Bumgarner, F. Duffield, V. F. Simmon, C. Hare, C. Rodriguez, L. Snow, M. D. Waters: in Waters, M. D., S. Nesnow, J. Lewtas Huisingh, S. S. Sandhu, L. Claxton (Eds.): *Application of short-term bioassay in the fractionation and analysis of complex environmental mixtures*, p 381, Plenum Press, New York, 1978
38. Slaga, T. J., L. L. Triplett, S. Nesnow: in Pepelko, W. E., R. M. Danner, N. A. Clarke (Eds.): *Health effects of diesel engine emissions*, Proceedings of an intern. Symposium, Vol. II, p 874, EPA publication No. EPA-600/9-80-057b, Govt. Printing Office, Washington DC, USA, 1980
39. Nesnow, S., L. L. Triplett, T. J. Slaga: in Waters, M., S. S. Sandhu, J. Lewtas Huisingh, L. Claxton, S. Nesnow (Eds.): *Short-term Bioassays in the Analysis of Complex Environmental Mixtures*, p 277, Plenum Press, New York, 1981
40. Nesnow, S., L. L. Triplett, T. J. Slaga: *J. nat. Cancer Inst. 68*, 829 (1982)
41. Kunitake, E., K. Shimamura, H. Katayama, K. Takemoto, A. Yamamoto, A. Hisanaga, S. Ohyama, N. Ishinishi: in Ishinishi, N., A. Koizumi, R. O. McClellan, W. Stöber (Eds.): *Carcinogenic and mutagenic effects of diesel engine exhaust*, p 235, Elsevier Sci. Publ., Amsterdam, New York, Oxford, 1986
42. Brune, H., G. Grimmer, R. Deutsch-Wenzel: Personal communication to the Commission, 1986
43. Kawabata, Y., K. Iwai, T. Udagawa, K. Tukagoshi, K. Higuchi: in Ishinishi, N., A. Koizumi, R. O. McClellan, W. Stöber (Eds.): *Carcinogenic and mutagenic effects of diesel engine exhaust*, p 213, Elsevier Sci. Publ., Amsterdam, New York, Oxford, 1986
44. Lies, K.-H., A. Hartung, A. Postulka, H. Gring, J. Schulze: in Ishinishi, N., A. Koizumi, R. O. McClellan, W. Stöber (Eds.): *Carcinogenic and mutagenic effects of diesel engine exhaust*, p 65, Elsevier Sci. Publ., Amsterdam, New York, Oxford, 1986
45. Heinrich, U., F. Pott, U. Mohr, R. Fuhst, J. König: *Exp. Path. 29*, 29 (1986)
46. Heinrich, U., F. Pott, S. Rittinghausen: in Ishinishi, N., A. Koizumi, R.O. McClellan, W. Stöber (Eds.): *Carcinogenic and mutagenic effects of diesel engine exhaust*, p 441, Elsevier Sci. Publ., Amsterdam, New York, Oxford, 1986
47. Bond, J. A., J. D. Sun, Ch. E. Mitchell, J. S. Dutcher, R. K. Wolff, R. O. McClellan: in Si Duk Lee, T. Schneider, L. D. Grant, P. J. Verkerk (Eds.): *Aerosols: Research, risk assessment and control strategies*, p 479, Lewis Publ., Chelsea, Mich., USA, 1986
48. Henry, M. C., C. D. Port, D. G. Kaufman: *Cancer Res. 35*, 207 (1975)
49. Sellakumar, A., F. Stenbäck, J. Rowlands: *Europ. J. Cancer 12*, 313 (1976)
50. Dalbey, W. E., P. Nettesheim, R. Griesemer, J. E. Caton, M. R. Guerin: *J. nat. Cancer Inst. 64*, 383 (1980)
51. Heinrich, U., F. Pott, S. Rittinghausen, L. Peters: *Carcinogenic effects after combined exposure to PAH-containing emissions and other respiratory tract carcinogens*, Lecture given at the 28th annual Spring Meeting of the Deutsche Gesellschaft für Pharmakologie und Toxikologie, D-6500 Mainz, 10–13 March 1987
52. Bernfeld, P., F. Homburger, E. Soto, K. J. Pai: *J. nat. Cancer Inst. 63*, 675 (1979)
53. International Agency for Research on Cancer (IARC): *IARC Monographs on the Evaluation of the Carcinogenic Risk of Chemicals to Humans*, Vol. 42, *Silica and Some Silicates*, Lyon, France (1987)
54. Holland, L. M., J. S. Wilson, M. I. Tillery, D. M. Smith: in Goldsmith, D. F., D. M. Winn, C. M. Shy (Eds.): *Silica, silicosis, and cancer. Controversy in occupational medicine*, p 267, Praeger Scientific Publ., New York, 1986
55. Martin, J. C, H. Daniel, L. Le Bouffant: in H. W. Walton (Ed.): *Inhaled Particles IV*, Vol. 1, p 361, Pergamon Press, Oxford, England, 1977
56. Lee, K. P., H. J. Trochimowicz, C. F. Reinhardt: Toxicol. appl. Pharmacol. *79*, 179 (1985)
57. Vostal, J. J.: in Ishinishi, N., A. Koizumi, R. O. McClellan, W. Stöber (Eds.): *Carcinogenic and mutagenic effects of diesel engine exhaust*, p 381, Elsevier Sci. Publ., Amsterdam, New York, Oxford, 1986
58. Langer, A. M., R. P. Nolan: in Beck, E. G., J. Bignon (Eds.): *In vitro effects of mineral dusts*, 3rd intern. workshop, Proceedings of the NATO Advanced Research Workshop, October 1984, p 9, NATO ASI Series G, Ecological Sciences No. 3, Springer, Berlin, 1985

59. Wang, Y. Y., S. M. Rappaport, R. F. Sawyer, R. D. Talcott, E. J. Wei: *Cancer Lett. 5*, 39 (1978)
60. Loprieno, N., F. DeLorenzo, G. M. Cornetti, G. Biaggini: in Pepelko, W. E., R. M. Danner, N. A. Clarke (Eds.): *Health effects of diesel engine emissions*, Proceedings of an internat. Symposium, Vol. I, p 276, EPA publication No. EPA 600/9-80-057a, Govt. Printing Office, Washington DC, USA, 1980
61. Matsushita, H., S. Goto, O. Endo, J.-H. Lee, A. Kawai: in Ishinishi, N., A. Koizumi, R. O. McClellan, W. Stöber (Eds.): *Carcinogenic and mutagenic effects of diesel engine exhaust*, p 103, Elsevier Sci. Publ., Amsterdam, New York, Oxford, 1986
62. Lewtas, J.: *Environm. Hlth Perspect. 47*, 141 (1983)
63. Pederson, T. C.: in Rionda, D., M. Cooke, R. K. Haroz (Eds.): *Mobile Source Emissions Including Polycyclic Organic Species*, p 227, D. Reidel Publishing Co., Dordrecht, NL, 1983
64. Casto, B. C., G. G. Hatch, S. L. Huang, J. L. Huisingh, S. Nesnow, M. D. Waters: in Pepelko, W. E., R. M. Danner, N. A. Clarke (Eds.): *Health effects of diesel engine emissions*, Proceedings of an internat. Symposium, Vol. II, p 843, EPA publication No. EPA 600/9-80-057b, Govt. Printing Office, Washington DC, 1980
65. Claxton, L. D.: *The Utility of Bacterial Mutagenesis Testing in the Characterization of Mobile Source Emissions: A review*, Elsevier Sci. Publ. Co. Inc., New York, 1982
66. Morimoto, K., M. Kitamura, H. Kondo, A. Koizumi: in Ishinishi, N., A. Koizumi, R. O. McClellan, W. Stöber (Eds.): *Carcinogenic and mutagenic effects of diesel engine exhaust*, p 85, Elsevier Sci. Publ., Amsterdam, New York, Oxford, 1986
67. U.S. Environmental Protection Agency: in *Short-Term Genetic Bioassays Used in the Evaluation of Unregulated Automobile Emission: 1981–1982 Contract Reports*: in Brusick, D. J., R. R. Young, D. R. Jagannath (Eds.): EPA-68-02-3382, Technical Directive 008, October 1983
68. Gibson, T. L., A. I. Ricci, R. L. Williams: in Bjoerseth, A., A. J. Dennis (Eds.): *Polynuclear Aromatic Hydrocarbons*, p 707, Battelle Press Columbus, OH, USA, 1981
69. Hartung, A., J. Schulze, H. Kieß, K.-H. Lies: *Staub 46*, 132 (1986)
70. Mitchell, A. D., E. L. Evans, M. M. Jody, E. S. Riccio, K. E. Mortelmans, V. F. Simmon: *Environm. International 5*, 393 (1981)
71. Chescheir, G. M., N. E. Garrett, J. D. Shelburne, J. L. Huisingh, M. D. Waters: in Waters, M. D., S. S. Sandhu, J. L. Huisingh, L. Claxton, S. Nesnow (Eds.): *Short-Term Bioassays in the Analysis of Complex Mixtures II*, p 337, Plenum Press, New York, 1981
72. Casto, B. C., G. G. Hatch, S. L. Huang, J. L. Huisingh, S. Nesnow, M. D. Waters: *Environm. International 5*, 403 (1981)
73. Li, A. P., R. E. Royer: *Mutat. Res. 103*, 349 (1982)
74. Barfknecht, T. R., R. A. Hites, E. L. Cavalieri, W. G. Thilly: in Lewtas, J. (Ed.): *Toxicological Effects of Emissions from Diesel Engines*, p 277, Elsevier Sci. Publ. Co. Inc., New York, 1982
75. McCormick, J. J., R. M. Zator, B. B. DaGae, V. M. Maher: in Pepelko, W. E., R. M. Danner, N. A. Clarke (eds): *Health effects of diesel engine emissions*, Proceedings of an internat. Symposium, Vol. II, p 423, EPA publication No. EPA 600/9-80-057b, Govt. Printing Office, Washington DC, USA, 1980
76. Curren, R. D., R. E. Kouri, C. M. Kim, L. M. Schechtman: *Environm. International 5*, 411 (1981)
77. National Academy Press: *Health Effects of Exposure to Diesel Exhaust*, Washington DC, USA, 1981
78. Schiff, L. J., S. F. Elliot, S. J. Moore, M. S. Urcan, J. A. Graham: p 114, U.S. Environmental Protection Agency, Cincinnati, OH, USA, 1981
79. McCoy, E. C., M. Anders, M. McCartney, P. C. Howard, F. A. Beland, H.S. Rosenkranz: *Mutat. Res. 139*, 115 (1984)
80. Heflich, R. H., N. F. Fullerton, F. A. Beland: *Mutat. Res. 161*, 99 (1986)
81. Swenberg, J. A., G. L. Petzold, P. R. Harbach: *Biochem. biophys. Res. Commun. 72*, 732 (1976)
82. Lewtas, J.: in Rondia, D., M. Cooke, R. K. Haroz (Eds.): *Mobile Source Emissions Including Polycyclic Organic Species*, p 165, Reidel Publishing Co., Dordrecht, NL, 1983
83. Guerrero, R. R., D. E. Rounds, J. Orthoefer: Environm. International 5, 445 (1981)
84. Pereira, M. A.: in Lewtas, J. (Ed.): *Toxicological Effects of Emissions from Diesel Engines*, p 265, Elsevier Sci. Publ. Co. Inc., New York, 1982

85. Russel, L. B., W. M. Generoso, W. L. Russel, E. F. Oakberg: in U.S. Environmental Protection Agency, EPA 600/51-81-056, p 1, Research Triangle Park, NC., USA, 1981
86. Schuler, R. L., R. W. Niemeier: in Pepelko, W. E., R. M. Danner, N. A. Clarke (Eds.): *Health effects of diesel engine emissions*, Proceedings of an internat. Symposium, Vol. II., p 914, EPA publication No. EPA 600/9-80-057b, Govt. Printing Office, Washington DC, USA, 1980
87. Schairer, L. A., R. C. Sautkulis, N. R. Tempel: in Tice, R. R., D. L. Costa, K. M. Schaich (Eds.): *Monitoring Ambient Air Using the Higher Plant Tradescantia in Genotoxic Effects of Airborne Agents*, p 121, Plenum Press, 1981
88. Ma, T. H., V. A. Anderson, S. Sandhu: in *Short-Term Bioassays in the Analysis of Complex Mixtures*, p 351, Plenum Press, New York, 1981
89. Pelroy, R. A., D. L. Stewart, Y. Tominaga, M. Iwao, R. N. Castle, M. L. Lee: *Mutat. Res. 117*, 31 (1983)
90. McFall, T., G. M. Booth, M. L. Lee: *Mutat. Res. 135*, 97 (1984)
91. Rosenkranz, H. S., R. Mermelstein: *Mutat. Res. 114*, 217 (1983)
92. Beland, F. A., R. H. Heflich, P. C. Howard, P. P. Fu: in Harvey, R. G. (Ed.): *Polycyclic Hydrocarbons and Carcinogenesis*, p 371, American Chemical Society, Washington DC, USA, 1985
93. Wong, D., C. E. Mitchell, R. K. Wolff, J. L. Mauderly, A. M. Jeffrey: *Carcinogenesis 7*, 1595 (1986)
94. Messier, F., C. Lu, P. Andrews, B. E. McCarry, M. A. Quilliam, D. R. McCalla: *Carcinogenesis 2*, 1007 (1981)
95. Heflich, R. H., E. K. Fifer, Z. Djuric, F. A. Beland: *Environm. Hlth Perspect. 62*, 135 (1985)
96. Howard, P. C., R. H. Heflich, F. E. Evans, F. A. Beland: *Cancer Res. 43*, 2052 (1983)
97. Djuric, Z., E. K. Fifer, F. A. Beland: *Carcinogenesis 6*, 941 (1985)
98. Hsieh, L. L., D. Wong, V. Heisig, R. M. Santella, J. L. Mauderly, C. E. Mitchell, R. K. Wolff, A. M. Jeffrey: in Ishinishi, N., A. Koizumi, R. O. McClellan, W. Stöber (Eds.): *Carcinogenic and mutagenic effects of diesel engine exhaust*, p 223, Elsevier Sci. Publ., Amsterdam, New York, Oxford, 1986
99. Heflich, R. H., Z. Djuric, E. K. Fifer, C. E. Cerniglia, F. A. Beland: in Ishinishi, N., A. Koizumi, R. O. McClellan, W. Stöber (Eds.): *Carcinogenic and mutagenic effects of diesel engine exhaust*, p 185, Elsevier Sci. Publ., Amsterdam, New York, Oxford, 1986
100. El-Bayoumy, K., C. Sharma, Y. M. Louis, B. Reddy, S. S. Hecht: *Cancer Lett. 19*, 311 (1983)
101. Cerniglia, C. E., P. C. Howard, P. P. Fu, W. Franklin: *Biochem. biophys. Res. Commun. 123*, 262 (1984)

completed 18.5.1987

Dimethyl ether

Classification/MAK value:	**1000 ml/m³ (ppm)**
	1910 mg/m³
Classification/MAK value dates from:	**1988**
Synonyms:	methyl ether
	wood ether
Trade names:	Aeropur®
	Dymel A®
Chemical name (CAS):	oxybismethane
CAS number:	115-10-6
Structural formula:	$H_3C-O-CH_3$
Molecular formula:	C_2H_6O
Molecular weight:	46.07
Melting point:	$-138.5\,^\circ C$
Boiling point:	$-23.7\,^\circ C$
Vapour pressure at 20 °C:	5200 hPa

1 ml/m³ (ppm) = 1.91 mg/m³   **1 mg/m³ = 0.523 ml/m³ (ppm)**

1 Toxic Effects and Modes of Action

Dimethyl ether (DME) is a colourless gas with mild narcotic effects and a slightly sweet, ether-like smell. It is less lipophilic and less narcotic than diethyl ether.
DME is taken up in the respiratory passages. In animals inhalation of toxic doses causes sedation, progressive paralysis of motor function, loss of the righting reflex and possibly death after hypopnea and coma.

In numerous mutagenicity tests DME has proved not to be mutagenic. In rats after life-long inhalation it was not carcinogenic. A teratogenicity test with DME was also negative.

2 Pharmacokinetics

DME-air mixtures containing 750–2000 ml/m³ DME were administered to male Wistar rats intratracheally for 60 minutes. After 30 minutes exposure to 1000 ml/m³, equilibrium concentrations of 14–22 ppm were established in all organs studied (blood, heart, lung, liver, spleen, kidney, fat, muscle, brain). The penetration of adipose and muscle tissue was slowest. However, after 30 minutes the DME concentration in adipose tissue was about 30% higher than in the other tissues. At the end of exposure the DME concentration decreased rapidly in all organs. The half-life for the α-phase was 10 minutes and for the β-phase about 90 minutes. The concentrations in adipose and muscle tissue decreased a little more slowly. Storage was not seen in any of the organs. In the concentration range tested, the DME levels in the organs were directly proportional to the exposure concentration [1, 2]. The same results were obtained in another study in which rats inhaled labelled DME $(750-2000 \text{ ml/m}^3)$ for 6 hours [3].

3 Effects in Man

3.1 Inhalation

Inhalation of 50 000 or 75 000 ml/m^3 DME by test persons led to a slight reduction in their ability to concentrate; exposure to 82 000 ml/m^3 resulted after 21 minutes in incoordination and visual defects, after 30 minutes in slight facial analgesia. At 144 000 ml/m^3 the first symptoms of intoxication appeared after 7 minutes and after 26 minutes included unconsciousness and nausea on reawakening. 200 000 ml/m^3 produced unconsciousness in 17 minutes [4].

DME concentrations up to 50% in air inhaled during laboratory work were felt to be highly unpleasant. Further details were not given [5].

DME concentrations in venous blood from four healthy test persons were determined under conditions like those of a normal hair-spray application with DME as propellant. After a brief exposure (7 seconds) blood levels of 20–50 ppb were found. Shortly after a 15 minute exposure to 300 ml/m^3 the blood levels were 0.5 ppm. They fell to 0.2 ppm within 30 minutes [1, 2].

3.2 Medical application

Because of its good solubility both in organic solvents and in water and because of its rapid diffusion in tissues, DME has been used medically to determine cardiac output and lung tissue volume. No toxic effects were found in man after intravenous bolus injections of 0.2–0.3 ml doses [6, 7].

When DME was used as propellant and solvent in mouth, nose and throat sprays for the treatment of respiratory disorders, particularly of asthmatic diseases, the applied medicines took effect more rapidly than with chlorofluorocarbon propellants. The narcotic effect of DME conceivable in this context was not observed in a pharmacological study with 6 healthy persons. They were administered two doses of 26.6 ± 3.5 mg DME by spraying into the pharynx cavity. 3 minutes later the plasma DME levels were between 2842 and 179 ppb. A second application 60 minutes later gave no evidence of accumulative effects [8].

4 Effects on Animals

4.1 Acute toxicity

LC_{50} values and observations of the effects of acute and subacute inhalation are assembled in Table 1.

The lethal concentrations are relatively high, about 16 % DME in air (v/v) for rats and 40 % for mice, so that it is very likely not only the narcotic action of DME which causes asphyxiation and death of the animals but also the reduced oxygen supply. Accordingly, the animals always died during the exposure.

Concentrations up to 20 000 ml/m^3 did not cause behavioural changes in rats; the animals presumably kept their eyes closed because of the irritation (see Table 1 [12]). Rats who had been exposed to 50 000 ml/m^3 DME for 10 days (see Table 1) were uncoordinated and unresponsive. Their growth was delayed. They excreted alkaline urine, and blood urea nitrogen and leukocytes were reduced while neutrophils were increased. Pathological studies revealed no evidence of organ damage. 13 days after the end of exposure the animals had recovered completely [10].

The symptoms of a generalized anaesthesia developed in rabbits at a concentration of 400 000 ml/m^3 [9].

In studies with dogs exposed for 5 minutes to 200 000 ml/m^3 or more, DME had a mildly stimulating action on the heart in 2 of 12 animals (see Table 1, [13]).

4.2 Subchronic and chronic toxicity

After rats had been exposed to 0, 2000, 10 000 or 20 000 ml/m^3 for 13 weeks (see Table 2), shifts in the white blood count (reduction in lymphocytes, increase in neutrophils) were observed which, although statistically significant, were not considered to have toxicological significance. Likewise reduced serum protein levels in female rats and slight increases in SGPT activity in males were not considered to be of significance since they were not found when the experiment was repeated [15, 16].

In another 13 week inhalation study (see Table 2) with rats and hamsters a no effect level for the influence of DME on the white blood count was determined as 10 000 ml/m^3 for rats and 5000 ml/m^3 for hamsters [15].

In a 30 week inhalation study with rats and 0, 200, 2000 and 20 000 ml/m^3 DME, increased SGOT levels were conspicuous in the group of male rats at 2000 ml/m^3 but not at 20 000 ml/m^3. The SGPT values, on the other hand, were only increased at 20 000 ml/m^3. In the females too the SGPT values were only increased at 20 000 ml/m^3 and the SGOT values not at all. The authors deduce a "minimum effect" level below 20 000, perhaps below 2000 ml/m^3, and a no effect level at or above 200 ml/m^3 [17].

The data of most importance for the assessment come from a 2 year inhalation study. Here, in view of the controversial findings of the other studies, particular attention was given to the liver changes and the serum values. The no effect level was determined as 2000 ml/m^3 (see Table 2) [18].

Table 1. Acute and subacute inhalation toxicity of dimethyl ether in animals

Nominal conc. (measured mean) ml/m³	Species (strain)	Number ♂	♀	Exposure period	Symptoms and observations	Ref.
10–100% v/v	mouse	8		15 min	LC$_{50}$ at 49.4% v/v	[9]
10–100% v/v	mouse	8		30 min	LC$_{50}$ at 38.6% v/v	[9]
3.4–27% v/v	rat (Wistar)	n.s.		4 h	LC$_{50}$ (4 h) at 16.4% v/v	[10, 11]
20000	rat (Wistar)	5	5	4 h	eyes closed (eye irritation), no changes in behaviour, no organ damage	[12]
400000	rabbit	n.s.		45 min	reduced blood pressure, increased heart rate, reduced O$_2$ partial pressure (arterial and venous), CO$_2$ partial pressure increased (arterial and venous), reduced pH	[9]
100000 200000 300000	dog	6 12 6		5 min	at 200000 and 300000 ml/m³ slight stimulating effect on the heart in 16.7% and 33.3% of animals, resp.	[13]
0 10000 50000	rat (ChR-CD)	3 3 3		6 h/d, for 10 d	— from 10000 ml/m³: slight dose-dependent toxicity at 50000 ml/m³: incoordination, unresponsiveness, delayed growth; blood and urine values: see text pathological examination: no substance-related findings normalization after 13 days	[10]
0 100 1000 10000	rat (Wistar)	40 40 40 40	40 40 40 40	6 h/d, 5 d/week, 4 weeks	— — — slight but significant weight loss only in ♀♀ in the last week of exposure	[14]
0 2000 (1945) 10000 (9998) 20000 (19051)	hamster (Syrian)	5 5 5 5	5 5 5 5	6 h/d, 5 d/week, 4 weeks	— — from 10000 ml/m³: number of leukocytes significantly reduced in ♀♀	[15]

n.s.: not specified

Table 2. Subchronic and chronic inhalation toxicity of dimethyl ether in animals

Nominal conc. (measured mean) ml/m³		Species (strain)	Number ♂ ♀		Exposure period	Observations	Ref.
0		rat	10	10	6 h/d,	–	[16]
2 000	(1 943)	(Wistar)	10	10	5 d/week,	–	
10 000	(9 734)		10	10	13 weeks	–	
20 000	(19 466)		10	10		sign. reduction in lymphocytes and increase in neutrophiles; increased SGPT activity in ♂♂, reduced serum protein levels in ♀♀	
0		rat	10	10	6 h/d,	–	[15]
1 000	(988)	(Wistar)	10	10	5 d/week,	–	
5 000	(5 019)		10	10	13 weeks	–	
10 000	(9 734)		10	10		–	
20 000	(19 740)		10	10		increase in neutrophiles	
0		rat	25	25	6 h/d,	–	[17]
200	(1 972)	(Wistar)	25	25	5 d/week,	–	
2 000	(1 964)		25	25	30 weeks	2000 ml/m³: sign. increased SGOT values only in ♂♂;	
20 000	(18 830)		25	25		20 000 ml/m³: sign. reduction in liver weight in ♂♂, sign. increased SGPT values in ♂♂ and ♀♀	
0		rat	100	100	6 h/d,	–	[18]
2 000		(Sprague-	100	100	5 d/week,	–	
10 000		Dawley)	100	100	104 weeks	from 10 000 ml/m³: sign. increase in body weight and reduced life times in ♂♂ and ♀♀; serum parameters and liver weights without substance-related findings (also at the interim sacrifices after 3, 6, 9, 12 and 18 months)	
25 000			100	100			
0		hamster	30	30	6 h/d,	–	[15]
1 000	(988)	(Syrian)	30	30	5 d/week,	–	
5 000	(5 019)		30	30	13 weeks	–	
10 000	(10 050)		30	30		from 10 000 ml/m³: lymphocyte count reduced but neither significantly, nor dose-dependently	
20 000	(19 740)		30	30		at 20000 ml/m³: lymphocyte count in ♂♂ from d 56 sign. reduced	

5 Reproductive and Developmental Toxicity

In two studies 24 and 75 female Wistar rats were exposed to DME concentrations in air of $20\,000-28\,000$ ml/m^3, 6 hours daily for 13 days before mating. No effect on the mating behaviour nor on the number of pregnancies was observed. From day 6 to day 16 of gestation the same dams were exposed to the same DME concentrations. In the dams no DME related weight loss was seen; the autopsy findings were also normal. An increased frequency of foetuses with too many lumbar ribs was observed but the effect was not dose-dependent and has therefore little real significance [19].

6 Genotoxicity

DME concentrations of $30\,625$, $61\,250$ and $118\,750$ ml/m^3 produced negative results in the Ames test with the *Salmonella typhimurium* strains TA1535, TA1537, TA1538, TA98 and TA100 with and without the addition of rat liver microsomes [20].

The unscheduled DNA synthesis (UDS) test in rat hepatocytes produced negative results with DME concentrations of 5, 10, 25, 50 and 75 mM [21]. After 4 hours incubation with V79 Chinese hamster cells the same concentrations of DME also produced negative results with and without metabolic activation [21].

No chromosome aberrations were found in *Drosophila melanogaster* after exposure to $28\,000$ ml DME/m^3 for 14 days [21].

Escherichia coli K$_{12}$ 343/113 or *S. typhimurium* TA1538 bacteria were injected into the tail vein of mice (N : NIHSW) for a host-mediated assay. After the mice had been exposed for 3 hours to $10\,000$ or $20\,000$ ml DME/m^3 the bacteria were recovered from the liver and examined for mutations. All results were negative [21].

In an *in vitro* study DME was not mutagenic in Ehrlich ascites tumour cells from the mouse [22].

7 Carcinogenicity

Rats inhaled DME in a life-time study (104 weeks) at concentrations of 0, 2000, $10\,000$ and $25\,000$ ml/m^3 (see also Table 2). Interim sacrifices after 3, 6 and 12 months revealed substance-related haemolytic effects; the erythrocyte counts were reduced after 3 months in females of the highest dose group. In males from the highest dose group after 6 and 12 months there were not only reduced erythrocyte counts but also congestion in the spleen and reduced spleen weights. As these changes were not observed consistently during the course of the study they were considered to be transient and not an expression of long-term effects. In all cases histological examination of the bone marrow produced no substance-related findings. There was no association between body weight gain and reduced life-times in the males of the medium and high dose groups; there were no histological findings which could account for the reduced survival times.

An incidence of benign and malignant mammary tumours (52.8%) in the $25\,000$ ml/m^3 group which was significantly increased above that of the control group (36%) was not considered to be substance-related since mammary tumours had been present with a frequency of 53 % in 436 historical controls in the laboratory [18].

8 Manifesto (MAK value, classification)

The sparse data for effects of DME in man yield no basis for a MAK value. In animals, chronic inhalation of 10 000 ml/m³ has adverse effects on body weight gain and survival; 2000 ml/m³ had no effects. The MAK value can therefore be set at 1000 ml/m³; from fundamental considerations this has been set as the upper limit for the MAK values of organic substances. For the limitation of exposure peaks the substance is classified in Category IV.

9 References

1. Eckard, R., F. H. Kemper: *Naunyn-Schmiedeberg's Arch. Pharmacol., Suppl., R 19* (1979)
2. Kemper, F. H., R. Eckard: *Massenfragmentographische Untersuchungen zum pharmakokinetischen Verhalten und zur Organverteilung von Dimethyläther (DME)*, Inst. Pharmakol. Toxikol. Univ. Münster, D-4400 Münster, 1978
3. Daly, J. J., G. L. Kennedy: *Chem. Times and Trends 1*, 40 (1987)
4. Davidson, B. M.: *J. Pharmacol. exp. Ther. 26*, 43 (1926)
5. Brown, W. E.: *J. Pharmacol. exp. Ther. 23*, 497 (1924)
6. Brody, A. W., J. L. Kurowsky, T. C. Connoly, J. J. McGill, K. P. Lions, M. J. Weaver, J. J. Wagner: *J. New Drugs 6*, 121 (1966)
7. Brody, A. W., K. P.Lions, J. L. Kurowsky, J. J. McGill, M. J. Weaver: *J. appl. Physiol. 31*, 121 (1971)
8. Wolff, G.: *Deutsches Patentamt, Offenlegungsschrift* Nr. DE 33 40 991 A1, 23.5.1985
9. Caprino, L., G. Togna: *Eur. J. Tox. 5*, 287 (1975)
10. Brittelli, M. R., L. W. Smith: *The Toxicologist 1*, 79 (1981)
11. Daly, J. J., E. J. Ostermann: *Chem. Times and Trends 5*, 38 (1982)
12. Kruysse, A.: Report No. R 4520, Division for Nutrition and Food Research, TNO Zeist, Niederlande, 1974
13. Reinhardt, Ch. F., A. Azar, M. E. Maxfield, P. E. Smith, L. S. Mullin: *Arch. environm. Hlth 22*, 265 (1971)
14. Kruysse, A., V. M. H. Hollanders, H. R. Immel: Report No. R 50C4, Division for Nutrition and Food Research, TNO Zeist, Niederlande, 1976
15. Reutzel, P. G. J., R. A. Woutersen: *Inhalation Toxicity Studies of Dimethyl Ether: 4-Week Study in Hamsters and a 13-Week Study in Hamsters and Rats*, Division for Nutrition and Food Research, TNO Zeist, NL, 1983
16. Reutzel, P. G. J., J. P. B. Bruyntjes, R. B. Beems: *Aerosol report 20*, 23 (1981)
17. Collins, C. J., L. M. Cobb, D. A. Purser: *Toxicology 11*, 65, (1978)
18. Du Pont de Nemours & Co.: Haskell Laboratory for Toxicology and Industrial Medicine, Report No. 198-86, MR No. 4227-001, Elkton Road Newark, Delaware 19714, USA, 1986
19. Koeter, H. B. W. M., L. M. Appelmann: Report No. V81 064/200753/200754, Division for Nutrition and Food Research, TNO Zeist, Niederlande, 1981
20. Willems, M. J.: Report No. R 5293, Division for Nutrition and Food Research, TNO Zeist, Niederlande, 1978
21. Kramers, P. G. N., C. A. van der Heijden, C. E. Voogd, A. G. A. C. Knaap, P. J. A. Rombout, B. Bissumbhas, A. J. P. Verlaan, J. J. van der Stel, H. W. Verharen, P. G. Langenbroek, M. Marra: Report No. 627909001, Rijksinstituut voor de Volksgezondheid, Bilthoven, Niederlande, 1981
22. Okada, T. A., E. Roberts, A. F. Brodie: *Proc. Soc. exp. Biol. 126*, 583 (1967)

completed 19. 5. 1988

Dimethyl hydrogen phosphite

Classification/MAK value	**see Section III B** **MAK List 1989**
Classification/MAK value dates from:	**1989**
Synonyms:	dimethyl phosphite dimethyl phosphonate dimethyl hydrogen phosphonate dimethoxyphosphine oxide phosphorous acid, dimethyl ester phosphonic acid, dimethyl ester
Chemical name (CAS):	phosphonic acid, dimethyl ester
CAS number:	868-85-9
Structural formula:	

$$H_3CO-\overset{\overset{\textstyle O}{\|}}{\underset{\underset{\textstyle H}{|}}{P}}-OCH_3$$

Molecular formula:	$C_2H_7O_3P$
Molecular weight:	110.05
Melting point:	not specified
Boiling point:	$170\,°-171\,°C$
Vapour pressure at $20\,°C$:	not specified

1 ml/m³ (ppm) = 4.57 mg/m³   **1 mg/m³ = 0.22 ml/m³ (ppm)**

1 Toxic Effects and Modes of Action

Dimethyl hydrogen phosphite (DMHP), a neutral ester of phosphorous acid, is a clear colourless liquid. It is used as a phosphorylating agent and intermediate in insecticide and herbicide production, as a stabilizer for oil and PVC and as an additive in metal-working fluids. There are very few toxicological studies of DMHP.

In the mouse and rat, acutely lethal doses induce inactivity, weakness, shallow breathing and, in 2/10 male mice (after 4640 mg/kg or 6810 mg/kg body weight), opaque eyes. After multiple doses (15 times 250–3000 mg/kg body weight), hyperplastic gastritis and atrophy of the squamous epithelium of the stomach were observed in male and female mice but there were no dose-related findings in rats.

Oral administration of 400 mg/kg (rat) or 375 mg/kg (mouse) for three months produced eye lesions in the rat, lung damage in rat and mouse and testicular atrophy in the male mouse.

After oral administration of 200 mg/kg to male rats for 2 years, a significantly increased frequency of lung tumours was found; with female rats – dosed only up to 100 mg/kg – the results were equivocal.

Short term mutagenicity tests were negative with *Salmonella typhimurium* and *Drosophila melanogaster*, and positive in the mouse lymphoma assay in the presence of S9 mix. In Chinese hamster ovary cells with and without metabolic activation, DMHP induced sister chromatid exchange.

2 Effects in Man

There are no reports available of effects of DMHP on man, neither from industrial sources nor as specific studies in humans.

3 Effects on Animals

3.1 Acute toxicity

The same symptoms were seen in the rat and the mouse after administration of various single doses of DMHP to determine the LD_{50} (Table 1): inactivity, weakness and shallow breathing which, in the rat, began soon after oral intubation and ended in death on the same day. In the mouse the shallow breathing lasted for one or two days and the animals died correspondingly later. No LD_{50} could be determined for female mice because the gradient of the survival curve was too steep. Autopsy revealed gas in the stomach and/or intestine in a few rats dosed with 3160 mg/kg or more and white opaque eyes in 2/10 male mice from the high dose groups. Other substance-related lesions were not described. Histopathological studies were not carried out [1].

On repeated (15×) administration of various doses of DMHP, purity 96%, (Table 2) all mice which had been given 2000 mg/kg or more and all rats in the 1000 mg/kg group as well as 6 rats from the 500 mg/kg group died before the end of the study. Mice became inactive after receiving 1000 mg/kg or more, rats after 500 mg/kg or more. Microscopic examination of the mice revealed dose-dependent stomach lesions, particularly acute/chronic hyperplastic gastritis and squamous atrophy but also epithelial ulceration and hyperplastic gastropathy which were not observed in the vehicle (corn oil) control animals. Autopsy revealed irregular thickening of the squamous epithelial region of the stomach in 5/5 male and 4/5 female mice from the 1000 mg/kg group as well as slight irregular thickening and nodules in 2/5 female and 1/5 males from the 500 mg/kg group. There were no such findings in rats [1].

Table 1. Effects of single lethal doses of dimethyl hydrogen phosphite

Species, number, sex (strain)	Dose mg/kg	Purity of DMHP (solvent)	Admin. route	Survivors/ initial number	Observations/ LD_{50}	Ref.
Mouse 5 ♂ per group (B6C3F₁)	1470 2150 3160 4640 6810	~ 96% (corn oil)	gavage	5/5 5/5 1/5 0/5 0/5	− − − inactivity − shallow breathing; all animals died on days 1 or 2; opaque eyes in 2/10 animals (dose ≥ 4640 mg/kg)	[1]
therefore: Mouse ♂♂	2815 (2420–3273)	~ 96% (corn oil)	gavage		LD_{50}	[1]
Mouse 5 ♀ per group (B6C3F₁)	1470 2150 3160 4640 6810	~ 96% (corn oil)	gavage	5/5 5/5 0/5 0/5 0/5	− − − inactivity − shallow breathing; all animals died on days 1 or 2	[1]
Rat 5 ♂ per group (F344/N)	1470 2150 3160 4640 6810	~ 96% (corn oil)	gavage	5/5 5/5 3/5 0/5 0/5	− − − − − inactivity, weakness, shallow breathing; all animals died on day 1	[1]
therefore: Rat ♂♂	3283 (2729–3949)	~ 96% (corn oil)	gavage		LD_{50}	[1]
Rat 5 ♀ per group (F344/N)	1470 2150 3160 4640 6810	~ 96% (corn oil)	gavage	5/5 5/5 2/5 0/5 0/5	− − − − − inactivity, weakness, shallow breathing; all animals died on day 1	[1]
therefore: Rat ♀♀	3040 (2527–3656)	~ 96% (corn oil)	gavage		LD_{50}	[1]
Rat (n.s.)	3050	n.s.	oral		LD_{50}	[2]
Rat (n.s.)	3800	n.s.	oral		LD_{50}	[3]
Rat (n.s.)	4250	n.s.	oral		LD_{50}	[4]
Rat (Wistar)	2300 (2115–2493)	~ 98% (arachis oil)	s.c.		LD_{50}	[5]

n.s.: not specified

Table 2. Acute toxic effects of dimethyl hydrogen phosphite after multiple applications [1].

Species, number, sex (strain)	Dose mg/kg	Purity of DMHP (solvent)	Route of administration	Duration	Survivors/ initial number	Stomach lesions			
						epithelial ulceration	acute/chronic hyperplastic gastritis	squamous atrophy	hyperplastic gastropathy
Mouse 5 ♂ per group (B6C3F$_1$)	0	~96% (corn oil)	gavage	1×/d for 15 d	5/5	0	0	0	0
	250				5/5	0	1	0	0
	500				5/5	0	5	0	0
	1000				5/5	1	4	0	1
	2000				0/5	4	3	1	1
	3000				0/5	0	0	5	0
Mouse 5 ♀ per group (B6C3F$_1$)	0	~96% (corn oil)	gavage	1×/d for 15 d	5/5	0	0	0	0.
	250				4/5	0	1	0	2
	500				5/5	0	5	0	0
	1000				5/5	1	5	0	0
	2000				0/5	3	4	1	0
	3000				0/5	2	1	2	0
Rat 5 ♂ per group (F 344/N)	0	~96% (corn oil)	gavage	1×/d for 15 d	5/5	– no dose-dependent findings			
	250				5/5	– from 500 mg/kg body weight: animals inactive			
	500				1/5				
	1000	(without solvent)			0/5				
	2000				0/5				
	3000				0/5				
Rat 5 ♀ per group (F 344/N)	0	~96% (corn oil)	gavage	1×/d for 15 d	5/5	– no dose-dependent findings			
	250				5/5	– from 500 mg/kg body weight: animals inactive			
	500				3/5				
	1000	(without solvent)			0/5				
	2000				0/5				
	3000				0/5				

3.2 Local effects on skin and mucous membranes

The available information as to the acute effect of DMHP on skin and mucous membranes is very meagre: after 24 hours on rabbit skin 500 mg DMHP is said to be moderately irritating, 20 mg DMHP in the rabbit eye for the same period is a strong irritant [4].

3.3 Subchronic and chronic toxicity

3 month studies were carried out with F344/N rats and B6C3F$_1$ mice to establish the dose range for the 2 year carcinogenicity study [1]. On 5 days a week for 13 weeks, groups of 10 male and 10 female rats or mice were administered a solution of DMHP (purity ∼ 96%) in corn oil by gavage at doses of 0, 25, 50, 100, 200 or 400 mg/kg body weight or 0, 95, 190, 375, 750 or 1500 mg/kg body weight, respectively.

Of the *rats*, 9/10 males and 8/10 females from the 400 mg/kg group died before the end of the study, at which time the final body weight of the survivors was reduced by 46% and 39%, respectively. Females from the 200 mg/kg group had 14% less final body weight than the vehicle controls. Degeneration of the lens was diagnosed in the eyes of 4/9 females and 1/7 males, and diffuse corneal inflammation in one of the 9 females from the 400 mg/kg group. No eye lesions were found in the animals of the next lower dose group – 200 mg/kg.

Lung lesions such as diffuse and focal chronic inflammation and congestion were observed in rats from all dosage groups and the vehicle control group. The implications of these data, however, were not clear as tests for pneumonia and Sendai virus in blood samples taken from the control animals at the end of the study were positive.

Of the *mice*, all animals in the 1500 and 750 mg/kg groups died during the first four weeks of the trial. 2/10 males and 5/10 females from the 375 mg/kg group died later. The body weight gain of the survivors was comparable to that of the controls. Mice given 375 mg DMHP/kg body weight or more were inactive and had tremor. Pulmonary congestion in male and female animals, cardiac mineralization in males and hepatocellular vacuolization in females were probably DMHP-induced. Testicular atrophy with hypospermatogenesis and the formation of giant spermatids and syncytial cells were diagnosed in males given 375 mg/kg or more [1].

4 Reproductive and Developmental Toxicity

Reproduction or teratogenicity studies have not been published to date.

5 Genotoxicity

DMHP was not mutagenic for *S. typhimurium* TA98, TA100, TA1535 and TA1537 at concentrations of 100–10000 µg/plate. In each case the tests were carried out with and without liver microsomes from two different species (Aroclor-induced Sprague-Dawley rat and Chinese hamster) [1].

In *Drosophila melanogaster*, DMHP induced no mutagenic changes either after feeding with 650 ppm or after injection of 1500 ppm [1].

In the mouse lymphoma assay (L5178Y tk$^+$/tk$^-$) DMHP was shown to be weakly mutagenic in the presence of S9 mix at concentrations of 2100–2500 µg/ml (tested concentrations 1700–2500 µg/ml). Concentrations above 2500 µg/ml medium were toxic. No significant mutagenicity was found in the absence of S9 mix; as little as 500 µg/ml reduced the pH of the medium. This probably contributed to the toxicity which began at lower concentrations in the absence of S9 mix [6,7].

DMHP induced chromosome aberrations (ABS) and also sister chromatid exchange (SCE) in Chinese hamster ovary cells *in vitro*. Two ABS-tests with the substance were weakly positive without S9 mix (dose range: 0–1600 µg/ml, positive at 1600 µg/ml), with S9 mix one was negative (dose range: 0–1600 µg/ml) and one positive (dose range: 0–5000 µg/ml, positive at 5000 µg/ml). At this concentration, however, the chromosomes were fused together in most cells so that the aberration data is of little significance. Of the SCE-tests without S9 mix, one was negative (dose range: 0–500 µg/ml), the other yielded positive results at doses of 250 µg/ml or more (dose range: 0–1600 µg/ml). In the two tests with S9 mix, DMHP produced positive results at doses of 1600 µg/ml or more and 1000 µg/ml or more, respectively [8].

6 Carcinogenicity

In a 2 year study, daily oral intubation of male rats with 100 or 200 mg DMHP/kg body weight and of female rats with 50 or 100 mg DMHP/kg body weight, 5 times weekly for 103 weeks, produced neoplastic and non-neoplastic lesions in lungs and forestomach. In the mouse there were no indications of tumorigenic properties of the substance (Table 3, [1]).

In male F344/N rats, DMHP induced the highest incidence of lung tumours which has ever been recorded for a substance tested during the NCI National Toxicology Program [9]. The historical incidence of tumours in Fischer 344/N rat vehicle controls for the whole National Toxicology Program are as follows: alveolar/bronchiolar adenomas 3% (34/1143), alveolar/bronchiolar carcinomas 1.4% (16/1143), squamous epithelial lung carcinomas 0.2% (2/1143). The data for the historical incidence of tumours in vehicle controls in the test laboratory are given in Table 3. The incidence of total lung lesions in the high dose female rats was similar to that for the low dose male rats; the sexes are probably equally sensitive.

In the *rat*, non-neoplastic lesions were found in the hematopoietic system, the eyes and cerebellum in addition to those seen in the lungs and forestomach. The dose-dependent lesions of the lungs were characterized as alveolar epithelial hyperplasia, adenomatous hyperplasia and interstitial pneumonia. These terms were used to diagnose a complex lesion induced by the DMHP treatment and characterized by hyperplasia of the alveolar epithelium and thickening of the septal walls around the terminal bronchioles and adjacent alveoli. When the thickening of the interstitium was a prominent feature, the diagnosis was interstitial pneumonia. The interstitial pneumonia found in 7 male control animals (shown in Table 3) was, in contrast, of

Table 3. Chronic and carcinogenic effects of dimethyl hydrogen phosphite

Author:	National Toxicology Program [1], Dunnick et al. [9]
Substance:	DMHP, purity 97–98%, dissolved in corn oil
Species:	mouse, B6C3F$_1$: 50 ♂♂ and 50 ♀♀ vehicle control: 50 ♂♂ and 50 ♀♀
Administration:	gavage
Dose:	200, 100, 0 mg/kg body weight
Duration of administration:	5 d/wk for 103 weeks, sacrifice in week 104
Toxicity:	high dose ♂♂: after week 28 about 5–10% reduction in body weight, ♀♀: about 5%. Significantly reduced survival of ♂♂ in comparison with vehicle control

Tumours	200	100	0 (vehicle control)	0 mg/kg (historical control of the test laboratory)
Liver				
adenomas: ♂♂	8/50	8/47	12/50	
♀♀	3/50	6/49	0/50	4/148
carcinomas: ♂♂	7/50	2/47	9/50	
♀♀	0/50	0/49	2/50	

Author:	National Toxicology Program [1], Dunnick et al. [9]
Substance:	DMHP, purity 97–98%, dissolved in corn oil
Species:	rat, Fischer 344/N: 50 ♂♂ and 50 ♀♀ vehicle control: 50 ♂♂ and 50 ♀♀
Administration:	gavage
Dose:	♂♂ 200, 100, 0 mg/kg body weight ♀♀ 100, 50, 0 mg/kg body weight
Duration of administration:	5 d/wk for 103 weeks, sacrifice in week 104
Toxicity:	high dose ♂♂: after week 40 about 10% reduction in body weight and significantly reduced survival in comparison with vehicle control as a result of DMHP toxicity low dose ♂♂, high dose ♀♀: body weight only marginally reduced

Lesions, Tumours	♂♂ ♀♀	200 100	100 50	0 (vehicle control)	0 mg/kg 0 (historical control of the test laboratory)
Lung alveolar					
epithelial hyperplasia:	♂♂ ♀♀	16/50 11/50	7/50 0/49	2/50 1/50	
adenomatous hyperplasia:	♂♂ ♀♀	26/50 10/50	3/50 0/49	0/50 0/50	

Table 3 (continued)

Lesions, Tumours		200 100	100 50	0 (vehicle control)	0 mg/kg 0 (historical control of the test laboratory)
Lung					
chronic interstitial pneumonia:	♂♂ ♀♀	43/50 33/50	19/50 5/49	7/50 4/50	
squamous epithelial metaplasia:	♂♂	3/50	0/50	0/50	
squamous epithelial carcinoma:	♂♂	5/50	0/50	0/50	0/150
alveo-bronchiolar adenoma:	♂♂	5/50	0/50	0/50	2/150
alveo-bronchiolar carcinoma:	♂♂ ♀♀	20/50 3/50	1/50 1/49	0/50 0/50	3/150 1/150
Stomach					
hyperkeratosis:	♂♂	8/50	1/50	0/50	
hyperplasia:	♂♂ ♀♀	32/50 14/48	16/50 2/50	8/50 4/50	
squamous epithelial papilloma:	♂♂ ♀♀	3/50 1/48	1/50 0/50	0/50 0/50	0/147
squamous epithelial carcinoma:	♂♂ ♀♀	3/50 1/48	0/50 0/50	0/50 0/50	0/147

a quite different type and characterized primarily by focal aggregations of macrophages. The adenomatous hyperplasia of the lung which occurred simultaneously took the form of focally extensive proliferation of pneumocytes.

In the forestomach, the proliferative lesion was a diffuse to focal thickening of the squamous epithelium.

Mononuclear leukemia was increased particularly in low dose male animals, cataracts (whether unilateral or bilateral was not specified) particularly in high dose rats of both sexes (♂♂: 36/50 = 72%, vehicle control: 25/50 = 50%; ♀♀: 22/50 = 44%, vehicle control: 17/50 = 34%). Focal mineralization occurred in the cerebellum of 12/49 high dose male rats and was found in no other group [1].

In the *mouse*, no DMHP-related neoplastic changes were found. Non-neoplastic lesions in females took the form of dose-dependent increases in fatty metamorphosis in the liver (high dose group: 4/50 = 8%, low dose group: 1/49 = 2%, vehicle control: 0/50) and of focal calcification in the testes in males (high dose group: 24/50 = 48%, low dose group: 9/47 = 19%, vehicle control: 2/50 = 4%). The form (circular to oblong) and the location suggested calcification of the seminiferous tubules [1].

In 50 Wistar rats (25 ♂♂ and 25 ♀♀), weekly s.c. injections of maximally tolerated doses of 100–150 mg DMHP (~ 98% pure)/kg body weight for 2 years, up to a total dose of 7.55 g/kg body weight, produced no indication of a carcinogenic effect [5].

7 Manifesto (MAK value, classification)

In a 2 year carcinogenicity study, dimethyl hydrogen phosphite (DMHP) proved to be unequivocally carcinogenic after daily oral administration to rats; in mice there was no evidence of increased tumour formation under the conditions of this study. Subcutaneous application to Wistar rats produced negative results. Short-term tests with *S. typhimurium* and *Drosophila melanogaster* were negative with DMHP. In the mouse lymphoma assay in the presence of S9 mix, however, the results were positive; sister chromatid exchange was induced in Chinese hamster ovary cells. A valid assessment of the mutagenic potential is currently impossible in view of the limited number of investigations which have been carried out. To confirm or exclude the suspicion of a carcinogenic effect further studies are necessary on the mutagenicity, alkylating potential and inhalation toxicity of DMHP under conditions which are comparable to the human situation at work. The substance is to be classified provisionally in Section III B of the MAK list. A MAK value cannot be established because of the lack of quantitative inhalation studies and of knowledge of effects on man.

8 References

1. National Toxicology Program (NTP): *Toxicology and Carcinogenesis Studies of Dimethyl Hydrogen Phosphite in F 344/N Rats and B6C3F₁ Mice*, Techn. Rep. Ser. No. 287, USDHHS, Research Triangle Park, NC 27709, USA, 1985
2. Mobil Chemical Company: Product Information Bulletin on Dialkyl Hydrogen Phosphites and Trialkyl Phosphites, Industrial Chemicals Division, 1977; cited in [1]
3. Levin, L., K. L. Gabriel: *Amer. industr. Hyg. Ass. J. 34*, 286 (1973)
4. Marhold, J. V.: *Sbornik Vysledku Toxixologickeho Vysetreni Latek A Prinpravku*, p 215, Institut Pro Vychovu Vedoucien Pracovniku Chemickeho Prumyclu Praha, Czechoslovakia, 1972; cited in *Registry of Toxic Effects of Chemical Substances (RTECS)*, 1985–86 ed., Vol. 4, p 3347, USDHHS, Cincinnati, OH 45226, USA
5. Steinhoff, D.: Pharma-Bericht Nr. 5220, unpublished report, Bayer AG, D-5600 Wuppertal, February 1975
6. McGregor, D. B., A. Brown, P. Cattanach, I. Edwards, D. McBride, W. J. Caspary: *Environm. Mutag. 8* (Suppl. 6), 54 (1986)
7. McGregor, D. B., A. Brown, P. Cattanach, I. Edwards, D. McBride, W. J. Caspary: *Environm. Mutag. 11*, 91 (1988)
8. Gulati, D. K., K. Witt, B. Anderson, E. Zeiger, M. D. Shelby: *Environm. Mutag. 13*, 133 (1989)
9. Dunnick, J. K., G. A. Boorman, J. K. Haseman, J. Langloss, R. H. Cardy, A. G. Manus: *Cancer Res. 46*, 264 (1986)

completed 29. 5. 1989

Dimethylsulfamoyl chloride

Classification/MAK value:	**see Section III A2)** **MAK List 1983**
Classification/MAK value dates from:	**1983**
Synonyms:	dimethylaminosulfonyl chloride N,N-dimethylsulfamyl chloride N,N-dimethylsulfamoyl chloride
Chemical name (CAS):	dimethyl-sulfamoyl chloride
CAS number:	13360-57-1
Structural formula:	
Molecular formula:	$C_2H_6NSO_2Cl$
Molecular weight:	143.5
Melting point:	not specified
Boiling point:	182–184 °C

Structural formula:

$$\begin{array}{c} H_3C \\ \quad\quad\ \searrow \\ \quad\quad\quad N-SO_2-Cl \\ \quad\quad\ \nearrow \\ H_3C \end{array}$$

1 ml/m³ (ppm) = 5.954 mg/m³   **1 mg/m³ = 0.168 ml/m³ (ppm)**

1 Toxic Effects and Modes of Action

After subcutaneous administration to rats, dimethylsulfamoyl chloride induces malignant tumours at the injection site in a high percentage of animals [1].

2 Effects in Man

Toxic effects in man have not yet been described.

3 Effects on Animals

The structural similarity to N,N-dimethylcarbamoyl chloride raises the question of whether dimethylsulfamoyl chloride also possesses carcinogenic activity. In a range-finding carcinogenicity study, groups of 25 male and 25 female Sprague-Dawley rats were administered subcutaneous doses of 100 mg/kg or 10 mg/kg or intratracheal doses of 1 mg/kg once weekly [1]. Since dimethylsulfamoyl chloride is relatively unstable in water it was applied in arachis oil. Correspondingly, groups of 25 male and 25 female rats were treated subcutaneously or intratracheally with arachis oil alone. The subcutaneous dose of 100 mg/kg/week had been shown to be the maximal applicable dose because of its local irritant effect. The intratracheal dose of 1 mg/kg/week also approximates the maximum tolerable dose, or is at least very close to it, because the LD_{50} for single intratracheal instillation was shown to be 13 mg dimethylsulfamoyl chloride/kg body weight. The subcutaneous injections were given for 40 weeks; at this time the first substance-related tumours were detectable at the injection site. Intratracheal instillation was continued until week 102. After the end of treatment the animals were then kept under observation until they died naturally. There were no differences in body weights between the treated groups and the corresponding controls. Survival times after intratracheal treatment were not shorter than in the control group. Survival of both male and female rats administered dimethylsulfamoyl chloride subcutaneously was significantly and dose-dependently reduced in comparison to the controls. This reduction in survival time was caused by the development of malignant tumours at the injection site (s.c. fibrosarcomas). The frequency of such tumours in the groups of 25 male and 25 female rats (1 tumour per animal) is shown in the table below.

Total tumours	Number of animals with tumours		Treatment group	Mean survival in days	
	♂♂	♀♀		♂♂	♀♀
5	4	1	vehicle control	876	764
33	22	11	10 mg/kg/week	659	694
39	22	17	100 mg/kg/week	520	627

The number and distribution of the other malignant tumours and that of the benign tumours in the rats treated by subcutaneous injection was not related to the dimethylsulfamoyl chloride treatment. Apart from the local carcinogenic effect, there was no indication of other toxic effects of the dimethylsulfamoyl chloride after subcutaneous administration. After intratracheal (i.t.) instillation of dimethylsulfamoyl chloride (1 mg/kg/week) to male rats the number of malignant tumours (by admittedly somewhat better survival times) was increased in comparison with the i.t. control from 6 to 13. This is probably a chance finding because practically the same number (12) of malignant tumours was found with a similar distribution pattern in the s.c. control after subtraction of the 4 fibrosarcomas at the injection site. Three brain tumours (astrocytomas) were conspicuous after the intratracheal treatment with dimethylsulfamoyl chloride; they developed in one male and two female rats. The remaining malignant tumours in the female rats corresponded in number and distribution with those in the control animals. The same was true for the benign tumours in both sexes. There were also no other indications of toxic effects of dimethylsulfamoyl chloride after intratracheal instillation at a dose of 1 mg/kg/week.

4 Manifesto (MAK value, classification)

Dimethylsulfamoyl chloride was shown to have a marked local dose-dependent carcinogenic effect in the sensitive subcutaneous injection test in the rat using the relatively high doses of 100 mg/kg/week and 10 mg/kg/week. After intratracheal instillation of 1 mg/kg/week (LD_{50} i.t.: 13 mg/kg) the effect could no longer be demonstrated.

Dimethylcarbamoyl chloride, a substance which is structurally very similar to dimethylsulfamoyl chloride, revealed marked local carcinogenicity in animals after inhalation [2] as well as after intratracheal [3] or subcutaneous [1] administration. Considerably higher doses could be applied subcutaneously than by inhalation or by intratracheal instillation. Accordingly, the carcinogenic effect was most marked after subcutaneous injection.

Dimethylsulfamoyl chloride, compared with dimethylcarbamoyl chloride after subcutaneous and intratracheal administration, also proved to be an unambiguous local carcinogen after subcutaneous injection although the effect was clearly weaker than that of dimethylcarbamoyl chloride. This weaker activity could be confirmed in the instillation test in which – unlike dimethylcarbamoyl chloride – dimethylsulfamoyl chloride could not be shown to be carcinogenic. The results of this comparative study lead the Commission to the conclusion that a carcinogenic risk for man can also exist under exposure conditions like those at workplaces. The results do also indicate, however, that dimethylsulfamoyl chloride is above all a locally acting carcinogen without very pronounced effects. Dimethylsulfamoyl chloride is classified in Section III A2) of the List of MAK Values. A MAK value cannot be established.

5 References

1. Steinhoff, D., K. Künstler: Unpublished report No. 10315 , Bayer AG, Institut für Toxikologie, D-5600 Wuppertal 1, 1981
2. Sellakumar, A. R., S. Laskin, M. Kuschner, R. Rusch, G. V. Katz, C. A. Snyder, R. E. Albert: *J. environm. Path. Toxicol. 4*, 107 (1980)
3. Steinhoff, D., S. Gad, G. K. Hatfield, U. Mohr: *Exp. Pathol. 30*, 129 (1986)

completed 4. 7. 1983

Dinitrobenzene (all isomers)   H

Classification/MAK value:	**see Section III B**
	MAK List 1988
Classification/MAK value dates from:	**1988**
Synonyms:	DNB
	1,2-dinitrobenzene (o-DNB)
	1,3-dinitrobenzene (m-DNB)
	1,4-dinitrobenzene (p-DNB)
	binitrobenzene
Chemical name (CAS):	dinitrobenzene
CAS number:	25154-54-5

Structural formula:

Molecular formula: $C_6H_4N_2O_4$

Molecular weight: 168.11

Melting points:	117.9 °C	(o-DNB)
	89.9 °C	(m-DNB)
	173–174 °C	(p-DNB)

Boiling points:	319 °C	(o-DNB)
	300–303 °C	(m-DNB)
	299 °C	(p-DNB) sublimes

1 ml/m³ (ppm) = 6.98 mg/m³   **1 mg/m³ = 0.143 ml/m³ (ppm)**

1 Characterization of the individual dinitrobenzene isomers and of the mixture

Dinitrobenzene (DNB) production yields a mixture of the three isomers. Both this mixture and the individual isomers are available commercially. The *ortho*-isomer (o-DNB) forms colourless to yellow monoclinic plates, the *meta*-isomer (m-DCB) colourless to yellow rhombic needles or plates and the *para*-isomer (p-DNB) colourless to yellow monoclinic needles [1].

In the older literature nitration procedures are mentioned in which the main product is m-DNB together with 7–10% o-DNB and p-DNB which are removed by washing [2] or in which the yield of m-DNB is 95% and the remainder consists of o-DNB and p-DNB and "other impurities" [3].

Thus technical grade DNB is comprised mostly of *m*-DNB with traces of *o*-DNB and *p*-DNB [4, 5].

Since *m*-DNB is industrially the most important isomer, it has been studied in most detail.

2 Toxic Effects and Modes of Action

At the workplace DNB is taken up principally by absorption through the skin but also by inhalation and ingestion of dust and inhalation of mixtures with steam; it is very volatile in steam [4, 6–8].

The toxic effects of technical DNB are said not to be significantly different from those of pure *m*-DNB [8]; in man and in animals the blood, liver and CNS are most affected but damage to the spleen and, in animals, to the testes have also been observed.

In man the main effect of DNB intoxication is more or less severe cyanosis. To an extent depending on the severity of intoxication, increased metHb levels, Heinz body formation, reduced erythrocyte and haemoglobin values as well as an increase in reticulocytes, anisocytosis, relative lymphocytosis are seen and sometimes spleen enlargement and anaemia as well. The CNS effects in man take the form of dyspnoea, vertigo, aesthesia and paraesthesia. More or less marked liver enlargement as well as icterus are observed in man whereas diffuse infiltration of small fat droplets, vacuole formation and necroses are found in the animal liver.

After *longer* exposure to DNB, icteric discoloration of the sclera, visus damage such as reduced visual field, impaired colour vision, venous hyperaemia of the retina and inflammation of the optic papilla are observed as well as impairment of hearing. Yellowish brown discoloration of the skin (xanthoprotein reaction), nodular eczema with severe erythema and swelling and reddish yellow, dull dry hair are mentioned in *older publications* which also point out that female workers can suffer from amenorrhoea or, in rare cases, from increased menstrual bleeding with severe pain (summarized in [8]).

Of the three isomers, *p*-DNB is the most powerful methaemoglobin producer and is among the most effective of all aromatic amino and nitro compounds (see Section 5.1 – Acute and subacute toxicity in animals).

Recovery after dinitrobenzene poisoning, unlike after exposure to mononitrobenzene or other aromatic nitro compounds, takes weeks [6, 8–11]. The toxic effects of dinitrobenzene on the blood [3] are on average 20 times more severe than those of trinitrotoluene (see Trinitrotoluene (all isomers), this volume) and also include an increase in reticulocytes as well as the formation of larger and more obvious Heinz bodies [4].

Alcohol and sunlight increase the toxicity of *m*-DNB [3], hot summer weather increases the skin absorption [4, 8]. Solvents can increase or decrease the skin penetration of DNB and the subsequent metHb formation [12].

Positive test results for mutagenicity in *Salmonella typhimurium* have been obtained with *m*-DNB and *p*-DNB. With *o*-DNB the results were negative. Studies of teratogenicity or carcinogenicity are currently not known.

2.1 Pharmacokinetics

Intake, breakdown and excretion

There is only one finding reported for man. After experimental exposure of a volunteer to *m*-DNB, the 2,4-dinitrophenol level in urine correlated with the metHb concentration in blood [13].

After oral and subcutaneous administration of *m*-DNB to rabbits, the following main metabolites were identified in urine using paper chromatography: 2,4-diaminophenol (ca. 31% of the dose), *m*-phenylene diamine (21%), *m*-nitroaniline (14%) and 2-amino-4-nitrophenol (14%), traces of unchanged *m*-DNB (0.7%), 2,4-dinitrophenol (0.1%), 4-amino-2-nitrophenol (0.8%), *m*-nitrophenylhydroxylamine (0.8%), *m*-nitrosonitrobenzene (0.25%) and 3,3'-dinitroazoxybenzene (0.3%) [14].

Metabolism studies have been carried out with the three individual isomers of [U-14C]DNB and hepatocytes and enzyme preparations from the livers of male Fischer 344 rats. Under aerobic conditions the main degradation pathway of *m*-DNB and *p*-DNB in the hepatocytes was the reduction to *m*-nitroaniline or *p*-nitroaniline which contained $74 \pm 1.2\%$ and $81 \pm 0.6\%$, respectively, of the radioactivity after 30 minutes incubation. Under the same conditions *o*-DNB was reduced, with a maximum after 2 minutes, mostly to S-(2-nitrophenyl)-glutathione ($48.1 \pm 5.5\%$) and to a lesser extent to *o*-nitroaniline ($29.5 \pm 2.1\%$).

Incubation with liver microsomes yielded the corresponding nitroanilines and nitrophenylhydroxylamines (see Figure 1). HPLC yielded definite evidence for *m*-nitrosonitrobenzene and *p*-nitrosonitrobenzene but not for *o*-nitrosonitrobenzene,

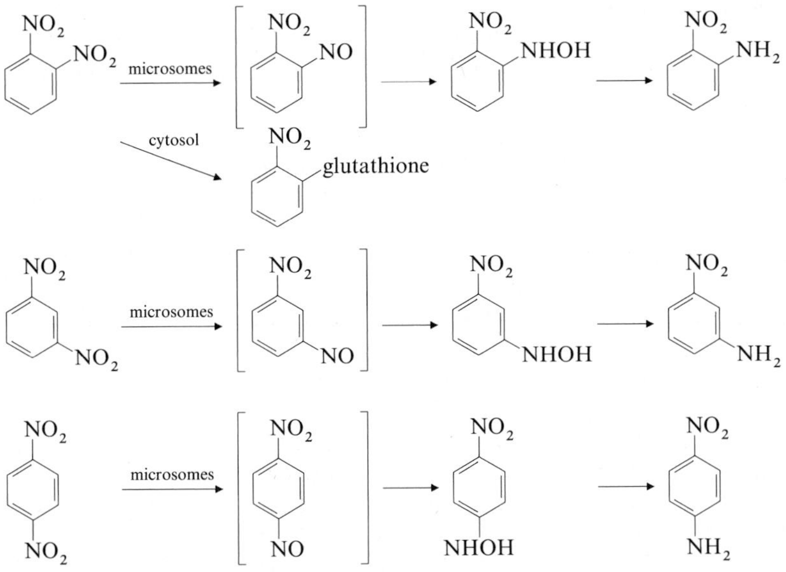

Figure 1. Breakdown of DNB isomers in hepatocytes of male Fischer 344 rats [15]

presumably because it is much less stable. The reduction of *o*-DNB and *m*-DNB was NADPH-dependent whereas that of *p*-DNB took place in the presence of either NADPH or, more slowly, NADH. *o*-DNB and *p*-DNB were reduced to the nitroaniline 3–5 times faster than *m*-DNB in either incubation medium [15].

Incubation with erythrocytes from Fischer 344 rats, Rhesus monkeys or man yielded with *o*-DNB or *p*-DNB the corresponding S-(nitrophenyl)-glutathione conjugate, not however with *m*-DNB [16, 17]. The authors conclude that the erythrocytes play an essential role in the conjugation and renal excretion of *o*-DNB and *p*-DNB. It is, however, unclear whether this process also yields reduction products.

Incubated with cytosol, *o*-DNB and *p*-DNB conjugated with glutathione; *m*-DNB did not. In intact hepatocytes only *o*-DNB formed a glutathione conjugate [15].

Other authors have shown that under aerobic conditions *p*-DNB, and to some extent also *o*-DNB and *m*-DNB, are reduced to the amino-nitro derivatives by rat liver mitochondria in a reaction which is almost exclusively NADH dependent. A number of other *para*-nitro compounds, on the other hand, are not reduced under these conditions [18, 19].

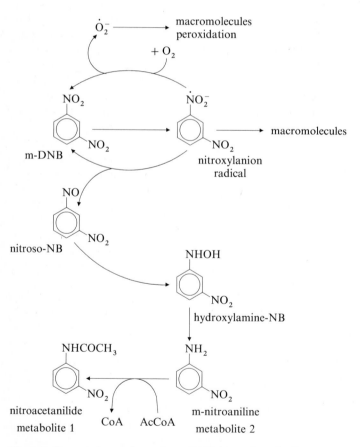

Figure 2. Degradation pathway for *m*-DNB in rat Sertoli cells [21]

o-DNB is a substrate for glutathione-S-aryltransferase [20]. The rapidity of the reaction suggests that this is the main pathway of metabolic *o*-DNB breakdown in the intact rat liver [15].

In vitro studies with cultured Sertoli cells from rat testes show that reduction of the nitro group is the main metabolic pathway for *m*-DNB in this tissue (see Fig. 2). The metabolism to (*in vitro*) non-toxic end products involves highly reactive intermediates which are very likely responsible for the testicular effects [22, 23].

[14]C-labelled *m*-DNB given orally to rabbits in doses of 50–100 mg/kg is excreted within two days in urine (65–93 %) and faeces (1–5 %). After that, only traces of radioactivity are found in the urine. After ingestion of radioactively labelled *m*-DNB, rabbits excrete ca. 30 % as the glucuronide and ca. 6 % as the sulfate [14].

3 Effects in Man

3.1 Acute toxicity

The toxic effects of dinitrobenzene were known as early as 1870 [24]. The first clinical cases involved munitions factory workers who became ill whenever DNB or similar nitro compounds were added to the explosives. From about the turn of the century until 1930, especially in Germany and England, numerous cases of intoxication with DNB were described [6, 7, 9, 25–30, reviewed in 2, 8]. In the Bavarian armaments industry alone during a single year – the year 1915–376 cases of intoxication were reported [9]. There are a few reports from the time of the Second World War and shortly afterwards [3, 4, 31, 32].

The case descriptions do not provide a clear picture of exposure levels, purity of the substance or degree of health impairment. Usually the workers are described simply as being occupied "in the production or processing of dinitrobenzene" and *m*-DNB is assumed to be the cause of the intoxication [3, 8, 26, 32].

The early reports can be summarized as follows: DNB intoxication is usually a result of skin absorption (soiled clothing and skin covered with dust) but also can result from inhalation and ingestion of the dust or from inhalation of vapour (review: [2]). Self-exposures confirmed the ready skin penetration of DNB and the consequent danger at the workplace [33]. Later it was recognized that the substances are readily soluble and volatile in steam [4, 7, 31].

The symptoms of *mild acute intoxication* are a greyish blue discoloration of the mucosa together with general indisposition, lack of appetite, nasty taste in the mouth, gastrointestinal disorders, palpitations, headaches, dizziness and disturbed sleep. They regress after 2 to 3 days. In cases of chronic mild intoxication the mucosa is always discoloured but the persons do not complain of significant indisposition. It is assumed that a certain acclimatization takes place.

In *moderately severe cases* not only the mucosa but also the skin is affected by the dark blue-grey discoloration. Other symptoms, which persist for about 10 days, include severe headaches, dizziness, nausea, respiratory distress, increased perspiration, marked weakness especially in the leg muscles. The affected persons complain of dizziness, headaches and general weakness for a long time afterwards.

The symptoms after *severe DNB intoxication* include severe respiratory distress, Cheyne-Stokes respiration with brief apneic periods, rapid pulse, headaches, pains in the limbs and chest, dizziness, nausea, lack of appetite, exhaustion, lack of energy and loss of weight, anaemia, brown coloured blood with damaged red blood cells, dark coffee-coloured urine, red discoloration of hair and nails, paraesthesia in the feet and hands, impaired hearing, markedly reduced corneal reflexes, nystagmus and increased irritability and spasms. The symptoms regress slowly after 20 days. In the most severe cases the dazed state can progress to unconsciousness, and death in coma can occur within the first 24 hours [4, 6, 11, 26, 30, 31, 34].

While emptying grenades, 12 male workers suffered DNB poisoning with the symptoms described above such as anaemia, severe cyanosis of skin and mucosa, brown discoloration of blood and urine, red discoloration of hair and nails; 3 also suffered mild and transient liver damage [31].

It was known that a DNB intoxication could appear with very different rapidity and severity in different individuals; some workers were said to be "giftfest" (resistant to the poison) [9, 25]. In two cases of subacute poisoning individual sensitivity was clearly described [32]. Of a number of female workers who all carried out identical procedures in a small *m*-DNB producing works, two became acutely ill and were admitted to hospital with the usual symptoms. In the first case the clinical findings were severe cyanosis with metHb levels up to 28% (of total haemoglobin), no Heinz bodies but an enlarged, soft liver and transient slight increase in serum bilirubin. In the second case the cyanosis was less severe with a metHb level of 16%, liver and liver parameters were normal but Heinz bodies were increased to 38%.

Alcohol increases the toxicity of DNB drastically [3, 9] as do high temperatures, so that there are a considerably larger number of cases of intoxication in the summer months. For example, in the years 1917/1918 in the Bavarian armaments industry 4.6% and 2.3% of workers became ill in November and December, respectively, compared with 20.2% and 30.8% in the summer months, July and August [9]. According to later observations, 16 of 22 patients became ill in the months May to August [4].

Multiple intoxications are frequently reported. For example, 28 out of 293 patients had been poisoned twice, 10 three times, 9 four times and 2 persons five times [9].

There are only a few *recent studies* available and they are described in more detail below.

In an electronics works a female employee was occupied regularly for 30–45 minutes of each working day in removing components from a chemical bath and arranging them so that they were ready to be welded together. During this period she wore latex rubber gloves.

Three days after introduction of an "improved" bath solution (containing 0.5% w/w *m*-DNB) her lips and finger nails became cyanotic and her face pale. After a day resting at home the symptoms disappeared but within two days back at work she developed cyanosis again with generalized indisposition and lack of appetite.

On admittance to hospital her sclera and facial skin were icteric and her liver palpable. During hospitalization most liver function tests and haematological studies yielded results in the normal range, apart from an increased icterus index and anaemia. The icterus disappeared within 10 days.

Only later did it become known that three of her colleagues had also been admitted to hospital with headaches, lack of appetite and/or sensitivity in the epigastric region. Meanwhile the use of the "improved" bath solution had been discontinued and so an attempt was made to simulate the course of events under the same working conditions but with air monitoring and the help of a male volunteer. Impinger measurements, however, could detect no *m*-DNB either in the breathing zone of the volunteer or above the pile of electronic components or elsewhere in the room air (the detection limit was 250 µg/m^3). Nevertheless, increased methaemoglobin (ca. 11%) was measured in the volunteer's blood immediately after completion of the procedure and it remained high for about 4 hours before returning to normal by the next morning. Increased 2,4-dinitrophenol levels were also found in the volunteer's urine. Therefore the gloves which had been worn were examined and it was shown that *m*-DNB had accumulated on the damp inner surface and so could be absorbed through the skin. It was concluded that the workers had been poisoned by skin absorption of *m*-DNB [13].

Increased GOT and GPT values were reported for workers exposed to DNB (isomer not specified!) [35].

In another works, a hot aqueous DNB solution splashed accidentally from a tank, dried on the outer surface and injured a worker's back (grade 1 and 2 burns). During the next week a total of 6 workers were employed in sequence in the mornings to chip the crystallized DNB from the surface of the tank which had overflowed. For this work they wore rubber gloves and gauze masks. Each of the 6 men became cyanotic on the day after beginning the work; some complained of slight headache, nausea and respiratory distress on exertion. In all cases anaemia was diagnosed a week after the development of cyanosis (specific weight of the whole blood samples reduced by 1.9%–15.5%) accompanied by palpitations, dizziness, fatigue and languor. Methaemoglobin was not measured. GOT and GPT values were normal. Urobilinogen tests were positive for 10 days for all 7 involved workers and bilirubin was detected in the highly positive urine samples. The authors [36] speculate that the workers not only inhaled the dust they produced but also swallowed it. The anaemia persisted for a relatively long period, 30–56 days depending on the duration of exposure. Follow-up examinations during the next 10 years did not reveal any late sequelae. The long recovery period is said by the authors [36] to be a characteristic effect of DNB. This has been confirmed in serial studies of cases of cyanosis with anaemia induced by various aromatic amino and nitro compounds. With other compounds the recovery period was on average only 4 days [37].

On the basis of 187 cases of occupational cyanosis from the ten years starting in 1956 and involving 13 amino and nitro compounds, DNB was said to have the most powerful cyanotic effect after the three chloroaniline isomers [38].

3.2 Subchronic and chronic toxicity

Subchronic and chronic intoxications with DNB are known only from older literature. The symptoms are given as more or less marked cyanosis, sometimes accompanied by marked icterus and, in particular, visus impairment. Permanent damage is described as well as lethal DNB exposures. A 16 year old youth had worked for 4 months with "dinitrobenzene". In the second and third month "slight attacks of intoxication" forced him to stay at home for a total of two days. At the end of the fourth month he was short of breath and cyanotic, had attacks of weakness and dizziness and an unsteady gait. After a week's rest, he took up different light work but did not feel well. He vomited and had cramp in the legs. In the middle of the fifth month headache and pains in the limbs developed as well. His skin was yellow, his urine dark in colour. The jaundice increased, he became agitated, coma and death followed at the end of the fifth month. The autopsy revealed yellow atrophy of the liver and fatty degeneration of the kidneys [39].

In another case a 58 year old worker had been employed for 15 years in the "production of dinitrobenzene" and so was exposed to vapour and dust. The first symptoms were progressive lack of appetite, weakness, headache, sleeplessness, confusion and severe itching (pruritis). Later, his visual acuity was reduced. In spite of this he went on working, apart from a brief spell in hospital, for another 5 months. Then a mild cyanosis developed, subicteric discoloration of the sclera, reduction of the visual acuity to 1/15, reduced field of vision, central scotoma with "pale pupilla" (diagnosis: neuritis retrobulbaris). His liver was swollen, erythrocyte and leukocyte counts were reduced [40].

According to Teleky [11] visus disorders usually only arise after long term DNB exposure – sometimes apparently induced by short-term higher exposure. Initially they take the form of blurred vision, opthalmoscopically a slight clouding of the peripapillary tissue, and reduced acuity of vision. Cords [29, 34] describes various grades of visus disorders which, for example, developed in 3 cases after 1–6 months *m*-DNB exposure, in 3 other cases after 6-12 months and in 8 cases after 1–3 years. They were particularly characterized by slight to severe clouding of the peripapillary region with hyperaemic discoloration and conspicuous distention of the veins, reduced central vision, peripheral reduction in field of vision, reduction in visual acuity to 1/10 to 1/50, central scotoma especially for red and green. Whereas the visual acuity returned to normal relatively rapidly after the end of exposure, the central scotoma for red and green persisted for a long time.

Cords subdivided the cases he had studied in detail into 4 groups:

– slight, transient disorders: 5 cases,
– severe disorders, reversible in time: 4 cases,
– severe disorders, not reversible: 12 cases,
– most severe disorders, progressive: 1 case.

In addition he had brief notes on "several dozen cases".

4 Effects on Animals

4.1 Acute and subacute toxicity

Increased methaemoglobin production and Heinz body formation are seen in experimental animals too after acute DNB intoxication. Cats are more sensitive than dogs, guinea pigs, rabbits and rats (see Table 1). In cats even a single i.p. dose of

Table 1. Acute toxic effects of single doses of *o*-DNB, *m*-DNB, *p*-DNB

Substance	Species (number)	Application route (solvent)	Dose (mg/kg)	Observations	Ref.
o-DNB	rat (n.s.)	oral	250	LD$_{low}$	[42]
o-DNB	rat (3) (3)	i.p. (corn oil)	60	metHb: 58.6% after 1.0 h 46.0% after 2.5 h	[43]
o-DNB + antibiotics	rat (3) (3)	i.p. (corn oil)	60	metHb: 62.5% after 1.0 h 42.8% after 2.5 h	[43]
o-DNB	rat (10) (10) (10) (10) (10)	i.p. (polyethylene glycol)	∼ 75.6	metHb: ∼ 16% after 5 min ∼ 49% after 30 min ∼ 31% after 60 min ∼ 15% after 120 min ∼ 2% after 240 min blood sugar: 9.5 mmol/l after 30 min	[44]
m-DNB	rat (n.s.)	oral	25	testicular effects, see text	[45]
m-DNB	rat (n.s.)	oral	27	LD$_{low}$	[42]
m-DNB	rat	oral (1% in corn oil)	83 (56−124)	LD$_{50}$	[46]
m-DNB	rat (10) (10) (10) (10) (10) (10)	i.p. (polyethylene glycol)	∼ 25.2	metHb: ∼ 18% after 5 min ∼ 57% after 30 min ∼ 60% after 60 min ∼ 52% after 120 min ∼ 49% after 240 min ∼ 1.5% after 24 h blood sugar: 7.5 mmol/l after 120 min	[44]
m-DNB	rat (5)	i.p. (poppyseed oil)	30	metHb: 40−60% (after 4 h) transient spasms and paralysis of rear extremities	[47]

Table 1 (continued)

Substance	Species (number)	Application route (solvent)	Dose (mg/kg)	Observations	Ref.
m-DNB	rat (3) (3) (3) (3)	i.p. (corn oil)	60	metHb: ~41% after 1.0 h ~56% after 2.5 h ~62% after 5.0 h ~45% after 8.0 h	[43]
m-DNB + antibiotics biotics	rat (3) (3) (3) (3)	i.p. (corn oil)	60	metHb: ~39% after 1.0 h ~55% after 2.5 h ~54% after 5.0 h ~34% after 8.0 h	[43]
m-DNB	guinea pig (1 per dose)	s.c. (n.s.)	10 20 50 100 140 180 200	animal survived animal survived animal survived animal died after 4 d animal died after 3 h animal died after 2 h animal died after 2 h	[41]
m-DNB	guinea pig (2) (2)	i.p. (2% in poppyseed oil)	10	metHb: 25% after 30 min 21% after 85 min	[41]
m-DNB	guinea pig (2) (2)	i.p. (2% in poppyseed oil)	20	metHb: 30% after 60 min 42% after 35 min	[41]
m-DNB	guinea pig (4) (4) (4) (4)	i.p. (2% in poppysed oil)	30	metHb: 28%, died after 4 h 33%, died after 2 d 34%, survived 36%, survived	[41]
m-DNB	guinea pig (2) (2)	i.p. (2% in poppyseed oil)	40	metHb: 40%, died after 3 h 42%, survived	[41]
m-DNB	guinea pig (1)	i.p. (2% in poppyseed oil)	50	metHb: 67%, died after 4 h	[41]
m-DNB	cat (1 per dose)	i.p. (poppyseed oil)	6.5 6.7 7.8	metHb: 65% Heinz bodies: 100% metHb: 68% Heinz bodies: 100% metHb: 60% Heinz bodies: 100%	[10]

Table 1 (continued)

Substance	Species (number)	Application route (solvent)	Dose (mg/kg)	Observations	Ref.
m-DNB	cat (10)	i.p. (n.s.)	10	metHb: 60–80%	[41]
m-DNB	dog (n.s.)	i.p. (n.s.)	10	metHb: 38–65% liver damage	[48]
m-DNB	rabbit (n.s.)	i.p. (n.s.)	30	metHb: 30–40%	[48]
m-DNB	dog (n.s.)	s.c. (olive oil or poppyseed oil)	1 2 10 20	no effect no effect 9/19 died 9/12 died	[49]
p-DNB	rat (n.s.)	oral (n.s.)	29	LD$_{low}$	[42]
p-DNB	rat (10)	i.p. (polyethylene glycol)	∼ 2.5	metHb: 86% after 5 min blood sugar: 8 mmol/l after 30 min	[44]
p-DNB	rat (3) (3) (3) (3) (3)	i.p. (polyethylene glycol)	∼ 3.4	metHb: ∼ 93% after 5 min ∼ 74% after 30 min ∼ 48% after 60 min ∼ 19% after 120 min ∼ 7% after 240 min	[44]
p-DNB	rat (3) (3)	i.p. (corn oil)	50	metHb: ∼ 84.2% after 1.0 h ∼ 43.6% after 2.5 h	[43]
p-DNB + antibiotics	rat (3) (3)	i.p. (corn oil)	50	metHb: ∼ 78.9% after 1.0 h ∼ 47.6% after 2.5 h	[43]

n.s.: not specified
s.c.: subcutaneous
LD$_{low}$: lowest published lethal dose

6.5–6.9 mg/kg body weight is enough to cause leukocytosis and anaemia as well [10, 41].

In male Fischer 344 rats a dose of 25 mg *m*-DNB/kg body weight yields 32% metHb in 3–6 hours; in specific pathogen-free animals of the same strain only slightly less metHb was formed. Since 30 μM *m*-DNB does not induce metHb formation *in vitro*, metabolites must be responsible for metHb formation *in vivo* [50]. In the specific pathogen-free animals, in contrast, the neurotoxicity was very much more apparent. In these animals the DNB levels in tissue, especially liver and brain, were higher than in the conventional animals and there are indications that *m*-DNB inhibits pyruvate utilization [50].

In incubations of erythrocytes from Fischer 344 rats, Rhesus monkeys and man with 100 μM concentrations of the single DNB isomers, *p*-DNB produced most metHb with all substrates. *m*-DNB had only little effect in rat erythrocytes and practically none in Rhesus monkey or human red cells. *o*-DNB produced relevant amounts of metHb only in human erythrocytes [17].

In rats a single oral dose of 25 mg/kg *m*-DNB or three daily doses of 5 mg/kg produced testicular changes after as little as 12 hours. Initial Sertoli cell vacuolation was followed by degeneration and/or exfoliation of the germ cells. 3 daily oral doses of 25 mg/kg caused reduction in testicular weight [22, 45].

The *in vivo* results were confirmed in studies of Sertoli cell co-cultures. *m*-DNB in concentrations of 5×10^{-6} to 10^{-4} M caused a dose-dependent loss of germ cells, vacuolation of the Sertoli cell monolayer and inclusion of degenerate cells. None of the metabolites studied in parallel was as effective as *m*-DNB at the same concentration; only at a concentration of 10^{-4} M were 2,4-dinitrophenol and 4-amino-2-nitrophenol able to cause damage in this cell system; 2,4-dinitrophenol was highly cytotoxic at this concentration [23, 51].

After lethal oral doses (56–126 mg/kg body weight), reduction in ambulatory motion, ataxia, weakness, dyspnoea, rapid heartbeat, cyanosis, coma and eventual respiratory failure are seen in rats [46].

Low i.p. doses of the individual isomers cause not only increased metHb levels in rats (see Table 1) but also increased blood sugar levels, increased leucine aminopeptidase and glutamate-pyruvate transaminase activities in serum as well as increased urinary catecholamine excretion [44].

In another study increased GOT and GPT values were seen in Wistar rats 5 hours after i.p. injection of 100 μmol/kg *p*-DNB or *m*-DNB but not with *o*-DNB [42].

Intraperitoneal administration of 30 mg *m*-DNB/kg to rats led not only to increased methaemoglobin but also to transient spasms and paralysis (see Table 1) [47].

16% reduction of the sciatic motor conduction velocity was seen in rats after *m*-DNB intoxication producing about 60% metHb. It returned to normal within 48 hours after regression of the methaemoglobinaemia. In comparison, carbon monoxide poisoning producing about 60% COHb brought about a 33% reduction in sciatic motor conduction velocity, which did not return to normal within 4 weeks [44, 52].

Single subcutaneous doses of 1 or 2 mg *m*-DNB/kg body weight (see Table 1) had no detectable effects in the dog. In contrast, repeated daily injections of 2 mg *m*-DNB/kg body weight caused lack of appetite in 3 of 5 animals on the second day, refusal of food by all animals on day 5 and spasms and lateral position of one animal and death of 4 of 5 animals in spite of discontinuation of the treatment on day 9 (see Table 3) [49].

A dog was injected subcutaneously with 6 mg/kg *m*-DNB on two consecutive days and, after a pause of 4 days, again on another three consecutive days, five times in all within nine days. Spasms developed after the last application and the animal died. The methaemoglobin level had risen to 5.5 g/100 ml (ca. 35% metHb) and 40% of the red blood cells contained Heinz bodies [49].

Symptoms of DNB poisoning in the dog too were especially apparent
– in the blood: methaemoglobinaemia, Heinz bodies, anaemia,
– in the central nervous system: nystagmus, stiffness of the limbs, hyperexcitability, extension spasms, spastic paralysis,
– in the liver: diffuse infiltration with small fat droplets, vacuolation, incipient necrosis of the central lobules, damaged parenchyma cells and endothelia, stroma residues and haemosiderin in the Kupffer cells,
– in the spleen: deposition of large amounts of red blood cell stroma residues and haemosiderin in the endothelia.
– in the kidney: fatty infiltration of the *tubuli renales contorti* and, in some cases, haemosiderin deposits were observed.

The cause of death in dogs after higher doses (≥ 20 mg/kg *m*-DNB) was taken to be the increased methaemoglobin level and anoxia; after lower doses which caused death only after several days, it was assumed to be damage to the central nervous system [49].

The main effect of repeated subcutaneous injections of 10 to 30 mg/kg *m*-DNB in guinea pigs was anaemia with an increase in reticulocytes. Histological studies revealed in particular lung damage. The severe oedema was probably a result of heart failure. Infiltration with large fat droplets and slight haemosiderosis were found in the liver and more pronounced haemosiderin deposits in the spleen [41].

Methaemoglobin production by the three isomers differs in time-dependency, potency and course of regression. *In vivo* in the cat [53, 54] and rat [43, 44] the potency decreases in the order *p*-DNB > *m*-DNB > *o*-DNB (see Table 1). At high concentrations (2 mM) in incubations with whole rat blood the order was *p*-DNB > *o*-DNB > *m*-DNB [42, 43]; here too on incubation with *p*-DNB the metHb production started immediately and had reached a maximum within an hour whereas with *o*-DNB the maximum level was measured after 8 hours (last measurement), with *m*-DNB after 5 hours.

A dose of 0.2 mg *p*-DNB was just as toxic for cats as 1–2 mg *m*-DNB or 3–6 mg *o*-DNB. After administration of *p*-DNB or *o*-DNB to cats the maximal metHb level was reached after 1 to 2 hours and simultaneous alcohol administration did not affect the metHb production. After *m*-DNB administration the maximal metHb value was never attained in less than 6 hours and on average it took 12 hours. The level then remained constant for 24–48 hours; simultaneous administration of alcohol increased the metHb production markedly [10, 53, 54]. Thus *p*-DNB is the most toxic of the three isomers. It is a more potent methaemoglobin producer than phenylhydroxylamine or nitrosobenzene [54, 55].

Table 2. Acute toxic effects of DNB (technical grade?) after dermal application

Species number ♂♀ (weight)	Dose	Application type (skin area)	Exposure time until death	Observations	Ref.
cat 1 (n.s.)	2×0.5g	rubbed into the fur (n.s.)	d1: 5 h d2: 3.5 h died	d1 after 3 h: restlessness, salivation, rapid breathing, groans, extension spasms, gradual recovery overnight, d2 like d1, coma and death, metHb, skin without erythema or signs of irritation	[57]
cat 1 ♀ (2350 g)	1 g (0.4 g/ kg bw)	occlusive (350 cm² back and part of flank)	28 h died	restlessness, cries, groans, pupils contracted, apathy, unconsciousness, blood: discoloured dark and with metHb lungs: greybrown, slightly oedematous	[58]
cat 1	5 g	occlusive (n.s.)	3 h died	groans, increased respiration rate, increased salivation, livid tongue and oral mucosa, blood: dark brown and with metHb spleen: lymph follicle slightly swollen skin: normal	[57]
cat 1 (n.s.)	50 g	occlusive (n.s.)	3.5 h died	groans, increased respiration rate, excessive salivation, tongue, oral mucosa and nose livid blood: dark brown and with metHb kidney: fatty infiltration spleen: lymph follicle swollen	[57]
cat (n.s.)	25% in lanolin ointment	occlusive (3-8 cm² shaved dorsal skin)	n.s.	extremities: stiff and extended cyanosis, salivation blood: brown and with metHb, red cells morphologically altered urine: dark liver: fatty infiltration kidney: toxic nephritis 3 animals died	[33]

Table 2 (continued)

Species number ♂♀ (weight)	Dose	Application type (skin area)	Exposure time until death	Observations	Ref.
rabbit 2 ♂ (1000 g)	1 g (1 g/ kg bw)	occlusive (250 cm² shaved dorsal and lateral skin)	25 h died 33 h died	tongue and oral mucosa livid, increased respiration rate, spasmic jerking, corneal and pupillary reflexes absent, blood and urine of one animal discoloured dark, no detectable metHb	[58]
rabbit 1 (n.s.)	2 × 50 g	occlusive (n.s.)	d1: 8 h d2: 9h died	d1: no reaction d2: after 4 h: restlessness, increased respiration rate, dsypnoea, jerking, extension spasms, died in the following night, blood: metHb urine: dark and bloody skin: normal	[57]

n.s.: not specified
bw: body weight
d1, d2, d3 ...: day 1, day 2, day 3 ...

From the data of older studies with cats Bodansky [55] concludes that *p*-DNB is the most potent methaemoglobin producer among 24 amino and nitro compounds. In a study comparing the methaemoglobin producing potency of various amino and nitro compounds* in the Wistar rat the most potent methaemoglobin producers were the two isomers *p*-DNB (29.5 ± 10.7%) and *m*-DNB (25.5 ± 5.5%) together with *m*-chloronitrobenzene (31.9 ± 5.8%) (measured 5 hours after i.p. injection of 100 μmole/kg body weight). *o*-DNB with 13.1 ± 1.0% was much less potent. In this study *p*-DNB was the only substance which caused the death of two rats [42].

In other comparative studies some of the rats were treated with antibiotics to eliminate intestinal bacteria. Here too, as in incubations with whole rat blood *in vitro*, *p*-DNB induced the highest methaemoglobin levels (see Table 1) although, because of its toxicity, it was used in smaller doses than the other nitroaromatics**. The results of these studies suggested that unlike other nitroaromatics, the DNB isomers require neither intestinal bacteria nor tissue nitroreductase for activation. The authors concluded that DNB itself penetrates the erythrocyte membrane and catalyses the oxidation of haemoglobin [43].

Incubation of rat erythrocytes and haemolysates with 14C-labelled *o*-DNB, *m*-DNB, *p*-DNB or mononitrobenzene demonstrated that although all four nitro compounds penetrate the membranes and accumulate in the erythrocytes, metHb production only takes place with the dinitro compounds even though in the 150 minute incubation period mononitrobenzene attained higher levels in the erythrocytes than, e.g., *p*-DNB. It is concluded that the mononitro and dinitro compounds must differ in their direct interaction with the haemoglobin and/or in their erythrocyte metabolism [56].

4.1.1 Dermal toxicity

Studies of the penetration of animal skin by DNB are only known in older literature and do not meet modern requirements (see Table 2). In general the DNB (probably technical!) applied is not specified in detail and the description of procedures and animals are incomplete. Nonetheless the studies demonstrate clearly that DNB readily penetrates intact skin and can cause systemic toxicity and death. No skin irritation was observed.

4.2 Subchronic and chronic toxicity

Although rats which were given 50, 100 or 200 mg *m*-DNB per litre drinking water for 8 weeks survived the treatment, apart from the animals in the highest dose group (see Table 3), histopathological changes were found in all animals. Particularly

---

  * substances studied: aniline, o-phenylenediamine, p-phenylenediamine, nitrobenzene, o-DNB, m-DNB, p-DNB, 1,3,5-trinitrobenzene, o-nitroaniline, m-nitroaniline, p-nitroaniline, 1,3-diamino-2,4,6-trinitrobenzene, o-chloroaniline, m-chloroaniline, pchloroaniline, o-chloronitrobenzene, mchloronitrobenzene, p-chloronitrobenzene, 1-chlor-2,4-dinitrobenzene

** substances studied: 3,5-dinitrobenzamide, nitrobenzene, niclosamide, nitrodan, 3,5-dinitrobenzoic acid and o-DNB, m-DNB and p-DNB

Table 3. Subacute, subchronic and chronic toxicity of DNB

Compound	Species (strain)	Number ♂♀	Dose	Application route	Duration	Observations	Ref.
m-DNB	rat (n.s.)	12 + 12 6 + 6 6 + 6 6 + 6	0 50 mg/l 100 mg/l 200 mg/l	in the drinking water	8 weeks	– dose-dependent reduction of growth rate and weight loss especially in ♂. Slight but consistent reduction of haemoglobin level in ♂ and ♀. Enlarged spleen in ♂ and ♀ from the 50 and 100 mg/l groups. Testes atrophy in all ♂ Histopathology see text. 200 mg/l: 4/6 ♂ died by week 6 and 2/6 ♀ died by week 8	[46]
m-DNB	rat (n.s.)	20 + 20 20 + 20 20 + 20 20 + 20	0 3 mg/l 8 mg/l 20 mg/l	in the drinking water	16 weeks	– no acute toxicity 8 and 20 mg/l: spleen weight increased in ♂ and ♀. Histopathology see text. 20 mg/l: testes weight markedly reduced in ♂; growth rate reduced in ♀. Haemoglobin levels initially reduced, then normal from week 10 or 14 resp. No deaths	[46]
m-DNB	dog (n.s.)	2	initial: 1 mg/kg then: 2 mg/kg then: 1 mg/kg	gruel i.g.	daily 4 months 7 times till month 9	condition normal, weight increase metHb level below 0.5 g/100 ml Heinz bodies in 0.1–1% of red blood cells After 5 doses of 2 mg/kg stiff gait, after 6 doses spasms and increased Heinz body values of 10–20% reduction of increased number of Heinz bodies	[49]

Table 3 (continued)

Compound	Species (strain)	Number ♂♀	Dose	Application route	Duration	Observations	Ref.
m-DNB	dog (n.s.)	1	0.1 mg/kg	in oil s.c.	4.5 months (142 d)	from d122: central nervous disorders (see text) from d126: spasms, died d144	[49]
m-DNB	dog (n.s.)	1	0.1 mg/kg	in oil s.c.	8 months	tolerated without symptoms, weight increase	[49]
m-DNB	dog (n.s.)	4	0.2 mg/kg	in oil s.c.	20, 25, 30 & 40 d	no visible damage	[49]
m-DNB	dog (n.s.)	3	0.2 mg/kg	in oil s.c.	> 70 d	long period without effects, from weeks 2–3 more active animals became quieter, central nervous disorders began between d42 and d70. 1/3 died on d49	[49]
m-DNB	dog (n.s.)	3	0.5 mg/kg	in oil s.c.	25–73 d	central nervous disorders on average from d40, deaths on d26, d40 and d74	[49]
m-DNB	dog (n.s.)	3	1 mg/kg	in oil s.c.	23–56 d	central nervous disorders on average from d23, deaths on d24, d33, d57	[49]
m-DNB	dog (n.s.)	12	1.5 mg/kg	in oil s.c.	16–~40 d not daily	central nervous disorders from d7–d25; in spite of discontinuation of injections disorders progressed to spasms, loss of weight and, in spite of repeated pauses in DNB administration, animals died between d18 and d114	[49]
m-DNB	dog (n.s.)	5	2.0 mg/kg	in oil s.c.	8–9 d	central nervous disorders from d5–d15, Heinz body values ∅ 24–54%. body weight loss, 4/5 died between d8 and d24	[49]

n.s.: not specified
s.c.: subcutaneous

conspicuous were the dose-dependent brownish yellow pigment deposits in the Kupffer cells in the liver, spleen enlargement, and signs of reduced spermatogenesis and reduced numbers of germinal cells in the testicular tissue in the 50 and 100 mg/l groups. More than half of the seminiferous tubules in the testes of animals from the 200 mg/l group were collapsed, neither germinal cells nor Sertoli cells were present in the tubules. In the ovaries no histopathological changes were seen in any group. Atrophy of the spleen with fibrosis and extensive haemosiderin deposits were present in male and female rats of the 200 mg/l group. Pathological changes were not found in any other tissues [46].

Rats which had been given 3, 8 or 20 mg *m*-DNB per litre drinking water for 16 weeks survived without any signs of acute toxicity and without deaths (see Table 3). The average daily intake of *m*-DNB in the 20 mg/l group was calculated to be 3.88 and 3.98 mg/kg/day, respectively, for female and male animals in the first weeks and 2.24 and 2.00 mg/kg/day in the last weeks. In the male rats of the high dose group haematocrit and haemoglobin values were reduced after 5 and 10 weeks but not after 16 weeks. Microscopic studies revealed haemosiderin deposits in the spleens of all animals, particularly in the high dose group. Spermatogenesis was slightly to moderately depressed in the males of the high dose group. Pathological changes were not found in any other tissues [46].

For urine studies two rats were treated initially with 30 mg/kg *m*-DNB by intraperitoneal injection and then either 3–4 times weekly or daily with a subcutaneous dose of 4 mg/kg. The first signs of a mild effect, occasional high stiff gait, hyperexcitability and refusal of food, developed later into symptoms of severe intoxication such as lateral position and spasms. For this reason the administration was interrupted repeatedly for increasing periods. One animal died within 6 months [47].

Chronic administration to dogs resulted in changed blood count, in the production of Heinz bodies without significant increase in methaemoglobin, in anaemia, central nervous disorders, spastic paralysis and spasms, as well as in liver and spleen lesions. Histopathological studies revealed structural changes in the liver, atrophy, necrosis, fatty degeneration and cloudy swelling as well as haemosiderosis in liver, spleen and occasionally in the kidneys.

Nervous disorders whose severity depended on the dose developed in dogs which were given subcutaneous injections of 0.1–2 mg/kg *m*-DNB dissolved in oil (see Table 3), initially stiff, uncertain gait, later complete stiffness of the front and rear extremities. The animals could no longer stand upright and fell flat on their chests with splayed out legs. These nervous disorders began whenever a total of 15–20 mg *m*-DNB/kg body weight had been administered; at this point the anaemia was also correspondingly advanced. The extent of methaemoglobin production and Heinz body formation, in contrast, depended on the daily dose and was less apparent in more chronic intoxications [49, 59].

5 Genotoxicity

m-DNB was a direct mutagen in the *S. typhimurium* strains TA98, TA1538, TA100 and D3052 [60-68]. In TA1538, TA98 and TA100 the lowest effective dose was 33 µg per plate [65]. Weak direct mutagenicity was also found in strain TA1537 (from 100 μg/plate) [64, 65]. Without S9 mix, positive results were obtained in TA1538 with up to 300 μg *m*-DNB/plate [66] or ~ 400 μg/plate [64] and in TA100 up to ~ 400 μg/plate [64]. At higher concentrations cytotoxicity reduced the number of revertants drastically.

Of the three isomers *m*-DNB was the strongest direct mutagen in the strains TA98, TA100 and TA1538 [62, 64, 67, 68] and, after metabolic activation, the strongest indirect mutagen in TA98 and TA100 [67].

In *Escherichia coli* W3110/polA$^+$ and p3478/polA$^-$ *m*-DNB was toxic for the bacteria at the concentrations tested, 100 μg to 10 mg per plate, both with and without S9 mix [65].

In the recombination test in yeast, *Saccharomyces cerevisiae* D5, no positive results were obtained with *m*-DNB at concentrations up to 32 mg/ml either with or without S9 mix [65].

p-**DNB** was also a direct mutagen in *S. typhimurium* TA98, TA1538 and TA100 [62, 64, 67–69]. In the nitroreductase-containing strains TA98 and TA1538 it was a strong direct mutagen, in the nitroreductase deficient strains TA98NR and TA1538NR, in contrast, the mutagenicity was weak [70].

o-**DNB** yielded only negative results in five tested *S. typhimurium* strains (TA98, TA1538, TA1537, TA100, TA1535) both with and without metabolic activation [63, 64] and in another study in TA98 in the concentration range 0.02–200 μg/plate [68]. Negative results were also obtained in the modified Ames test in 8 histidine auxotrophs of *S. typhimurium* and in two tryptophan auxotrophs of *E. coli* [62].

Listed below are those known and potential metabolites of DNB (see Section 2.1 – Pharmacokinetics) which have also been studied to date.

p-**Nitrophenylhydroxylamine** in doses of 5–50 μg/plate was mutagenic in *S. typhimurium* TA98 (up to 1844 ± 139 revertant colonies per plate) and even more so in TA1538 (up to 5243 ± 409 revertant colonies per plate) [70].

o-**Nitroaniline, *m*-nitroaniline and *p*-nitroaniline** were mutagenic in the "Rec Assay" in *Bacillus subtilis* strains H17 and M45 in the order of potency *p*-nitroaniline > *o*-nitroaniline > *m*-nitroaniline. In the Ames test *m*-nitroaniline was the most effective isomer and was a direct mutagen in the strains TA98, TA1538, TA100 and TA1535 (concentration range tested 0.05–10 mg/plate; toxic at 10 mg/plate). *p*-Nitroaniline was a direct mutagen in TA98 and TA1538, *o*-nitroaniline was not mutagenic in any of the strains tested (TA98, TA1538, TA1537, TA100, TA1535) up to 1 mg/plate with or without activation; 5 mg/plate was in the toxic range [71].

In another study, when the three isomers were tested in the concentration range 0.1–10 μmole/plate without metabolic activation in the strains TA98 and TA100, the only positive results were obtained with *m*-nitroaniline in TA98 [60].

2,4-Dinitrophenol was not mutagenic in *S. typhimurium* TA98 or TA100 in the concentration range 0.1–10 μmole/plate without metabolic activation [60].

6 Carcinogenicity

Studies of the carcinogenicity of DNB are currently not known.

7 Manifesto (MAK value, classification)

The most evident effects of DNB are the acute toxic effects on the blood. The dinitrobenzenes are among the most potent methaemoglobin producers (c.f Linch [38], Section 3.1 – Acute toxicity in man).

It is known from studies with acetanilide and acetophenetidin [1] that man is very sensitive to the effects of methaemoglobin-producing substances, less sensitive than the cat but more sensitive than the dog, rat, rabbit or monkey.

Systematic long-term studies of experimental animals under controlled exposure conditions have not been carried out with DNB. The symptoms described for man in many "historical" reviews cannot be associated with definite exposure levels. In particular, the significance of the liver effects cannot be adequately assessed. Therefore a MAK value cannot be deduced from these data.

The MAK value of 1 mg/m³, adopted from the USA value in 1958 and valid until now, was *deduced* from a comparison of the acute toxic effects of various aromatic and nitroaromatic compounds and is not well founded [72].

More recent publications demonstrate (see Section 3.1 – Acute toxicity in man) that persons can suffer intoxication (cyanosis, etc.) even at concentrations below 250 µg/m³ in the air (1/4 of the MAK value of 1 mg/m³) if there is direct contact with the substance so that it can be taken up through the intact skin.

The studies of metabolism and genotoxicity reveal marked differences between the three DNB isomers. Thus *o*-DNB is the least potent metHb producer and yields negative results in various Ames tests. The main component of DNB mixtures, *m*-DNB, and *p*-DNB are both potent metHb producers and mutagenic in *S. typhimurium* strains.

Comparison with other amino and nitro aromatics (e.g. 2-amino-4-nitrotoluene, 2-amino-4-nitroanisidine, 2-nitro-4-aminophenol, dinitrotoluene) suggests that DNB has carcinogenic potential. Further studies on the genotoxic and carcinogenic effects of these substances and a basis for the establishment of a MAK value are therefore urgently required.

Mixtures containing *m*-DNB or *p*-DNB are therefore classified in Section III B of the List of MAK Values. A MAK value cannot be established; it would make sense to apply exposure control according to the BAT value concept for the dinitrobenzenes and efforts should be made in this direction. Because of the danger of uptake of toxic amounts of the substances through the skin, the dinitrobenzenes are designated with an H.

8 References

1. Beard, R. R., J. T. Noe: in Clayton, G. D., F. E. Clayton (Eds.): *Patty's Industrial Hygiene and Toxicology*, 3rd rev. ed., Vol. 2A, p 2413, John Wiley & Sons, New York, Chichester, Brisbane, Toronto, 1981
2. v. Oettingen, W. F.: *Publ. Health Bulletin No. 271*, p 94, Washington DC, U.S.A., 1941
3. Rejsek, K.: *Acta med. scand. 127*, 179 (1947)
4. Schwarz, L.: *Zbl. Arbeitsmed. 8*, 104 (1958)
5. *Ullmanns Encyklopädie der technischen Chemie* Vol. 12, 768 (1960)
6. Koelsch, F.: *Zbl. Gewerbehyg. 5*, 60, 142 (1917)

7. Stukowski, J.: *Dtsch. med. Wschr. 48*, 1377 (1922)
8. Taeger, H.: *Die Klinik der entschädigungspflichtigen Berufskrankheiten*, p 153, Springer-Verlag, Berlin, 1941
9. Koelsch, F.: *Öff. Gesundheitspflege 51*, 257 (1919)
10. v. Bredow, M., F. Jung: *Naunyn-Schmiedeberg's Arch. exp. Path. Pharmak. 200*, 335 (1942)
11. Teleky, L.: *Gewerbliche Vergiftungen*, p 300, Springer-Verlag, Berlin, Göttingen, Heidelberg, 1955
12. Ishihara, N., M. Ikeda: *Int. Arch. occup. environm. Hlth 44*, 91 (1979)
13. Ishihara, N., A. Kanaya, M. Ikeda: *Int. Arch. occup. environm. Hlth 36*, 161 (1976)
14. Parke, D. V.: *Biochem. J. 78*, 262 (1961)
15. Cossum, P. A., D. E. Rickert: *Drug Metab. Dispos. 13*, 664 (1985)
16. Cossum, P. A., D. E. Rickert: *Pharmacologist 27*, 250 (1985)
17. Cossum, P. A., D. E. Rickert: *Toxicol. Lett. 37*, 157 (1987)
18. Abou-Khalil, S., W. H. Abou-Khalil, A. A. Yunis: *Pharmacology 31*, 301 (1985)
19. Abou-Khalil, S., W. H. Abou-Khalil, C. Saadeh, A. A. Yunis: *Fed. Proc. 44*, 1254 (Abstr.) (1985)
20. Asaoka, K., K. Takahashi: *J. Biochem. (Tokyo) 90*, 1237 (1981)
21. Mason, R. P., P. D. Josephy (1984), cited in [23, 51]
22. Foster, P. M. D., C. M. Sheard, S. C. Lloyd: *Excerpta med. Int. Cong. Ser.* (1986), cited in [23]
23. Foster, P. M. D., S. C. Lloyd, M. S. Prout: *Toxic. in vitro 1*, 31 (1987)
24. Starkow, W.: *Virchows Arch. path. Anat. 52*, 464 (1971), cited in [32]
25. Monks, E. H.: *Lancet I*, 89 (1902)
26. Steiner, O.: *Korresp.-Bl. schweiz. Ärz. 48*, 1139 (1918)
27. Curschmann, F.: *Zbl. Gewerbehyg. 6*, 93 (1918)
28. Curschmann, F.: *Zbl. Gewerbehyg. 6*, 162 (1918)
29. Cords, R.: *Zbl. Gewerbehyg. 7*, 6 (1919)
30. Floret: *Zbl. Gewerbehyg. 16*, 19 (1929)
31. Glahn, M., P. Schack-Schou: *Nord. Med. 36*, 2135 (1947)
32. Beritic, T.: *Brit. J. industr. Med. 13*, 114 (1956)
33. White, R. P., J. Hay: *The Lancet*, Aug. 31, 582 (1901)
34. Cords, R.: *Augenschädigungen bei Munitionsarbeitern*, Report of the 41st Meeting of the Ophthalmologischen Gesellschaft, D-6900 Heidelberg, p 127, 1918
35. Onishi (1975), cited in [13]
36. Okubo, T., S. Shigeta: *Industr. Hlth 20*, 297 (1982)
37. Wuertz, R. L., W. H. Frazee, W. G. Hume, A. L. Linch, J. M. Wetherhold: *Arch. environm. Hlth 9*, 478 (1964)
38. Linch, A. L.: *Amer. industr. Hyg. Ass. J. 35*, 426 (1974)
39. Walker, E.: *Lancet II*, 717 (1908), cited in [11]
40. Cappelini, A., G. G. Zanotti: *Med. d. Lavoro 37*, 265 (1946), cited in [11]
41. Kunz, G.: *Naunyn-Schmiedeberg's Arch. exp. Path. Pharmak. 199*, 508 (1942)
42. Watanabe, T., N. Ishihara, M. Ikeda: *Int. Arch. occup. environm. Hlth 37*, 157 (1976)
43. Facchini, V., L. A. Griffiths: *Biochem. Pharmacol. 30*, 931 (1981)
44. Pankow., D., W. Ponsold: *Toxicology 11*, 377 (1978)
45. Blackburn, D. M., S. C. Lloyd, A. J. Gray, P. M. D. Foster: *Toxicologist 5*, 121 (Abstr. 482) (1985)
46. Cody, T., S. Witherup, L. Hastings, K. Stemmer, R. T. Christian: *J. Toxicol. environm. Hlth 7*, 829 (1981)
47. Kiese, M., G. Siems: *Naunyn-Schmiedeberg's Arch. exp. Path. Pharmak. 206*, 528 (1949)
48. Kiese, M., F. Jung, cited in [41]
49. Kiese, M.: *Naunyn-Schmiedeberg's Arch. exp. Path. Pharmak. 206*, 361, 505 (1949)
50. Philbert, M. A., A. J. Gray, T. A. Connors: *Toxicol. Lett. 38*, 307 (1987)
51. Lloyd, S. C., P. M. D. Foster: *Arch. Toxicol., Suppl. 11*, 281 (1987)
52. Pankow, D., W. Glatzel, K. Tietze, W. Ponsold: *Arch. Toxicol. 34*, 325 (1975)
53. Heubner, W., Lo-Sing: *Naunyn-Schmiedeberg's Arch. exp. Path. Pharmak. 188*, 143 (1938)
54. v. Issekutz, B.: *Naunyn-Schmiedeberg's Arch. exp. Path. Pharmak. 193*, 551 (1939)
55. Bodansky, O.: *Pharmacol. Rev. 3*, 144 (1951)
56. Goldstein, R. S., D. E. Rickert: *Life Sci. 36*, 121 (1985)

57. Zieger, J.: *Studien über die Wirkung von Nitrobenzol, Dinitrobenzol, Nitrotoluol, Dinitrotoluol von Lunge und Haut aus.* Thesis, D-8700 Würzburg, 1913
58. Dambleff, J.: *Beiträge zur Kenntnis der giftigen Wirkung nitrierter Benzole und Toluole insbesondere von der Haut aus.* Thesis, D-8700 Würzburg, 1908
59. Kiese, M.: *Naunyn-Schmiedeberg's Arch. exp. Path. Pharmak. 208*, 43 (1949)
60. Chiu, C. W., L. H. Lee, C. Y. Wang, G. T. Bryan: *Mutat. Res. 58*, 11 (1978)
61. Matsuda, A.: *Acta Sch. med. Univ. Gifu 29*, 278 (1981)
62. Probst, G. S., R. E. McMahon, L. E. Hill, C. Z. Thompson, J. K. Epp, S. B. Neal: *Environm. Mutag. 3*, 11 (1981)
63. Spanggord, R. J., K. E. Mortelmans, A. F. Griffin, V. F. Simmon: *Environm. Mutag. 4*, 163, (1982)
64. Shimizu, M., Y. Yasui, N. Matsumoto: *Mutat. Res. 116*, 217 (1983)
65. McGregor, D. B., C. G. Riach, R. M. Hastwell, J. C. Dacre: *Environm. Mutag. 2*, 531 (1980)
66. McGregor, D., R. D. Prentice, M. McConville, J. J. Lee, W. J. Caspary: *Environm. Mutag. 6*, 545 (1984)
67. Furukawa, H., K. Kawai: *Mutat. Res. 147*, 256 (1985)
68. Furukawa, H., N. Kawai, K. Kawai: *Nucleic Acids Symp. Ser. 16*, 5 (1985)
69. Rao, T. K., L. D. Claxton: *Environm. Mutag. 5*, 426 (1983)
70. Corbett, M. D., C. I. Wei, B. R. Corbett: *Carcinogenesis 6*, 727 (1985)
71. Shimizu, M., E. Yano: *Mutat. Res. 170*, 11 (1986)
72. ACGIH (American Conference of Governmental Industrial Hygienists Inc.): *Documentation of the Threshold Limit Values and Biological Exposure Indices*, 5th ed., Cincinnati, OH., U.S.A., 1986

completed 11. 4. 1988

Hydrazine

H S

Classification/MAK value:	see Section III A 2) **MAK List 1989**
Classification/MAK value dates from:	**1989**
Synonyms:	diamide diamine
Chemical name (CAS):	hydrazine
CAS number:	302-01-2
Structural formula:	H_2N-NH_2
Molecular formula:	N_2H_4
Molecular weight:	32.05
Melting point:	1.5 °C
Boiling point:	113.5 °C
Vapour pressure at 20 °C:	13.3 hPa

1 ml/m³ (ppm) = 1.332 mg/m³   **1 mg/m³ = 0.751 ml/m³ (ppm)**

1 Toxic Effects and Modes of Action

Hydrazine (liquid or vapour) is a strong irritant of skin and mucous membranes [1]. In addition hydrazine causes marked skin sensitization [2, 3].

The principle symptoms of a systemic intoxication are vomiting, muscle tremor, convulsions, paresthesia and, after chronic exposure, also anorexia, weight loss, kidney damage and centrolobular fatty metamorphosis of the liver [1, 4–7].

Hydrazine interferes in intermediary metabolism, in particular by inhibition of pyridoxal phosphate-dependent enzyme systems [8–12]. In animals it has also been shown to inhibit gluconeogenesis [8] and to cause an increase in plasma concentrations of all amino acids [13] and of free fatty acids [14].

Hydrazine is rapidly absorbed and distributed in the organism. After parenteral injection of hydrazine into mice half the dose is metabolized and the other half excreted unchanged in the urine [15]. 1,2-Diacetylhydrazine is detectable in the urine of rabbits but not of dogs [16].

It has long been known that hydrazine is a carcinogen in animals [17–21]. There is no evidence for cumulative effects [22, 23].

2 Effects in Man
(see also "Carcinogenicity")

Ingested liquid hydrazine produces local irritation which leads to protracted vomiting. Then the main symptoms are of central nervous origin – somnolence, ataxia, restlessness, incoordination and paresthesia. With medical treatment these symptoms regress within a few days. The transient respiratory and cardiac rhythm disorders are also likely to be of central nervous origin [24, 25].

Exposure to hydrazine vapour causes, sometimes after a latent period of several hours, nausea and vomiting as well as local eye irritation, especially of the conjunctiva, irritation of the mucous membranes of the upper respiratory tract – with respiratory distress – and of exposed skin areas [1, 22]. One investigator also found liver enzyme values in exposed persons to be increased, at times considerably [26].

There are no reports available in which industrial exposures are accompanied by analytical data and, in particular, none of exposures to vapour concentrations below the odour and irritation thresholds [1, 22, 27].

Skin lesions caused by direct contact with hydrazine have often been described [28–32]. Particularly frequent are reports of inflammatory skin conditions in persons involved in the production of hydrazine and its derivatives [28, 29]. Even workers whose uncovered skin was splashed with soldering fluid containing hydrazine hydrobromide or who handled metal components which had been soldered using this fluid developed dermatitis on the exposed skin areas [3]. Allergic eczema after contact with hydrazine has also been described frequently [31]. With one exception [26] there are no reports of systemic intoxication after wetting the skin with hydrazine.

The sharp ammoniacal smell of hydrazine vapour is very noticeable. The odour threshold is about 3–4 ppm [27] so that the danger of acute intoxication is small but chronic intoxication can readily occur [1].

3 Effects on Animals

3.1 Acute toxicity

The results of studies on the acute toxicity of hydrazine are presented in Table 1.

The main symptoms include hypopnea followed by increased excitability and tonicoclonic convulsions, drop in blood pressure, nerve conduction disturbances and, after oral administration, vomiting (as a result of irritation of the mucous membranes of the stomach). Histopathological changes include fatty metamorphosis of the liver and kidney changes.

3.2 Subchronic toxicity

Anorexia, vomiting, weight loss, lethargy and increased levels of SGOT and bilirubin were observed in Rhesus monkeys who received up to 20 injections of 20 mg/kg

Table 1. Acute toxicity

	Administration route	Species	LD$_{50}$/LC$_{50}$	Ref.
LD$_{50}$	i.v.	dog	25 mg/kg	
		rat	55 mg/kg	[33]
		mouse	57 mg/kg	
		rabbit	34 mg/kg	[34]
	i.p.	rat	59 mg/kg	[33]
		mouse	62 mg/kg	
	oral	rat	60 mg/kg	[33]
		mouse	59 mg/kg	
	dermal	rabbit	91 mg/kg	[35]
		guinea pig	190 mg/kg	[36]
LC$_{50}$	inhalation	rat	$\sim$ 200 ppm	[23]
	(4h)		570 ppm	[27]
		mouse	252 ppm	[27]

hydrazine. Pathological-anatomical investigations revealed fatty deposits in the liver, myocardium, kidneys and skeletal muscles [37].

The results of studies on the toxicity of inhaled hydrazine are shown in Table 2. The main symptoms include hyperexcitability, locomotor disturbances, anorexia, vomiting and weight loss and, at concentrations above 5 ppm, dyspnoea.

4 Carcinogenicity

4.1 Human evidence

In 1978 an attempt at risk evaluation for persons exposed to hydrazine was carried out in an international cooperative project involving nine hydrazine producers [45]. Four of the nine producers had not begun hydrazine production until 1960 or later and so were not included in the study. Production in the other five works began in the period between 1940 and 1956. For three of these five hydrazine producers there were no indications of a carcinogenic effect of hydrazine; there were, however, also no detailed data for the risk evaluation. In the period between 1940 and 1974 the fourth producer employed 53 people who had been exposed to hydrazine for more than 10 years (for 35 cases the average exposure was 15 years and the average interval since the first exposure 21 years). For this works too there was no evidence for a carcinogenic effect of hydrazine; once more, however, the data base was very limited. For the fifth producer more extensive data were available – documentation for 272 persons who had been employed in hydrazine production between 1945 and 1970. The collective was divided into three groups according to roughly estimated expo-

Table 2. Toxicity of inhaled hydrazine

Species	Conc. (ppm)	Exposure duration	Mortality (no. died/ total no.)	Symptoms/ pathological-anatomical changes	Ref.
mouse	900	8 × 1h during 1.5 weeks	4/11, 7/11 moribund and killed	irritation, anaemia, weight loss	[38]
rat, mouse	225	5 × 6 h	16/20 (rat) 8/10 (mouse)	irritation weight loss	[23]
mouse	100	1 h/d 6 d/week 4 weeks	0/20	anaemia	[39]
rat mouse	54	6 h/d 5 d/week up to 13x	14/16 (rat) 7/10 (mouse)	irritation weight loss	[23]
rat mouse	20	6 h/d 5 d/week up to 30x	11/13 (rat) 7/10 (mouse)	behaviour normal weight loss	[23]
dog	14	6 h/d 5 d/week up to 194 ×	2/4	deaths after 13 and 74 exposures. 2 dogs survived with forced feeding because of anorexia	[23]
rat mouse guinea pig	14	6 h/d 5 d/week up to 105 ×	23/30 (rat) 15/20 (mouse) (remainder killed) 8/10 (guinea pig)	inactivity	[23]
guinea pig	2–6	6 h/d 47 × during 69 d	1/8 (1 other killed)	no certain signs of damage	[40]
dog (mongrel)	2–4	6 h/d 7 × during 9 d	1/2 (the other dog killed)	general weakness, motor coordination disturbed	[40]
dog	5	6 h/d 5 d/week 26 weeks	0/2	weight loss, anorexia, vomiting, muscle tremor, dyspnoea; symptoms reduced on exposure-free weekends	[23]
rat	5	6 h/d 5 d/week 26 weeks	2/10	inactivity, no weight loss	[23]
rat	0.7–3.5	4 h/d 6 d/week 3 months	1/9	irritation, weight loss, anaemia, leukocytosis, increased excitability	[41]

Table 2. Continued

Species	Conc. (ppm)	Exposure duration	Mortality (no. died/ total no.)	Symptoms/ pathological-anatomical changes	Ref.
mouse	0.7–3.5	4 h/d 6 d/week 3 months	several of 20	central excitability	[41]
monkey rat mouse	1	90 d continuous	2/10 (monkey) 48/50 (rat) 98/100 (mouse)	not specified	[42]
rat	0.07–0.6	4 h/d ? d/week 7 months	0/20	delayed weight gain, reduced Hb, reversibly increased excitability 3 weeks after end of exposure: behaviour normal	[41]
rat rabbit	0.4–0.7	7 months	0/23	no clinical symptoms specified gluconeogenesis inhibited, disturbance of lipolysis with fatty deposits in liver and kidney	[43, 44]

sure. There were 79 workers who had been exposed for 10 years or more (most exposed: 10, intermediate: 43, least: 26); 193 persons had been exposed for less than 10 years (most exposed: 33, intermediate: 84, least: 76). This study also produced no evidence for a carcinogenic effect of hydrazine. Some years later (1984) the same cohort was studied again in more detail. Of the 427 exposed workers 406 were still available for the second study [46]. Once again a carcinogenic effect of hydrazine could not be demonstrated. There were, however, only 78 persons in the highest exposure group (estimated hydrazine concentration 1–10 ppm) and only a total of 707 man years available for evaluation in this group (and a period of at least 10 years since the first exposure).

4.2 Carcinogenicity studies

Because of the wide technical interest in hydrazine it has been studied for possible carcinogenic effects in a whole series of animal experiments. In two studies in which hydrazine sulfate was administered orally to Syrian golden hamsters there were no indications of a carcinogenic effect. Both studies, however, were unsatisfactory. In one case the dose administered by oral intubation (60 times 3 mg or 100 times 2.8 mg) produced severe liver damage so that all hamsters died within 64 weeks [47]. In the second hamster study hydrazine sulfate was administered for the life-time of the animals at a concentration of 0.012% in the drinking water. All the various kinds of tumours which developed were considered to be spontaneous. The significance of the study is reduced by the fact that no direct control group was included although 1,2-dimethylhydrazine which was tested at the same time under the same conditions did reveal – in spite of the ten times lower concentration applied – a marked carcinogenic effect [48].

Two earlier studies with hydrazine sulfate in rats are so unsatisfactory that they are exceedingly difficult to evaluate. In one study Osborne Mendel rats were given intraperitoneal injections of hydrazine sulfate at doses of 60 mg/kg, 5 times weekly for 30 weeks. Survival was so poor that the study was over in 709 days. Two of the 17 rats which could be evaluated had lung tumours. There was no control group [49]. In the second study hydrazine sulfate was administered to Cb/Se rats in daily doses of 15 mg/rat by oral intubation for 68 weeks and the animals observed for the rest of their lives. All 32 rats were examined for the presence of lung tumours; in 26 of the 32 the possibility of liver tumours was investigated as well(!). In the exposed group lung tumours were found in 25% of the animals and liver tumours in 15% (♂♂: 4/13, ♀♀: 0/13) [20].

After life-time administration of hydrazine to Swiss mice at a concentration of 0.001% in the drinking water 51% of the animals (50 ♂♂, 50 ♀♀) developed lung tumours, 16% lymphomas and 22% other tumours. In all, tumours were found in 89% of the treated mice. In parallel groups treated with ammonium hydroxide the proportion of animals with tumours was between 26% and 43%. There was no direct control group. Instead reference is made to earlier controls. The survival times given for the hydrazine-treated mice were longer than those for the control mice [50].

Life-time studies with 80 AKR mice and the much higher hydrazine sulfate concentration, 0.012% in drinking water, produced no evidence for tumour induction. In the treated group 80% of the mice developed tumours compared with 89% in the control group [19]. Under similar conditions after hydrazine sulfate treatment of 81 C3H mice 7.5% of the animals developed lung tumours compared with 0% of the control group; at the same time the frequency of mammary adenocarcinomas in the treated group was lower (37.5%) than in the control group (77%) [19]. With the same experimental protocol 64% of the treated Swiss albino mice and 30% of the control mice developed tumours. In 49% of the treated mice and 11.5% of the control mice there were lung tumours (mostly adenomas) [19]. After 48 weeks, 0.03% hydrazine sulfate in the drinking water induced lung tumours in 34 of 37 and 38 of 38 male A/J mice (3.1 and 3.9 lung tumours/mouse). In the control group such tumours developed in 11 of 20 and in 12 of 20 mice (0.8 lung tumours/mouse) [51].

When hydrazine was administered to female Swiss mice by oral intubation in doses of 0.25 mg/animal 5 times weekly for 40 weeks, only 13 of 25 mice were still alive at the end of treatment; in 6 of these mice a total of 23 lung tumours developed. In the control group in the same period 11 such tumours developed in 8/79 mice. The small number of animals in the treated group, the poor survival rate and the lack of data for other tumours make this study difficult to evaluate [17]. When hydrazine sulfate was administered by oral intubation to 42 CBA/Cb/Se mice for 36 weeks in daily doses of 1.13 mg/animal, lung tumours developed in 83% and liver tumours in 67% of animals. Among the 84 animals of the control group 6% developed lung tumours and 7% liver tumours. Tumours other than lung and liver tumours are not mentioned in this report [20]. Mice were given 150 doses of hydrazine sulfate by oral intubation in life span studies. For both male and female BALB/c/Cb/Se mice the lung tumour frequencies were as follows:

single dose/mouse 1.13 mg 90%
0.56 mg 70%
0.28 mg 76%
0.14 mg 43%
untreated control 14%

Tumours other than lung tumours were not mentioned [52]. For CBA/Cb/Se mice (both sexes) the following values are given for animals with liver tumours:

single dose/mouse 1.13 mg 61%
0.56 mg 57%
0.28 mg 18%
0.14 mg 2%
untreated control 7%

Data for other tumours were not given [47]. The influence of hormone status on the effect of hydrazine sulfate was investigated in a life span study with female BALB/c/Cb/Se mice. The animals were given a total of 150 doses of 1.13 mg/mouse by oral intubation. This treatment led to the development of lung tumours in 20/22 virgin mice (controls 1/25), in 25/25 mated mice (controls 2/25) and in 15/25 ovariectomized mice (controls 7/26) [53]. The results of another test series in which hydrazine sulfate was administered by oral intubation (1.1 mg/mouse 6 times weekly for up to 15 months) while various other parameters (partial hepatectomy, protein deficiency, vitamin B deficiency, mating, various strains of mice) were varied, cannot be evaluated with confidence because the number of animals (6–14 mice evaluated per experiment) is too small [54].

After receiving in 46 days 16 intraperitoneal injections of hydrazine hydrate in physiological saline, about 25 mg/kg body weight per injection, 26 of the 60 treated "white mice" died during the first 80 days of the study. Of the remaining 34 mice 13 died with tumours (leukemia or reticulosarcomas) within 100–313 days. Two of the 60 control mice died with tumours (lung adenoma, lymphosarcoma) during the same period [21]. 30 male (BALB/cXDBA/2)F_1 mice were given intraperitoneal injections of hydrazine sulfate (8 times 2.6 mg/animal) in a life span study. In the treated group lung tumours developed in 6 of 30 mice; in the control group one such tumour was found among 9 mice. When twice the dose (8 times 5.2 mg/animal) was given by oral intubation, 13 of the 28 treated mice had lung tumours compared with 1 of 10 control mice [55]. No clear effect of hydrazine could be demonstrated after intraperitoneal injection of hydrazine sulfate (5 times or 10 times 95 mg/kg) when the animals were irradiated (400 R) simultaneously or treated with croton oil [56].

These findings provide evidence for a carcinogenic effect of toxic doses of hydrazine in the rat and mouse, even though all the early studies have significant gaps in the data. In this situation a large hydrazine inhalation study was carried out with a total of 800 hamsters, 1100 Fischer 344 rats and 2000 C57Bl/6 mice [57]. For each species the maximum tolerated concentration was applied, 1 ppm for the mice and

5 ppm for the rats and hamsters, as well as two lower concentrations. The animals were exposed 6 hours per day and 5 days per week for 1 year and then observed for the rest of their lives. The mice were exposed to 0.05, 0.25 and 1 ml/m^3 (400 female mice per group) and 0 ml/m^3 (800 female mice). There was no evidence for a carcinogenic effect of hydrazine. Groups of 200 male hamsters were exposed to hydrazine at concentrations of 0.25, 1, 5 and 0 ml/m^3. At the highest concentration benign tumours of the nasal cavity (polyps) developed in 12% of the hamsters. The rats were exposed to 0.05, 0.25,1 and 5 ml/m^3 (100 male and 100 female animals per group) and to 0 ml/m^3 (150 males and 150 females). At 5 ml/m^3, 50% of the rats developed benign tumours of the nasal cavity (adenomas) and 6% malignant tumours at the same site (adenocarcinomas); at 1 ml/m^3 benign tumours of the nasal cavity (adenomas) developed in 7% of the rats. In the rats of the high concentration group, inflammation was demonstrated definitely in the epithelia of the upper respiratory passages.

Thus, in this inhalation study the local irritant, hydrazine, induced in hamsters and rats but not in mice tumours only of the epithelium of the nasal cavity. As it is known that this tissue is highly sensitive to the local effects of carcinogens in rodents, it is difficult to extrapolate the results of this study to the human situation. It seems to provide evidence for a low carcinogenic potential of hydrazine.

All together the carcinogenic effects of hydrazine (or hydrazine sulfate) have been demonstrated to date only with maximally tolerated, unambiguously toxic doses or locally irritating concentrations (in the inhalation study) [58].

This statement can be illustrated with the example of hydrazine or hydrazine sulfate administered to mice in the drinking water. In the early studies a hydrazine concentration of 10 mg/l was shown to be a weak or questionable carcinogen (no control group) [50], 30 mg/l was carcinogenic in one study and not carcinogenic in two others [19], 75 mg/l had a weak carcinogenic effect [51]. In a 2 year carcinogenicity study which is satisfactory according to present day standards and in which hydrazine was administered in the drinking water to groups of 50 male and 50 female NMRI mice, 10 mg/l proved to be the maximal tolerable concentration on the basis of effects on body weight whereas 50 mg/l was unambiguously toxic (body weights reduced by 20% in comparison with controls) [59]. Even under these conditions, however, the survival times were not reduced. The study produced no evidence of a carcinogenic effect of hydrazine nor could other tissue damage be demonstrated macroscopically or microscopically, not even in the liver. In contrast to these results obtained after daily ingestion of toxic doses of 5–6 mg hydrazine/kg with the drinking water in the recent study described above, daily doses of 0.7–1.5 mg hydrazine/kg administered by oral intubation produced increased tumour frequencies in mice, however, in early studies which are now considered unsatisfactory [47, 52]. Daily administration of hydrazine by oral intubation probably led to markedly higher (= more toxic) concentrations in the tissues than did ingestion with the drinking water. The toxic effects of bolus dosing is emphasized by two early studies in which hydrazine was administered orally to hamsters. In one study ∼7 mg hydrazine/kg (as sulfate) was administered daily by oral intubation [47], in the other about the same daily dose in the drinking water (120 mg hydrazine sulfate/l) [48]. Administered by oral intubation, the dose was highly toxic; all animals died within

64 weeks. In the drinking water, in contrast, the hydrazine was well tolerated. In neither study could a carcinogenic effect of hydrazine sulfate be demonstrated.

In a more recent study hamsters were administered even higher hydrazine sulfate concentrations with the drinking water: 170, 340 or 510 mg/l for 2 years (average doses expressed as hydrazine: 4.6, 8.3 or 10.3 mg/kg body weight) [60]. In a preliminary experiment in the same laboratory these concentrations had produced 10%, 15% or 20% inhibition of body weight gain and so were taken to be maximally tolerated to toxic doses [61]. In the carcinogenesis study, however, even the highest concentration had little effect on the body weights but all doses produced as toxic effect a reduction of the life span. After about 18 months, necrosis, hypertrophy and nodular hyperplasia developed in the liver to an extent depending on the dose. Towards the end of the 2 year period the hydrazine ingestion resulted in massive degeneration of liver tissue. The first liver tumours after hydrazine exposure were found in two animals which were killed after 18 months. The overall frequency of the hepatocellular carcinomas which were evidence for a carcinogenic effect of hydrazine in this study were: control 0/31, 170 mg/l 0/31, 340 mg/l 4/34 (12%), 510 mg/l 11/34 (32%). In view of the negative results of the other two carcinogenesis studies with oral administration of hydrazine sulfate to hamsters [47, 48] and the inhalation study which also produced no liver tumours in hamsters [58] it becomes clear that a carcinogenic effect can only be demonstrated for hydrazine when it is administered for practically the whole life of the animals in toxic doses which do not reduce the life span very much.

After daily administration by oral intubation of evidently toxic doses of hydrazine sulfate to 32 rats, lung tumours were found in 25% of the animals and liver tumours in 15% [20]. Although this study is far from satisfactory it did provide evidence that hydrazine, administered orally in toxic doses, is able to induce lung and liver tumours in the rat.

Therefore, in a carcinogenesis study carried out according to currently acceptable standards, hydrazine was administered to rats in the drinking water [62]. In 90 day preliminary studies the effects on body weights had revealed that a concentration of 10 mg hydrazine/l may be considered to be the maximum tolerated concentration and that a concentration of 50 mg/l is unambiguously toxic. This toxic concentration was still included in the carcinogenesis study because the carcinogenic effect was expected only with this dose. To increase the power of the study even further the treatment was continued until the spontaneous death of all animals (or until the animals were killed in a moribund state). The concentrations administered to groups of 50 male and 50 female Wistar rats were 0 mg/l (control), 2 mg/l, 10 mg/l and 50 mg/l. 2 mg/l was tolerated well; 10 mg/l was the maximum tolerable concentration in terms of body weight effects and 50 mg/l was unambiguously toxic (20% reduction in body weight, effects on appearance and behaviour). Yet the life span was practically unaffected even at the highest dose (mean survival after start of study: 915 days, end of study after 3 years). Under these severe study conditions a weak carcinogenic effect of hydrazine could only be demonstrated for the highest concentration and only as the very late development of small, mostly benign, hepatocellular tumours (first tumour detected after 686 days of treatment). The frequency of these tumours was 11.5% compared with 0% in the control group (historical control

9/652 = 1.4% (0-2.7%)). The mean daily doses for the highest concentration were about 3 mg hydrazine/kg body weight [62].

The results of this study may be summarized as follows: only the unambiguously toxic concentration after the longest possible period produced a weak carcinogenic effect. This is in agreement with the results of several exploratory life span studies in which not toxic but maximum tolerated doses were administered. In these studies hydrazine administered subcutaneously or intratracheally to Sprague-Dawley rats was without any demonstrable carcinogenic effect. Even together with benzo[*a*]pyrene (Sprague-Dawley rats intratracheal or mice intraperitoneal) hydrazine did not increase the carcinogenic effect of benzo[*a*]pyrene [62]. In a publication which deals with the mechanism of action of hydrazine it is mentioned briefly that unpublished results of the authors show that hydrazine does not induce liver tumours [63].

5 Genotoxicity

In extensive comparative studies with the Ames test, hydrazine had a weak mutagenic effect which was reduced in the presence of liver homogenate [64]. For hydrazine sulfate as well, a not very pronounced mutagenicity was demonstrated with *Salmonella typhimurium* TA1535 with and without metabolic activation [65]. The sometimes contradictory results of other authors may possibly be explained by the apparent relative weakness of the effect [66-70]. In mouse lymphoma cells *in vitro* hydrazine proved to be a direct mutagen and the mutagenicity was correlated with the cytotoxicity [71]. In the host mediated assay (*S. typhimurium*) in the mouse a marked mutagenic effect was seen after subcutaneous injection of a highly toxic single dose of hydrazine (150 mg hydrazine sulfate/kg body weight) [72].

Thus in extensive studies with the Ames test hydrazine has revealed a not very pronounced mutagenic effect which may be demonstrated in practice only in the bacteriotoxic range.

In various *in vitro* tests hydrazine proved to be a direct mutagen and its mutagenicity was correlated with its cytotoxicity. In the host-mediated assay (*S. typhimurium*) hydrazine was mutagenic after highly toxic doses.

In an international comparative test program hydrazine was tested among other compounds in many different kinds of assays. In the final evaluation the following comment was made for hydrazine:

> "The majority of the bacterial repair and mutation assays gave weak positive responses for this chemical but there was little consistency among laboratories about the nature or origin of these responses ... This chemical gave a positive response in most of the eukaryotic assays in which it was tested, but the occasional requirement for high dose levels or growing cells again indicates the elusive nature of its activity." [73].

Very high concentrations of hydrazine (0.01-0.2 mol/l) were mutagenic in yeast but even under optimal conditions the mutagenicity was not very pronounced and the author concludes that "hydrazine mutagenesis in yeast differs from mutation induced by other physical and chemical mutagens ('atypical mutagen')" [74].

In a more recent study hydrazine (as hydrate and sulfate) was tested in a DNA repair test (UDS) in primary cultures of rat and mouse hepatocytes. For hydrazine too the test can be expected to be very sensitive. Hydrazine produced negative results with the rat hepatocytes and positive results with the mouse cells. The authors emphasized that the UDS level for the positive result in the mouse cells "was relatively low compared to that of other types of carcinogenic chemicals" [75].

The mammalian spot test in the mouse is an *in vivo* procedure to detect gene mutations and recombinations in somatic cells. In a recent study hydrazine chloride is described as being mutagenic in this test and inducing a significant increase ($p = 0.049$) in the number of genetically relevant fur spots after a single intraperitoneal dose of 80 mg/kg (38 mg/kg as hydrazine). After reduction of the dose to 60 or 40 mg/kg no more statistically significant effects were found [76]. Because there were indications that faulty methods could have led to an overestimation of the effects, the spot test with hydrazine was repeated. After an intraperitoneal dose of 80 mg hydrazine/kg body weight, all eight treated dams died; at 40 mg/kg there was still marked embryotoxicity. 40 mg/kg is thus the highest possible test dose. At this dose in the spot test hydrazine revealed only a weakly mutagenic effect which was not statistically significant ($p > 0.05$). After the hydrazine treatment there were 7 genetically relevant fur spots among the 357 F_1 mice examined (2%); in the control there was only one such spot among 196 F_1 mice (0.5%). Experience with this test indicates that this difference is of biological significance [77]. Thus the highest dose which could be tested, which was still highly embryotoxic, was shown in this test to be only weakly mutagenic. This result agrees well with the results of the carcinogenesis studies.

Investigations into the mechanism of action of hydrazine in the rat and mouse led to the demonstration of DNA methylation in the liver after oral administration of 60 or 10 mg hydrazine/kg ($LD_{50} \sim 60$ mg/kg) simultaneously with intraperitoneal injection of methionine. Similar methylation of liver DNA has also been found after administration of other liver toxins and weak carcinogens, e.g., carbon tetrachloride or thioacetamide [78]. Other authors [63] obtained similar results with mice but not with rats after intraperitoneal injection of hydrazine doses in the range of the LD_{50} and simultaneous injection of formate or methionine. However, in the toxic range (30–90 mg/kg) a single oral dose of hydrazine alone was sufficient to induce formation of 7-methylguanine and O^6-methylguanine in liver DNA. The increase in these two bases was small after hydrazine doses in the range 45–75 mg/kg body weight; 90 mg/kg (a lethal dose), however, caused a marked increase. The administration of 3 mg hydrazine/kg body weight and day by oral intubation for 1, 2, 3 or 4 days caused, after the fourth dose, a 6.6% loss of body weight; at the same time the livers appeared pale with fatty deposits. Also at the same time the formation of 7-methylguanine but not of O^6-methylguanine was observed in the liver DNA [79]. The authors compare the effect of hydrazine to that of carbon tetrachloride and ethanol for which DNA methylation has also been demonstrated [80]. It was suggested that treatment with hydrazine or hepatotoxicity in general could disturb the balance of methylation and demethylation on N-7 and O-6 of guanine by inhibiting the demethylation preferentially which would result in accumulation of the methylated purines in the liver DNA [79]. Later the hypothesis was put forward that hydrazine forms a condensation product with endogenous formaldehyde in liver cells [61, 81] and that this product could be metabolized to a methylating agent by alcohol and/or acetaldehyde dehydrogenase [82] or by catalase or catalase-like enzymes [83].

6 Manifesto (MAK value, classification)

Hydrazine proved to be weakly carcinogenic in the rat, mouse and hamster only after practically life-long administration of toxic doses (close to or in the lethal range). Hydrazine is genotoxic but the overall effect is weak – even when toxic doses are applied *in vivo* or high concentrations *in vitro*. It has been suggested that hydrazine produces indirectly an increase in 7-methylguanine and O^6-methylguanine particularly in the liver and only when administered in the highly toxic range.

The findings presented here are considered sufficient to justify the classification of hydrazine in Section III A2) of the List of MAK Values. A MAK value cannot be established.

7 References

1. Sutton, W. L.: in Patty, F.A. (Ed.): *Industrial Hygiene and Toxicology*, 2nd rev. ed., Vol. II, p 2218, Interscience Publishers, New York, London, 1963
2. Hoevding, G.: *Acta derm. venereol. (Stockh.) 47*, 293 (1967)
3. Wheeler, C. E., S. R. Penn, E. P. Cawley: *Arch. Derm. 91*, 235 (1965)
4. Thienes, C. H., T. J. Haley: *Clinical Toxicology*, Lea R. Febiger, Philadelphia, 1964
5. Wells, G. H.: *J. exp. Med. 10*, 457 (1908)
6. Ganote, C. E.: *Amer. J. Path. 52*, 5a (1968)
7. Wong, E. T.: *Toxicol. appl. Pharmacol. 8*, 51 (1966)
8. Fortney, S. R., D. A. Clark, E. Stein: *J. Pharmacol. exp. Ther. 156*, 277 (1967)
9. Killam, K. F., J. A. Bain: *J. Pharmacol. exp. Ther. 119*, 255 (1957)
10. Greenberg, L. A.: *Ann. Rev. Biochem. 26*, 209 (1957)
11. Cornish, H. H., C. E. Wilson: *Toxicol. appl. Pharmacol. 12*, 265 (1968)
12. Reinhardt, C. F., B. D. Dinman: *Arch. environm. Hlth 10*, 859 (1965)
13. Korty, P., F. L. Coe: *J. Pharmacol. exp. Ther. 160*, 212 (1968)
14. Trout, D. L.: *J. Pharmacol. exp. Ther. 152*, 529 (1966)
15. Dambrauskas, T., H. H. Cornish: *Toxicol. appl. Pharmacol. 6*, 653 (1964)
16. McKennis, H., A. S. Yard, J. H. Weatherby, J. A. Hagy: *J. Pharmacol. exp. Ther. 126*, 109 (1959)
17. Roe, F. J. C., G. A. Grant, D. M. Millican: *Nature (Lond.) 216*, 375 (1967)
18. Biancifiori, C., R. Ribacchi: *Nature (Lond.) 194*, 488 (1962)
19. Toth, B.: *J. nat. Cancer Inst. 42*, 469 (1969)
20. Severi, L., C. Biancifiori: *J. nat. Cancer Inst. 41*, 331 (1968)
21. Juhasz, J., J. Balo, B. Szende: *Z. Krebsforsch. 70*, 150 (1967)
22. Byrkit, G. D., G. A. Michalek: *Ind. Eng. Chem. 42*, 1862 (1950)
23. Comstock, C. C., L. H. Lawson, E. A. Greene, F. W. Oberst: *Arch. industr. Hyg. 10*, 476 (1954)
24. Drews, A., K. Eversmann, E. Fritze: *Med. Welt* 1295 (1960)
25. Reid, F. J.: *Brit. med. J. II*, 1246 (1965)
26. Ehrlicher, H.: personal communication, Ärztliche Abteilung, Betriebshygienische Untersuchungsstelle der Farbenfabriken Bayer AG, D-5090 Leverkusen, 1970

27. Jacobson, K. H., J. H. Clem, H. J. Wheelwright, W. E. Rinehart, N. Mayes: *Arch. industr. Hlth* *12*, 609 (1955)
28. Brandt, B.: *Derm. Wschr. 141*, 376 (1960)
29. Sonneck, H. J., H. Umlauf: *Z. Haut- u. Geschl.-Kr. 31*, 179 (1961)
30. Gardenghi, G.: *Rass. Med. industr. 21*, 279 (1952), ref. *Zbl. Haut- u. Geschl.-Kr. 86*, 160 (1953/54)
31. Evans, D. M.: *Brit. J. industr. Med. 16*, 126 (1959)
32. Schultheiss, E.: *Berufsdermatosen 7*, 131 (1959)
33. Witkin, L. B.: *Arch. industr. Hlth 13*, 34 (1956)
34. Thienes, H., H. P. Roth: Report AL 731, North American Aviation, Inc. (1948), cited in Krop, S.: *Arch. industr. Hyg. 9*, 199 (1954)
35. Horton, R. G., L. W. Conn: cited in Krop, S.: *Arch. industr. Hyg. 9*, 199 (1954)
36. Rothberg, S., O. B. Cope: U.S. Army Chem. Warfare Lab. Rept. 2027, Army Medical Centre, Maryland (1956); cited in Sutton, W. L.: in Patty, F. A. (Ed.): *Industrial Hygiene and Toxicology*, 2nd rev. ed., Vol. II. p 2220,, Interscience Publishers, New York, London, 1963
37. Patrick, L. R., K. C. Back: Bericht, Wright-Patterson Air Force Base, Dayton, Ohio, USA, 1964, cited in *Chem. Abstracts 62*, 5789 (1965)
38. Thienes, C. H., H. P. Roth, E. A. Swenson, V. C. Morgan, C. F. Lombard: Report for North American Aviation, Inc., 1948
39. Cier, A., J. P. Rouganne, M. Schmitt: *C. R. Soc. Biol. (Paris) 161*, 854 (1967)
40. Weatherby, J. H., A. S. Yard: *Arch. industr. Hlth 11*, 413 (1955)
41. Kulagina, N. K.: *Toksikol. Nowykh Prom. Khim. Veshchestv 4*, 65 (1962) (Toxicology of the new industrial chemicals) (Russian)
42. Thomas, A. A., K. C. Back in: Honma and Crosby (Eds.): *A Symposium on Toxicity in the Closed Ecologic System*, Lockheed Missiles and Space Co., Palo Alto, CA, USA, 1964; cited in: American Conference of Governmental Industrial Hygienists, Inc. (ACGIH): *Documentation of TLV*, Cincinnati, OH, USA, 1966
43. Velling, E. I., A. A. Preobrajenskaya: *Gig. Tr. prof. Zabol. No. 2*, 56 (1961)
44. Maskimova-Voznesenskaya, G. A.: *Gig. Tr. prof. Zabol. No. 10*, 48 (1961)
45. Roe, F. J. C.: *Ann. occup. Hyg. 21*, 323 (1978)
46. Wald, N., J. Boreham, R. Doll, J. Bonsall: *Brit. J. industr. Med. 41*, 31 (1984)
47. Biancifiori, C.: *J. nat. Cancer Inst. 44*, 943 (1970)
48. Toth, B.: *Cancer Res. 32*, 804 (1972)
49. Ribacchi, R., G. Giraldo: *Lav. Ist. Anat. Univ. Perugia 21*, 5 (1968)
50. Toth, B.: *Int. J. Cancer 9*, 109 (1972)
51. Yamamoto, R. S., J. H. Weisburger: *Life Sci. 9*(II), 285 (1970)
52. Biancifiori, C.: *Lav. Ist. Anat. Univ. Perugia 30*, 89 (1970)
53. Biancifiori, C.: *J. nat. Cancer Inst. 45*, 965 (1970)
54. Bhide, S. V., R. A. D'Souza, M. M. Sawai, K. J. Ranadive: *Int. J. Cancer 18*, 530 (1976)
55. Kelly, M. G., R. W. O'Gara, S. T. Yancey, K. Gadekar, C. Botkin, V. T. Oliverio: *J. nat. Cancer Inst. 42*, 337 (1969)
56. Mirvish, S. S., L. Chen, N. Haran-Ghera, I. Berenblum: *Int. J. Cancer 4*, 318 (1969)
57. MacEwen, J. D., E. H. Vernot, C. C. Haun, E. R. Kinkead, A. Hall: Air Force Aerospace Medical Research Laboratory, Wright-Patterson Air Force Base, Ohio 45433, AF AMRL-TR-81-56, 1981
58. Vernot, E. H., J. D. MacEwen, R. H. Bruner, C. C. Haun, E. R. Kinkead, D. E. Prentice, A. Hall, R. E. Schmidt, R. L. Eason, G. B. Hubbart, J. T. Young: *Fundam. appl. Toxicol. 5*, 1050 (1985)
59. Steinhoff, D., U. Mohr, W. M. Schmidt: *Exp. Path.* (1990), in press
60. Bosan, W. S., R. C. Shank, J. D. MacEwen, C. L. Gaworski, P. M. Newberne: *Carcinogenesis 8*, 439 (1987)
61. Bosan, W. S., R. C. Shank: *Toxicol. appl. Pharmacol. 70*, 324 (1983)
62. Steinhoff, D., U. Mohr: *Exp. Path. 33*, 133 (1988)
63. Quintero-Ruiz, A., L. L. Paz-Neri, S. Villa-Treviño: *J. nat. Cancer Inst. 67*, 613 (1981)
64. DeFlora, S.: *Carcinogenesis 2*, 283 (1981)
65. Rogan, E. G., B. A. Walker, R. Gingell, D. L. Nagel, B. Toth: *Mutat. Res. 102*, 413 (1982)

66. Herbold, B., W. Buselmaier: *Mutat. Res. 40*, 73 (1976)
67. Purchase, I. F. H., E. Longstaff, J. Ashby, J. A. Styles, D. Anderson, P. A. Lefevre, F. R. Westwood: *Brit. J. Cancer 37*, 873 (1978)
68. Shimizu, H., K. Hayashi, N. Takemura: *Jap. J. Hyg. 33*, 474 (1978)
69. Rosenkranz, H. S., L.A. Poirier: *J. nat. Cancer Inst. 62*, 873 (1979)
70. Simmon, V. F.: *J. nat. Cancer Inst. 62*, 893 (1979)
71. Rogers, A. M., K. C. Back: *Mutat. Res. 89*, 321 (1981)
72. Schöneich, J.: *Mutat. Res. 41*, 89 (1976)
73. Ashby, J.: *Progr. Mutat. Res. 1*, 112 (1981)
74. Lemontt, J. F.: *Mutat. Res. 43*, 165 (1977)
75. Mori, H., S. Sugie, N. Yoshimi, H. Iwata, A. Nishikawa, K. Matsukubo, H. Shimizu, I. Hirono: *Jap. J. Cancer Res. (Gann) 79*, 204 (1988)
76. Neuhäuser-Klaus, A., P. S. Chauhan: *Mutat. Res. 191*, 111 (1987)
77. Fahrig, R.: Final Report, Spot-Test No. 191–192, Fraunhofer-Institut für Toxikologie und Aerosolforschung, D-3000 Hannover, 1989
78. Barrows, L. R., R. C. Shank: *Proc. Amer. Ass. Cancer Res. 21*, 110 (Abstract No. 439), 1980
79. Becker, R. A., L. R. Barrows, R. C. Shank: *Carcinogenesis 2*, 1181 (1981)
80. Barrows, L. R., R. C. Shank: *Toxicol. appl. Pharmacol. 60*, 334 (1981)
81. Lambert, C. E., W. S. Bosan, R. C. Shank: *Carcinogenesis 7*, 419 (1986)
82. Bosan, W. S., C. E. Lambert, R. C. Shank: *Carcinogenesis 7*, 413 (1986)
83. Lambert, C. E., R. C. Shank: *Carcinogenesis 9*, 65 (1988)

completed 29. 5. 1989

Limonene

Classification/MAK value:	**not yet established** **see Section IIb) MAK list 1989**
Synonyms:	4-isopropenyl-1-methyl-1-cyclohexene 1-methyl-4-isopropenyl-1-cyclohexene 1,8(9)-p-menthadiene p-mentha-1,8-diene dipentene $d(+)$-limonene, $l(-)$-limonene inactive limonene
Chemical name (CAS):	1-methyl-4-(1-methylethenyl)cyclohexene (d,l-limonene)
CAS number:	d,l-limonene: 138-86-3 d-limonene: 5989-27-5 dipentene: 7705-14-8
Structural formula:	

Molecular formula:	$C_{10}H_{16}$
Molecular weight:	136.24
Melting point:	$-74.35\,°C$
Boiling point:	$176-178\,°C$
Vapour pressure at 20 °C:	not specified

1 ml/m³ (ppm) = 5.65 mg/m³   **1 mg/m³ = 0.18 ml/m³ (ppm)**

1 Toxic Effects and Modes of Action

Limonene is a lemon scented liquid and belongs to the menthadienes. The dextrorotatory form, d-limonene (($+$)-limonene), occurs in essential oils (Seville orange peel oil, celeriac oil, caraway oil) and has been studied preferentially because it is used widely in the foodstuff and cosmetic industries. It is used medicinally to dissolve postoperative gallstones by infusion into the common bile duct. The pure stereoiso-mer, *l*-limonene, also occurs naturally, e.g., in pine essence and in turpentine [1].

Technical-grade dipentene, a mixture of monocyclic terpenes (e.g., cymene, ter-pinene, menthane, menthene, etc.) is a frequent component of solvents in the paint and varnish industry and in the do-it-yourself trade (e.g., strippers, paint brush cleaners, wood varnishes, cleaning materials).

Being lipophilic, limonene is absorbed very readily through the skin. It is, howev-er, relatively rapidly excreted in the urine.

d-Limonene irritates the digestive system in man and animals; it irritates the skin without inducing skin tumours after long-term application. In studies involving dermal application to mice the substance was shown to have a promoting effect for papillomas. On the other hand, after oral application it has tumour inhibiting prop-erties for a number of other tumours.

There is evidence that the substance, even at low doses, affects the immune system first as a stimulant and then as an inhibitor.

Nephropathological findings (formation of hyaline droplets, cell changes in cer-tain tubulus epithelia) have been described only for male rats.

In 2 year studies an increased incidence of renal adenomas and adenocarcinomas is found only in male rats. Nephropathological changes, which depend on the pres-ence of a protein ($\alpha_{2\mu}$-globulin) produced in the liver under testosterone control, are a prerequisite for the development of these tumours. The carcinogenesis is still not fully understood. According to current opinion (see "Carcinogenicity") renal tu-mours are not to be expected in other species. To what extent man is affected is currently a matter of controversial debate because the occurrence of $\alpha_{2\mu}$-globulin in the human kidney has not yet been adequately investigated.

d-Limonene is relatively readily oxidized because of its double bonds and can be converted to the hydroperoxide by the oxygen in the air. The carcinogenicity of a similar compound, 1-vinylcyclohexene-3, has been attributed to the presence of traces of its carcinogenic autooxidation product, 1-hydroperoxy-1-vinyl-cyclohex-ene-3 [2].

1.1 Pharmacokinetics

Mice ($\male$ dd) were subjected to a bubble bath (Pinimenthol) containing five tritium-labelled substances. The bath water (temperature not specified) contained *d,l*-limonene at the concentration recommended by the manufacturer, 2.62 µg *d,l*-limonene per ml. The duration of bathing (5–40 minutes) and the area of skin which had been shaved and depilated (1–6 cm^2) were varied. After 10 minutes skin contact with the bath water the blood concentrations of the labelled terpenes had reached a maximum and were directly proportional to the area of shaved skin: ∼ 112 ng limonene/ml blood for 6 cm^2 skin area after 10 minutes bath time in water containing 2.62 µg limonene/ml [3].

The results of this experiment may not be extrapolated to man without reservation because, on the one hand, the depot effect in human skin plays a role and, on the other, the surface area to blood volume ratio is not the same in man and mouse [3].

d-Limonene is rapidly distributed in the body tissues. Rats ($\male$ Wistar) were given a single dose of 800 mg/kg radioactively labelled *d*-limonene (purity not specified) by oral intubation. Maximum radioactivity in the tissues was reached after 1–2 hours, the values in liver, kidney, adrenals and serum being particularly high. 48 hours after intubation only negligible levels of radioactivity remained in any of the tissues [4]. Dose effect studies have shown that orally administered *d*-limonene increases the formation of hyaline droplets in the rat kidney: after a dose of 0.1 mmol [^{14}C]-*d*-limonene per kg body weight the radioactivity was similarly distributed in the kidneys of male and female rats; after 1 mmol/kg, however, the kidneys of the male rats contained significantly higher concentrations of metabolites. As the most radioactive fraction coincided with the $\alpha_{2\,\mu}$-globulin fraction in the droplets, there are grounds for the assumption that *d*-limonene or its metabolites binds to $\alpha_{2\,\mu}$-globulin [5].

The metabolites are mostly (60–90%) excreted in the urine and only to a small extent in faeces (5–7%) and expired air (2%) [4, 6]. Excretion is complete within 24 hours (rat) or 72 hours (rabbit) after administration of *d*-limonene. In rats with a cannulated bile duct 25% of the metabolized *d*-limonene was recovered in the bile within 24 hours [4]. Of the identified metabolites which arose by oxidation of the double bonds, p-menth-1-en-8,9-diol occupied a key position (see Figure 1).

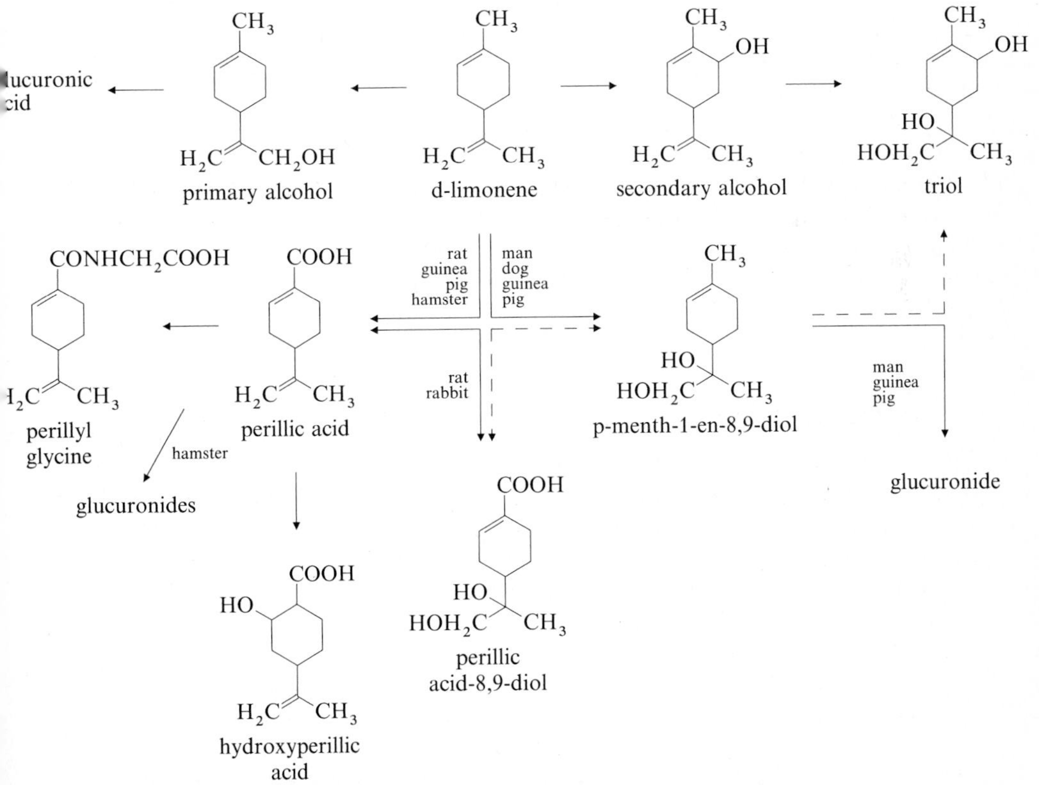

Figure 1. Probable degradation pathways for *d*-limonene according to [7]

2 Effects in Man

2.1 Acute toxicity

Five healthy male volunteers swallowed a capsule containing 20 g *d*-limonene (purity not specified). All complained of nonbloody diarrhoea and tenesmus. Functional examinations of liver, kidneys and pancreas, and urinalysis revealed mild transient proteinuria as the only abnormality [8].

A limonene preparation was injected through a specially designed resistant catheter into the bile duct of 15 patients to dissolve postoperatively retained gallstones. The preparation, consisting of 97% *d*-limonene (purity not specified), 2.1% polysorbate 80 and 0.9% sorbitan monooleate, was intended to increase contact of the solvent with the gallstones which was poor when *d*-limonene was used on its own. Very different doses – even in the one patient – and several to many 30 minute infusions at 2 day intervals were necessary to achieve dissolution of the gallstones: in 3 cases 5–8 ml (one infusion), in one case 10 ml (2 infusions) and mostly (14 cases) 20 ml (3–23 infusions). Side effects like pain and tenderness radiating from the upper abdomen to the anterior chest, nausea and vomiting, tenesmus and diarrhoea were usually observed only during the first infusion. No other symptoms were seen. Some of the patients were followed for more than 2 years (X-ray and clinical laboratory parameters) and no anomalies arose [8].

2.2 Acute dermal toxicity

Women who had continual contact with Seville orange peel oil (ca. 90% *d*-limonene) at work (details not specified) developed blisters on the skin and erysipelas [9].

Using the method of Oettel [11], limonene was applied to the skin of the volar surface of the lower arm after the skin had been washed with soap and water. A small glass dish, 1 cm diameter, was filled with the liquid and attached for 1 hour to the volunteer's arm (number not specified). The limonene (purity not specified) had been obtained by distillation of an old, resinous limonene sample. The distillation residue had no effect but the distillate produced an erythema which remained evident for several days and pigmentation which was still visible 14 days to 3 weeks later [12].

A 54 year old man who was occupationally exposed to lemon oil (constituents: citral, limonene, citronellal) had a several week old scaly eczematous eruption on the dorsa of the hands and on the wrists. A patch test with dipentene (10% in acetone) produced a widespread erythema with intense edema (grade 1–2 plus). Since similar tests with citral and citronellal produced negative results the hypersensitivity to lemon oil was put down to its content of limonene [13].

2.3 Chronic toxicity

There is no information available as to chronic toxicity in man.

3 Effects on Animals

3.1 Acute toxicity

The lethal doses of limonene given in the literature are assembled in Table 1. According to Moreno [17, 18], the LD_{50} values for *d*-limonene, *l*-limonene and dipentene are similar (see Table 1).

A depressive effect on the CNS was observed in mice after a single dose of *d*-limonene [14, 16]. Nephrosis with formation of hyaline droplets – exclusively in male rats – and a slight effect on some liver parameters were observed after short-term administration. Repeated high doses administered over several days resulted in weight loss and death. These findings are assembled in Table 2.

Studies to elucidate the effect of *d*-limonene on the immune system of mice demonstrated a slight but not dose-dependent increase in an antibody to keyhole limpet hemocyanin [25]. The significance of this finding for persons occupationally exposed to limonene is unclear.

3.2 Subchronic and chronic toxicity

After administration of limonene to experimental animals by various routes (see Table 3) weight loss, nausea and, in male rats, nephropathy and granular deposits in the renal tubules were observed. Higher doses led to hepatocellular changes. Conspicuous destruction of the bronchi after intratracheal instillation of *d*-limonene has been reported in only one publication [28].

3.3 Dermal toxicity

Cats (5 groups with 5 ♂ and 5 ♀ per group, Domestic Shorthair) were shaved to remove a 10 cm by 10 cm area of fur and then wetted thoroughly with various concentrations of a commercial insecticidal dip (78.2% limonene). Immersion at the concentration recommended by the manufacturer (ca. 11.25 g/l water) produced no signs of toxicity; at 5 times this concentration there were mild clinical symptoms (brief hypersalivation, ataxia, muscle tremor). After an increase of the concentration to 15 times that recommended, the hypersalivation persisted for 15 to 30 minutes, the muscle tremor for 1 to 4 hours and the ataxia for 1 to 5 hours. Even after this highest dose there were no permanent lesions. However, the male cats developed severe inflammation of the scrotal skin (acute epidermitis with multifocal erosions and ulcerations) [29].

Chronic application of limonene to the shaved abdominal skin of the rat, painted three times daily and allowed to dry in the fresh air, produced after about 10 applications (time, concentration and quantity not specified) eczematous inflammation which began in skin creases and extended gradually over the whole of the treated area. Thick encrustations, scabs and markedly dilated blood vessels developed in the subcutis when the treatment was continued. 8 days after termination of the treatment the inflammation was completely healed [12].

Table 1. Lethal single doses of *d*-limonene, *l*-limonene and dipentene

Substance (purity)	Species (strain)	Appl. route	Obs. time	LD$_{50}$ ♂	♀	DL$_0$ ♂	Ref.
d-limonene ("purum")	mouse (Swiss)	p.o.				3.50 g	[14]
d-limonene (n.s.)	mouse (ddN)	p.o.		5.6 g/kg (4.8–6.5 g)	6.6 g/kg (5.5–7.9 g)		[15]
d-limonene (n.s.)	mouse (ddN)	p.o.	7 d	6.3 ml/kg	8.1 ml/kg		[16]
d-limonene (n.s.)	rat (Wistar JCL)	p.o.		4.4 g/kg (3.4–5.9 g)	5.2 g/kg (3.9–7.0 g)		[15]
d-limonene (n.s.)	rat (n.s.)	p.o.		> 5 g/kg (sex n.s.)			[17]
l-limonene (n.s.)	rat (n.s.)	p.o.		> 5 g/kg (sex n.s.)			[19]
dipentene (n.s.)	rat (n.s)	p.o.		> 5.3 g/kg (sex n.s.)			[17]
d-limonene ("purum")	mouse (Swiss)	i.p.				0.62 g	[14]
d-limonene (n.s.)	mouse (ddN)	i.p.		1.3 g/kg (1.2–1.5 g)	1.3 g/kg (1.2–1.5 g)		[15]
d-limonene (n.s.)	mouse (ddN)	i.p.	3 d	3.7 ml/kg	3.6 ml/kg		[16]
d-limonene (n.s.)	mouse (ddN)	i.p.	10 d	0.7 ml/kg	0.6 ml/kg		[16]
d-limonene (n.s.)	rat (Wistar JCL)	i.p.		3.6 g/kg (2.7–4.9 g)	4.5 g/kg (3.4–6.6 g)		[15]
d-limonene (n.s.)	rat	i.v.		0.125 g/kg (0.093– 0.168 g)	0.110 g/kg (0.104– 0.117 g)		[15]
d-limonene (n.s.)	mouse (ddN)	s.c.		>41.5 g/kg	> 41.5 g/kg		[15]
d-limonene (n.s.)	mouse (ddN)	s.c.	7 d	>25.6 ml/kg	> 25.6 ml/kg		[16]
d-limonene (n.s.)	rat (Wistar JCL)	s.c.		20.2 g/kg	20.2 g/kg		[15]
d-limonene (n.s.)	rabbit (n.s.)	dermal		> 5 g/kg (sex n.s.)			[17]
l-limonene (n.s.)	rabbit (n.s.)	dermal		> 5 g/kg (sex n.s.)			[19]

DL$_0$: maximal nonlethal dose
n.s.: not specified

Table 2. Short-term administration of *d*-limonene

Species (strain number, sex)	Appl. route	*d*-Limonene: purity, solvent	Dose in mg/kg bw	Exposure duration	Observations and findings	Ref.
mouse (Swiss 10–12, n.s.)	i.p.	"purum", 1% Tween 20	0		—	[14]
			50–150	once	50% of animals: reduction in reflex nervous behaviour (animals less curious and less observant)	
	oral		3000	once	50% of animals: inactive	
mouse (B6C3F$_1$ 5 ♂ + 5 ♀ per group)	gavage	> 99%, in corn oil	0	daily 5 d/week for 16 d	—	[21]
			413		no compound-related findings	
			825		no compound-related findings	
			1650		1/5 ♂ and 1/5 ♀ died within 3 d	
			3300		4/5 ♂ and 5/5 ♀ died within 3 d	
			6000		5/5 ♂ died within 1 d 5/5 ♀ died within 2 d	
mouse (ddN, n.s.) and rat (Wistar JCL, n.s.)	oral	n.s.	3 ml/kg	once	CNS depression: reduction of spontaneous motor activity, hyperthermia	[16]
rat (Wistar 4–6, ♂)	oral	n.s., in gum tragacanth solution	200	once	no compound-related findings	[22]
			400	once	no compound-related findings	
			600	once	no compound-related findings	
			800	once	slight reduction in glycogen level in the liver	
			1200	once	slight increase in cytochrome P-450 and δ-aminolaevulinic acid in the liver	
rat (Wistar n.s. ♂)	oral	n.a., in gum-tragacanth solution	400	2 d	no compound-related findings	[22]
			400	3 d	no compound-related findings	
rat (Wistar 5 ♂ per group)	gavage	n.s., in gum arabic	0		—	[23]
			8.5	once	no compound-related findings	
			25	once	no compound-related findings	
			85	once	bile secretion slightly increased	
			250	once	– at 250 mg/kg and above:	
			426	once	dose-dependent increase	
			850	once	in bile secretion	

Table 2 (continued)

Species (strain number, sex)	Appl. route	*d*-Limonene: purity, solvent	Dose in mg/kg bw	Exposure duration	Observations and findings	Ref.
rat (F344/N 5 ♂ per group)	gavage	n.s., in corn oil	0	5 d	—	[24]
			75	5 d	1/5: chronic nephrosis* and formation of hyaline droplets in the kidney	
			150	5 d	1/5: chronic nephrosis and formation of hyaline droplets in the kidney	
			300	5 d	2/5: chronic nephrosis and formation of hyaline droplets in the kidney	
rat (F344/N 5 ♂ + 5 ♀ per group)	gavage	> 99%, in corn oil	0	daily 5 d/week for 16 d	—	[21]
			413		no compound-related findings	
			825		no compound-related findings	
			1650		♂♂: 10% reduced body weight, no other findings	
			3300		♀♀: 8% reduced body weight 5/5 ♂ and 3/5 ♀ died within 2 d	
			6000		5/5 ♂ and 5/5 ♀ died within 1 d	
dog (mongrel 2 ♂ per group)	gavage	n.s., in gum arabic	0		—	[23]
			250	once	bile secretion ca. 70% increased	
pig (Mini Japan, n.s.)	into the gallbladder with tube	limonene preparation**	20 ml/pig	once	liver function normal, direct contact surfaces unchanged, liver and kidneys without pathological changes	[8]

n.s.: not specified

  * Chronic nephrosis includes cytoplasmic basophilia in the epithelial cells of the tubuli renales contorti, tubular dilatation, increased number of nuclei in some tubular sections, tubular epithelial cell hyperplasia.

** Limonene preparation consisted of 97% limonene, 2.1% polysorbat 80 and 0.9% sorbitan monooleate.

4 Reproductive and Developmental Toxicity

Rats were given 591 or 2869 mg *d*-limonene/kg body weight and day orally from day 9 to day 12 of gestation. The high dose caused body weight loss and death of 40% of the dams; at the lower dose no effects were observed. Several weeks post partum delayed ossification of the foetal metacarpal bones and the proximal phalanx of the

Table 3. Subchronic and chronic administration of *d*-limonene by various routes

Species (strain)	Number ♂ ♀	Dose	Appl. route (purity, solvent)	Exposure duration	Observations	Ref.
mouse (B6C3F₁)	10 10	0	gavage (> 99%, corn oil)	daily 5 d/week 13 weeks	–	[21]
	10 10	125 mg/kg bw			no compound-related findings	
	10 10	250 mg/kg bw			no compound-related findings	
	10 10	500 mg/kg bw			1/10 ♀ died in week 5 rough hair coats, reduced activity	
	10 10	1000 mg/kg bw			rough hair coats, reduced activity ♂♂: 11% reduced body weight ♀♀: 2% reduced body weight	
	10 10	2000 mg/kg bw			1/10 ♂ and 2/10 ♀ died within 4 weeks 1/10 ♀ alveolar adenoma	
rat (F344/N)	10 10	0	gavage (> 99%, corn oil)	daily 5 d/week 13 weeks	–	[21]
	10 10	150 mg/kg bw			no compound-related findings*	
	10 10	300 mg/kg bw			no compound-related findings*	
	10 10	600 mg/kg bw			♂♂*: 6% reduced body weight	
	10 10	1200 mg/kg KG			♂♂*: 12% reduced body weight, rough hair coats, lethargy, excessive lacrimation	
	10 10	2400 mg/kg bw			survivors: 5 ♂*: 23% reduced body weight, rough hair coats, lethargy, excessive lacrimation 1 ♀: 11% reduced body weight	
rat (Sprague Dawley-JCL)	10 10	0	gavage (n.s., 1% Tween 80)	daily for 4 weeks	–	[15]
	10 10	227 mg/kg bw			in ♂♂ at all doses granular deposits in the kidneys	
	10 10	554 mg/kg bw				
	10 10	1385 mg/kg bw			♂♂: reduced body weight	
	9 9	2770 mg/kg bw			♀♀: no compound-related findings	

Table 3 (continued)

Species (strain)	Number ♂	Number ♀	Dose	Appl. route (purity, solvent)	Exposure duration	Observations	Ref.
Dog (Japanese Beagle)	3	3	0 0.4 ml/kg bw	gavage (n.s.)	daily for ~6 months	– all animals and doses: nausea and vomiting	[26]
		3	1.2 ml/kg bw			♂♂ + ♀♀: protein casts in the renal tubule ♀: reduced body weight Cholesterol and blood sugar levels reduced (sex n.s.)	
		3	3.6 ml/kg bw			♂: reduced body weight	
rat (Sprague-Dawley)	25	25	0 800 mg 8000 mg	in the diet (> 99%)	daily for 7 months	– body weight and blood parameters unchanged (no histopathological studies)	[27]
rat (n.s.)	n.s.		0.2 ml	intra-tracheal (aerosol)	weekly for 6 weeks	after 3 weeks: destruction of the bronchial and bronchiolar epithelium with alveolar hemorrhage after 6 weeks: enlarged pale lungs most animals died	[28]
hamster (n.s.)	n.s.		0.2 ml	intra-tracheal (aerosol)	weekly for 6 weeks	destruction of the bronchial and bronchiolar epithelium with alveolar hemorrhage after 6 weeks: enlarged, pale, vesiculated lungs	[28]

n.s.: not specified

* In all groups with ♂♂ dose-dependent nephropathy: degeneration of the epithelium in the tubuli renales contorti, granular casts in the tubulus lumen, especially in the outer regions of the medulla, hyaline droplet formation in the kidney.

offspring had been compensated. The authors consider that at a dose of 2869 mg/kg body weight and day *d*-limonene is a weak teratogen [30].

5 Genotoxicity

In the Ames test *d*-limonene is not mutagenic (*Salmonella typhimurium* TA98, TA100, TA1535, TA1537, TA1538), neither with nor without S9 mix [21, 33–35].

Trifluorothymidine resistance (loss of thymidine kinase) could not be induced in mouse L5178Y lymphoma cells with *d*-limonene (with or without S9 mix) [21].

In CHO cells *d*-limonene (with or without S9 mix) caused neither chromosome aberrations nor sister chromatid exchange [21].

In the mammalian spot test too the test for mutagenicity gave negative results (215 mg *d*-limonene/kg body weight, i.p., C57BL/6J Han mice on days 9–11 of gestation) [36, 37].

The effect of the carcinogen ethylnitrosourea (ENU) in combination with *d*-limonene was tested in the mammalian spot test in mice ($♀$: C57BL/6JHan, $♂$: T-stock). The dams were given 30 mg ENU together with 172 mg *d*-limonene by intraperitoneal injection on day 9 of gestation and then 215 mg *d*-limonene on its own on each of days 10 and 11. The results showed that *d*-limonene markedly reduced the effectiveness of the ENU (up to ca. 50%) [37, 38].

6 Carcinogenicity

In a lung carcinogenicity study A/He mice of both sexes were given 200 or 1000 mg *d*-limonene/kg body weight by intraperitoneal injection once each week for 24 weeks. No lung tumours were found [39].

d-Limonene (90%) on its own was not carcinogenic for mouse skin but produced epithelial hyperplasia [40].

A 2 year study of mice and rats revealed frequent tubular hyperplasia and neoplasia in male rats exposed to *d*-limonene. Tumours were observed only in the kidneys of male rats. The incidence of adenomas and adenocarcinomas in the renal tubules was 5/50 (16%) at the low dose (75 mg) and 11/50 (22%) at the higher dose (150 mg) (Table 4, [21]). The development of these renal tumours is currently explained as follows:

Rats have a low molecular weight transport globulin ($\alpha_{2\mu}$-G) which is synthesized in the liver, filtered in the glomerulus and largely reabsorbed in the tubuli. The concentration of this protein in the urine of male rats is 120 times higher than in that of females. Reabsorbed $\alpha_{2\mu}$-G is degraded by lysosomal enzymes more slowly than are other renal proteins. When foreign substances bind reversibly to the already "indigestible" $\alpha_{2\mu}$-G, a protein complex is formed which accumulates in the tubulus cells of the P2 segment and initiates the so-called $\alpha_{2\mu}$-G nephropathy which is characterized by the occurrence of hyaline droplets and single cell necrosis. This cytotoxicity leads to increased cellular regeneration and, on chronic treatment of the

Table 4. Carcinogenic Effects of *d*-limonene (> 99 % in corn oil, gavage) [21]

Species (strain)	Number ♂	♀	Dose in mg/kg bw	Exposure duration	Observations
mouse (B6C3F$_1$)	50		0	daily	—
	50		250	5 d/week	4/36: multinucleated hepatocytes
	50		500	103 weeks	32/50: multinucleated hepatocytes
		50	0	daily	—
		50	500	5 d/week	no substance-related findings
		50	1000	103 weeks	5–15% reduced body weight
rat (F344/N)	50		0	daily	—
	50		75	5 d/week 103 weeks	renal tubulus lesions: 4/50: hyperplasia 4/50: adenomas 4/50: adenocarcinomas
	50		150		4–7% reduced body weight from week 2 renal tubulus lesions: 7/50: hyperplasia 8/50: adenomas 3/50: adenocarcinomas
		50	0	daily	—
		50	300	5 d/week	no substance-related findings
		50	600	103 weeks	4–6% reduced body weight from week 28

animals, to a continual proliferation stimulus. The increased cell proliferation then has the effect that the frequency of the otherwise rare spontaneous adenomas and adenocarcinomas of the kidney is increased in a dose-dependent manner [41].

The cause of these tumours, therefore, is the $\alpha_{2\mu}$-G nephropathy which is brought about not only by limonene but also by many other substances such as, e.g., 1,4-dichlorobenzene, isophorone and 2,2,4-trimethylpentane exclusively in male rats and not in female rats nor in mice. Where these substances have been tested in long-term carcinogenicity studies, they have been shown to produce renal tumours in male rats but not in female rats and not in mice. Since a protein analogous to $\alpha_{2\mu}$-G is very likely not produced in man in sufficient quantities, the tumours found in the male rats may be assumed to have no relevance for man [42].

6.1 Tumour promotion and tumour suppression

Whether *d*-limonene acts as a tumour promoter or tumour suppressor seems to depend on the route of administration (Table 5).

Administered in the diet, neither orange oil nor *d*-limonene had a promoter effect after initiation with dimethylbenzanthracene. *d*-Limonene reduced the number and

Table 5. Tumour promotion and suppression with *d*-limonene

Species (strain)	Number ♂ ♀	Initiator, application route	Promoter, (purity) application route	time of application	Observation time	Findings	Ref.
mouse (101)	10 10	300 µg DMBA in acetone, topical	–	–	33 weeks	1 papilloma in untreated submandibular region	[40]
	10 10	300 µg DMBA in acetone, topical	0.25 ml orange oil (> 90% *d*-l.) topical	3 weeks after DMBA appl. 1 × /week for 33 weeks	33 weeks	39 papillomas in 13 mice	
mouse (CD-1)	– 24	51.2 µg DMBA in acetone, topical	0.2 ml acetone topical	2 weeks after DMBA appl. 2 × /week for 40 weeks	40 weeks	no substance-related findings	[43]
	– 24	51.2 µg DMBA in acetone, topical	0.2 ml *d*-l. (n.s.) topical	2 weeks after DMBA appl. 2 × /week for 40 weeks	40 weeks	from week 34: 0.86 papillomas per animal, no skin carcinomas	
	– 24	51.2 µg DMBA in acetone, topical	0.2 ml orange oil (> 95% *d*-l.) topical	2 weeks after DMBA appl. 2 × /week for 40 weeks	40 weeks	from week 18: 1.56 papillomas per animal skin carcinomas sign. increased	
	– 24	51.2 µg DMBA in acetone, topical	1% *d*-l. in the diet	1 week after DBMA appl. for 4 weeks	40 weeks	no substance-related findings	
	– 24	0	1% orange oil (> 95% *d*-l.) in the diet	1 week after DMBA appl. for 40 weeks	40 weeks	no substance-related findings	

Table 5 (continued)

Species (strain)	Number ♂ ♀	Initiator, application route	Promoter, (purity) application route	time of application	Observation time	Findings	Ref.
mouse (Stock Albino)	17 (♂ + ♀)	50 µg DBP in polyethylene glycol, gavage	–	–	> 8 weeks	2 forestomach tumours, 1 glandular stomach tumour, 4 lung adenomas	[44]
	23 (♂ + ♀)	50 µg DBP in polyethylene glycol, gavage	0.05 ml *d*-l. (highly pure) gavage	time n.s.: 1 × /week for 40 weeks	> 8 weeks	8 forestomach tumours, 1 glandular stomach tumour, no lung adenomas	
	23 (♂ + ♀)	50 µg DBP in polyethylene glycol, gavage	0.05 ml orange oil (n.s.) gavage	time n.s.: 1 × /week for 40 weeks	> 8 weeks	22 forestomach tumours (incl. 1 squamous cell carcinoma), no other tumours	
rat (Sprague-Dawley)	– 25	0	–	–	27 weeks	–	[27]
	– 25	65 mg DMBA/kg bw in sesame oil, gavage	0.1% *d*-l. (> 99%) in the diet	1 week before until 27 weeks after DMBA admin.	27 weeks	number of mammary tumours significantly reduced	
	– 25	65 mg DMBA/kg bw in sesame oil, gavage	1% *d*-l. (> 99%) in the diet	1 week before until 27 weeks after DMBA admin.	27 weeks	number of mammary tumours significantly reduced	

Table 5 (continued)

Species (strain)	Number ♂	Number ♀	Initiator, application route	Promoter, (purity) application route	time of application	Observation time	Findings	Ref.
rat (W/FuX xF344)	–	10	130 mg DMBA/kg bw in sesame oil, gavage	–	–	~18 weeks	5/6 animals with mammary tumours	[45]
	–	10	130 mg DMBA/kg bw in sesame oil, gavage	10% *d*-l. (>99%) in the diet	*d*-l. given from when 1 tumour >15 mm^3	until 1 tumour >4000 mm^3 or ~18 weeks	2/7 animals with mammary tumours, sign. regression of primary mammary tumours, formation of subsequent tumours inhibited	
rat (Sprague-Dawley)	–	n.s.	0	–	–	25 weeks	–	[46]
	–	n.s.	65 mg DMBA/kg bw in sesame oil, gavage	5% *d*-l. (n.s.) in the diet	1 week before until 1 week after DMBA admin.	25 weeks	number of mammary tumours significantly reduced, appearance of first tumour delayed	
	–		65 mg DMBA/kg bw in sesame oil, gavage	5% *d*-l. (n.s.) in the diet	1 week after DMBA admin. for 25 weeks	25 weeks	number of mammary tumours significantly reduced	

DMBA: dimethylbenz[*a*]anthracene
DBP: dibenzopyrene
d-l.: *d*-Limonene
bw: body weight
n.s.: not specified

size of mammary tumours when administered in this way [43]. After initiation with dibenzopyrene (subcutaneous) in mice (C57BL/6Jax), subcutaneous *d*-limonene is also said to cause a significant reduction in the number of tumours formed (no details given) [47].

After intragastric administration both *d*-limonene and orange oil were shown to be promoters of forestomach tumours in mice. In such cases the forestomach was frequently grossly shrunken and scarred and there were small ulcers in the squamous epithelium [44]. Topically applied orange oil ($> 90\%$ *d*-limonene) had a promoting effect on skin papillomas and carcinomas in mice (strain 101) after a single application of the initiator, dimethylbenzanthracene [40]. Limonene (purity not specified) had a weak inhibiting effect on the induction of skin papillomas by benzopyrene in mice (JCR/Ha Swiss). No carcinogenic effects of *d*-limonene were seen in this experiment; the tumour promoting activity was not studied [48].

7 Manifesto (MAK value, classification)

The acute toxicity of *d*-limonene for man is considered to be low; dermal toxicity is likely but not well documented. Long-term studies from which dose-response relationships could be derived for man are currently not available.

In all the genotoxicity tests carried out to date *d*-limonene has produced negative results (Ames test, chromosome aberrations, sister chromatid exchange). In the mammalian spot test mutagenicity reducing properties were found.

The results obtained in animal experiments reveal toxic effects on the lungs, CNS or digestive system, depending on the route of administration.

Orally ingested *d*-limonene has tumour suppressing properties; topically applied, it is a promoter.

Nephropathy (hyaline droplets, damage to the tubular epithelium and renal tumours after chronic administration) is specific for the post-pubertal male rat and dependent on the presence of $\alpha_{2\mu}$-globulin. The demonstration of the existence of this or a similar protein in man is the subject of intensive studies, the results of which are still outstanding. Until they are available, *d*-limonene will be classified in Section IIb of the List of MAK Values. There are insufficient data available for the establishment of a MAK value.

8 References

1. Gildemeister, E., F. Hoffmann: in Treibs, W., D. Merkel (Eds.): *Die ätherischen Öle*, Vol. 3a, p 45, Akademie Verlag, Berlin, 1960
2. Van Duuren, B. L., N. Nelson, L. Orris, E. D Palmes, F. L. Schmitt: *J. nat. Cancer Inst. 31*, 41 (1963)
3. Schäfer, R., W. Schäfer: *Arzneimittel-Forsch. 32*, 56 (1982)
4. Igimi, H., M. Nishimura: *Xenobiotica 4*, 77 (1974)
5. Lehman-McKeeman, L. D., D. Caudill: *The Toxicologist 8*, 1 (1988)
6. Kodama, R., K. Noda, H. Ide: *Xenobiotica 4*, 85 (1974)
7. Kodama, R., T. Yano, K. Furukawa, K. Noda, H. Ide: *Xenobiotica 6*, 377 (1976)
8. Igimi, H., T. Hisatsugu, M. Nishimura: *Amer. J. dig. Dis. 21*, 926 (1976)
9. Imbert-Gourbeyre: *Gaz. méd Paris* 38 (1853); cited in [10]

10. Madaus, G.: *Lehrbuch der biologischen Heilmittel*, Vol. 1, p 646, Thieme, Leipzig, DDR, 1938
11. Oettel, H. J.: *Naunyn-Schmiedeberg's Arch. exp. Path. Pharmak. 183*, 641 (1936)
12. Riedel, H.: *Klin. Wschr. 19*, 1034 (1940)
13. Keil, H.: *J. invest. Derm. 8*, 327 (1947)
14. Le Bourhis, B., A.-M. Soenen: *Food Cosmet. Toxicol. 11*, 1 (1973)
15. Tsuji, M., Y. Fujisaka, Y. Arikawa, S. Masuda, S. Kinoshita, A. Okubo, K. Noda, H. Ide, Y. Iwanaga: *Oyo Yakuri 9*, 387 (1975)
16. Tsuji, M., Y. Fujisaka, K. Yamachika, K. Nakagami, F. Fujisaka, M. Mito, T. Aoki, S. Kinoshita, A. Okubo, I. Watanabe: *Oyo Yakuri 8*, 1439 (1974)
17. Moreno, O. M., 1972: cited in [18]
18. Opdyke, D. L. J.: *Food Cosmet. Toxicol. 13*, 825 (1975)
19. Moreno, O. M., 1975: cited in [20]
20. Opdyke, D. L. J.: *Food Cosmet. Toxicol. 16*, 809 (1978)
21. National Toxicology Program (NTP): *Toxicology and carcinogenesis studies of d-limonene in F344/N rats and B6C3F$_1$ mice (gavage studies)*, NTP Techn. Rep. 347, (Draft) 4/88, NIH Publ. No. 88-2802, US Dept. of Health and Human Services, Research Triangle Park, NC 27709, USA, 1988
22. Ariyoshi, T., M. Arakaki, K. Ideguchi, Y. Ishizuka, K. Noda, H. Ide: *Xenobiotica 5*, 33 (1975)
23. Kodama, R., H. Inove, K. Noda, H. Ide: *Life Sci. 19*, 1559 (1976)
24. Kanerva, R. L., C. L. Alden: *Food chem. Toxicol. 25*(5), 355 (1987)
25. Evans, D. L., D. M. Miller, K. L. Jacobsen, P. B. Bush: *J. Toxicol. environm. Hlth 20*, 51 (1987)
26. Tsuji, M., Y. Fujisaki, Y. Arikawa, S. Masuda, T. Tanaka, K. Sato, K. Noda, H. Ide, M. Kikuchi: *Oyo Yakuri 9*, 775 (1975)
27. Elegbede, J. A., C. E. Elson, A. Qureshi, M. A. Tanner, M. N. Gould: *Carcinogenesis 5*, 661 (1984)
28. Leroy, E. P.: *Fed. Proc. 43(4)* 1984, Abstract 3473
29. Hooser, S. B., V. R. Beasley, J. I. Everitt: *J. Amer. vet. med. Ass. 189*, 905 (1986)
30. Kodama, R., A. Okubo, E. Araki, K. Noda, H. Ide, T. Ikeda: *Oyo Yakuri 13*, 863 (1977); cited in [31]
31. Sandmeyer, E. E.: in Clayton, G. D., F. E. Clayton (Eds.): *Patty's Industrial Hygiene and Toxicology*, 3rd rev. ed., Vol. 2B, pp 3232, 3238, John Wiley & Sons, New York, Chichester, Brisbane, Toronto, 1981
32. Tsuji, M., Y. Fujisaki. A. Okubo, Y. Arikawa, K. Noda, H. Ide, T. Ikeda: *Oyo Yakuri 10*, 179 (1975)
33. Watabe, T., A. Hiratsuka, M. Isobe, N. Ozawa: *Biochem. Pharmacol. 29*, 1068 (1980)
34. Watabe, T., A. Hiratsuka, N. Ozawa, M. Isobe: *Xenobiotica 11*, 333 (1981)
35. Florin, I. L., M. Rutberg, M. Curvall, C. R. Enzell: *Toxicology 15*, 219 (1980)
36. Styles, J. A., M. G. Penman: *Mutat. Res. 154*, 183 (1985)
37. Fahrig, R.: *Progr. clin. Biol. Res. 109*, 339 (1982)
38. Fahrig, R.: *BGA Schriften 6*, 58 (1985)
39. Stoner, G. D., M. B. Shimkin, A. J. Kniazeff, J. H. Weisburger, E. K. Weisburger, G. B. Gori: *Cancer Res. 33*, 3069 (1973)
40. Roe, F. J. C., W. E. H. Peirce: *J. nat. Cancer Inst. 24*, 1389 (1960)
41. Charbonneau, M., J. A. Swenberg: *CIIT Activities 8*(6), 1988
42. Short, B. G., J. A. Swenberg: *CIIT Activities 8*(7), 1988
43. Elegbede, J. A., T. H. Maltzman, A. K. Verma, M. A. Tanner, C. E. Elson, M. N. Gould: *Carcinogenesis 7*, 2047 (1986)
44. Field, W. E. H., F. J. Roe: *J. nat. Cancer Inst. 35*, 771 (1965)
45. Elegbede, J. A., C. E. Elson, M. A. Tanner, A. Qureshi, M. N. Gould: *J. nat. Cancer Inst. 76*, 323 (1986)
46. Elson, C. E., T. H. Maltzman, J. L. Boston, M. A. Tanner, M. N. Gould: *Carcinogenesis 9*, 331 (1988)
47. Homburger, F., A. Treger, E. Boger: *Oncology 25*, 1 (1971)
48. Van Duuren, B. L., B. M. Goldschmidt: *J. nat. Cancer Inst. 56*, 1237 (1976)

completed 29. 5. 1989

2-Methoxy-1-propanol

Classification/MAK value:	**20 ml/m³ (ppm)** **75 mg/m³**
Classification/MAK value dates from:	**1988**
Synonyms:	propylene glycol 2-methylether
Chemical name (CAS):	2-methoxy-1-propanol
CAS number:	1589-47-5
Structural formula:	$H_3C-CH-CH_2OH$ 　　　　$|$ 　　　OCH_3
Molecular formula:	$C_4H_{10}O_2$
Molecular weight:	90.1
Melting point:	$< -50\,°C$
Boiling point (range):	$130-133\,°C$
Vapour pressure at 20°C:	5.5 hPa

1 ml/m³ (ppm) = 3.74 mg/m³　　　　　**1 mg/m³ = 0.27 ml/m³ (ppm)**

1 Toxic Effects and Modes of Action

High doses of 2-methoxy-1-propanol affect the central nervous system, are mildly irritating in the eyes and respiratory tract and are teratogenic in rabbits. The toxicological profile of the substance is practically identical with that of 2-methoxypropyl-1-acetate, from which the acetyl group is rapidly saponified in the organism [1]. The toxic effects of the same molar doses (with the units mmol/kg) of the two substances, therefore, are equivalent.

2 Effects in Man

There are no reports available on the effects of 2-methoxy-1-propanol in man.

3 Effects on Animals

3.1 Acute toxicity

LD_{50} rat, oral: > 5000 mg/kg   [2]
LD_{50} rat, inhalation: > 6 mg/l (4 h)   [3]

The principal symptoms were effects on the central nervous system (sedation, narcosis).

On the dorsal skin of the rabbit no irritation was observed after occlusive treatment of intact and scarified skin for 24 hours (Draize test) [2]. The substance caused slight irritation of the eyes.

3.2 Subacute toxicity

1800 mg/kg and day, administered ten times within two weeks to 10 male rats by oral intubation, produced a slight reduction in erythrocyte numbers and in haemoglobin level but no testis or bone marrow damage nor leukopenia such as occurred when ethoxyethanol was administered under the same conditions [4]. The slight reduction in erythrocyte numbers could be a haemolytic effect. It was not seen after an equimolar dose of 2-methoxypropyl-1-acetate (2600 mg/kg body weight and day) [4].

4 Reproductive and Developmental Toxicity

Screening studies with limited numbers of animals (5 rats per dose group) revealed that inhalation of 3000 ppm 2-methoxy-1-propanol for 6 hours daily from day 6 to day 15 of gestation caused cleft spine (thorax vertebrae) just as was seen when testing 2-methoxypropyl-1-acetate in rats [5]. With 2000 and 1000 ppm, only indentations were seen on the corresponding vertebrae. 2000 and 3000 ppm induced mild sedation in the dams and 3000 ppm produced irritation of the respiratory organs.

In a test of the isomer 1-methoxy-propan-2-ol for teratogenicity in the rat and rabbit [6] the inhaled test substance contained 1.32% 2-methoxy-1-propanol. Since no teratogenic effects were found at the highest dose, 3000 ppm, it may be concluded that 40 ppm 2-methoxy-1-propanol has no teratogenic effects in the rat or rabbit.

A series of concentrations of 2-methoxy-1-propanol, 145, 225, 350 day and 545 ppm, were tested by inhalation for 6 hours daily from day 6 to day 18 of gestation in Himalaya rabbits (12 animals per dose group). Marked maternal toxicity was found only at 545 ppm – body weight gain and uterus weight at the end of the observation period were reduced. Placenta weights were increased and an increased frequency of foetal absorptions was also demonstrated. The number of living foetuses at the end of the observation period was reduced, as were their body weights. Two animals aborted. In addition to a large number of variations, malformations were found in the extremities, sternum and ribs as well as the vessels in the heart region. At 350 ppm the same effects were recorded but they were less marked. At 225 ppm the uterus weights were still slightly reduced and there was a slight increase (trend) in rib and sternum variations as well as a slightly increased frequency of malformations. 145 ppm had no effect [7].

5 Manifesto (MAK value, classification)

The data available is not sufficient for the establishment of a MAK value. There is no information as to effects in man. There is, however, an analogy with 2-ethoxyethanol. Therefore, the MAK value for 2-methoxy-1-propanol is to be 20 ml/m^3; it requires, however, substantiation with appropriate occupational medical studies and inhalation experiments.

Since the toxic effects in the low concentration range may be seen as systemic effects and the half-life of the substance is expected to be less than 2 hours because of its rapid enzymatic conversion, 2-methoxy-1-propanol is classified in category II,1 for the limitation of exposure peaks.

2-Methoxy-1-propanol was shown to be teratogenic in the rat and rabbit. The teratogenic potential is of the same order of magnitude as that of 2-ethoxyethanol. Therefore, like 2-ethoxyethanol, 2-methoxy-1-propanol is classified in pregnancy group B.

6 References

1. Gelbke, H.-P.: *Spaltung von 2-Methoxypropylacetat in Rattenplasma*, personal communication of unpublished results, BASF Aktiengesellschaft, D-6700 Ludwigshafen, 1984
2. Gelbke, H.-P., H. Zeller: *Bericht über die gewerbetoxikologische Grundprüfung von 2-Methoxy-propanol-1*, personal communication of unpublished results, BASF Aktiengesellschaft, D-6700 Ludwigshafen, 1979
3. Gelbke, H.-P.: *Bericht über die Bestimmung der akuten Inhalationstoxizität (LC$_{50}$) von 2-Methoxypropanol bei 4stündiger Exposition an Sprague-Dawley-Ratten*, personal communication of unpublished results, BASF Aktiengesellschaft, D-6700 Ludwigshafen, 1979
4. Gelbke, H.-P.: *Kurzbericht über einen Vorversuch mit 10maliger Sondierung an Ratten mit Ethyl-glykol, 2-Methoxypropanol-1 und 2-Methoxypropyl-1-acetat*, personal communication of unpublished results, BASF Aktiengesellschaft, D-6700 Ludwigshafen, 1982
5. Merkle, J., H.-J. Klimisch, R. Jäckh: *Fund. appl. Toxicol. 8*, 71 (1987)
6. Hanley, T. R., L. L. Calhoun, B. L. Yano, K. S. Rao: *Fund. appl. Toxicol. 4*, 784 (1984)
7. Gelbke, H.-P.: *Prenätale Toxizität von 2-Methoxypropanol-1 am Kaninchen nach inhalativer Auf-nahme*, personal communication of unpublished results, BASF Aktiengesellschaft, D-6700 Ludwigshafen, 1988

completed 11.4.1988

2-Methoxypropyl-1-acetate

Classification/MAK value:	**20 ml/m^3 (ppm)**
	110 mg/m^3
Classification/MAK value dates from:	**1988**
Synonyms:	2-methoxypropanol-1-acetate
	propylene glycol-2-methylether-1-acetate
Chemical name (CAS):	2-methoxy-1-propanol acetate
CAS number:	70657-70-4
Structural formula:	$H_3C-CH-CH_2OOC-CH_3$
	$\quad\quad\ \ \overset{\vert}{O}CH_3$
Molecular formula:	$C_6H_{12}O_3$
Molecular weight:	132.2
Melting point:	$< -20\,°C$
Boiling point (range):	$150-151\,°C$
Vapour pressure at 20 °C:	2.9 hPa

1 ml/m^3 (ppm) = 5.49 mg/m^3   **1 mg/m^3 = 0.182 ml/m^3 (ppm)**

1 Toxic Effects and Modes of Action

2-Methoxypropyl-1-acetate irritates the respiratory passages at high concentrations; in high doses it affects the central nervous system and is teratogenic in rabbits. After absorption into the organism, saponification rapidly removes the acetyl group to yield 2-methoxy-1-propanol. The half-life in rat plasma *in vitro* is about 10 minutes [1]. Thus, applied at the same molar dose (with the units mmol/kg) the toxicity of 2-methoxypropyl-1-acetate is much the same as that of 2-methoxy-1-propanol.

2 Effects in Man

There are no reports available on effects of 2-methoxypropyl-1-acetate in man.

3 Effects on Animals

3.1 Acute toxicity

LD$_{50}$ rat, oral: > 5000 mg/kg   [2]
LD$_{50}$ rabbit, dermal   > 2000 mg/kg   [3]

The principal symptoms were effects on the central nervous system (sedation, narcosis). Beagle dogs and rabbits exposed once for 6 hours (whole body exposure) to an atmosphere containing 400 ppm 2-methoxypropyl-1-acetate tolerated the exposure without serious toxic effects [4]. Initially, increased salivation and blinking was observed in dogs.

3.2 Subacute toxicity

10 doses of 2600 mg 2-methoxypropyl-1-acetate/kg and day administered within 2 weeks by gavage to 5 male Wistar rats produced no changes in macroscopically visible or clinical laboratory parameters whereas ethoxyethanol, tested in parallel, caused testis damage and leukopenia [5].

During a 28 day inhalation study (6 hours daily, 5 days per week) with Wistar rats, irritation of the respiratory organs, delayed body weight gain, atrophy of the thymus and, in male animals, increased absolute liver weights were observed at inhaled concentrations of 14.9 mg/l (2800 ppm). The exposure did not damage the testis, bone marrow or peripheral blood. At 560 ppm slight irritation was still seen; 110 ppm had no effect [6].

4 Reproductive and Developmental Toxicity

Signs of maternal toxicity seen in pregnant Wistar rats (25 animals per dose group) exposed by inhalation to a 2-methoxypropyl-1-acetate concentration of 14.9 mg/l (2800 ppm, 6 hours daily, from day 6 to day 15 of gestation) included irritation of the mucosa, sedation, reduced body weight on days 15 and 20 of gestation and reduced uterus weight at the end of the observation period. At 3.0 mg/l (560 ppm) sedation, ruffled fur and irregular breathing were still seen during the exposure (with subsequent recovery), but to a lesser extent. Macroscopic examination of organs revealed no toxic effects. At 14.9 mg/l foetotoxicity took the form of increased frequency of foetal absorption and a slight reduction in foetal body weight.

Cleft spine (thorax vertebrae) was observed in 12 of 189 foetuses from the highest dose group but not at any of the other doses. An anomalous unilateral open eye was found twice in the 3.0 mg/l (560 ppm) group and once in the 0.6 mg/l (110 ppm) group. There were no such findings in the control group [3].

Maternal toxicity was not observed in Himalaya rabbits (15 animals per dose group) which were exposed to 2-methoxypropyl-1-acetate concentrations of 0.2, 0.8 and 3.0 mg/l (about 36, 145 and 560 ppm) for 6 hours daily from day 6 to day 18 of gestation. All foetuses which were examined from the highest dose group, however, had malformations (particularly of the sternum, the paws, the heart and larger vessels). At 145 ppm and in the control group there were no malformations. In the 36 ppm group there were anomalies in 3 of the 65 foetuses examined (1 diaphragmatic hernia, 1 scoliosis, 1 foetus without a gall bladder). They could be classified as spontaneous pathological findings [3].

No signs of maternal or foetal toxicity were found after dermal application of 1000 or 2000 mg/kg to Himalaya rabbits daily from day 6 to day 18 of gestation. The undiluted test substance was applied under semi-occlusive conditions for 6 hours daily to 22×9 cm of the shaved dorsal skin (10 animals per dose group) [3].

5 Manifesto (MAK value, classification)

There are no data available from animal studies which may be applied directly for the determination of a MAK value. Industrial experience with 2-methoxypropyl-1-acetate is also completely lacking. There is, however, an analogy with ethoxyethanol and 2-methoxy-1-propanol so that the MAK value for 2-methoxypropyl-1-acetate is also to be 20 ml/m^3. This value must be considered to be preliminary. Studies are needed to substantiate the value, both in the industrial situation and with animals.

Since 2-methoxypropyl-1-acetate, like its analogues, also acts systemically, it is classified in category II,1 for the limitation of exposure peaks.

2-Methoxypropyl-1-acetate was unambiguously teratogenic in rabbits and doubtfully so in the rat. Since the substance is rapidly and quantitatively metabolized to 2-methoxy-1-propanol, the risk during pregnancy must be considered to be the same for the two compounds. 2-methoxypropyl-1-acetate is therefore classified in the pregnancy group B.

6 References

1. Gelbke, H.-P.: *Spaltung von 2-Methoxypropylacetat in Rattenplasma*, personal communication of unpublished results, BASF Aktiengesellschaft, D-6700 Ludwigshafen, 1984
2. Gelbke, H.-P.: *Bericht über die Prüfung der akuten oralen Toxizität an Ratten von 2-Methoxypropylacetat-1*, personal communication of unpublished results, BASF Aktiengesellschaft, D-6700 Ludwigshafen, 1984
3. Merkle, J., H.-J. Klimisch, R. Jäckh: *Fund. appl. Toxicol. 8*, 71 (1987)
4. Gelbke, H.-P.: *Information über einmalige Inhalation von 2-Methoxypropylacetat-1 über 6 Stunden an Kaninchen und Hund*, personal communication of unpublished results, BASF Aktiengesellschaft, D-6700 Ludwigshafen, 1984
5. Gelbke, H.-P.: *Kurzbericht über einen Vorversuch mit 10maliger Sondierung an Ratten mit Ethylglykol, 2-Methoxypropanol-1 und 2-Methoxypropyl-1-acetat*, personal communication of unpublished results, BASF Aktiengesellschaft, D-6700 Ludwigshafen, 1982
6. Gelbke, H.-P.: Personal communication of unpublished results, BASF Aktiengesellschaft, D-6700 Ludwigshafen, 1984
7. Gelbke, H.-P.: *Prenätale Toxizität von 2-Methoxypropanol-1 am Kaninchen nach inhalativer Aufnahme*, personal communication of unpublished results, BASF Aktiengesellschaft, D-6700 Ludwigshafen, 1988

completed 11.4.1988

N-Methyl-bis(2-chloroethyl)amine HS

Classification/MAK value:	**see Section III A 1)** **MAK List 1987**
Classification/MAK value dates from:	**1987**
Synonyms:	nitrogen mustard N-methyl lost N,N-bis(2-chloroethyl)-N- methylamine 2,2'-dichloro-N-methyldiethylamine bis(ß-chloroethyl)methylamine di(2-chloroethyl)methylamine N-methyl-2,2'-dichlorodiethylamine chlormethine mechlorethamine mustargen HN2
Chemical name (CAS):	2-chloro-N-(2-chloroethyl)- N-methyl-ethanamine
CAS number:	51-75-2
Structural formula:	

$$H_3C-N \begin{array}{l} CH_2-CH_2Cl \\ CH_2-CH_2Cl \end{array}$$

Molecular formula:	$C_5H_{11}Cl_2N$
Molecular weight:	156.1
Melting point:	$-60\,°C$
Boiling point:	$87\,°C$ at 18 mm Hg
Vapour pressure at 20 °C:	not specified

1 ml/m³ (ppm) = 6.48 mg/m³   **1 mg/m³ = 0.154 ml/m³ (ppm)**

1 Toxic Effects and Modes of Action

N-Methyl-bis(2-chloroethyl)amine (nitrogen mustard) is an alkylating agent and so reacts with nucleic acids and proteins. Rapidly proliferating tissues such as the haematopoietic systems are affected most. It has adverse efects on all essential enzymes.

Both the oily liquid and its vapour are corrosive and raise blisters on skin and mucous membranes, characteristically after a latent period of several hours. The substance readily penetrates the skin.

Inhalation of sublethal doses by man causes eye injury, hoarseness, toxic pneumonia, liver damage, urticaria, oedema of the lips and severe indisposition as a result of extensive enzyme damage. The symptoms continue for months after the end of exposure.

The main effects observed in animals after inhalation of toxic or lethal doses were neurological symptoms such as increased irritability, incoordination and balance disorders but lacrimation, salivation, nasal discharge, production of viscid bronchial phlegm, diarrhoea, urination, miosis and convulsions were seen as well; the testis tissues were severely damaged.

The water-soluble hydrochloride of nitrogen mustard is used both internally and externally as a cytostatic medicine. It is poorly absorbed through the skin but its effects are otherwise not different from those of nitrogen mustard itself. Intravenous administration causes massive side-effects such as high temperature, vomiting, anorexia, nausea, alopecia, severe headache due to irritation of the meninges, hypocalcaemia, severe depression of bone marrow activity, damage to liver, heart muscle and gonads.

Nitrogen mustard yields positive results in all short term tests for mutagenicity and is unambiguously carcinogenic and teratogenic in animals. Therapeutic doses lead to the development of secondary tumours in man, most frequently to leukaemia.

The substance has a high sensitization potential.

1.1 Pharmacokinetics

In aqueous solution the substance undergoes rapid cyclization to the quaternary ethylenimonium ion (50% in 2 minutes at 37 °C and pH 7) [1]. This form is more reactive than its precursor and reacts with organic and inorganic ions in tissues as well as with important functional groups such as amino groups, sulfides and sulfhydryl groups [2]. In the course of several days the ethylenimonium ion is converted to other hydrolysis and dimerization products (Figure 1) whose alkylating potential decreases progressively [3]. The monofunctional hydrolysis product N-methyl-2-chloroethyl-2-hydroxyethylamine has antimitotic activity and is acutely toxic [4, 5]; the piperazinium ion (Figure 1) is said not to be toxic [5].

In a study with mice, enrichment of the substance in brain, spinal cord, lungs and submaxillary gland was found 5 minutes after intravenous injection of 35 mg nitrogen mustard hydrochloride per animal; the growth of yeast on whole body sagittal sections of the mice was used as an indicator [6].

The distribution of nitrogen mustard or its alkylating metabolites in the rat was studied using the 4-*p*-nitrobenzylpyridine reaction. Of the 500 µg (= 3.3 mg/kg) administered by intraperitoneal injection only 16% could be found in the organs studied (liver, lungs, spleen and kidneys). The maximal concentrations in blood (4 µg/ml), liver (4 µg/g), kidney (7 µg/g) and lung (8 µg/g) were reached within

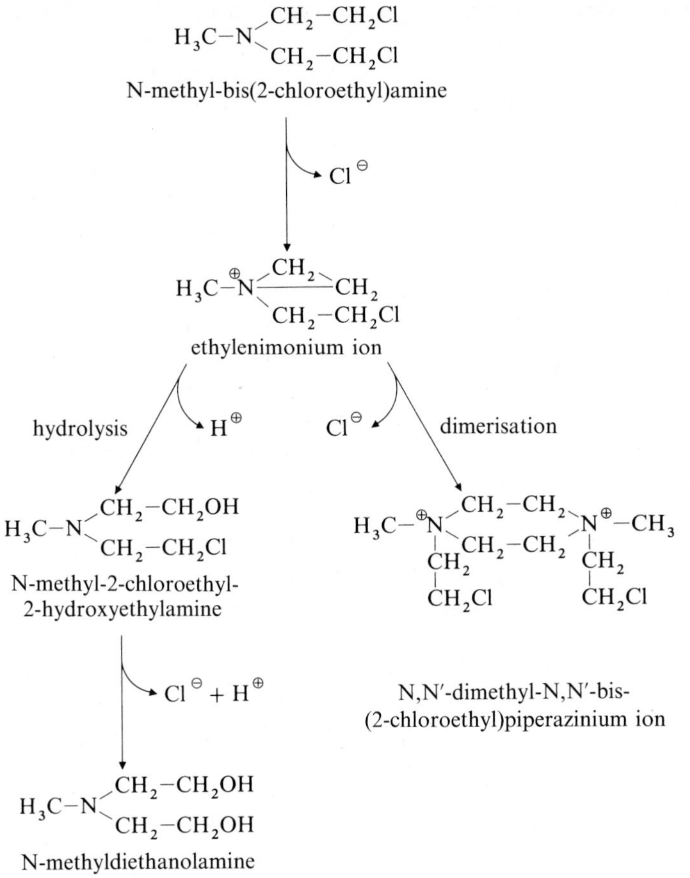

Figure 1. Reactions of N-methyl-bis(2-chloroethyl)amine in aqueous milieu [7]

5 minutes. Only in the spleen did the concentration go on rising in the subsequent 5 minutes (to 7.5 μg/g) and the value then remained almost constant for 12 hours. In the lung 40 % of the maximal value was still present after 12 hours. Nitrogen mustard was no longer detectable in the blood after 30 minutes, in the liver after 60 minutes and in the kidney after 12 hours. 20 μg alkylating agent/ml was found in the 1.5 hour urine sample. In the subsequent hours the elimination increased and reached a maximum of 83 μg/ml after 12 hours. At this time 17 % of the administered dose had been excreted. The concentration of alkylating activity then decreased rapidly. The author accounts for these results in terms of a loss of alkylating activity of the urinary metabolites [8].

1.2 DNA-binding studies

Nitrogen mustard reacts with DNA molecules to form N^7-guaninyl and N^7-bis-guaninyl derivatives which can take the form of irreversible cross-links either within a DNA strand, between two complementary DNA strands or between DNA and other molecules (e.g. proteins) [9, 10].

2 Effects in Man

2.1 Industrial intoxications

Intoxications at the workplace are described in only one publication which describes 7 cases of occupational intoxication with nitrogen mustard during production of Dolantin. The vapour released (concentration not specified) during process irregularities attacked first the eyes and upper respiratory passages of the exposed persons. The eyes were reddened, the conjunctiva inflamed, the eye colour altered (yellowish tinge in 2/7) and night blindness occurred (1/7). All affected persons were hoarse, often for days. There was one case of toxic pneumonia. This patient suffered even one month later from recurring urticarial wheals, especially on the face, as well as from oedema of the lips.

All exposed persons were severely indisposed and liver damage (seen as increased urobilinogen and bilirubin in urine and a positive galactose test) persisted for months after stopping work. The author concluded that nitrogen mustard caused generalized enzyme damage [11].

2.2 Use in cancer therapy

Nitrogen mustard hydrochloride is used as an alkylating cytostatic in cancer therapy, internally especially for the treatment of Hodgkin's lymphoma and externally for skin diseases such as mycosis fungoides, psoriasis and alopecia areata. Intravenous administration of therapeutic doses (0.7–0.9 mg/kg) has severe side-effects such as thrombophlebitis at the injection site, increased temperature, vomiting, nausea, severe headache caused by irritation of the meninges, anorexia, alopecia, severe bone marrow depression (granulocytes $< 1000/mm^3$, thrombocytes $< 50000/mm^3$), hypocalcaemia (7.5–8.4 mg/dl compared with 9–10.6 mg/dl before treatment) and damage to liver and heart muscle [12].

After administration of 0.2 mg/kg on two consecutive days, the severe granulocytopenia and thrombocytopenia persisted for 5 and 8 days respectively; bone marrow recovery took more than 2 weeks [12].

Nitrogen mustard is gonadotoxic for both male and female patients. Testis atrophy has been reported in men treated with nitrogen mustard [13]. Combination therapies such as MOPP (nitrogen mustard, vincristine, procarbazine, prednisone) and MVPP (nitrogen mustard, vinblastine, procarbazine and prednisolone) caused irreversible sterility in 90% of 158 male patients [14].

There are no reports on the effects of pure nitrogen mustard, not combined with other substances, on the female gonads. Nonetheless it appears that the substance impairs ovarial function markedly. Four women – 25, 26, 30 and 31 years old – who had been given 26 mg nitrogen mustard followed by daily doses of 6–8 mg chlorambucil developed irregular menstrual cycles and amenorrhoea [15]. After 6 cycles of MOPP or MVPP therapy, total irreversible failure of ovarian function was found in 85% of the women over 25 years old. The extent of gonadotoxicity is often not immediately recognizable because the process of ovarian damage is progressive and continues after termination of therapy [14].

Risk assessment attempted on the basis of published reports of secondary tumours arising after therapy with nitrogen mustard met with difficulties [16–19] because the patients often died before the secondary tumour had developed or this was not recognized (or not published). In addition, nitrogen mustard is frequently used in combination therapy.

In a recent summary of 89 well documented cases of secondary tumours after nitrogen mustard administration, the main types of cancer observed were acute leukaemia (60%), erythroleukaemia (3%), bladder carcinoma (10%), skin carcinoma (3%) and bronchial carcinoma (6%). From these data a mean carcinogenic dose of 42 mg and a mean latency period of 44 months were calculated [20].

Nitrogen mustard hydrochloride applied topically as an aqueous solution has promoting properties for skin cancer as well as initiating properties. Thus squamous epithelial carcinoma and kerato-acanthoma were observed on skin sites exposed to the sun in 10% of 202 patients after local therapy with nitrogen mustard hydrochloride. In 2 of these patients the cancers also developed on treated sites which had not been exposed to the sun [21].

2.3 Dermal toxicity and allergenic effects

Nitrogen mustard causes severe skin burns with blisters which develop after a latency period of up to 8 days and which heal leaving hyperpigmentation and scarring. The oily substance readily penetrates the skin and so acts systemically [11]. The aqueous nitrogen mustard hydrochloride solution which is used for external treatment of skin disorders seems not to be as readily absorbed through the skin [7]. One case, however, has been reported in which the spleen and lymph nodes of a 56 year old man were enlarged and the bone marrow was hyperplastic after a nitrogen mustard hydrochloride solution (1 : 5000) had been used for local treatment for two years [22].

Sensitization of the skin and to a slight extent of the mucosa as well was observed after exposure to nitrogen mustard gas [11].

50% of mycosis fungoides patients who were painted daily with the usual nitrogen mustard hydrochloride solution (1 : 5000) became sensitized [7]. Other reports describe sensitization of 51 of 76 mycosis fungoides patients [23], 15 of 20 psoriasis patients [24] and 2 of 11 patients with alopecia areata [25] after topical treatment with nitrogen mustard hydrochloride. Allergic contact dermatitis developed in general 2–4 weeks after the therapy began [7]; rarely it only appeared on the diseased skin sites [26]. A slightly higher concentration (1 :4000) used to treat the whole body for a period of 5 years (over 100 applications) caused urticaria and anaphylactic reactions. Epicutaneous, non-occlusive application of 0.02 ml of a 1 : 100000 dilution in water was an adequate provocation dose [27].

2.4 Embryotoxicity and teratogenicity

It is assumed that nitrogen mustard, being an alkylating agent, can affect the rapidly proliferating cells of human foetal tissue. In fact, however, only very few observations have been reported since pregnancy is avoided when possible during cancer chemotherapy.

There were no malformations among the children of three women treated during pregnancy for Hodgkin's disease with nitrogen mustard (not in combination). The children's' development was still normal when they were 7.5, 8.5 and 9.5 years old. Later examinations were not reported [28].

On the other hand, 2 cases of malformations have been described in foetuses after the mothers had been subjected to combination therapy with MVPP (nitrogen mustard, vincristine, procarbazine, prednisone) before and during the first trimester of pregnancy. In one case there was malformation of the kidneys [29], in the other skeletal malformation (only 4 toes on each foot with webbing of two toes on the right foot, bowing of the tibia) and a large haemorrhage in the right cerebral hemisphere [30].

3 Effects on Animals

3.1 Acute toxicity

The LD_{50} values found in the literature are assembled in Table 1.

Intravenous injection of more than lethal doses (20 mg/kg) into rabbits led after 5–15 minutes to incoordination, convulsions, salivation and urination, defaecation, lacrimation, miosis and production of viscid bronchial phlegm [31]. 2.5 mg/kg ad-

Table 1. LD_{50} values (mg/kg) for N-methyl-bis(2-chloroethyl)amine administered by various routes

Species	Application route					Observation time	Ref.
	dermal*	subcu- taneous	intra- venous	oral	intra- peritoneal		
mouse	29	2.6	~ 2.0	20		15 d	[31]
mouse		4				n.s.	[5]
mouse					4.13	n.s.	[32]
rat	22	1.9	1.1	10		15 d	[31]
rat		2				n.s.	[5]
rat					1.75	n.s.	[33]
rat**		1.5				n.s.	[34]
rabbit	~ 15		~ 1.6			15 d	[31]
dog			1.0			15 d	[31]

* substance on the uncovered skin for 2 hours, then skin cleaned with ether
** newborn rats
n.s.: not specified

ministered intravenously to rabbits caused after 8 hours an initial granulocytosis (from 4000 to 8000 granulocytes/mm^3) which developed after 44 hours into granulocytopenia with a maximum (30 cells/mm^3) after 90 hours. The granulocyte count returned to normal in 8–9 days [35].

Intravenous administration of doses in the range of the LD$_{50}$ or **inhalation** of concentrations in the range of the LC$_{50}$ led after 3–4 days to increased irritability, motor disorders and, in serious cases, to balance disorders in the rat. Generally the animals died shortly after the CNS symptoms appeared; survivors were over-excitable for weeks. Pathological studies revealed demyelination of the peripheral nerves in one third of the animals [31]. The lowest published concentrations which were lethal after 10 minutes inhalation are 370 mg/m^3 (mouse), 290 mg/m^3 (cat), 290 mg/m^3 (dog), 690 mg/m^3 (rabbit) and 440 mg/m^3 (guinea pig) [36].

Subcutaneous injection of 20 mg/kg into mice caused depression, trembling and intermittent convulsions. Incoordination, over-excitability, balance disorders, diarrhoea and nasal discharge were observed in mice which survived longer (exact times not specified) [31].

The effect of nitrogen mustard on testis tissue was studied after a single **intraperitoneal injection** of 4 mg/kg or 6.3 mg/kg or 7 times 0.6 mg/kg in mice. Histological examination revealed that the testis tissue was damaged markedly as soon as 24 hours after injection of 4 mg/kg or 6.3 mg/kg. In the following days all stages of cytoplasmic degeneration and nuclear pyknosis were seen including the formation of giant cells and marked decrease in the numbers of mature spermatozoa. None of the animals in these two groups survived longer than 20 or 8 days, respectively.

The 7 intraperitoneal injections of 0.6 mg/kg (interval between injections not specified) produced more severe testis damage than did the same dose administered as a single injection. The pathological cell changes described above appeared one day after the first injection and progressed to final dissolution of the seminiferous tissue. Two to three weeks after the end of treatment the testis epithelium began to recover slowly. All animals survived [32].

3.2 Subchronic and chronic toxicity

When 115 female RF mice were treated four times by intravenous injection of 2.4 mg/kg with two weeks between doses, 10% of the animals were dead within 30 days of the end of treatment. The life expectancy of the 101 animals evaluated was reduced by 22.7% in comparison to that of 112 controls. This was not only the result of neoplasia but also of a number of delayed effects such as abscesses of the heart (1%), kidneys (2%), lungs (1%), liver (4%), spleen (1%) and uterus (2%) as well as colitis (3%), nephrosclerosis (7%), cystitis of uterus and ovaries (2%), ascites (7%) and hydrothorax (2%). These disorders were also frequent in the control group but were less numerous and/or developed appreciably later [37].

3.3 Toxicity to skin and mucous membranes

Nitrogen mustard was tested for local tissue damaging potential on the shaved dorsal skin of guinea pigs. The dose for the guinea pig, 0.5 mg/animal, was calculated to correspond to the therapeutic dose for man, 20 mg/m^2. Intradermal injection of 90% of this dose led within a few hours to ulceration which was still present after 7 days. 9% of the dose caused black, necrotic changes and tissue ulceration, 1% and 0.3% only hyperaemia. After subcutaneous injection of the same doses these reactions were not observed [38]. Epicutaneous treatment of each of 30 mice with 0.1 mg nitrogen mustard once weekly for 33 weeks induced dermatitis in a small percentage of animals (no further details given). The same dose 3 times weekly or 0.3 mg once weekly produced dermatitis, alopecia and scarring in most of the treated mice [38].

2 drops of a 0.1%, 0.5%. 1.0% or 10% solution of nitrogen mustard in 0.15 molar NaCl in the eyes of male rabbits caused, after 30 minutes, hyperaemia of the iris and conjunctiva, dose-dependent miosis and increased intraocular pressure as well as injury to the blood aqueous humour barrier [39]. In further studies with vertebrates (rabbits, guinea pigs, ducks, cats and owl monkeys) the reaction to nitrogen mustard in the eyes was different from species to species. After application of 50 or 25 µl of a 1% nitrogen mustard hydrochloride solution into the conjunctival sac, an increase in intraocular pressure could be measured in all species except for the owl monkeys; in rabbits and guinea pigs two maxima were recorded (immediately after application and 3–6 hours later) and in ducks and cats a maximum within the first hour. Contraction of the pupil was only observed in rabbits, cats and monkeys, erythema and cellular invasion of the anterior chamber of the eye only in rabbits, cats and guinea pigs [40].

3.4 Allergenic effects

To date there is only one negative test result available with animals. A total dose of 1 mg nitrogen mustard per animal was applied to the back of the neck of guinea pigs (numbers not specified) by simultaneous subcutaneous and intramuscular injections. A challenge dose of 1.5 µg/animal applied 3 weeks after this treatment revealed no sensitization [41].

4 Reproductive and Developmental Toxicity

Nitrogen mustard is very embryotoxic and teratogenic both *in vitro* and *in vivo*. *In vitro* 0.1 µg/ml nitrogen mustard caused chromosome aberrations in 14% of metaphases in rat embryo cells, 1 µg/ml inhibited mitosis [42]. The *in vivo* studies on the rat are presented in Table 2.

Applied at the beginning of pregnancy (on day 4), the substance is blastotoxic. After intraperitoneal injection between day 10 and day 16 of gestation the main anomalies observed, apart from a generalized growth retardation, meningocele and encephalocele, were skeletal. In 108 foetuses examined with skeletal malformation the details of the bones affected were as follows: ribs (49.5%), sternum (36.1%), occipital bone (26.1%), shoulder blade (24%), cheek bone (12.9%), ulna (13.9%), radius (9.2%), fibula (4.6%), humerus (5.5%), femur (1.9%) [33].

Malformation of the limbs was observed in the embryos of chickens and quails after nitrogen mustard application. 0.6–0.9 µg nitrogen mustard in aqueous solution

Table 2. Embryotoxicity and teratogenicity of N-methyl-bis(2-chloroethyl)amine, tested in rats

Dose mg/kg	Application route	Application time days post coitum	Number of ♀♀ (strain)	Time of examination days post coitum	Foetal malformation frequency %	Observations; Malformations	Findings in dams	Ref.
0.8	i.p.	4	4 (BDII)	13	0	nidation affected adversely, no foetuses developed		[43]
1	s.c.	12 and 13	7 (n.s.)	20 and 21	90	general growth retardation; meningocele; syndactyly; short mandible; short kinky tail		[42]
0.2–0.3	i.p.	12	n.s. (Wistar)	21		all foetuses normally developed		[33]
0.3–0.5	i.p.	9, 10, 11, 12, 14–16	2–6 (Wistar)	21	0, 5, 25, 50, 40	general growth retardation; encephalocele; circular cranial defects involving the parietal, interparietal frontal and occipital bones; widening of the cervical vertebral canal; angulation of the ribs; fusion and bifurcation of the sternebrae		[34]

Table 2 (continued)

Dose mg/kg	Application route	Application time days post coitum	Number of ♀♀ (strain)	Time of examination days post coitum	Foetal malformation frequency %	Observations; Malformations	Findings in dams	Ref.
0.7	i.p. i.p.	12 12	66* 61** (Wistar)	21 21	27 36	general growth retardation; syndactylous forepaws (13.8%) and rear paws (3.9%); short kinky tail (4.6%); cleft palate (4.6%); encephalocele (2.3%)	no unambiguous weight changes of spleen or thymus, slight bone marrow depression, involution of lymphatic tissue	[33]
0.7	i.p.	12	16 (Wistar)	21		litter LD_{50}		[33]
1.4	i.p.	12	n.s. (Wistar)	21		all foetuses died		[33]
1.75	i.p.	12	n.s. (Wistar)	21			LD_{50} for dams	[33]

* animals whose litters survived almost entirely
** animals whose litters were largely reabsorbed
litter LD_{50}: dose which killed the majority of the foetuses in 50% of the treated animals
n.s.: not specified

was applied to the yolk sac membrane of 155 chicken eggs which had been incubated for 36–55 hours. Examination on days 8 and 10 revealed malformations in 73.6% of the embryos, 21.9% of which were affected with hemisomia, the rest with one or more limb malformations (hemimelia, amelia). Also when applied after 4.5–5 days incubation, 0.3 ml of a 0.03–0.1 mg nitrogen mustard/ml H_2O on the yolk sac membrane caused malformations in 59.3% of the right wing bones and 86.5% of the foot bones of the chicken embryos; 0.3 ml of a solution of 0.4 mg/ml nitrogen mustard on the yolk sac membrane of quail eggs (after 4.5–5 days incubation) led to malformation of 56.3% of foot bones [44]. In another study on chicken eggs embryotoxic doses (not specified in more detail) applied on day 2 of development led to malformations in the heart (50%), eye (17%) and rump (33%), on days 3 and 4 to anomalies in the brain (100% and 88%, respectively), the facial bones (100% and 88%) and the limbs (100% and 88%) [45].

5 Genotoxicity

Nitrogen mustard is a notorious direct mutagen. It is one of the first substances for which genotoxicity (in *Drosophila melanogaster*) was demonstrated [46, 47].

All mutagenicity tests with prokaryotes and eukaryotes are unambiguously positive. The studies are so numerous – especially since, being a known mutagen, the substance is often used as a positive control and for validation of test systems – that the extensive literature cannot be cited here completely. The publications which appeared before 1962 are summarized in a report by Wheeler [47].

More recent *in vivo* studies in mice and *in vitro* short term tests are assembled in Tables 3 and 4.

Chromosome aberrations were found 4 days after the injection in 4.5% of the blood cells of a patient who had been given 12 mg nitrogen mustard intravenously [72].

6 Carcinogenicity

The substance is unambiguously carcinogenic in animals. After percutaneous and subcutaneous administration to mice, tumours were observed at the application site (see Table 5); after subcutaneous, intravenous or intraperitoneal application lung tumours and leukaemia were most common (see Table 6).

7 Manifesto (MAK value, classification)

N-Methyl-bis(2-chloroethyl)amine (nitrogen mustard) has long been known to be highly mutagenic. It has proved to be carcinogenic and teratogenic in various animal species. Human therapy with nitrogen mustard has caused numerous cases of secondary tumours. Therefore N-methyl-bis(2-chloroethyl)amine is classified in Sec-

Table 3. Positive *in vivo* mutagenicity tests with N-methyl-bis(2-chloroethyl)amine in mice

Strain, sex, number	Test	Dose mg/kg	Appl. route	Mating times	Females/group	Observations	Ref.
♂	dominant lethal	2.5	i.p.	1 ×/week, for 8 weeks	2	examined on day 13 after mating: pregnancies: > 80% foetal deaths: increased in weeks 1 to 3 implantations: reduced in weeks 1 and 3	[48]
		3.5	i.p.	1 ×/week, for 8 weeks	2	as above but: foetal death rate even higher in week 2	
ICR, ♂	dominant lethal	2.25	i.v.	5 weeks after injection	40	85% mated, fertilization rate unchanged; embroys removed at 2 cell stage and cultured for 3 days in egg culture medium; development of the trophectoderm affected adversely, mutation frequency: 14%	[49]
ICR/Ha, ♂, 7	dominant lethal	1.0	i.p.	1 ×/week, for 8 weeks	3	examination on day 13 after mating: increased foetal deaths (3 of 7.9 implantations/pregnancy died)	[50]
AB/Jena Gat ♀	injected with ascites tumour cells	0.07	i.p.			chromosome aberration frequency 66–96%, maximum after 36–48 h inhibition of mitosis	[51]
		0.68	i.p.				
		0.68	s.c.			chromosome aberrations 6% after 12 h	
		6.78	s.c.			chromosome aberrations 55% after 48 h	
Swiss 15–20	injected with ascites tumour cells	0.1	i.p.			conc. = D_0 for ascites cells 2.5×10^4 alkylations/cell = 2.5×10^3 cross-links/cell	[9]
AB/Jena Gat ♀	bone marrow studies	0.68	s.c.			chromosome aberrations in bone marrow cells: 38% after 12 h	[51]
		6.78	s.c.			chromosome aberrations in bone marrow cells: 98.7% after 24–36 h	

D_0: concentration at which 1/3 of the cells survived

Table 4. *In vitro* short term tests with N-methyl-bis(2-chloroethyl)amine since 1962

Organism	Conc. µg/µl (time)	Mutation	Observations	Ref.
coliphage T$_4$ RII	n.s.	reversion; Gc →AT	32% spontaneous mutants 22% induced mutants 47% deletions	[52]
coliphage T$_7$	7.8 (30 min)	DNA interstrand cross-links	17 alkyl groups/DNA molecule at 63% lethality; maximum 90 min after treatment, minimum after 2 days; then another increase	[53]
E. coli S	n.s.	lac − → lac + base pair substitution deletion	reversible not reversible	[54]
E. coli K-12 (and derived strains)	1.56–312	mutation to rifampicin resistance by mutation at rif locus		[55]
S. typhimurium LT2	n.s.	gal-chl deletions HIPA resistance	mutation frequency increases with exposure time, after 30 min. exposure the number of mutants/plate is five times that of the control (7% survivors)	[56]
S. typhimurium strain not specified	n.s.	reversion of base pair substitutions	dose-effect curve linear with plateau at 250 µg/ml	[57, 58]
S. typhimurium TA1537, TA1534 TA100	n.s.	—	no frameshift mutations	[57, 58]
S. typhimurium his G 46 his C$_{3076}$	n.s.	base pair mutations —	no frameshift mutations	[59]

Table 4 (continued)

Organism	Conc. µg/µl (time)	Mutation	Observations	Ref.
Sacch. cerevisiae S 211	n.s.	base pair substitution		[59]
S 138		–	no frameshift mutations	
Paramecium aurelia	n.s.	recessive lethal mutations	maximal mutation rate after treatment during or close to the G1 phase	[60]
Neurospora crassa	156–780 µg/plate (1 h)	DNA-DNA cross-links, DNA-protein cross-links	increased thymidine incorporation	[61]
Chinese hamster (CHO cells)	0.047 0.468	SCE (doubled) SCE (increased 10 times)	of 20 cells examined in M_2: 2 chromosome aberrations (ring) 1 chromatid aberration (isochromatid)	[62]
mouse lymphoma cells P 388	0.0126 (30 min)	$IUdR^s \rightarrow IUdR^r$ $TdR^s \rightarrow TdR^r$	conc. = D_0; after 48 h maximal expression, then until 144 h no change in mutation frequency	[63]
mouse testis cells	1.56–78 (3 h)	UDS		[64]
human lymphocytes	7.8×10^{-3}	SCE	in S_1 phase largest effect in G_1 phase smallest effect (because the damage is repaired in this phase)	[65]
human lymphocytes	0.156–15.6 (1 h)	UDS	thymidine incorporation increased 3 × (plateau after 8 h incubation time)	[66–68]

Table 4 (continued)

Organism	Conc. µg/µl (time)	Mutation	Observations	Ref.
human fibroblasts	46.8×10^{-3} (30 min)	chromosome aberrations double strand breaks		[69]
human lymphoblastoid cells		cross-links	inhibition of [^{3}H]TdR-incorporation	[70]
Raji	0.06		1/3 of cells survived, dose-effect relationship linear	
TK6	0.02		1/3 of cells survived, dose-effect relationship linear	
AHH-1 TK$^{+/-}$	0.036–0.15	aneuploidy (additional Y chromosome)		[71]
human bone marrow cells	0.156–15.6	UDS	concentration dependent thymidine incorporation	[68]

SCE: sister chromatid exchange
D_0: concentration at which 1/3 of the cells survive
UDS: unscheduled DNA synthesis
n.s.: not specified

Table 5. Tumours at the site of application after percutaneous and subcutaneous application of N-methyl-bis(2-chloroethyl)amine to mice

Total dose	Solvent	Application route	Number of doses (time)	Mouse strain	number (initial) evaluated	Tumours %	kind	month*	Ref.
0	95% ethanol 0.2 ml	p.c., 3×/week	120 (40 weeks)	Swiss	36	0			[38]
6.9 mg/mouse	95% ethanol 0.2 ml	p.c., 3×/week	69 (23 weeks)	Swiss	(36) 33	27.2	squamous cell carcinoma	7.9	
						3	papilloma	7.9	
0	H₂O	n.i.		n.s.	40	0			[73]
1 mg/kg		s.c., 1×/week	50 (50 weeks)	n.s.	(20) 14	7.1	sarcoma	n.s.	
0		n.i.		C3H	(40) 35	0			[74]
0.15–0.20 mg/mouse	H₂O	s.c., 1×/week	6–8 (6–8 weeks)	C3H	(40) 36	8.3	sarcoma	15.3	
						5.5	sarcoma (neurogenic)	17	
						2.6	haemangioendothelioma	20	
0	H₂O	n.i.		C3Hf	(40) 39	0			[74]
0.15 mg/mouse		s.c., 1×/week	6 (6 weeks)	C3Hf	(41) 37	5.4	sarcoma	17	
						2.7	papilloma	21	

* appearance of tumours, months after the beginning of treatment. Animals were observed until death.

n.i.: not injected

n.s.: not specified

p.c.: *per cutem*

Table 6. Tests for carcinogenicity of N-methyl-bis(2-chloroethyl)amine in mice and rats

Total dose (mg/kg)	Sol-vent	Appl. route	Number of doses (treatment period)	Species Strain	Number (initial) evaluated	Tumours %	kind	number per animal	Appearance of tumours * or time of sacrifice	Ref.
0		n.i.		mouse n.s.	40	15 / 5	lung tumours / lymphosarcoma		13–17* / 11–19*	[73]
50	H_2O	s.c. 1×/week	50 (50 weeks)	mouse n.s.	(20) 14	57.1 / 2.5	lung tumours / uterus fibromyoma		9.3–19.1* / 18.3*	
0	H_2O	n.i.		mouse C3Hf	(40) 39	15.4	lung tumours		20*	[74]
0.15*	H_2O	s.c. 1×/week	6 (6 weeks)	mouse C3Hf	(41) 37	56.8	lung tumours		17.8*	
0	NaCl-soln	n.i.		mouse A	30	20	lung tumours		15–24*	[75]
0.1 mg/animal	NaCl-soln	1×/week	5 (5 weeks)	mouse A	27	63	lung tumours		9–21*	
0	H_2O	i.p. 3×/week	12 (4 weeks)	mouse A	(360) 339	31.3	lung tumours	0.38	died week 39	[76]
0.00385	H_2O	i.p. 3×/week	12 (4 weeks)	mouse A	(60) 47	30	lung tumours	0.3	died week 39	
0.21	H_2O	i.p. 3×/week	12 (4 weeks)	mouse A	(60) 53	40	lung tumours	0.6	died week 39	
0.86	H_2O	i.p. 3×/week	12 (4 weeks)	mouse A	(60) 51	69	lung tumours	1.2	died week 39	
3.37	H_2O	i.p. 3×/week	12 (4 weeks)	mouse A	(60) 38	95	lung tumours	2.8	died week 39	

Table 6 (continued)

Total dose (mg/kg)	Sol-vent	Appl. route	Number of doses (treatment period)	Species	Strain	Number (initial) evaluated	Tumours %	kind	number per animal	Appearance of tumours* or time of sacrifice	Ref.
0	T	i.p. 3×/week	12 (4 weeks)	mouse	A	(120) 108	34	lung tumours	0.44	died week 39	[76]
0.081	T	i.p. 3×/week	12 (4weeks)	mouse	A	(30) 26	46	lung tumours	0.8	died week 39	
0.2	T	i.p. 3×/week	12 (4 weeks)	mouse	A	(30) 28	50	lung tumours	0.6	died week 39	
0.83	T	i.p. 3×/week	12 (4 weeks)	mouse	A	(30) 28	29	lung tumours	1.2	died week 39	
3.3	T	i.p. 3×/week	12 (4 weeks)	mouse	A	(30) 30	63	lung tumours	1.0	died week 39	
0		n.i.		mouse	A	30	13	lung tumours	0.17	died week 16	[77]
2–4	H$_2$O	i.v. every 2 days	2–4 (4d–8d)	mouse	A	29	100	lung tumours	3.48	died week 16	
0		n.i.		mouse	A	32	62.5	lung tumours	0.81	died month 10	[78]
4	H$_2$O	i.v. every 2 days	4 (8 d)	mouse	A	32 (20)	100	lung tumours	9.6	died month 10	
0		n.i.		mouse	A	31	58	lung tumours	0.94	died month 10	[78]
4	H$_2$O	i.v.	1	mouse	A	(35) 9	100	lung tumours	7.56	died month 10	

Table 6 (continued)

Total dose (mg/kg)	Solvent	Appl. route	Number of doses (treatment period)	Species Strain	Number (initial) evaluated	Tumours %	kind	number per animal	Appearance of tumours* or time of sacrifice	Ref.
0		n.i.		mouse RF	(113) 112	15	lung tumours		18.7*	[37]
						10	thymus lymphoma		19.8*	
						4	leukaemia (myeloid)		18.6*	
						37	leukaemia (others)		21.8*	
						20	ovarian tumour		21.4*	
9.6	phys. NaCl soln	i.v. every 2 weeks	4 (8 weeks)	mouse RF	(115) 104	68	lung tumour		13.8*	
						21	thymus lymphoma		11.9*	
						2	leukaemia (myeloid)		16.5*	
						34	leukaemia (others)		18.4*	
						26	ovarian tumour		16.7*	
0		n.i.		rat BR46	65	4.6	mammary sarcoma		23 ± 5*	[79]
						1.54	mammary fibroma			
						3	thymoma			
5.72	H₂O	i.v. 1×/week	52 (52 weeks)	rat BR46	(48) 27	3.7	leukaemia (lymphocytic)		16 ± 3*	
						3.7	leukaemia (myeloid)			
						3.7	reticulosarcoma			
						3.7	liposarcoma			
						3.7	adenosarcoma of the large intestine			
						3.7	meningiosarcoma			
						3.7	haemangioendothelioma			

* The appearance of tumours is given in months after the start of treatment. Animals were observed until death.

T : tricaprylin

n.i.: not injected

tion III A1) of the List of MAK Values. Because of the danger of skin absorption and of sensitization the designations H and S are necessary.

8 References

1. Lambert, B., K. Hansson, T. H. Bui, F. Funes-Cravioto, J. Lindsten, M. Holmberg, R. Strausmanis: *Ann. hum. Genet. 39*, 293 (1976)
2. Ross, W. C. J.: *Ann. N.Y. Acad. Sci. 68*, 669 (1958)
3. Inch, W. R., J. A. Credie: *Canad. J. Biochem. 41*, 417 (1963)
4. Van Scott, E. J., R. J. Yu: *J. invest. Derm. 62*, 378 (1974)
5. Boyland, E.: *Brit. J. Pharmacol. 1*, 247 (1946)
6. Tubaro, E., M. J. Buegini: *Nature (Lond.) 218*, 395 (1968)
7. Vonderheid, E. C.: *Int. J. Derm. 23*, 180 (1984)
8. Obrecht, P.: *Z. Krebsforsch. 66*, 151 (1964)
9. Chun, E. H. L., L. Gonzales, F. S. Lewis, J. Jones, R. Rutman: *Cancer Res. 29*, 1184 (1969)
10. Hemminki, K., S. Kallama: *IARC Sci. Publ. No. 78*, 55 (1986)
11. Jordi, A.: *Helv. med. Acta 15*, 470 (1948)
12. Hartmann, D. W.: *Cancer Treatm. Rep. 65*, 327 (1981)
13. Spitz, S.: *Cancer (Philad.) 1*, 383 (1948)
14. Chapman, R. M.: *Amer. J. industr. Med. 4*, 149 (1983)
15. Sobrinho, L. G., R. A. Levine, R. C. Deconti: *Amer. J. Obstet. Gynec. 109*, 135 (1971)
16. Schmähl, D., M. Habs, M. Lorenz, J. Wagner: *Cancer Treatm. Rev. 9*, 167 (1982)
17. Henne, T., D. Schmähl: *Cancer Treatm. Rev. 12*, 77 (1985)
18. Lien, E. J., X.-C. Ou: *J. clin. hosp. Pharm. 10*, 223 (1985)
19. Tester, W. J., T. J. Kinsella, B. Waller, R. W. Makuch, P. A. Kelley, E. Glatstein, V. T. DeVita: *J. clin. Oncol. 2*, 762 (1984)
20. Schmähl, D.: *IARC Sci. Publ. No. 78*, 29 (1986)
21. DuVivier, A., E. C. Vonderheid, E. J. van Scott, F. Urbach: *Brit. J. Derm. 99*, 61 (1978)
22. Wadell, C. C., M. A. Zubler, W. S. Gore: *Arch. Derm. 118*, 179 (1982)
23. Ramsay, D. L., R. E. Parnes, N. Dubin: *Arch. Derm. 120*, 1585 (1984)
24. Mauduit, G., O. Silvestre, J. Thivolet: *Brit. J. Derm. 113*, 515 (1985)
25. Arrazola, J. M., E. Sendagorta, A. Harto, A. Ledo: *Int. J. Derm. 24*, 608 (1985)
26. Shelley, W. B.: *Acta derm.-venereol. (Stockh.) 61*, 161 (1981)
27. Daughters, D.: *Arch. Derm. 107*, 429 (1973)
28. Sokal, J. E.: *J. Amer. med. Ass. 172*, 1765 (1960)
29. Mennuti, M. T., T. H. Shepard, W. J. Mellmann: *Obstet. gynec. Surv. 46*, 194 (1975)
30. Garret, M. J.: *Arch. intern. Med. 80*, 667 (1974)
31. Anslow, W. P., D. A. Karnofsky, B. ValJager, H. W. Smith: *J. Pharmacol. exp. Ther. 91*, 224 (1947)
32. Landing, B. H.: *Cancer (Philad.) 2*, 1075 (1949)
33. Murphy, M. L., A. Del Moro, C. Lawn: *Ann. N.Y. Acad. Sci. 68*, 762 (1958)
34. Murphy, M. L., D. A. Karnofosky: *Cancer 9*, 955 (1956)
35. Herion, J. C., R. I. Walker, W. B. Herring, J. G. Palmer: *Blood 25*, 522 (1965)
36. National Defence Research Committee, Office of Scientific Research and Development, Progress Report; cited in: NIOSH *Registry of Toxic Effects of Chemical Substances (RTECS)*, 1983 Supplement to the 1981–1982 edition, p 629, USDHHS, USA, 1983
37. Conklin, J. W.: *Cancer Res. 25*, 20 (1965)
38. Zackheim, H. S., E. A. Snuckler: *Experientia (Basel) 36*, 1211 (1980)
39. Maul, E., M. L. Sears: *Invest. Ophthal. 15*, 308 (1976)
40. Klein, E. M., L. Z. Bito: *Invest. Ophthal. 24*, 184 (1983)
41. Barr, R. D., S. G. Benton, L. W. Belbeck: *J. nat. Cancer Inst. 66*, 1129 (1981)
42. Boyland, E., E. S. Hornig: *Brit. J. Cancer 3*, 118 (1949)
43. Heston, W. E.: *J. nat. Cancer Inst. 14*, 131 (1953)
44. Duhig, J. T.: *Arch. Path. 79*, 177 (1965)

45. Shimkin, M. B.: *J. nat. Cancer Inst. 36*, 915 (1966)
46. Heston, W. E.: *J. nat. Cancer Inst. 10*, 125 (1949)
47. Heston, W. E.: *J. nat. Cancer Inst. 11*, 415 (1950)
48. Schmähl, D., H. Osswald: *Arzneimittel-Forsch. 20*, 1461 (1970)
49. Soukup, S.: *J. Embryol. exp. Morph. 18*, 215 (1967)
50. Brock, N., Th. v. Kreybig: *Naunyn-Schmiedeberg's Arch. exp. Path. Pharmak. 249*, 117 (1964)
51. Salzgeber, B.: *Ann. Embryol. Morph. 5*, 145 (1972)
52. Jelinek, R.: *Teratog. Carcinog. Mutagen. 2*, 255 (1982)
53. Auerbach, C.: *Genetics 32*, 3 (1947)
54. Wheeler, G. P.: *Cancer Res. 22*, 651 (1962)
55. Anderson, D., D. B. McGregor, I. F. H. Purchase, M. C. E. Hodge, J. A. Cuthbert: *Mutat. Res. 43*, 231 (1977)
56. Goldstein, L. S.: *Mutat. Res. 140*, 193 (1984)
57. Epstein, S. S., E. Arnold, J. Andre, W. Bass, Y. Bishop: *Toxicol. appl. Pharmacol. 23*, 288 (1972)
58. Wobus, A. M., J. Schöneich, R. Thieme: *Mutat. Res. 58*, 67 (1978)
59. Corbett, T. H., C. Heidelberger, W. F. Dove: *Molec. Pharmacol. 6*, 667 (1970)
60. Brakier, L., W. G. Verley: *Biochim. biophys. Acta (Amst.) 213*, 296 (1970)
61. Zampieri, A., J. Greenberg: *Genetics 57*, 41 (1967)
62. Fram, R. J., J. Sullivan, M. G. Marinus: *Mutat. Res. 166*, 229 (1986)
63. Alper, M., B. N. Ames: *J. Bact. 121*, 259 (1975)
64. Commoner, B.: Nat. Techn. Inform. Serv., PB 256 934, 1976; cited in: Fox, M., D. Scott: *Mutat. Res. 72*, 131 (1980)
65. Benedict, W. E.: *Cancer Res. 37*, 2209 (1977)
66. Brusnick, D. J., E. Zeiger: *Mutat. Res. 14*, 271 (1972)
67. Kimball, R. F.: *Mutat. Res. 9*, 261 (1970)
68. Baker, J. M., J. H. Parish, J. P. Curtis: *Mutat. Res. 132*, 171 (1984)
69. Perry, P., H. J. Ewans: *Nature (Lond.) 258*, 121 (1975)
70. Anderson, D., M. Fox: *Mutat. Res. 25*, 107 (1974)
71. Bleikirch, H.: *Arch. Toxicol. 37*, 195 (1977)
72. Perticone, P., B. Lambert: *Mutat. Res. 175*, 171 (1986)
73. Lambert, B., M. Sten, S. Soederhaell: *Mutat. Res. 111*, 171 (1983)
74. Clarkson, J. M., H. J. Evans: *Mutat. Res. 14*, 413 (1972)
75. Liebermann, M. W., R. N. Baney, R. E. Lee, S. Sell, E. Farber: *Cancer Res. 31*, 1297 (1971)
76. Sen, P., W. N. Hittelman: *Mutat. Res. 129*, 359 (1984)
77. Dean, S. W., M. Fox: *Mutat. Res. 132*, 63 (1984)
78. Crespi, C. L., G. M. Seixas, B. W. Penman: *Mutat. Res. 190*, 69 (1987)
79. Conen, P. E., G. S. Lansky: *Brit. med. J. 2*, 1055 (1961)

completed 11. 4. 1988

Methyl 2-cyanoacrylate and Ethyl 2-cyanoacrylate

Esters of 2-cyanoacrylic acid with the general structure:

$$H_2C{=}C{-}C{-}O{-}R$$

with substituents $N{\equiv}C$ and O (the $-C{\equiv}N$ nitrile group and the $C{=}O$ ester carbonyl).

	MCA	**ECA**
Classification/MAK value:	2 ml/m^3 (ppm) 8 mg/m^3	not yet established see Section IIb, MAK List 1978
Classification/MAK value dates from:	1978	
Synonyms:	2-cyanoacrylic acid methyl ester, methyl α-cyanoacrylate, mecrylate	2-cyanoacrylic acid ethyl ester, ethyl α-cyanoacrylate,
Chemical name (CAS):	2-cyano-2-propenoic acid, methylester	2-cyano-2-propenoic acid, ethyl ester
CAS number:	137-05-3	7085-85-0
Structural formula, monomer:	$H_2C{=}C{-}C{-}O{-}CH_3$	$H_2C{=}C{-}C{-}O{-}C_2H_5$
Molecular formula:	$C_5H_5NO_2$	$C_6H_7NO_2$
Structural formula, polymer:	$\left[-CH_2{-}C{-} \atop COOR \right]_n$	
Molecular weight, monomer:	111.10	125.07
polymer:	∅ 2204	∅ 1533
Melting point, monomer:	2.5 °C	not specified
polymer:	168 °C	not specified
Boiling point, monomer:	47−49 °C (at 2.4−2.7 mbar)	60 °C (at 3.99 mbar)
Vapour pressure at 20 °C:	not specified	not specified

1 ml MCA/m^3 (ppm) = 4.6 mg/m^3

1 mg MCA/m^3 = 0.216 ml/m^3 (ppm)

1 ml ECA/m^3 (ppm) = 5.2 mg/m^3

1 mg ECA/m^3 = 0.192 ml/m^3 (ppm)

1 Toxic Effects and Modes of Action

1.1 Effects of the substance

Methyl 2-cyanoacrylate (MCA) and ethyl 2-cyanoacrylate (ECA) are strong local irritants. Airborne cyanoacrylates are characterized by an unpleasant acrid smell and by the symptoms that they cause, lacrimation and irritation of the mucous membranes of the nose and eyes.

On undamaged skin the liquids can produce unwanted adhesions and mechanical injury can result from the subsequent attempts to separate the adhering parts. Acute dermal toxicity could not be demonstrated in animals [1]. Injudicious contact with the eyes can cause adhesion of the eyelids as well as irritation and corneal injury [2, 3]. Severe local irritation in the form of inflammation, pus formation, oedema and necrosis can be the result of tissue exposure to MCA or ECA for medical purposes (implants, surgery on internal organs) [4–13] while systemic toxic effects are not known [14, 15].

After oral administration of polymerized cyanoacrylates to animals in the diet, neither local nor systemic toxic effects could be demonstrated [16, 17].

Local sarcomas had developed in rats 19.5 months after a single i.p. injection of MCA monomer but not in dogs after 24 months nor in various strains of mice after a 6 month observation period [16, 18]. These studies, however, suffer from methodic shortcomings and do not meet present day requirements.

Cyanoacrylates polymerized on tissues were shown in long term studies not to be carcinogenic [8, 19–22].

With monomeric MCA as well as with MCA adhesives positive results were obtained in the Ames test in the presence of S9 mix but only with the *Salmonella typhimurium* strain TA100. With ECA, positive results have not been obtained in any of the short term tests used to date [23–29].

Various occupational medical studies have shown that MCA and ECA cause sensitization of skin and mucous membranes [30–36].

1.2 Absorption and metabolism

Metabolism studies have been carried out in particular with a view to the medical applications of cyanoacrylates. They are used extensively as single component glues for a variety of very different materials and – of particular importance – as biodegradable tissue adhesives in surgery and dentistry [16, 37–41].

The extremely rapid adhesion is the result of an anionic polymerization reaction which is catalyzed by even minimal amounts of water or weak bases; the NH_2 groups in tissue proteins may also be considered to be initiators. The reaction is highly exothermic. The higher homologues polymerize more rapidly than MCA or ECA whereas the polymers of the lower homologues are more rapidly metabolized [4, 7, 11, 42–46]. Studies of *in vivo* degradation of MCA in rats revealed that after about 5 months less than 10% of the implant remained. The *in vivo* degradation rate was ~0.6% per day [47]. n-Butyl 2-cyanoacrylate, on the other hand, was present unchanged 6 months after use (to glue the mesentery) in dogs and rabbits [48] and

Table 1. Excretion in urine and faeces after oral administration of 100 g labelled methyl or butyl cyanoacrylate to rats (2 animals per group) in % of administered ^{14}C (mean values) [53].

Excreted in	Cyanoacrylate	day 1	day 2	day 3	day 4	Total
urine	methyl	7.6	7.2	1.2	0.1	15.9
	butyl	2.0	0.2	0.1	–	2.2
faeces	methyl	1.6	14.1	2.0	0.1	17.8
	butyl	54.4	14.6	2.9	1.3	73.1

also in guinea pigs after 8 months [49]. The degradation rate for n-butyl 2-cyanoacrylate was 0.03% per day [50]. Isobutyl 2-cyanoacrylate was still detectable in dogs 9 months after use (peripheral nerves) and in chimpanzees even after 14 months whereas MCA had disappeared almost completely after only 7 weeks [8]. The degradation rate of MCA in chicken embryo organ cultures was 75% in 24 hours [51, 52]. These tests also confirm that the degradation rate decreases with increasing length of the alkyl chain.

In studies of absorption of cyanoacrylates after ingestion, rats were given a single dose of 100 g ^{14}C3-labelled powdered polymer in vegetable oil. Urine and faeces were collected for 4 days. The urine radioactivity is taken to represent absorbed metabolites whereas the faeces radioactivity represents unabsorbed polymer (Table 1). These results indicate that a considerable proportion of ingested polymer is metabolized and markedly more rapidly than are implants. Again there is a large difference between the degradability of the two homologues [53].

The degradation rate of polymeric MCA applied in the monomeric form to the intact oral mucosa of rats is similar to that of implants; about 1% of the applied MCA appears in the urine each day [53].

Percutaneous absorption of radioactive monomers or their polymers was investigated for 3 homologues in rats. Absorption through intact skin was compared with that through split-thickness skin-graft donor sites. There was markedly less radioactivity in the 6 day urine from animals with intact skin than from those whose skin was damaged. The total amounts decreased in the order: MCA > n-butyl 2-cyanoacrylate > heptyl 2-cyanoacrylate [54].

It is likely that MCA monomer, which polymerizes relatively slowly, is better absorbed through skin than the more rapidly polymerizing higher homologues. Unlike the monomers, the polymers are only slightly soluble in lipids. Polymer degradation on intact skin could be facilitated by the action of sweat, sebum, water, body temperature and bacteria. The degradation products are all soluble in water. If the suggestion that the pilosebaceous unit is the main percutaneous transit route for cyanoacrylates is correct, skin absorption must be slower in man than in the rat. It is not known, however, in what proportions monomer, polymer and degradation products are absorbed [54].

When ^{14}C-labelled MCA was applied to incisions in the skin of rats radioactivity could subsequently be demonstrated in the liver and other organs. The radioactivity decreased with time until after 24 days it was only slightly in excess of the control values [55].

The polymers may be hydrolyzed to yield formaldehyde and alkyl cyanoacetate; both compounds are potentially toxic [17, 42, 53, 56, 57]. The presumed mechanism involves ester hydrolysis to yield low molecular weight, water soluble fractions [58]. It is also thought possible that the acetate is further degraded to yield calcium malonate [57].

Formaldehyde production was demonstrated in ^{14}C-labelling experiments with MCA [58]: when substance labelled at C2, C3 or CN was implanted subcutaneously in dogs, ^{14}C-activity appeared in the urine only from the [14]C3-compound. The formaldehyde enters C_1-metabolism and appears, e.g., as urea in urine and as CO_2 in expired air [53, 58]. In experiments with organ cultures, 0.21% of the labelled MCA applied to the culture was recovered as CO_2 [52]. About 5% of the cyano groups were released as cyanide ion, converted to thiocyanate and excreted in the urine [53, 59].

2 Effects in Man

2.1 Irritation

In 24 series of tests, 14 volunteers were exposed to vapour concentrations of 1–60 ml/m³ MCA monomer in a simulated work situation [45]. Air samples were collected in the breathing zone of the test persons at about 5 minute intervals and at the same time their subjective impressions were noted. The observations recorded were:

odour threshold	at ca.	1 ml/m³
irritation of the nose and throat	at ca.	3 ml/m³
burning irritation of the eyes	at ca.	5 ml/m³
lacrimation and nasal discharge	at ca.	20 ml/m³
painful irritation of the eyes	at ca.	50 ml/m³
blurred vision for about 2 hours	at ca.	50–60 ml/m³
(beginning some hours after the test)		

On the basis of these results the author suggests that the maximal exposure concentration should be ≤ 3 ml/m³ [45].

During experiments in which large amounts of isoamyl cyanoacrylate were applied to animals the investigators suffered from burning of their eyes and a watery discharge [60].

2.2 Histotoxicity

There are numerous reports of medicinal use of cyanoacrylates in man as well as of accidents resulting from careless handling of adhesives (skin adhesions, eye lesions) [61, 62 and others]. Thus one patient suffered from transient visual impairment after treatment of an ocular aneurysm with ECA. Another patient with the same disorder was blind in one eye after operative application of ECA and the other eye developed a visual field loss [63].

The marked histotoxicity of cyanoacrylate adhesives, especially of MCA, has been confirmed in more recent reviews [64, 65]. One patient, for example, died 3 days after the dome of an aneurysm in the cranial cavity had been coated with 2 drops of MCA monomer. The patient died because of a repeat subarachnoid haemorrhage. Histological examination revealed a severe inflammatory reaction and necrosis of the wall of the aneurysm [64]. Cases of thrombosis are known as well [63]. Thrombosis occurs if cyanoacrylate monomer enters a blood vessel and polymerizes on the intima [37].

2.3 Sensitization of the skin and respiratory tract

The following report [30] describes an incident from a factory producing cigarette lighters where 10 workers joined component parts using a cyanoacrylate adhesive. Each worker used 10 g adhesive per day. The adhesive delivery nozzle was cleaned every evening with a dimethyl formamide solvent.

About 2–3 hours after starting work, 8 of the 10 workers developed irritation in the nasopharyngeal region: shooting pains in the nose and throat, nasal discharge, and conjunctivitis with lacrimation. One of the women who had previously suffered from asthma developed symptoms of respiratory distress again. Psoriasiform lesions on the underarm were reactivated in another. One worker who was exposed to particularly large amounts of cyanoacrylate vapour (regulation of the adhesive delivery system) also complained of shooting pains in the mucous membranes of the nose and eyes, then some days later of itching and headaches, finally of a scarlatiniform rash first on the arms, shoulders and back, then on the whole body and a temperature increase to 39–40 °C. After 3–4 days in hospital the patient's condition returned to normal. There is no definite proof of a causal relationship. Dimethyl formamide is excluded by the author as the agent responsible because of its use in very small quantities and only at the end of the working day. Since the installation of a fresh air supply as a screen between the workbenches and the faces of the workers there have been no more symptoms of illness.

In the same year, 1979, in an electronics factory an outbreak of dermatitis among users of an ECA adhesive (containing 90.6% ECA, 9.0% polymethyl methacrylate, 0.4% hydroquinone, traces of organic sulfonic acid) was reported [31]. Five cases of itching rashes on the cheeks, forehead and lips or eyelids of women using the adhesive were described. The symptoms usually developed 1–2 hours after the women started work and, for one worker, they always worsened when she used the soldering iron.

At normal relative humidity the volatile monomeric cyanoacrylates polymerize rapidly; at low relative humidity, however, increased monomer concentrations can accumulate. In the factory in question the humidity was found to be between 30 and 40 percent. The ECA monomer concentrations in the air were not measured. It is claimed that there were no further complaints after the relative humidity at the workbenches had been increased to above 55 percent.

Later and almost simultaneously in England and in the USA cases of asthma and rhinitis were observed after use of cyanoacrylates at work or for hobbies [32–34]. Further studies in two different factories hardened the suspicion that ECA had a sensitizing effect on the employees [35, 36]. In five cases in clinically controlled tests provocation with cyanoacrylate adhesives produced asthma in persons who had very likely become sensitized previously at work. They are described below.

A 52 year old man who was employed in the production of scientific instruments developed respiratory difficulties when he had been using MCA adhesive for about one month. He stopped using the adhesive; 11 weeks later he was subjected to a clinical examination. Scratch tests with common inhaled allergens were negative; no reduction in the FEV_1 (forced expiratory volume) could be induced with histamine. However, when the patient worked with the MCA adhesive for 25 minutes in the same way as he did at work, his FEV_1 was reduced after 15 hours by 42% and rhinitis symptoms persisted for the whole day.

Three women who used ECA adhesives in two different work areas – soldering electronic components and producing lamp shades – developed symptoms of sneezing, coughing and/or respiratory distress 2 and 3 weeks after introduction of the adhesive, respectively. The symptoms sometimes became less severe at weekends or during lengthy absence from work. Scratch tests were negative in two of the women and positive for 4 common inhaled allergens in the third. In all three, ECA adhesives reduced the FEV_1 in blind inhalation trials. In two cases the FEV_1 sank immediately after the exposure and again after 7–8 hours; in the third it was not reduced until 7 hours after the exposure.

In the fifth reported case, that of a 34 year old woman who used an alkyl cyanoacrylate adhesive (not specified more particularly!) in the assembly of loud speakers, respiratory difficulties developed one month after she began the work. The symptoms became apparent about 4 hours after she started work each day and increased in intensity in the course of the working week, becoming better at weekends, on bank holidays and during vacations. The installation of a humidifier at her workbench led to an improvement in her symptoms on those days when the device was operating. Routine recordings of PEF (peak expiratory flow rates) demonstrated that the values became worse at work but less so on those days when the relative humidity was high (> 55%). In a clinical examination, histamine provoked no decrease in the patient's FEV_1. In blind inhalation trials in which provocation was carried out for 30 minutes with alkyl cyanoacrylate-containing and alkyl cyanoacrylate-free adhesives at various relative humidities, delayed reduction of the FEV_1 by 17% at 49% relative humidity and by 10% at 66% relative humidity was induced after inhalation of alkyl cyanoacrylate-containing adhesives but there was no asthmatic reaction after inhalation of alkyl cyanoacrylate-free adhesives. Scratch tests were positive with three common inhaled allergens [32].

Another case of asthma and rhinitis was observed in a 32 year old white man who had been using an ECA adhesive for his hobby [33]. The man was examined clinically because of a 12 month history of asthma, wheezing, cough, chest tightness, dyspnoea and rhinorrhoea. Questioning revealed that the symptoms had developed about a year after he had started using an ECA adhesive to build model aeroplanes at home in a closed room. Shortness of breath, puffy lips and rhinorrhoea developed 30 minutes to 1.5 hours after he had applied the glue to Balsa wood; wheezing, dyspnoea and chest tightness occurred 3 to 5 hours later, often awakening him at night. Profuse watery rhinorrhoea was noted 12 to 24 hours after exposure. These symptoms lasted for several days and were treated medicinally. The attacks of asthma only occurred after the patient had used cyanoacrylate adhesives, not after the use of alkyl cyanoacrylate-free adhesives. He remained free of symptoms after continued avoidance of the instant glue.

In order to throw light on these observations, a series of measurements of the patient's peak expiratory flow (PEF) were carried out in his home while he was using the ECA adhesive for his hobby. A one hour exposure (from 9 p.m.) induced such severe symptoms that the measurements had to be discontinued at about 11 p.m. and the patient had to take medication. The PEF values at this time had decreased abruptly. The patient had nasal symptoms from about 6 a.m. and at about 12 noon rhinorrhoea developed. The PEF values did not return to normal until the morning of the following day.

Another case of chronic dermatitis which was not of occupational origin [34] involved a 66 year old white woman with an 18 month history of a scaly, mildly itching eruption which appeared first on the breasts and then spread to the scapular areas, abdomen and thighs. The spots took the form of sharply circumscribed, 5 to 15 cm, pink, barely palpable plaques on generally thin, dry skin. The clinical impression was of small plaque parapsoriasis. More specific questioning revealed that for some time the patient had been strengthening her brittle fingernails with tea bag paper and ECA adhesive (Krazy Glue) before applying her nail polish. The occlusive patch tests which were then carried out were negative with 29 common allergens including epoxide resin and four different kinds of nail polish which the woman used. With dried Krazy Glue, however, the ECA adhesive which had been used, and with another commercially available ECA product the patch tests were positive within 48 hours; the vesicular reactions (grade 3^+) were evident for more than a week. Tests with other components of adhesives such as hydroquinone or polyalkyl methacrylate or with formaldehyde (degradation product) produced negative results. The eruptions cleared within a month after the patient had removed the ECA adhesive from her fingernails.

In a company producing automotive products workers exposed to ECA vapour while glueing plastic components or to 2-butanone (methyl ethyl ketone) during cleaning procedures were examined. Respiratory symptoms in about 80 employees were sufficient reason to determine the concentrations of the substances in the air. For 2-butanone (personal samplers) $17-430$ mg/m^3 (MAK value $= 590$ mg/m^3) was found and values up to 1.6 mg/m^3 for ECA during application of the adhesive.

At the same time a questionnaire was filled in by 73 employees. Of these, 26 complained of respiratory symptoms (19 reported wheezing or whistling breath, 16 reported episodes of shortness of breath and 15 reported chest tightness); 47 had no symptoms. Three months later 43 of the employees, 23 with and 20 without symptoms, were subjected to PEF measurements every three hours for 7 days, spirometry was carried out before and after the work shift and clinical laboratory parameters were determined. In 5 cases two doctors agreed on the diagnosis of occupational asthma; for 8 persons the diagnosis of "probably occupational" asthma was made by only one of the doctors; three of these persons had previously used ECA adhesives at work. Occupational asthma was finally agreed upon in 8 cases. The authors [36] emphasize, however, that it is not possible to conclude from the results of this study that ECA exposure results in occupational asthma.

The same authors [35] had previously examined 5 persons exposed to lead and 16 exposed to ECA in a factory producing metal products. Medical questionnaires were filled in by these employees and air concentrations were determined. Lead in the air did not exceed the detection limit and biological monitoring results were in the normal range. ECA was determined as 4.6 mg/m^3 (25 cm and 75 cm from the automatic ECA applicator). Persons exposed to ECA reported more symptoms of the upper respiratory passages – stuffy nose, irritation or inflammation of the throat – than did those exposed to lead. The employees exposed to ECA were therefore studied again by means of another questionnaire. Some reported shortness of breath, often starting in the evening or during the night after they had worked with ECA; at times their sleep was disturbed. Many had used the ECA adhesive since it had first been introduced into the process at a time when poorer ventilation had probably led to higher exposure concentrations. A few individuals reported that even minimal contact with ECA resulted in irritation and shortness of breath.

3 Effects on Animals

3.1 Histotoxicity – cytotoxicity

The use of ECA during surgery in animals (e.g. on the rabbit brain [64], in the cat middle ear [65], during experimental osteosynthesis in the rabbit [66]) leads either to inflammation and necrosis or to inhibition of bone growth at the contact sites and to an associated inflammatory reaction with round cell and macrophage infiltration.

Commercial-grade and medical-grade ECA adhesives were introduced transorbitally into the subarachnoid space of 25 cats in the vicinity of the right middle cerebral artery. Neuropathological examination after intervals between 2 days and 6 months revealed with both types of ECA adhesive, in comparison with sham operated controls, acute and chronic granulotamous inflammation of the meninges and severe vascular damage including vessel wall necrosis, inflammation, thrombosis and occasional haemorrhage. Most treated animals had cerebral infarcts of variable size in the ECA distribution region [67]

MCA implants induce, for example, severe axonal and neuronal damage in nerve tissue. In peripheral nerves one finds epineurial inflammation, the perineurium is also affected and tubular demyelination is produced. In the cortex there is necrosis and occasionally abscess production and glial degeneration [4, 8].

There are numerous studies on tissue tolerance of cyanoacrylates. The most important results are described below.

Cyanoacrylate implants and cyanoacrylates added to cell cultures are cytotoxic; MCA is the most toxic, followed by ECA; homologues with longer alkyl chains are less effective [6–9, 15, 43, 44, 56, 68, 69]. MCA and ECA produce severe inflammation, pus formation and necrosis and prevent both collagen production and granulation [7, 9].

One hour after the application of MCA monomer (saturated filter paper discs) to monolayer cultures of mouse fibroblasts, clear zones indicating cytotoxicity were already apparent [68].

In long term studies on the local toxicity of 4 different technical-grade cyanoacrylate adhesives in the rabbit eye, a thin layer of adhesive was applied with a brush to the cornea, conjunctiva and sclera of 47 rabbits [70]. Mechanical irritation and tissue reaction of various severity and duration were the result. In the rabbit eye one drop of another technical-grade adhesive consisting primarily of MCA caused adhesions of the lids, irritation of the conjunctiva and staining of the cornea. The eye returned to normal within 14 days [1]. Similar results were obtained by Seabaugh *et al.* [71] in the rabbit eye with 9 cyanoacrylate adhesives containing MCA or ECA: they produced severe tissue reaction with iritis, conjunctivitis and opacity.

The cytotoxic effects seen in chicken embryo liver culture after an 8 hour exposure to MCA were described as follows [52]: pyknotic nuclei, nuclear fragmentation and denaturation of the nucleoplasm, cytoplasmic vacuolization, mitochondrial damage, absence of glycogen granules. Lysosomes, lipofuscin, denuded rough endoplasmic reticulum and free ribosomes indicate extensive, non-specific cellular damage. The local toxic effects of MCA monomer and polymer are similar. There is a positive correlation between the absorption rate of the polymer and the degree of local inflammation it produces [69]. Cyanoacrylates with longer alkyl chains, however, produce proliferation of the surrounding connective tissue, foreign body response with giant cell development, leukocytic infiltration, phagocytosis and transient localized inflammation [5, 6, 9, 15, 49, 56, 72, 73].

Factors which have been suggested to be responsible for the histotoxicity include:

1. the release of the metabolites formaldehyde, cyanoacetate and also cyanide [6, 56, 74],
2. the temperature increase associated with polymerization [6, 74],
3. the loss of intracellular and extracellular water to the polymer [74],
4. mechanical irritation caused by the polymer [75].

The higher toxicity of short chain cyanoacrylates could be caused by their more rapid release of formaldehyde and cyanoacetate, the relatively high proportion of cyano groups, the more exothermic reaction producing coagulation necrosis. No statistically significant difference could be demonstrated between the homologues with respect to loss of tissue water to the polymerization reaction nor could a correlation between water loss and tissue damage be shown [74].

Cyanoacrylates inhibit the growth of some microorganisms [8, 76, 77]. According to Blum [78] this is an effect of cyanoacrylate vapour; they do not diffuse in agar. Freshly polymerized isobutyl 2-cyanoacrylate is said to be more cytotoxic than that which was exposed to the air for 24 hours prior to polymerization. It is not clear whether the volatile toxic component is an additive (e.g., SO_2 which prevents spontaneous polymerization) [79] or a contaminant in the monomer (e.g., formic acid [73]).

3.2 Inhalation

There are no studies available on inhalation of MCA or ECA by animals. Experiments in which isobutyl 2-cyanoacrylate, as used in dentistry, was sprayed into the oral cavity of rats revealed no deleterious effects on the respiratory or gastrointestinal tract [14].

3.3 Oral administration

Experiments with animals which were not described in more detail are said to indicate that monomeric MCA adhesive administered directly into the stomach and allowed to polymerize there is non-toxic [1].

Young rats were fed for 10 days on a diet containing powdered butyl 2-cyanoacrylate polymer (0.4–6.4 mg/day). After the tenth day they received standard chow again and after 90 days they were sacrificed for examination. Neither an effect on weight gain nor any systemic toxic effects on the internal organs could be demonstrated. It was not possible to feed the animals a lethal dose [17].

3.4 Dermal application

Acute dermal toxicity could not be demonstrated with a technical-grade MCA adhesive when 10 ml/kg body weight was applied to guinea pigs [1]. There are no other available studies on dermal toxicity of MCA or ECA.

More detailed studies of dermal toxicity have been carried out with isoamyl 2-cyanoacrylate which produced erythema and oedema on rabbit skin after a single application of monomer, which polymerized on the skin, and an exposure time of 24 hours to 2 weeks. Repeated application within 21 days (0.05–2.0 ml/kg bw/week) was not lethal and produced no behavioural changes. Skin irritation was dose-dependent. Histological examination revealed slight capillary dilatation, moderate oedema between the epidermis and dermis and slight focal accumulation of round cell infiltrate [60].

3.5 Allergenic effects

21 different acrylates including methyl and butyl 2-cyanoacrylate were tested for their ability to induce contact dermatitis in guinea pigs. Negative results in the Polak sensitization test were obtained with all C2-substituted acrylates including methyl methacrylate, which has been shown to cause contact dermatitis in man [80].

4 Reproductive and Developmental Toxicity

There are no reproduction or teratogenesis studies available with ECA or MCA.

5 Genotoxicity

MCA (Eurecryl 2400®) and ECA (Eurecryl 2450®) were tested as suspensions of their powdered polymers in the standard plate test with *S. typhimurium* TA1535,

TA100, TA1537, TA1538 and TA98 and concentrations ranging from 0.01 to 5 mg per plate with and without metabolic activation. ECA was not mutagenic in any of the bacterial strains whereas MCA with S9 mix was shown reproducibly to be a weak, dose-dependent mutagen in TA100 [23, 24].

Commercial-grade cyanoacrylate adhesives – methyl, ethyl, allyl and butyl 2-cyanoacrylate – were tested in a spot test according to Ames as well as in a spot test designed for volatile compounds with the *S. typhimurium* strains TA100, TA1535, TA98 and TA1538. Only the two MCA adhesives (Tixo K 100 and Cyanolite 102) were mutagenic in both tests in *S. typhimurium* TA100 with and without metabolic activation but not in the other strains [25]. Also in the plate incorporation assay according to Ames the two MCA adhesives were mutagenic in TA100 without metabolic activation. The authors concluded that the methyl 2-cyanoacrylate monomer itself is responsible for the mutagenic effect and not any impurities or breakdown products.

These positive results have been confirmed in other studies of commercial-grade cyanoacrylate adhesives and their corresponding cyanoacrylic ester monomers [26, 27]. The plate assay was used with the *S. typhimurium* strains TA1535, TA1537, TA1538, TA98 and TA100 with and without metabolic activation as well as the modified spot test for volatile substances with TA100, as previously described by Andersen *et al.* [25]. In both test systems MCA and the MCA commercial-grade adhesives (Amicon CY-2000 and Loctite 493) were mutagenic with and without S9 mix, in the plate test at $\sim$ 300 µg/plate and more. With ECA the results were negative in both tests.

Of the cyanoacrylic esters and cyanoacrylate adhesives tested – methyl, ethyl, n-butyl and isobutyl 2-cyanoacrylate, methyl 2-cyano-3-phenylacrylate, methyl 2-cyano-3-(2-methylphenyl)acrylate, methyl 2-cyano-3-(2-bromophenyl)acrylate – the only direct mutagen apart from MCA was methyl 2-cyano-3-(2-bromophenyl)acrylate in TA1535; MCA was the most toxic substance tested ($>$ 500 µg/plate) [26, 27].

MCA was shown to be bacteriostatic with a variety of different kinds of bacteria (*Staphylococcus aureus*, *Proteus sp.*, *Pyozyaneus sp.*, *Escherichia coli* and enterococci) [28].

In another study too, MCA was mutagenic in *the S. typhimurium* strain TA100 both with and without metabolic activation with rat or hamster liver microsomes. Negative results were obtained with the strains TA1535, TA1537 and TA98 [29].

Weak, dose-dependent mutagenicity was also found with a n-butyl 2-cyanoacrylate adhesive (histoacryl blue) in TA1537 but only after activation with mixed function oxidases [81].

MCA (Eurecryl 2400®) was tested in two independent HGPRT tests with V 79 Chinese hamster cells. Because the substance was more cytotoxic in the absence of S9 mix lower concentrations had to be used in the tests without metabolic activation (5, 15, 25, 35 µg/ml) than in those with S9 mix (20, 50, 70, 90 µg/ml). The results of both tests were negative both with and without metabolic activation [82].

6 Carcinogenicity

Sprague-Dawley rats (60 males and 55 females, controls: 14 males and 12 females) received a single injection of 0.1 or 0.4 ml MCA monomer (containing 20% polymer) into a wide, shallow pocket dissected in the dorsal subcutis and were observed for 19.5 months. In all animals a firm lump of polymer developed within 1 minute and within 24 hours at the implant site there was a marked inflammatory reaction which subsided within two weeks in some rats and persisted longer in others. The MCA masses decreased in size only slowly: in the 0.1 ml group palpable masses were present at the implant site in 56% of the animals after 3 months, in 42% after 6 months and still in 14% after 12 months. In all rats in the 0.4 ml group MCA masses were still palpable after 1 year, in 10/11 animals after 15 months. Fibrosarcomas developed at the implant site in 12% of the animals from the high dose group, 2 metastasized to the lung. The first tumour was observed after 11 months. At termination after 19.5 months metaplasia and focal anaplastic proliferation of the cells of the injected site were found in one rat of the 0.1 ml group [16].

Dogs were injected with 0.1 or 0.4 ml MCA in the same way in a flat subcutaneous pocket in the proximal thigh. Although there was an initial inflammatory reaction which persisted for 2 to 3 weeks no other effects were observed during the subsequent 24 months. After 6 to 8 months the palpable lumps of MCA at the injection sites had disappeared. All of the organs were histologically normal. Dogs, therefore, degraded the locally formed MCA polymer more rapidly than did rats in which tumours developed at the injection site in those animals in which large palpable masses of polymer persisted for longer than 11 months. [16].

In three strains of mice which differ in their susceptibility to carcinogenic substances (C 3H, Swiss albino, C-57 Black) a single subcutaneous injection of 0.3 ml MCA or MCA adhesives produced no tumours within 6 months [18]; this observation period is, however, too short.

7 Manifesto (MAK value, classification)

Industrial experience and studies of model inhalation exposures at work indicate that MCA concentrations ≥ 3 ml/m^3 can cause localized lesions. Since no long-term studies have been published on inhalation of cyanoacrylates by animals, it is not possible to predict long-term effects.

Methyl 2-cyanoacrylate (MCA) and ethyl 2-cyanoacrylate (ECA) have been shown in numerous studies from the occupational medical sector to be severe sensitizers of skin and mucous membranes. Although it has been reported several times that at high relative humidity the monomer polymerizes so rapidly that the sensitization reactions may be kept in check, studies on sensitized persons have shown that under conditions which are like those at work, attacks may still be induced even after a considerable increase in humidity. It must also be taken into consideration that under workplace conditions the effectiveness of humidifiers is variable and that accidental breakdown would lead to a rapid increase in the monomer concentration.

MCA in the pure form as well as in MCA adhesives has been shown reproducibly to be mutagenic in one *Salmonella* strain (TA100); negative results were obtained in the HGPRT test. With ECA, on the other hand, the various forms of the Ames test all yielded negative results. The reason for this difference between MCA and ECA is not known.

In studies in which MCA was injected into rats local tumours, some of which metastasized, were formed at the injection site. These studies do not fulfill present day requirements. Their relevance for the carcinogenic risk for man is also difficult to estimate for the following reasons:

- rapid polymerization in the aqueous milieu of tissues inhibits the genotoxic action of the monomer;
- the polymer produced at the injection site is degraded at different speeds in different animal species. In comparison to rats, dogs break down the depots more rapidly and, presumably for this reason, do not develop tumours;
- implant studies with plastics and metals have shown that physical form is a critical factor in local tumorigenesis.

These interpretative difficulties and the low probability that MCA or ECA could have an effect at workplaces in the form tested in this experiment make it impossible to use the data to estimate the risk for man or to classify the substances into one of the existing groups of occupational carcinogens.

A MAK value of 2 ml/m^3 corresponding to 8 mg/m^3 suffices to prevent acute irritation. The danger that exposure might not be noticed is very small because the odour threshold is about 1 ml/m^3.

There is not enough information available to establish a MAK value for ECA.

For the reasons given above MCA and ECA must be designated with an "S".

It is not possible to classify MCA or ECA in one of the groups of germ cell mutagens because reproductive toxicity studies are not available.

Because of the mutagenicity of MCA observed in *S. typhimurium* TA100 there is a need for further studies to clarify the mutagenic potential of this substance and for longer term inhalation studies with appropriate animal species to throw light on a possible carcinogenic effect.

8 References

1. Eastman Chemical International Company: Unpublished communication, Eastman Kodak Company, Kingsport, Tennessee, USA, February 9, 1977
2. Eastman Chemical International Company: Unpublished report *Eastman 910 Adhesive*, 1958
3. Schering AG: Unpublished report, *Cyanacrylat* WOK/D2-C6, Schering AG, D-4619 Bergkamen, July 1974
4. Kline, D. G., G. J. Hayes: *J. Neurosurg. 20*, 647 (1963)
5. Woodward, S. C., J. B. Herrmann, F. Leonard: *Fed. Proc. 23*, 495 (1964)
6. Woodward, S. C., J. B. Herrmann, J. L. Cameron, G. Brandes, E. J. Pulaski, F. Leonard: *Ann. Surg. 162*, 113 (1965)
7. Woodward, S. C.: *Ann. N.Y. Acad. Sci. 146*, 225 (1968)
8. Lehman, R. A. W., G. J. Hayes, F. Leonard: *Arch. Surg. 93*, 441 (1966)
9. Lehman, R. A. W., G. J. Hayes: *Surgery 61*, 915 (1967)

10. Mastalerski, J., S. Leszczynki, W. Zagorski, J. Bokwa, Z. Jezewksi: *Pol. Rev. Radiol. Nucl. Med.* *35*, 753 (1971)
11. Herrmann, J. B., S. C. Woodward, L. S. Meriwether, L. E. Benjamin: *Res. Commun. chem. Path. Pharmacol. 3*, 155, (1972)
12. Schenker, J. G., W. Z. Polishuk: *Contraception 7*, 145 (1973)
13. Gennaro, A. R., C. A. Moreira: *Dis. Colon Rect. 19*, 245 (1976)
14. Bhaskar, S. N., D. E. Cutright, J. D. Beasley, J. P. Ward: *Oral Surg. 29*, 313 (1970)
15. Nelson. R. A., E. H. Banitt, D. C. Kvam, J. K. Harrington, J. E. Robertson, J. S. Buelow: *Arch. Surg. 100*, 295 (1970)
16. Page, R. C., E. J. Larson, E. Siegmund: "Chronic toxicity studies of methyl-2-cyanoacrylate in dogs and rats" p 11: in Healey, J. E. (Ed.): *A Symposium on Physiological Adhesives*, University of Texas, Houston, USA, 3./4.2.1966
17. Ousterhout, D. K., H. W. Larsen, P. M. Margetis, F. Leonard: *Oral Surg. 27*, 275 (1969)
18. Just Viera, J. O., G. A. Escalera, G. H. Yeager: *Bal. Ass. Med. Puerto Rico 62*, 181 (1970)
19. Woodward, S. C.: *J. Amer. med. Ass. 201*, 1052 (1967)
20. Collins, J. A., K. C. Pani, M. M. Seidenstein, G. Brandes, F. Leonard: *Surgery 65*, 256 (1969)
21. Matsumoto, T., C. A. Heisterkamp: *Amer. Surg. 35*, 825 (1969)
22. Greer, R. O., *Oral Surg. 40*, 659 (1975)
23. Lang, R.: *Prüfung von Eurecryl 2400® auf mutagene Wirkung an Salmonella typhimurium TA1535, TA100, TA1537, TA1538 und TA98 ("Ames-Test")*, Unpublished report, Fa. Schering AG, Pharma-Forschung, D-1000 Berlin, 4.1.1980
24. Lang, R.: *Prüfung von Eurecryl 2450® auf mutagene Wirkung an Salmonella typhimurium TA1535, TA100, TA1537, TA1538 und TA98 ("Ames-Test")*, Unpublished report, Fa. Schering AG, Pharma-Forschung, D-1000 Berlin, 4.1.1980
25. Andersen, M., M.-L. Binderup, P. Kiel, H. Larsen, J. Maxild, S. H. Hansen: *Mutat. Res. 102*, 373 (1982)
26. Rietveld, E. C., M. A. Garnaat, F. Seutter-Berlage: *Naunyn-Schmiedeberg's Arch. Pharmacol. 330*, R 22 (1985)
27. Rietveld, E. C., M. A. Garnaat, F. Seutter-Berlage: *Mutat. Res. 188*, 97 (1987)
28. Heiss, W. H.: *Progr. Pediat. Surg. 1*, 99 (1970)
29. Zeiger, E., B. Anderson, S. Haworth, T. Lawlor, K. Mortelmans, W. Speck: *Environm. Mutag. 9, Suppl. 9*, 1 (1987)
30. Soubrier, R., J. Paquet: *Arch. Mal. prof. 33*, 204 (1972)
31. Calnan, C. D.: *Contact Dermatitis 5*, 165 (1979)
32. Lozewicz, S., A. G. Davison, A. Hopkirk, P. S. Burge, D. A. R. Boldy, J. F. Riordan, D. V. McGivern, B. W. Platts, D. Davies, A. J. Newman Taylor: *Thorax 40*, 836 (1985)
33. Kopp, S. K., R. T. McKay, D. R. Moller, K. Cassedy, S. M. Brooks: *Ann. intern. Med. 102*, 613 (1985)
34. Shelley, E. D., W. B. Shelley: *J. Amer. med. Ass. 252*, 2455 (1984)
35. Lee, S. A., M. A. London: Health Hazard Evaluation Report No. HETA-84-011-1567, KP Industries, Delphos, Ohio, NIOSH, USDHHS, Cincinnati, OH 45226, USA, 1985
36. London, M. A., S. A. Lee: Health Hazard Evaluation Report No. HETA-84-371-1729, Orbitron Products, Delphos, Ohio, NIOSH, USDHHS, Cincinnati, OH 45226, USA, 1986
37. Anon.: *Food Cosmet. Toxicol. 11*, 314 (1973)
38. Editorial: *J. Amer. med. Ass. 201*, 195 (1967)
39. Refojo, M. F.: in Polack, F. M. (Ed.): *Corneal and external diseases of the eye*. First Inter-American Symposium, p 183, Charles C. Thomas, Springfield, Ill., USA, 1970
40. Gazarian, A. V.: *Zh. Eksp. Klin. Med. 15*, 107 (1975)
41. Orlowski, T., A. Badowski, W. Kurnatowski: *Zbl. Chir. 101*, 1301 (1976)
42. Leonard, F., R. K. Kulkarni, G. Brandes, J. Nelson, J. J. Cameron: *J. appl. Polymer Sci. 10*, 259 (1966)
43. Leonard, F., R. K. Kulkarni, J. Nelson: *J. Biomed. Mater. Res. 1*, 3 (1967)
44. Matsumoto, T., R. M. Hardaway, C. A. Heisterkamp, K. C. Pani, F. Leonard: *Arch. Surg. 94*, 861 (1967)
45. McGee, W. A., F. L. Oglesy, R. L. Raleigh, D. W. Fassett: *Amer. industr. Hyg. Ass. J. 29*, 558 (1968)

46. Florence, A. T., M. E. Haq, J. R. Johnson: *J. Pharm. Pharmacol. 28*, 539 (1976)
47. Cameron, J. L., S. C. Woodward, E. J. Pulaski, H. K. Sleeman, G. Brandes, R. K. Kulkarni, F. Leonard: *J. Surgery 58*, 424 (1965)
48. Leroy, J. P., J. A. Barra, J. F. Charles: *Arch. Anat. path. 22*, 147 (1974)
49. Saeger, W., J. Plage, R. Pfalz: *Z. Laryng. Rhinol. 51*, 118 (1972)
50. Pani, K. C., G. V. Gladieux, G. Brandes, R. K. Kulkarni, F. Leonard: *Surgery 63*, 481 (1968)
51. Hegyeli, A. F.: *In Vitro 7*, 267 (1972)
52. Hegyeli, A. F.: *J. Biomed. Mater. Res. 7*, 205 (1973)
53. Ousterhout, D. K., G. V. Gladieux, C. W. R. Wade, G. Brandes, P. M. Margetis, F. Leonard: *Oral Surg. 27*, 410 (1969)
54. Ousterhout, D. K., G. V. Gladieux, F. Leonard: *J. Biomed. Mater. Res. 2*, 157 (1968)
55. Reynolds, R. C. et. al.: *Proc. of a Symposium on Physiological Adhesives*, University of Texas, p 24, 1966, cited in: Houston, S., D. K. Ousterhout, K. H. Sleeman, F. Leonard: *J. Biomed. Mater. Res. 4*, 25 (1970)
56. Leonard, F.: *Ann. N.Y. Acad. Sci. 146*, 203 (1968)
57. Lindenau, K.-F., H. A. Hackensellner, D. Oldag: *Dtsch. Gesundh.-Wes. 28*, 218 (1973)
58. Wade, C. W. R., F. Leonard: *J. Biomed. Mater. Res. 6*, 215 (1972)
59. Kulkarni, R. K., G. A. Hanks, K. C. Pani, F. Leonard: *J. Biomed. Mater. Res. 1*, 11 (1967)
60. Arthaud, L. E., G. R. Lewellen, W. A. Akers: *J. Biomed. Mater. Res. 6*, 201 (1972)
61. Balent, A.: *Amer. J. Ophthal. 82*, 501 (1976)
62. De Fonseka, C. P.: *Brit. med. J. 2*, 234 (1976)
63. Chou, S. N.: *J. Neurosurg. 46*, 266 (1977)
64. Zumpano, B. J., L. R. Jacobs, J. B. Hall, G. Margolis, E. Sachs: *Surg. Neurol. 18*, 452 (1982)
65. Koltai, P. J., A. R. Eden: *Ann. Otol. (St. Louis) 92*, 29 (1983)
66. Forssell, H., H. Aro, A. J. Aho: *Arch. orthop. traumat. Surg. 103*, 278 (1984)
67. Smith, T. W., U. DeGirolami, R. M. Crowell: *J. Neurosurg. 62,* 108 (1985)
68. De Renzis, F. A., J. J. Aleo: *Oral Surg. 30*, 803 (1970)
69. Bischoff, F.: *Clin. Chem. 18*, 869 (1972)
70. Khodak, R. A., A. M. Poliakova, K. A. Mager: *Oftal. Zh. 30*, 539 (1975)
71. Seabaugh, V. M., G. W. Bierbower, C. A. Hoheisel, J. McLaughlin: *Toxicol. appl. Pharmacol. 33*, 141 (1975)
72. Wade, G. W.: *Oral Surg. 28*, 226 (1969)
73. Aronson, S. B., P. R. B. McMaster, T. E. Moore, M. A. Coon: *Arch. Ophthal. 84*, 342 (1970)
74. Aleo, J. J., F. A. De Renzis: *Pharmacol. Ther. Dent. 2*, 21 (1975)
75. Gasset, A. R., C. I. Hood, E. D. Ellison, H. E. Kaufman: *Invest. Ophthal. 9*, 3 (1970)
76. Bhaskar, S. N., J. Frisch, P. M. Margetis, F. Leonard: *Oral Surg. 22*, 526 (1966)
77. Jandinski, J., S. Sonis: *J. dent. Res. 50*, 1557 (1971)
78. Blum, G. N., W. A. Nolte, P. B. Robertson: *J. dent. Res. 54*, 500 (1975)
79. Spangberg, L., H. Rodrigues, K. Langeland: *Oral Surg. 37*, 438 (1974)
80. Parker, D., J. L. Turk: *Contact Dermatitis 9*, 55 (1983)
81. Marck, P. A., J. E. Cummins, K. Galil, I. Schofield, G. Z. Wright: *J. dent. Res. 61*, Abstr. 983 (1982)
82. LMP Darmstadt: *Test report of study LMP 049 – Test compound: Eurecryl® 2400*, Unpublished report, Laboratorium für Mutagenitätsprüfung an der Techn. Hochschule, D-6100 Darmstadt, 11. 11. 1983

completed 29. 5. 1989

4,4'-Methylene-bis(N,N-dimethylaniline)

Classification/MAK value:	**see Section III A2)** **MAK List 1988**
Classification/MAK value dates from:	**1988**
Synonyms:	4,4'-bis(dimethylamino)diphenyl- methane p,p'-bis(dimethylamino)diphenyl- methane tetramethyldiaminodiphenylmethane bis(p-(dimethylamino)phenyl)- methane methane base methylene base Michler's base Michler's hydride Michler's methane reduced Michler's ketone N,N,N',N'-tetramethyl-p,p'-diamino- diphenylmethane
Chemical name (CAS):	4,4'-methylenebis(N,N-dimethyl)- benzenamine
CAS number:	101-61-1
Structural formula:	$(CH_3)_2N$—⟨◯⟩—CH_2—⟨◯⟩—$N(CH_3)_2$
Molecular formula:	$C_{17}H_{22}N_2$
Molecular weight:	254.4
Melting point:	90–91 °C
Boiling point:	390 °C (sublimation)

1 ml/m³ (ppm) = 10.55 mg/m³   **1 mg/m³ = 0.094 ml/m³ (ppm)**

1 Toxic Effects and Modes of Action

4,4'-Methylenebis(N,N-dimethylaniline) seems, from the few available reports, not to be very poisonous when administered for a short period. After chronic administration, 4,4'-methylenebis(N,N-dimethylaniline) induces follicular adenomas and carcinomas of the thyroid gland in rats and increases the frequency of hepatocellular adenomas in mice. In addition in both species non-neoplastic proliferative changes are produced in the thyroid gland.

The bladder tumours in persons working in auramine production in so-called methane base works, could not be unambiguously related to 4,4'-methylenebis(N,N-dimethylaniline) exposure.

In short-term tests, 4,4'-methylenebis(N,N-dimethylaniline) and all its demethylated breakdown products have been shown to be mutagenic, but to varying extents.

4,4'-Methylenebis(N,N-dimethylaniline) binds to RNA and DNA.

1.1 Pharmacokinetics

One and three hours after i.p. injection of methylene-[^{14}C]-labelled 4,4'-methylenebis(N,N-dimethylaniline) into Osborne-Mendel rats, the radioactivity was found mostly in the small intestine, adipose tissue and the liver, 24 hours later mostly in the large intestine and the adipose tissue. After oral administration, most of the radioactivity (73%) was still in the animal after 24 hours; 15.2% was detected in the urine, 5.1% in the faeces and none in the exhaled air [1].

Demethylation, acetylation and hydroxylation of the methylene group seem to be the principal metabolic reactions of 4,4'-methylenebis(N,N-dimethylaniline) in the rat; N,N'-diacetyl-4,4'-(hydroxymethylene)dianiline was the main metabolite, making up 36% of the radioactivity found in the urine. Attempts to identify the smaller peaks were not successful [1].

Incubation of 4,4'-methylenebis(N,N-dimethylaniline) with rat liver microsomes in the presence of NADPH yields the unsymmetrical twice demethylated N,N-dimethyl-4,4'-methylenedianiline (44.7%) as main product together with the three times demethylated metabolite, N-methyl-4,4'-methylenedianiline (11.8%), the four

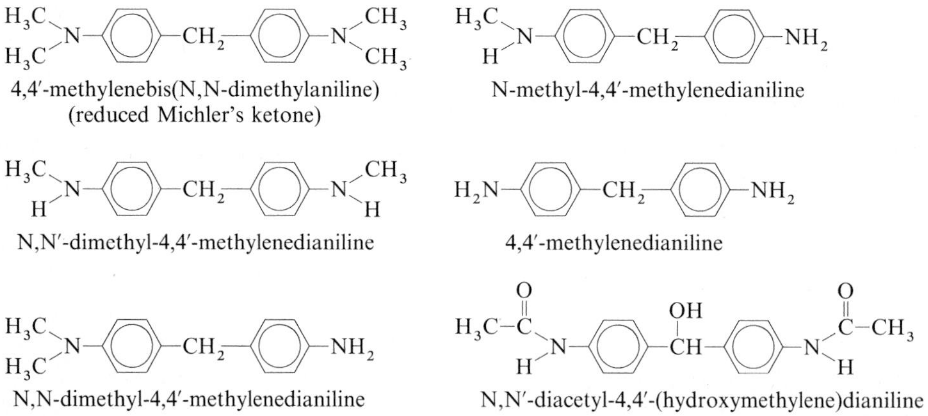

Figure 1. Chemical structures of 4,4'-methylenebis(N,N-dimethylaniline) and its metabolites identified *in vivo*, according to McCarthy *et al.* [1].

fold demethylated 4,4'-methylenedianiline (6.9%) and the symmetrical twice demethylated N,N'-dimethyl-4,4'-methylenedianiline (5.3%) (see Figure 1) [1].

1.2 Binding studies

When 4,4'-methylenebis(N,N-dimethylaniline), unspecifically labelled with tritium, was injected i.p. as a solution in dimethylsulfoxide into male Fischer rats, metabolites were bound irreversibly to the liver DNA and RNA. The binding potential of 4,4'-methylenebis(N,N-dimethylaniline) was, however, less than that of Michler's ketone [2].

Methylene-[^{14}C]-labelled 4,4'-methylenebis(N,N-dimethylaniline) incubated with liver microsomes in the presence of NADPH also caused irreversible binding to macromolecules. More binding was found with S9 mix from mouse liver than with that from rat liver. The binding index was higher with 4,4'-methylenebis(N,N-dimethylaniline) than with Michler's ketone [3].

2 Effects in Man

In retrospective studies of cases of bladder cancer in the German and English dyestuff industries an increased frequency of bladder cancer was found in persons involved in auramine production [4, 5, 6]. It was not possible to incriminate specifically the end product, auramine, an intermediate or the starting material, 4,4'-methylenebis(N,N-dimethylaniline). Three bladder cancer patients from a methane base plant seemed to have been exposed mainly to 4,4'-methylenebis(N,N-dimethylaniline) but also to auramine and/or dimethylaniline and diethylaniline. One of the workers had left the methane base/auramine plant one month before his cancer was diagnosed and had been briefly in contact with benzidine and β-naphthylamine [4].

3 Effects on Animals

3.1 Acute toxicity

The substance seems not to be very poisonous when administered for short periods. An oral LD$_{50}$ for the mouse is given as 3160 mg/kg [7]. The lowest lethal oral dose for the rat was 500 mg/kg [8].

3.2 Subchronic and chronic toxicity

The only available report on the chronic toxicity of 4,4'-methylenebis(N,N-dimethylaniline) describes the range-finding experiment for the NCI carcinogenicity study. 4,4'-Methylenebis(N,N-dimethylaniline), administered for 4 weeks to male and female rats in doses of 145–3155 mg/kg diet, caused no deaths within the subsequent 14 days and no other signs of intoxication in the female animals. All five male animals from the highest dose group (3155 ppm) had rough hair and arched backs. In both sexes but more particularly in the males body weight gain was reduced in a dose-dependent manner:

680 ppm:	♂ 37%,	♀ 11%,
1466 ppm:	♂ 107%,	♀ 49%,
3155 ppm:	♂ 135%,	♀ 61%.

Chronic administration of 750 or 375 mg 4,4'-methylenebis(N,N-dimethylaniline) per kg diet in the NCI studies did not cause any delay in growth but produced

Table 1. Studies on the carcinogenic effects of 4,4'-methylenebis(N,N-dimethylaniline)

Author:	National Cancer Institute [9]
Substance:	technical 4,4'-methylenebis(N,N-dimethylaniline)*
Species:	mouse, B6C3F$_1$, 50 ♂ + 50 ♀, control: 20 ♂ + 20 ♀
Application route:	in the diet
Concentration:	2500, 1250, 0 mg/kg diet
Duration:	78 weeks, killed week 91
Toxicity:	10–15% body weight reduction for males by the end of the study, dose-dependent body weight reduction for females from week 30

	2500	1250	0 mg/kg
survivors in week 91	♂ 50/50 (100%)	47/50 (94%)	20/20 (100%)
	♀ 42/50 (84%)	46/50 (92%)	18/20 (90%)

lesions/tumours in week 91:

liver

	2500	1250	0 mg/kg
adenomas:	♂ 16/48	3/50	2/20
	♀ 22/48	18/49	1/19
carcinomas:	♂ 6/48	9/50	3/20
	♀ 1/48	1/49	0/19
adenomas and carcinomas together:	♂ 22/48 (46%)	12/50 (24%)	5/20 (25%)
	♀ 23/48 (48%)	19/49 (39%)	1/19 (5%)

thyroid gland:

	2500	1250	0 mg/kg
papillary and focal hyperplasia:	♂ 13/49	10/45	0/20
	♀ 6/43	7/43	0/19
adenomatous and colloid goitre:	♂ 24/49	4/45	0/20
	♀ 35/43	25/43	0/19

In some thyroid glands haemosiderin deposits, exfoliated follicular cells and mineralized tissue debris were found in the colloid.

Table 1 (continued)

Author:	National Cancer Institute [9], Murthy [25], Weisburger *et al.* [26]
Substance:	technical 4,4'-methylenebis(N,N-dimethylaniline) *
Species:	rat, Fischer 344, 50 ♂ + 50 ♀, control: 20 ♂ + 20 ♀
Application route:	in the diet
Concentration:	750, 375, 0 mg/kg diet
Duration:	59 weeks, killed in week 104
Toxicity:	merely slightly reduced body weights in ♂ + ♀ at the end of the study

	750	375	0 mg/kg
survivors in week 104:	♂ 44/50 (80%) ♀ 37/50 (74%)	39/50 (78%) 41/50 (82%)	16/20(80%) 17/20(85%)

lesions/tumours in week 104:

thyroid
follicular cell

	750	375	0 mg/kg
cysts:	♂ 3/46 ♀ 1/45	4/50 3/46	0/18 0/20
hyperplasia:	♂ 7/46 ♀ 5/45	0/50 1/46	0/18 0/20
adenomas:	♂ 13/46 (28%) ♀ 13/45 (29%)	0/50 1/46 (2%)	0/18 0/20
carcinomas:	♂ 21/46 (46%) ♀ 23/45 (51%)	4/50 (8%) 3/46 (7%)	1/18 (6%) 0/20
neoplasms: (nos)	♂ 1/46 (2%) ♀ 1/45 (2%)	0/50 0/46	0/18 0/20

C-cell

	750	375	0 mg/kg
hyperplasia:	♂ 1/46 ♀ 1/45	5/50 1/46	0/18 0/20
adenomas:	♂ 3/46 ♀ 1/45	0/50 1/46	2/18 2/20
carcinomas:	♂ 1/46 ♀ 0/45	2/50 1/46	0/18 0/20

pituitary

	750	375	0 mg/kg
adenomas:	♂ 14/48 (29%) ♀ 21/48 (44%)	12/47 (26%) 18/47 (38%)	2/19 (11%) 11/20 (55%)

adrenals

	750	375	0 mg/kg
pheochromocytoma:	♂ 5/48 (10%)	3/47 (6%)	1/20 (5%)

* Technical 4,4'-methylenebis(N,N-dimethylaniline) melting at 85–87°C; thin layer chromatographic determination of purity always revealed only a single spot.

nos: not otherwise specified

substance-related non-neoplastic proliferative changes in the thyroid gland (see Table 1).

Mice tolerated 4,4'-methylenebis(N,N-dimethylaniline) administration in doses of 370–11830 mg/kg diet for four weeks and two weeks recovery period without deaths, signs of toxicity or clinical anomalies. Average weight gain was reduced but the reduction was only about 2–4% and was not dose-dependent. Substance-related non-neoplastic proliferative changes were observed in the thyroid gland after chronic feeding of 1250 or 2500 mg 4,4'-methylenebis(N,N-dimethylaniline) per kg diet (see Table 1) [9].

4 Mutagenicity

4,4'-Methylenebis(N,N-dimethylaniline) has been tested for mutagenicity by a number of authors. In the presence of activating enzymes (rat or mouse liver microsomes), it was mutagenic in *Salmonella typhimurium* TA98 and TA100 [3, 10–12] or only in TA100 [13]. These results were supported and underlined by the finding that also the metabolites found *in vivo*, N,N'-dimethyl-4,4'-methylenedianiline, N,N-dimethyl-4,4'-methylenedianiline, N-methyl-4,4'-methylenedianiline and 4,4'-methylenedianiline (see Figure 1), are unambiguously mutagenic [1]. The strongest mutagen was 4,4'-methylenedianiline from which the authors conclude that the N-methyl groups are not necessary for the activation. 4,4'-Methylenedianiline was mutagenic in TA100, TA97 and TA98 with either hamster or rat liver microsomes, in TA1535 only with microsomes from the hamster liver [14].

Negative results were obtained in the Ames test in some early experiments [15], possibly as a result of insufficient activation [3], and also in TA98 by Dean *et al.* [13].

4,4'-Methylenebis(N,N-dimethylaniline) was also listed in a NTP/NCI review as not mutagenic [16]. Analysis of the results of the 4 laboratories involved, however, revealed repeated weakly mutagenic effects. These were ignored in the rigid, conservative evaluation scheme designed to deal with results from a large number of compounds.

Dean *et al.* [13] also obtained negative results in *Escherichia coli* WP$_2$, WP$_2$uvrA, *Saccharomyces cerevisiae* JD1 and in a rat liver chromosome assay from Dean and Hodson-Walker.

4,4'-Methylenebis(N,N-dimethylaniline) induced weak sister chromatid exchange in rabbit lymphocyte cultures without exogenous metabolic activation [11] and morphological transformation in hamster embryo cells [17].

4,4'-Methylenebis(N,N-dimethylaniline) yielded negative results in the mouse pulmonary tumour bioassay (20–30 strain A mice of both sexes) [18].

Negative results were also obtained with 4,4'-methylenebis(N,N-dimethylaniline) at doses of 2.6 and 1.55 µg per 5.2×10^4 cells in the embryo cell assay with cells from rats infected with Rauscher leukaemia virus [19].

In a host-mediated assay with mice after i.m. administration of 125 mg/kg body weight, 4,4'-methylenebis(N,N-dimethylaniline) yielded positive results in *S. typhimurium* but, after oral administration of 1600 mg/kg body weight, negative results in *S. cerevisiae* [20].

In a DNA repair test in primary cultures of hepatocytes 4,4'-methylenebis(N,N-dimethylaniline) was initially considered to yield weak positive results [21]. Meanwhile, however, the authors describe the result as "according to present day standards definitely – not only weakly – positive" [22].

In a preliminary publication of the results of short-term tests from the NTP programme it is reported that 4,4'-methylenebis(N,N-dimethylaniline) yields positive results in 5 short-term tests, i.e., in the Ames test, in the mouse lymphoma cell mutagenesis assay (positive results in two different laboratories), in the UDS (unscheduled DNA synthesis) assay in primary cultures of rat hepatocytes and in two transformation assays, in mouse lymphoma cells: Balb/c 3T3 cells and in the rat retrovirus system: Rauscher leukaemia virus/rat embryo assay [23, 24].

5 Carcinogenicity

The only available carcinogenicity studies are the two from the NTP programme which are shown in Table 1. It is remarkable that the administration period for rats was only 59 weeks (reason not specified), that the dose for this species was very likely less than the MTD and that the control groups for both species contained only 20 animals. Nevertheless, increased tumour frequencies were obtained. In the rat there were follicular cell adenomas and carcinomas affecting either parts of the thyroid gland or one or both of its lobes and exerting pressure on neighbouring tissues. One follicular cell carcinoma metastasized to the lung. In the mouse 4,4'-methylenebis(N,N-dimethylaniline) induced neoplasia of the liver (adenomas and carcinomas) and follicular cell hyperplasia of the thyroid. The non-neoplastic proliferative changes in the thyroid which are listed together with the tumours for both species were not observed in the controls.

6 Manifesto (MAK value, classification)

4,4'-Methylenebis(N,N-dimethylaniline) and its partly or completely demethylated metabolites are mutagenic in numerous short-term tests. It has been demonstrated that the activation products bind covalently to nucleic acids. Thus 4,4'-methylenebis(N,N-dimethylaniline) has genotoxic potential. It also produced positive results in a transformation test. On long-term administration to rats in animal studies, technical 4,4'-methylenebis(N,N-dimethylaniline), which was, however, pure according to thin layer chromatography, induced follicular cell adenomas and carcinomas of the thyroid in both sexes. In the mouse it increased the frequency of hepatocellular adenomas in both sexes. Hepatocellular carcinomas were observed as well. The spectrum of tumours is the same as is caused by 4,4'-methylenedianiline, the potency is slightly less. The two substances are linked by the stepwise demethylation of 4,4'-methylenebis(N,N-dimethylaniline) demonstrated *in vivo*. Since 4,4'-methylenebis(N,N-dimethylaniline) is a genotoxic substance it is assumed that the thyroid tumours are not the result of a purely hormonal effect. As for other aromatic amines, the increase of the frequency of liver tumours in mice cannot be explained in terms of a purely promoting effect. Together with the structural analogy with 4,4'-methylenedianiline, the results of the animal studies are therefore taken as evidence of a carcinogenic effect of 4,4'-methylenebis(N,N-dimethylaniline). Therefore the substance is classified in Section III A2) of the List of MAK Values.

7 References

1. McCarthy, D. J., R. F. Struck, T.-W. Shih, W. J. Suling, D. L. Hill, S. E. Enke: *Cancer Res. 42,* 3475 (1982)
2. Scribner, J. D., G. Koponen, S. R. Fisk: *Cancer Lett. 9,* 117 (1980)
3. McCarthy, D. J., W. J. Suling, D. L. Hill: *Mutat. Res. 119,* 7 (1983)
4. Gropp, D.: *Zur Ätiologie des sogenannten Anilin-Blasenkrebses,* Thesis, Johannes-Gutenberg-Universität Mainz, D-6500 Mainz, 1958
5. Case, R. A. M., J. T. Pearson: *Brit. J. industr. Med. 11,* 213 (1954)
6. Deutsche Forschungsgemeinschaft (DFG): "Auramine/Auraminebase" In: Henschler D. (Ed.) *Gesundheitsschädliche Arbeitsstoffe, toxikologisch-arbeitsmedizinische Begründung von MAK-Werten.* Verlag Chemie, Weinheim, 1987
7. NCI/Litton Bionetics, Inc. 1972; "Progress Report NO NIH-NCI-C-C-72-3252", submitted for NCI by Litton Bionetics, Inc. (Bethesda), cited in *RTECS, Registry of Toxic Effects of Chemical Substances,* p 395, 1981–82,
8. Dieke, S. H., G. S. Allen, C. P. Richter: *J. Pharmacol. exp. Therap. 90,* 260 (1947)
9. NCI, National Cancer Institute: *Bioassay of 4,4'-Methylene-bis(N,N-dimethyl)-benzamine for possible carcinogenicity,* Techn. Rep. Ser. No. 186, 1979, U.S.D.H.E.W., Public Health Service, N.I.H., U.S.A.
10. Dunkel, V. C., V. F. Simmon: *IARC Sci. Publ. No. 27,* 283 (1980)
11. Waalkens, D. H., H. F. P. Joosten, T. D. Yih, A. Hoekstra: *Mutat. Res. 89,* 197 (1981)
12. Spillman, J. E., J. Gridley, W. D. Ross, V. L. Bell: *Environm. Mutagen. 4,* 322 (1982)
13. Dean, B. J., T. M. Brooks, G. Hodson-Walker, D. H. Hutson: *Mutat. Res. 153,* 57 (1985)
14. Zeiger, E., B. Anderson, S. Haworth, T. Lawlor, K. Mortelmans: *Environm. mol. Mutagen. 11,* Suppl. 12, 1 (1988)
15. International Agency for Research on Cancer (IARC), *IARC Monographs on the Evaluation of the Carcinogenic Risk of Chemicals to Humans, Vol. 27,* p 119 (1982)
16. Dunkel, V. C., E. Zeiger, D. Brusick, E. McCoy, D. McGregor, K. Mortelmans, H. S. Rosenkranz, V. F. Simmon: *Environm. Mutagen. 7, Suppl. 5,* 1 (1985)
17. Pienta, R. J., J. A. Poiley, W. B. Lebherz: *Int. J. Cancer 19,* 642 (1977)
18. Maronpot, R. R., H. P. Witschi, L. H. Smith, J. L. McCoy: *Environm. Sci. Res. 27,* 341 (1983)
19. Traul, K. A., K. Takayama, V. Kachevsky, R. J. Hink, J. S. Wolff: *J. appl. Toxicol. 1,* 190 (1981)
20. Simmon, V. F., H. S. Rosenkranz, E. Zeiger, L. A. Poirier: *J. Nat. Cancer Inst. 62,* 911 (1979)
21. Williams, G. M., M. F. Laspia, V. C. Dunkel: *Mutat. Res. 97,* 359 (1982)
22. Williams, G. M.: Personal communication to the Commission, 5.1.1987
23. Mitchell, A. D., C. J. Rudd, B. C. Myhr, W. C. Caspary, S. Poulton, Y. J. Lee: *Environm. Mutagen. 4,* 394 (1982)
24. NTP: *Technical Bulletin No. 9,* 1983, U.S. Department of Health and Human Services, Research Triangle Park, 27709, N.C.,U.S.A
25. Murthy, A. S. K.: *Toxicol. Lett. 6,* 391 (1980)
26. Weisburger, E. K., K. Murthy, H. Lilja, J. C. Lamb: *J. Nat. Cancer Inst. 72,* 1457 (1984)

completed 19.5.1988

4-Nitrobiphenyl   H

Classification/MAK value:	see Section III A 2) MAK List 1985
Classification/MAK value dates from:	1985
Synonyms:	p-nitrobiphenyl p-nitrodiphenyl 4-nitrodiphenyl 4-phenyl-nitrobenzene p-phenyl-nitrobenzene PNB
Chemical name (CAS):	4-nitro-1,1′-biphenyl
CAS number:	92-93-3
Structural formula:	
Molecular formula:	$C_{12}H_9NO_2$
Molecular weight:	199.2
Melting point:	113.8 °C
Boiling point:	340 °C

1 ml/m³ (ppm) = 8.26 mg/m³   **1 mg/m³ = 0.12 ml/m³ (ppm)**

1 Toxic Effects and Modes of Action

4-Nitrobiphenyl seems no longer to be produced on a commercial scale anywhere in the world [1]. The possibility that it occurs in not inconsiderable amounts as an impurity in occupational chemicals, however, cannot be ruled out with certainty.

Administered acutely to animals, 4-nitrobiphenyl proved not to be very toxic [2]. However, the central question with this compound is whether it has carcinogenic activity. 4-Aminobiphenyl, which has proved to be markedly carcinogenic in man [5], was shown to be a metabolite of 4-nitrobiphenyl *in vivo* in rats [3] and also in liver homogenates *in vitro* [4]. In monkeys and dogs after administration of 4-nitro-biphenyl, small amounts of N-hydroxy-4-aminobiphenyl and 4-nitrosobiphenyl were found [6]. Bladder carcinoma was induced in the dog after oral administration of 4-aminobiphenyl [7].

In *Salmonella typhimurium* a mutagenic effect of 4-nitrobiphenyl could be demonstrated [8, 9] and in *Escherichia coli* both binding to DNA [10] and DNA damage [11]. A carcinogenic effect of 4-nitrobiphenyl in man has not yet been unambiguously demonstrated [1, 12].

2 Effects in Man

In the past 4-nitrobiphenyl seems to have served exclusively as an intermediate in the production of 4-aminobiphenyl [1]. The proof of a causal relationship between a carcinogenic effect and 4-nitrobiphenyl exposure in man has never been demonstrated. When persons handling 4-nitrobiphenyl developed bladder cancer, they had always been exposed to 4-aminobiphenyl as well [1, 12].

3 Effects on Animals

3.1 Acute toxicity

Acute oral administration of 4-nitrobiphenyl to the rat and rabbit revealed that the substance is not very toxic. The LD_{50} after oral administration is given as 2230 mg/kg for the rat and 1970 mg/kg for the rabbit [2].

3.2 Chronic toxicity

Groups of 29–35 newborn male and female Sprague-Dawley rats received a total of eight (weekly) subcutaneous injections of 50 or 100 μmoles 4-nitrobiphenyl (in dimethylsulfoxide) per kilogramme body weight. The study was terminated after 62 weeks. Unlike 1-nitropyrene, which was tested using equimolar doses, 4-nitrobiphenyl revealed no carcinogenic activity in this study [13].

Four female mongrel dogs were each given 0.3 gramme 4-nitrobiphenyl (capsule) three times weekly for 33 months. Within this period and after a total dose of 7–10 g/kg malignant bladder tumours developed in three of the four dogs [7]. In another study six female beagles were each given 1 milligramme of 4-nitrobiphenyl (capsule) per kilogramme body weight five times weekly for the whole of the study which lasted for about 3 years (total dose ~ 0.7 g/kg). None of the six dogs developed a bladder tumour. There were also no other indications of a carcinogenic effect of 4-nitrobiphenyl under these conditions. However, neither 2-naphthylamine nor benzidine yielded evidence of carcinogenic potential under the same conditions in the same study; only with 4-aminobiphenyl were bladder tumours (in 3 cases malignant) found in all six treated dogs [14]. In a similar study five female beagles were each given 0.1 g 4-nitrobiphenyl (capsule) three times weekly. After 31 months and a total dose of about 2 g/kg the study was terminated. Bladder tumours or other growths which could have indicated a carcinogenic effect of 4-nitrobiphenyl did not develop in any of the five dogs. With 2-naphthylamine which was tested at the same time in a similar way, bladder tumours were found in four of five dogs. When the two substances were given together there was evidence of an additive effect in all of the five treated dogs [15].

4 Genotoxicity

4-Nitrobiphenyl was shown to be mutagenic in *S. typhimurium* [8, 9], to cause DNA binding [10] or DNA damage [11] in *E. coli* and *in vitro* transformation of mammalian cells [9, 16].

5 Manifesto (MAK value, classification)

4-Nitrobiphenyl is mutagenic in *Salmonella typhimurium*. After administration of 4-nitrobiphenyl to rats, 4-aminobiphenyl, a substance which is very carcinogenic in man, was detected as a metabolite; in monkeys and dogs N-hydroxy-4-amino-biphenyl and 4-nitrosobiphenyl were found. In the dog 4-nitrobiphenyl has bladder-cancer inducing activity which appears to be weaker than that of 4-aminobiphenyl. Although the evidence for carcinogenicity of 4-nitrobiphenyl comes from only one study and the study has limitations because of the very small numbers of animals treated (4 dogs), the carcinogenic effect in this experiment is still unambiguous. 4-Nitrobiphenyl is therefore classified in Section III A2) of the List of MAK Values. A MAK value cannot be established.

Like 2-naphthylamine and benzidine, e.g., it must be assumed that 4-nitro-biphenyl also penetrates the skin relatively readily. Therefore the designation H is necessary.

6 References

1. International Agency for Research on Cancer (IARC): *IARC Monographs on the Evaluation of the Carcinogenic Risk of Chemicals to Man*, Vol. 4, p 113, Lyon, France, 1974
2. National Institute for Occupational Safety & Health (NIOSH): *Registry of Toxic Effects of Chemical Substances*, p 231, US Department of Health, Education and Welfare, Cincinnati, OH 45226, USA, 1977
3. Laham, S.: *Canad. J. Biochem. 38*, 1383 (1960)
4. Uehleke, H., K. Nestel: *Naunyn-Schmiedeberg's Arch. exp. Path. Pharmak. 257*, 151 (1967)
5. International Agency for Research on Cancer (IARC): *IARC Monographs on the Evaluation of the Carcinogenic Risk of Chemicals to Man*, Vol. 1, p 74, Lyon, France, 1972
6. Radomski, J. L., G. M. Conzelman, A. A. Ray, E. Brill: *J. nat. Cancer Inst. 50*, 989 (1973)
7. Deichmann, W. B., W. M. MacDonald, M. M. Coplan, F. M. Woods, W. A. D. Anderson: *Industr. Med. Surg. 27*, 634 (1958)
8. Simmon, V. F.: *J. nat. Cancer Inst. 62*, 893 (1979)
9. Purchase, I. F. H., E. Longstaff, J. Ashby, J. A. Styles, D. Anderson, P. A. Lefevre, F. R. West-wood.: *Brit. J. Cancer 37*, 873 (1978)

10. Kubinski, H., G. E. Gutzke, Z. O. Kubinski: *Mutat. Res. 89*, 95 (1981)
11. Rosenkranz, H. S., L. A. Poirier: *J. nat. Cancer Inst. 62*, 873 (1979)
12. Cartwright, R. A.: *Environm. Hlth Perspect. 49*, 13 (1983)
13. Hirose, M., M. S. Lee, C. Y. Wang, C. M. King: *Cancer Res. 44*, 1158 (1984)
14. Deichmann, W. B., J. Radomski, E. Class, W. A. D. Anderson, M. Coplan, F. Woods: *Industr. Med. Surg. 34*, 640 (1965)
15. Deichmann, W. B., T. Scotti, J. Radomski, E. Bernal, M. Coplan, F. Woods: *Toxicol. appl. Pharmacol. 7*, 657 (1965)
16. Pienta, R. J., J. A. Poiley, W. B. Lebherz: *Int. J. Cancer 19*, 642 (1977)

completed 10.1.1985

N-Nitrosamines

Classification/MAK value: see Section III A 2)
                                  MAK List 1987

Classification/MAK value dates from: 1987

A report on the carcinogenic effects of the following N-nitrosamines which have been detected in workplace air:

Chemical name:	CAS number:
N-nitrosodi-n-butylamine	924-16-3
N-nitrosodiethanolamine	1116-54-7
N-nitrosodiethylamine	55-18-5
N-nitrosodimethylamine	62-75-9
N-nitrosodi-*i*-propylamine	601-77-4
N-nitrosodi-*n*-propylamine	621-64-7
N-nitrosoethylphenylamine	612-64-6
N-nitrosomethylethylamine	10595-95-6
N-nitrosomethylphenylamine	614-00-6
N-nitrosomorpholine	59-89-2
N-nitrosopiperidine	100-75-4
N-nitrosopyrrolidine	930-55-2

Structural formula:

$$O = N - N \begin{smallmatrix} \diagup R_1 \\ \diagdown R_2 \end{smallmatrix}$$

1 Toxic Effects and Modes of Action

The nitrosamines belong to one of the most intensively studied classes of substances in modern toxicology. The literature – including numerous reviews and monographs – is so extensive that it has become practically impossible to keep track of it. One reason for this development is that nitrosamines are excellent model substances for experimental cancer research. Most of them are very potent carcinogens with which malignant tumours can be induced, frequently selectively and in high yield, in practically any of the essential organs of any the many and various kinds of experimental animal, depending on the kind of N-nitrosamine used and independently of the application route. Some of these dangerous N-nitrosamines are also found in the human environment.

Since a very powerful carcinogenic effect has been demonstrated in animal studies for about 90% of the N-nitrosamines tested to date, the question of carcinogenicity is clearly the key issue in the toxicological assessment.

2 N-Nitrosamines in the occupational environment

It has been possible to synthesize N-nitrosamines since the early years of organic chemistry by means of the reaction of secondary amines with nitrosation agents such as acidic nitrite. More recent studies have shown that nitrosation of the secondary, tertiary and quaternary amino compounds in the human environment can also occur under conditions such as are found, e.g., in the digestive systems of animals and man [1–3]. In addition, nitrogen oxides are evidently able to convert nitrosatable amines into N-nitrosamines. Since nitrogen oxides are ubiquitous in our environment and their occurrence at the workplace in particular is frequently unavoidable (exhaust fumes from internal combustion engines, etc.), the formation of N-nitrosamines must be expected in all places where nitrosatable amines are encountered [see also "The Nitrosation of volatile Amines at the Workplace", this volume].

Extensive measurement programmes in recent years have revealed that not inconsiderable concentrations of N-nitrosamines can occur in the air in foundries, in metal processing workshops and at workplaces in the leather and rubber industries [4, 4a]. The nitrosamines detected in the air at such workplaces are generally not present in the starting materials but are formed spontaneously during the production processes by various mechanisms from nitrosatable amino compounds and nitrosation agents.

According to the measurements which have been carried out to date, we must expect to find not only dimethylnitrosamine, which was classified years ago as "carcinogenic in animals" (III A 2)), but also other N-nitrosamines in the air of more than a few workplaces. Frequently several nitrosamines are formed simultaneously. Present information indicates that the following N-nitrosamines have been detected in workplace air [4, 4a]:

N-nitrosodimethylamine
N-nitrosomethylethylamine
N-nitrosodiethylamine
N-nitrosodi-*n*-propylamine
N-nitrosodi-*i*-propylamine
N-nitrosodi-*n*-butylamine
N-nitrosodiethanolamine
N-nitrosomethylphenylamine
N-nitrosoethylphenylamine
N-nitrosomorpholine
N-nitrosopiperidine
N-nitrosopyrrolidine

3 Combined Action of N-Nitrosamines

Since it is not uncommon to detect more than one N-nitrosamine at the one time in the workplace air, the question of their combined effects is of great practical significance.

In animal studies the N-nitrosamines as a group are carcinogenic in a multitude of organs and tissues. As a rule that is also true for the individual N-nitrosamines, whereby the tumour localization does not only depend on the kind of nitrosamine but also on the species and the dose. Mostly, however, a preferred target organ (or even several) can be recognized. This is frequently the liver, as in the case of ten of the twelve N-nitrosamines listed above (including N-nitrosodimethylamine) (Table 1). Similar tumour localization must be expected in man although additional tumour induction by these N-nitrosamines in other organs and tissues cannot be excluded.

Additive carcinogenic effects have been demonstrated after simultaneous or consecutive administration of carcinogens with very different chemical structures but identical organ specificity; this was not the case for substances with different organ specificities [5]. Studies of the combined application of various N-nitroso compounds to rats indicated that the effects are additive when the substances have the same target organ but that even when the target organs are different a certain additive effect is apparent [6, 7].

Without doubt, almost all questions in the field of combined action of chemicals have still to be answered and that is also true for the combined effects of N-nitrosamines [8]. It is, however, highly likely that at least structurally related N-nitrosamines with similar organ specificity operate additively (Table 1).

Table 1. Principle target organs established in animal studies for the twelve N-nitrosamines shown to occur at places of work

N-nitrosodimethylamine	liver, kidney, lung, blood vessels
N-nitrosomethylethylamine	liver, oesophagus, blood vessels, nasal cavity, bile duct, haematopoietic system
N-nitrosodiethylamine	liver, kidney, oesophagus, respiratory tract, forestomach
N-nitrosodi-*n*-propylamine	liver, kidney. oesophagus, respiratory tract, upper digestive tract, brain, haematopoietic system
N-nitrosodi-*i*-propylamine	liver, respiratory tract
N-nitrosodi-*n*-butylamine	liver, oesophagus, urinary bladder, digestive tract, respiratory tract
N-nitrosodiethanolamine	liver, kidney, respiratory tract
N-nitrosomethylphenylamine	oesophagus, urinary bladder, lung, upper digestive tract
N-nitrosoethylphenylamine	not studied
N-nitrosomorpholine	liver, kidney, respiratory tract, haematopoietic system
N-nitrosopiperidine	liver, oesophagus, respiratory tract, upper digestive tract
N-nitrosopyrrolidine	liver, bile duct, nasal cavity

4 Carcinogenicity

Only those animal studies which have been carried out in the region of the lowest effective dose have been included in the data summaries which follow. This selection of data was made because the question of effectiveness is of particular significance for the carcinogenic N-nitrosamines.

N-Nitrosodimethylamine

Structural formula $O=N-N\begin{smallmatrix}CH_3\\CH_3\end{smallmatrix}$ CAS number: 62-75-9

Species	Number of animals	Treatment	Duration of study	Animals with tumour(s) of the main target organs	Ref.
rat ♂♀	120 per dose	33 ppb in drinking water (2 µg/kg/d) (total dose: ∼ 2 mg/kg)	life	♂: hyperplastic liver nodules (details not specified)	[9]
		132 ppb in drinking water (8 µg/kg/d) (total dose: ∼ 8 mg/kg)	life	♂: carcinogenic (details not specified)	
rat ♂	30	5 mg/l drinking water, 5× weekly for 30 weeks, only at night (total dose: ∼ 45 mg/kg)	2 years	27% liver	[10]
rat ♂♀	6	5 ppm in the diet for 2 years (total dose: ∼ 250 mg/kg)	2 years	0%	[11]
	6	10 ppm in the diet for 2 years (total dose: ∼ 500 mg/kg)	2 years	33% liver	
	6	20 ppm in the diet for 2 years (total dose: ∼ 1000 mg/kg)	2 years	83% liver	
	36	1 × 30 mg/kg p.o.	2 years	20% kidneys	
rat ♂♀	37	2 ppm in the diet for 2 years (total dose: ∼ 100 mg/kg)	2 years	3% liver	[12]
	68	5 ppm in the diet for 2 years (total dose: ∼ 250 mg/kg)	2 years	7% liver	
♀	5	10 ppm in the diet for 2 years (total dose: ∼ 500 mg/kg)	2 years	40% liver	

Species	Number of animals	Treatment	Duration of study	Animals with tumour(s) of the main target organs	Ref.
rat ♂♀	87	0.005 mg/m^3 continuous inhalation (total dose: $\sim$ 1.5 mg/kg)	25 months	no carcinogenic effects	[13]
	61	0.2 mg/m^3 continuous inhalation (total dose: $\sim$ 40 mg/kg)	25 months	12/61 lung (control 5/77) 12/61 liver (control 3/77) 32/61 kidney (control 2/77)	
rat ♂♀	141	1 $\times$ 0.125 mg/rat s.c. (1–7 days old) (total dose: $\sim$ 10 mg/kg)	life	62% kidney 12% liver	[14]
mouse ♂♀	61	10 ppb in drinking water (*in utero* + 25 weeks) (total dose: $\sim$ 0.4 mg/kg)	28 weeks	♂ 8/25 (32%) lung (control 1/23 (4.3%) lung) ♀ 6/36 (17%) lung (control 4/38 (10%) lung) ♂ + ♀ 14/61 (23%) lung (control 5/61 (8.2%) lung)	[15]
mouse ♂♀	77	0.005 mg/m^3 continuous inhalation (total dose: $\sim$ 2 mg/kg)	17 months	no carcinogenic effects	[13]
	101	0.2 mg/m^3 continuous inhalation (total dose: $\sim$ 100 mg/kg)	17 months	19/101 lung (control 3/81) 6/101 liver (control 0/81) 4/101 kidney (control 0/81)	
mouse ♂♀	96	1 $\times$ 0.03 mg/mouse s.c. (1 day old) (total dose: $\sim$ 1 mg/kg)	52 weeks	25% ♂ lung (control 1%) 58% ♀ lung (control 0%) 37% ♂ liver (control 0%) 43% ♀ liver (control 0%)	[16]
mouse ♂♀	7	1 $\times$ 1 mg/kg s.c. (1 day old)	100 weeks	1/7 vessels (control 0/100) 1/7 liver (control 0/100)	[17]
	22	1 $\times$ 10 mg/kg s.c. (1 day old)	100 weeks	6/22 vessels 10/22 liver	
mouse ♂ ♀	47	1 $\times$ 0.025 mg/mouse s.c. (1 day old) (total dose: $\sim$ 1 mg/kg)	life	13/47 liver (control 2/69) 16/47 lung (control 4/69)	[18]
mouse ♂♀ (Swiss)	218	control	life	15% lung, 2% malignant	[19]
	40	1 $\times$ 0.5 mg/kg s.c.	life	17% lung, 7% malignant	
	40	1 $\times$ 1 mg/kg s.c.	life	29% lung, 16% malignant	
	40	1 $\times$ 2 mg/kg s.c.	life	35% lung, 19% malignant	
	40	1 $\times$ 4 mg/kg s.c.	life	39% lung, 21% malignant	
	40	1 $\times$ 8 mg/kg s.c.	life	67% lung, 44% malignant	

Species	Number of animals	Treatment	Duration of study	Animals with tumour(s) of the main target organs	Ref.
mouse (ASW/SN)	145	control	life	37% lung, 9% malignant	[19]
	40	1 × 0.5 mg/kg s.c.	life	49% lung, 6% malignant	
	40	1 × 1 mg/kg s.c.	life	36% lung, 14% malignant	
	40	1 × 2 mg/kg s.c.	life	46% lung, 30% malignant	
	40	1 × 4 mg/kg s.c.	life	41% lung, 28% malignant	
	40	1 × 8 mg/kg s.c.	life	81% lung, 58% malignant	
(A)	144	control	life	22% lung, 1% malignant	
	40	1 × 0.25 mg/kg s.c.	life	29% lung, 8% malignant	
	40	1 × 0.5 mg/kg s.c.	life	28% lung, 8% malignant	
	40	1 × 1 mg/kg s.c.	life	19% lung, 8% malignant	
	40	1 × 2 mg/kg s.c.	life	25% lung, 8% malignant	
	40	1 × 4 mg/kg s.c.	life	34% lung, 5% malignant	

Tumours at other localizations were not indicative of a carcinogenic effect of N-nitrosodimethylamine [19].

Species	Number of animals	Treatment	Duration of study	Animals with tumour(s) of the main target organs	Ref.
mouse ♂	22	1 × 5 mg/kg i.p.	life	50% lung (control 48%)	[20]
	22	1 × 10 mg/kg i.p.	life	84% lung	
	20	1 × 15 mg/kg i.p.	life	80% lung	
mouse ♂♀	34	6 × 1 mg/kg i.p. (7–22 days old)	66 weeks	26% liver (control 0%) 9% lung (control 0%)	[21]
	39	6 × 2 mg/kg i.p. (7–22 days old)	66 weeks	56% liver 15% lung 3% haemangiomas (control 0%)	
	54	6 × 4 mg/kg i.p. (7–22 days old)	66 weeks	72% liver 37% lung 17% haemangiomas	
mouse ♂♀	100	10 × 6 mg/kg i.p.	life	22% vessels (control 3%)	[22]
golden hamster ♂	24	6 × 0.25 mg/hamster s.c. (total dose: ~ 15 mg/kg)	life	50% liver vessels	[23]
Chinese hamster ♂♀	40	control	life	0/40 liver vessels	[24]
	40	0.9 mg/kg/week s.c. (total dose: ~ 32 mg/kg)	life	37/40 liver vessels	
European hamster ♂	10	1.4 mg/kg/week s.c. (total dose: ~ 55 mg/kg)	life	10% liver 20% kidneys } mostly vessel tumours	[25]
♀	10	2.2 mg/kg/week s.c. (total dose: ~ 72 mg/kg)	life	80% liver 50% kidneys }	

Species	Number of animals	Treatment	Duration of study	Animals with tumour(s) of the main target organs	Ref.
golden hamster ♂	15	1.4 mg/kg/week s.c. (total dose: ~ 62 mg/kg)	life	53% liver	[26]
♀	15	1.7 mg/kg/week s.c. (total dose: ~ 54 mg/kg)	life	13% liver	

It may be concluded from the studies listed above that a carcinogenic effect of N-nitrosodimethylamine may be demonstrated in some tests after a total dose of as little as 1 mg/kg body weight.

N-Nitrosomethylethylamine

Structural formula $O=N-N\begin{smallmatrix} CH_3 \\ C_2H_5 \end{smallmatrix}$ CAS number: 10595-95-6

Species	Number of animals	Treatment	Duration of study	Animals with tumour(s) of the main target organs	Ref.
rat ♂	20	6 mg/l drinking water 5× weekly for 30 weeks 0.6 mg/rat/week total dose: 18 mg/rat (total dose ~ 55 mg/kg)	life	15% liver	[27]
	20	30 mg/l drinking water 5× weekly for 30 weeks 3 mg/rat/week total dose: 90 mg/rat (total dose: ~ 270 mg/kg)	life	45% liver 20% nasal cavity 5% oesophagus	
rat ♂	20	150 mg/l drinking water 5× weekly for 30 weeks total dose: 450 mg/rat (total dose: ~ 1350 mg/kg)	life	95% liver (malignant) 85% liver vessels 35% oesophagus 40% leukaemia 15% bile duct (malignant)	[28]
rat ♂♀	11	daily 1 mg/kg in the drinking water (total dose: ~ 420 mg/kg)	life	6/11 liver	[29]
	4	daily 2 mg/kg in the drinking water (total dose: ~ 750 mg/kg)	life	4/4 liver	

These results seem to indicate that N-nitrosomethylethylamine is less carcinogenic as well as being a less potent DNA-alkylating agent [30] than N-nitrosodimethylamine or N-nitrosodiethylamine. Nevertheless, N-nitrosomethylethylamine must be recognized as a very strong carcinogen.

N-Nitrosodiethylamine

Structural formula $O=N-N\begin{smallmatrix} \diagup C_2H_5 \\ \diagdown C_2H_5 \end{smallmatrix}$ CAS number: 55-18-5

Species	Number of animals	Treatment	Duration of study	Animals with tumour(s) of the main target organs	Ref.
rat ♂ ♀	120 per dose	132 ppb in drinking water (8 µg/kg/day) (total dose: ~ 8 mg/kg)	life	♂: carcinogenic (details not specified)	[9]
rat ♂ ♀	24	1.5 mg/rat/day with the drinking water (total dose: ~ 600 mg/kg)	~ 138 days	22/24 liver	[31]
rat ♂	25	0.55 mg/rat, 5 × weekly, oral intubation (total dose: ~ 240 mg/kg)	~ 35 weeks	25/25 liver	[32]
rat ♂ ♀	4	1 × 280 mg/kg i.v.	~ 330 days	4/4 kidney 1/4 ovary	[33]
	3	1 × 280 mg/kg p.o.	485 days	1/3 liver	
	4	4 × 25–35 mg/kg p.o. (total dose: 100–140 mg/kg)	~ 500 days	2/4 kidney 1/4 liver 1/4 oesophagus	
rat ♂ ♀	60	0.075 mg/kg/day with the drinking water (total dose: ~ 65 mg/kg)	life	5/60 liver 3/60 oesophagus	[34]
	45	0.15 mg/kg/day with the drinking water (total dose: ~ 90 mg/kg)	life	22/45 liver 22/45 oesophagus	
	80	0.3 mg/kg/day with the drinking water (total dose: ~ 120 mg/kg)	life	63/80 liver 30/80 oesophagus	
	60	0.6 mg/kg/day with the drinking water (total dose: ~ 210 mg/kg)	life	51/60 liver 9/60 oesophagus	
rat ♂ ♀	14	2 × 11.2 mg/kg/week rectal instillation (total dose: ~ 630 mg/kg)	~ 30 weeks	14/14 liver	[35]
rat ♂ ♀	20	1 × 1.25 mg/kg i.v.	life	1/20 kidney	[36]
	20	1 × 2.5 mg/kg i.v.	life	2/20 kidney	
	20	1 × 5 mg/kg i.v.	life	3/20 kidney	
	20	1 × 10 mg/kg i.v.	life	3/20 kidney	

Species	Number of animals	Treatment	Duration of study	Animals with tumour(s) of the main target organs	Ref.
rat ♂ ♀	20	1 × 20 mg/kg i.v.	life	1/20 kidney	
	20	1 × 40 mg/kg i.v.	life	7/20 kidney	
	20	1 × 80 mg/kg i.v.	life	9/20 kidney	
	20	1 × 160 mg/kg i.v.	life	11/20 kidney	
mouse ♂ ♀	28	daily 13 mg/kg with the drinking water (total dose: ~ 2300 mg/kg)	~ 180 days	28/28 liver (control 0/18)	[37]
mouse ♂ ♀	24	daily 8 mg/kg with the drinking water (total dose: ~ 1400 mg/kg)	~ 170 days	14/24 liver (control 0/20)	[38]
	19	daily 3 mg/kg with the drinking water (total dose: ~ 870 mg/kg)	~ 290 days	19/19 liver	
mouse ♂	162	control	~ 25 months	41% lung 4% liver	[39]
	32	0.6 mg/kg/day with the drinking water (total dose: ~ 57 mg/kg)	~ 19 months	84% lung 17% liver 62% forestomach	
	63	2 mg/kg/day with the drinking water (total dose: ~ 213 mg/kg)	~ 17 months	77% lung 47% liver 92% forestomach	
	30	6 mg/kg/day with the drinking water (total dose: ~ 321 mg/kg)	~ 14 months	68% lung 87% liver 100% forestomach	
mouse ♂ ♀	31	2 × weekly 2 drops (0.2% solution), dermal (total dose: ~ 350 mg/kg)	~ 8 months	27/31 nasal cavity	[40, 41]
mouse ♂ ♀		4 × 3 mg/kg i.p.; (newborn) (total dose: 12 mg/kg)	life	72% liver (control 0?)	[42]
mouse		pregnant; 80–240 mg/kg s.c.	1 year	F_1 generation: 63% lung (control 10%)	[43]
golden hamster ♂ ♀	54	1 × 5.5 mg/kg; (newborn)	life	18/54 respiratory tract	[44]
	48	1 × 11 mg/kg; (newborn)	life	21/48 respiratory tract	
	54	1 × 33 mg/kg; (newborn)	life	23/54 respiratory tract	
	48	1 × 55 mg/kg; (newborn)	life	19/48 respiratory tract	

Species	Number of animals	Treatment	Duration of study	Animals with tumour(s) of the main target organs	Ref.
golden hamster ♂	35	12 × 0.5 mg/hamster s.c. 1 × weekly (total dose: ∼ 60 mg/kg)	life	29/35 respiratory tract	[45]
	36	12 × 1 mg/hamster s.c. 1 × weekly (total dose: ∼ 120 mg/kg)	life	35/36 respiratory tract	
	36	12 × 2 mg/hamster s.c. 1 × weekly (total dose: ∼ 240 mg/kg)	life	36/36 respiratory tract	
golden hamster ♀	20	1 × 0.5 mg/hamster s.c. (total dose: ∼ 5 mg/kg)	25 weeks	0/20 respiratory tract	[46]
	20	1 × 0.75 mg/hamster s.c. (total dose: ∼ 7.5 mg/kg)	25 weeks	5/20 respiratory tract	
	20	1 × 1 mg/hamster s.c. (total dose: ∼ 10 mg/kg)	25 weeks	3/20 respiratory tract	
	20	1 × 1.5 mg/hamster s.c. (total dose: ∼ 15 mg/kg)	25 weeks	4/20 respiratory tract	
	20	1 × 2 mg/hamster s.c. (total dose: ∼ 20 mg/kg)	25 weeks	6/20 respiratory tract	
	20	1 × 3 mg/hamster s.c. (total dose: ∼ 30 mg/kg)	25 weeks	12/20 respiratory tract	
	20	1 × 4 mg/hamster s.c. (total dose: ∼ 40 mg/kg)	25 weeks	13/20 respiratory tract	
golden hamster	174	1 × 45 mg/kg (on one of the first 11 days of pregnancy)		F_1 generation: 0/174 respiratory tract	[47]
	10	1 × 45 mg/kg (on d12 of pregnancy)		4/10 respiratory tract	
	20	1 × 45 mg/kg (on d13 of pregnancy)		8/20 respiratory tract	
	24	1 × 45 mg/kg (on d14 of pregnancy)		17/24 respiratory tract	
	20	1 × 45 mg/kg (on d15 of pregnancy)		19/20 respiratory tract	
	36	control		0/36 respiratory tract	
Chinese hamster ♂♀	40	11.6 mg/kg/week s.c. (total dose: ∼ 270 mg/kg)	life	95% liver, respiratory and digestive tract (control: 0/40)	[24]

Species	Number of animals	Treatment	Duration of study	Animals with tumour(s) of the main target organs	Ref.
European hamster ♂	10	1 × 20 mg/kg/week s.c. (total dose: ~ 500 mg/kg)	25 weeks	10/10 respiratory tract	[48]
guinea pig ♂		drinking water		liver 50% tumorigenic dose = 122 mg/guinea pig	[49]

N-Nitrosodiethylamine has also been shown to have a strong carcinogenic effect in the dog [50, 51], chicken [52], cat [52], hedgehog [53], pig [54, 55], rabbit [56, 57], budgerigar [58], gerbil [59, 60], in various species of fish [61, 62] and in the snake [63] as well as in various monkey species [64, 65, 66]. Taking the data as a whole, the liver is the foremost target organ although the respiratory tract – including the nasal cavity – is frequently very sensitive as well. In spite of the wide span of species tested, the various N-Nitrosodiethylamine doses required for tumour induction do not differ very much.

N-Nitrosodiethylamine is a very strong carcinogen for which the carcinogenic potential could be demonstrated very readily in all species tested to date.

N-Nitrosodi-*n*-propylamine

Structural formula $O=N-N\diagdown^{C_3H_7}_{C_3H_7}$ CAS number: 621-64-7

Species	Number of animals	Treatment	Duration of study	Animals with tumour(s) of the main target organs	Ref.
rat ♂	20	45 mg/l drinking water 5 × weekly for 30 weeks total dose: 135 mg/rat (total dose: ~ 400 mg/kg)	life	100% oesophagus (malignant) 60% forestomach 30% tongue 30% leukaemia	[28]
rat ♀	12	gastric intubation 2 × weekly for 30 weeks total dose: 132 mg/rat (total dose: ~ 400 mg/kg)	life	75% liver	[67]
♂	20	gastric intubation 2 × weekly for 30 weeks total dose: 264 mg/rat (total dose: ~ 800 mg/kg)	life	100% liver	

Species	Number of animals	Treatment	Duration of study	Animals with tumour(s) of the main target organs	Ref.
rat ♂	15	90 mg/l drinking water 5× weekly for 30 weeks total dose: 270 mg/rat (total dose: ~ 800 mg/kg)	life	9/15 liver 14/15 oesophagus 8/15 nasal cavity	[68]
rat ♂ ♀	14	4 mg/kg/day in the diet (total dose: ~ 3000 mg/kg)	life	12/14 liver 6/14 root of tongue 3/14 oesophagus	[29]
rat ♂ ♀	20	24 mg/kg/week s.c. (total dose: ~ 2400 mg/kg)	life	85% nasal cavity 20% oesophagus 15% brain 5% lung	[69]
	20	49 mg/kg/week s.c. (total dose: ~ 4900 mg/kg)	life	90% nasal cavity 25% oesophagus 20% lung 15% kidney 15% brain	
	20	97 mg/kg/week s.c. (total dose: ~ 9700 mg/kg)	life	65% nasal cavity 55% liver 30% lung	
mouse ♂ ♀	68	control	72 weeks	2/68 liver 3/68 oesophagus, forestomach 13/68 lymphoma 4/68 lung	[70]
	70	oral intubation 2× weekly for 50 weeks total dose: 3 mg/mouse (total dose: ~ 70 mg/kg)	72 weeks	4/70 liver 9/70 oesophagus, forestomach 12/70 lymphoma 9/70 lung	
mouse ♂	15	control	72 weeks	1/15 nasal cavity 10/15 respiratory tract 1/15 digestive tract	[71]
	15	1× weekly 35 mg/mouse s.c. (total dose: ~ 45 g/kg)	72 weeks	13/15 nasal cavity 14/15 respiratory tract 13/15 digestive tract	
	15	1× weekly 69 mg/mouse s.c.	72 weeks	12/15 nasal cavity 13/15 respiratory tract 7/15 digestive tract 1/15 liver	
	15	1× weekly 138 mg/mouse s.c.	life	9/15 nasal cavity 8/15 respiratory tract 7/15 digestive tract 4/15 liver	

Species	Number of animals	Treatment	Duration of study	Animals with tumour(s) of the main target organs	Ref.
golden hamster ♂♀	40	control	life	—	[72]
	40	3.75 mg/kg/week s.c. (total dose: ~ 200 mg/kg)	life	22/40 nasal cavity 21/40 upper respiratory tract 5/40 lung	
	40	7.5 mg/kg/week s.c. (total dose: ~ 375 mg/kg)	life	22/40 nasal cavity 32/40 upper respiratory tract 8/40 lung	
	40	15 mg/kg/week s.c. (total dose: ~ 600 mg/kg)	life	30/40 nasal cavity 34/40 upper respiratory tract 6/40 lung	
	40	30 mg/kg/week s.c. (total dose: ~ 990 mg/kg)	life	26/40 nasal cavity 39/40 upper respiratory tract 12/40 lung	
	40	60 mg/kg/week s.c. (total dose: ~ 2200 mg/kg)	life	34/40 nasal cavity 37/40 upper respiratory tract 25/40 lung	
golden hamster ♂♀	30	control	life	7% urogenital tract 3% vessels 7% other sites	[73]
	30	6.5 mg/hamster, 1 × weekly s.c. (total dose: ~ 2000 mg/kg)	life	100% respiratory tract 7% digestive tract 7% other sites	
golden hamster		pregnant, 1 × 100 mg/kg s.c.		weak or borderline transplacental carcinogenic effect	[74]

The available data indicate that N-nitrosodi-n-propylamine must be considered to be a very strong carcinogen

N-Nitrosodi-*i*-propylamine

Structural formula

$$O=N-N \overset{\overset{\displaystyle CH_3}{\underset{\displaystyle |}{CH-CH_3}}}{\underset{\underset{\displaystyle CH_3}{\underset{\displaystyle |}{CH-CH_3}}}{}}$$

CAS number: 601-77-4

Species	Number of animals	Treatment	Duration of study	Animals with tumour(s) of the main targe organs	Ref.
rat ♂ ♀	20	25–50 mg/kg/day in the diet (total dose: ∼ 11–14 g/kg)	life	45 % liver	[29]
rat ♂	15	90 mg/l drinking water 5 × weekly for 50 weeks total dose: 450 mg/rat (total dose: ∼ 1400 mg/kg)	life	8/15 nasal cavity 1/15 lung	[68]
	15	600 mg/l drinking water 5 × weekly for 40 weeks total dose: 2400 mg/rat (total dose: ∼ 7500 mg/kg)	life	10/15 nasal cavity 3/15 liver 1/15 lung	

In the first limited study with N-nitrosodi-*i*-propylamine the substance seemed to be a relatively weak carcinogen in comparison, for example, with N-nitrosodiethylamine [29]. In the second study – of equally limited scale – the substance revealed a markedly stronger effect [68].

N-Nitrosodi-*n*-butylamine

Structural formula

$$O=N-N \overset{\displaystyle C_4H_9}{\underset{\displaystyle C_4H_9}{}}$$

CAS number: 924-16-3

Species	Number of animals	Treatment	Duration of study	Animals with tumour(s) of the main target organs	Ref.
rat ♂ ♀	10	10 mg/kg/day in the diet (total dose: ∼ 7000 mg/kg)	life	60 % urinary bladder 40 % oesophagus 30 % pharynx 30 % liver 10 % forestomach	[29]

Species	Number of animals	Treatment	Duration of study	Animals with tumour(s) of the main target organs	Ref.
rat ♂ ♀	10	20 mg/kg/day in the diet	life	80% oesophagus 70% urinary bladder 40% liver	[29]
	16	37.5 mg/kg/day in the diet	life	81% liver 31% oesophagus 31% urinary bladder	
	4	75 mg/kg/day in the diet	life	100% liver	
	20	1 × weekly 200–400 mg/kg s.c.	life	10% liver 15% oesophagus 90% urinary bladder	

In the data shown above N-nitrosodi-n-butylamine is seen to be a strong carcinogen with the urinary bladder as the main target organ. Subsequently a very large number of studies were carried out with relatively high doses of the compound to study the tumorigenesis of the urinary bladder cancer; not all of these will be detailed here.

Species	Number of animals	Treatment	Duration of study	Animals with tumour(s) of the main target organs	Ref.
mouse ♂		1 × 3 mg/mouse, oral intubation (total dose: ~ 90 mg/kg)	10 months	18% liver + 8% digestive tract or 9% liver + 18% digestive tract	[75]
mouse ♂♀	100	7.6 mg/kg/day with the drinking water (total dose: ~ 5000 mg/kg)	life	100% gastrointestinal tract, urinary bladder	[76]
mouse ♂	39	50 ppm in the diet for 12 months (total dose: ~ 3600 mg/kg)	15 months	33/33 forestomach 15/33 liver 8/33 lung 4/34 oesophagus (control: 3/30 tumours)	[77]
mouse ♂ ♀	29	10 µl every 2nd week s.c. for 40 weeks (total dose: ~ 6000 mg/kg)	life	48% urinary bladder	[78]
mouse ♂ ♀	52	4 × 105 mg/kg s.c. (newborn)	1 year	73% lung 50% liver (control: 4% lung, 2% liver)	[79]
guinea pig ♂ ♀	19	5 × weekly 40 mg/kg with the drinking water (total dose: ~ 2000 mg/kg)	life	13/19 liver 7/19 urinary bladder	[80]

Species	Number of animals	Treatment	Duration of study	Animals with tumour(s) of the main target organs	Ref.
golden hamster ♂♀	10	control	life	0/10 respiratory tract	[81]
	10	1 × 200 mg/kg i.p.	life	4/10 respiratory tract	
	10	1 × 400 mg/kg i.p.	life	6/10 respiratory tract	
	10	1 × 800 mg/kg i.p.	life	7/10 respiratory tract	
	10	1 × 150 mg/kg s.c.	life	3/10 respiratory tract	
	10	1 × 300 mg/kg s.c.	life	4/10 respiratory tract	
	10	1 × 600 mg/kg s.c.	life	5/10 respiratory tract	
	10	1 × 1200 mg/kg s.c.	life	7/10 respiratory tract	
	10	1 × 400 mg/kg p.o.(gavage)	life	3/10 respiratory tract	
	10	1 × 800 mg/kg p.o.(gavage)	life	5/10 respiratory tract	
	10	1 × 1600 mg/kg p.o.(gavage)	life	7/10 respiratory tract	
golden hamster ♂♀	20	control	life	0% respiratory tract, 0% urinary bladder	[82]
	20	22 mg/kg/week s.c.	life	59% respiratory tract, 22% urinary bladder	
	20	44 mg/kg/week s.c.	life	65% respiratory tract, 32% urinary bladder	
	20	88 mg/kg/week s.c.	life	61% respiratory tract, 41% urinary bladder	
	20	176 mg/kg/week s.c.	life	74% respiratory tract, 47% urinary bladder	
	20	352 mg/kg/week s.c.	life	78% respiratory tract, 48% urinary bladder	
	20	control	life	0% respiratory tract, 0% urinary bladder	
	20	29 mg/kg/week gastric intubation	life	0% respiratory tract, 5% urinary bladder	
	20	58 mg/kg/week gastric intubation	life	0% respiratory tract, 11% urinary bladder	
	20	116 mg/kg/week gastric intubation	life	13% respiratory tract, 13% urinary bladder	
	20	232 mg/kg/week gastric intubation	life	60% respiratory tract, 25% urinary bladder	
	20	464 mg/kg/week gastric intubation	life	50% respiratory tract, 44% urinary bladder	

In the golden hamster there were also indications that N-nitrosodi-n-butylamine is a transplacental carcinogen [83].

The effects of N-nitrosodi-n-butylamine in the Chinese hamster [84-86] and the European hamster [87] are similar to those in the golden hamster.

N-Nitrosodiethanolamine

Structural formula O=N−N⟨ $\begin{array}{l} C_2H_4OH \\ C_2H_4OH \end{array}$ CAS number: 1116-54-7

Species	Number of animals	Treatment	Duration of study	Animals with tumour(s) of the main target organs	Ref.
rat ♂♀	16	~ 600 mg/kg/day with the drinking water (total dose: 150 g/kg)	300 days	16/16 liver	[29]
	4	~ 1000 mg/kg/day with the drinking water (total dose: 300 g/kg)	325 days	4/4 liver	
rat ♂	88	control	life	—	[88]
	72	1.5 mg/kg/day with the drinking water (total dose: 860 mg/kg)	life	10% liver	
	72	6 mg/kg/day with the drinking water (total dose: 3470 mg/kg)	life	60% liver 3% nasal cavity	
	36	25 mg/kg/day with the drinking water (total dose: 11140 mg/kg)	life	92% liver 17% nasal cavity	
rat ♀	16	400 mg/l drinking water (total dose: ~ 6000 mg/kg)	life	15/16 liver 3/16 nasal cavity	[89]
rat ♂♀	40	control	life	5/40 liver (all benign)	[90]
	78	28 mg/l drinking water (total dose: ~ 800 mg/kg)	life	16/78 liver (5 malignant) 1/78 kidney	
	40	64 mg/l drinking water (total dose: ~ 1800 mg/kg)	life	25/40 liver 3/40 kidney	
golden hamster ♂♀	30	27 × 565 mg/kg s.c. (total dose: 15.3 g/kg)	life	12/30 nasal cavity 7/30 trachea 3/30 injection site	[91]
	30	7 × 2260 mg/kg s.c. (total dose: 15.8 g/kg)	life	10/30 nasal cavity 8/30 trachea 3/30 liver	
golden hamster ♂♀	27	250 mg/kg/week s.c. (total dose: ~ 12 g/kg)	life	13/27 nasal cavity 2/27 trachea 3/27 larynx	[92]
	29	500 mg/kg/week s.c. (total dose: ~ 24 g/kg)	life	14/29 nasal cavity 5/29 trachea 4/29 larynx	

Species	Number of animals	Treatment	Duration of study	Animals with tumour(s) of the main target organs	Ref.
golden hamster ♂♀	30	1000 mg/kg/week s.c. (total dose: ~ 48 g/kg)	life	22/30 nasal cavity 9/30 trachea 9/30 larynx	[92]
golden hamster ♂♀	29	58 mg/kg/week s.c. (total dose: ~ 3 g/kg)	19 months	2/29 trachea	[93]
	29	170 mg/kg/week s.c. (total dose: ~ 9 g/kg)	19 months	7/29 nasal cavity 4/29 trachea	
	30	500 mg/kg/week s.c. (total dose: ~ 27 g/kg)	19 months	19/30 nasal cavity 7/30 trachea 2/30 larynx	
golden hamster ♂♀	30	~ 25 mg/kg 3 × weekly dermal (total dose: ~ 2700 mg/kg)	20 months	–	[94]
	30	~ 80 mg/kg 3 × weekly dermal (total dose: ~ 8600 mg/kg)	20 months	1/30 trachea	
	30	~ 250 mg/kg 3 × weekly dermal (total dose: ~ 27000 mg/kg)	20 months	4/30 nasal cavity 4/30 trachea 1/30 larynx	

Although when N-nitrosodiethanolamine is administered orally with the drinking water, it is a less potent carcinogen in the rat than, e.g., N-nitrosodimethylamine or N-nitrosodiethylamine, the compound must still be seen as a very strong carcinogen since a total dose of ~ 800 mg/kg was still enough to induce liver tumours in ~ 10% of animals.

After receiving the compound by subcutaneous injection, the golden hamster proved to be slightly less sensitive (after a total dose of ~ 3 g/kg tracheal tumours developed in 7% of the animals). In this species after subcutaneous injection the upper respiratory tract was the preferred site of tumour induction.

N-Nitrosomethylphenylamine

Structural formula $O=N-N\underset{}{\overset{\diagup CH_3}{\diagdown}}$ ⟨phenyl ring⟩

CAS number: 614-00-6

Species	Number of animals	Treatment	Duration of study	Animals with tumour(s) of the main target organs	Ref.
rat ♂♀	48	1 × 2 mg/kg/week s.c. (total dose: 78 mg/kg)	life	46% oesophagus	[95]
	48	1 × 10 mg/kg/week s.c. (total dose: 240 mg/kg)	life	84% oesophagus	
	48	daily 0.3 mg/kg with the drinking water (total dose: 61 mg/kg)	life	80% oesophagus	
	48	daily 1.5 mg/kg with the drinking water (total dose: 232 mg/kg)	life	87% oesophagus	
rat ♂♀	33	2 mg/rat, 5× weekly with the drinking water (total dose: ∼ 1.5 g/kg)	life	7/33 oral cavity 16/33 oesophagus 8/33 forestomach	[96]
♂	20	2 × 7.5 mg/rat, 2× weekly oral intubation (total dose: ∼ 4.5 g/kg)	life	2/20 oral cavity ⎫ all 5/20 oesophagus ⎬ be- 2/20 forestomach ⎭ nign	
rat ♂♀	20	daily 10 mg/kg in the diet (total dose: ∼ 3.4 g/kg)	life	8/20 oesophagus 1/20 urinary bladder	[29]
rat ♂♀	32	0.2–0.1% in drinking water ∼ 15-8 mg/kg, 6× weekly (total dose: ∼ 6 g/kg)	life	30/32 oesophagus 5/32 forestomach	[97]
mouse ♂♀	160	control	40 weeks	14% lung 1.3 lung tumours per tumour-bearing mouse	[98]
	40	70 mg/l drinking water (total dose: ∼ 4 g/kg)	40 weeks	61% lung 3.3 lung tumours per tumour-bearing mouse	

N-Nitrosomethylphenylamine is carcinogenic in the rat and mouse after oral administration and after subcutaneous injection. A total oral dose of ∼ 60 mg/kg is already very potent in the rat and oesophagus tumours are clearly most predominant.

N-Nitrosoethylphenylamine

Structural formula   O=N–N⟨CH₂–CH₃ / ⬡   CAS number: 612-64-6

In comparative studies the effect of N-nitrosoethylphenylamine in an *in vitro* cell transformation test system was similar to that of N-nitrosodimethylamine and of N-nitrosodiethylamine [99]. In a teratogenicity test N-nitrosoethylphenylamine was teratogenic in the rat after i.p. injection of a high dose (1 × 180 mg/kg); the same results were obtained with N-nitrosomethylphenylamine (1 × 140 mg/kg) [100].

There are no carcinogenicity studies available for N-nitrosoethylphenylamine. The very similar compound, N-nitrosomethylphenylamine, proved to be a very potent carcinogen in animal studies. It must be assumed that the carcinogenic potency of N-nitrosoethylphenylamine is similar to that of N-nitrosomethylphenylamine.

N-Nitrosomorpholine

Structural formula   O=N–N⟨   ⟩O   CAS number: 59-89-2

Species	Number of animals	Treatment	Duration of study	Animals with tumour(s) of the main target organs	Ref.
rat ♂	30	8 mg/l drinking water for 30 weeks (total dose: ~ 70 mg/kg)	life	11/30 liver	[101]
	30	40 mg/l drinking water for 30 weeks (total dose: ~ 330 mg/kg)	life	16/30 liver	
rat ♂	20	16 mg/l drinking water 5 × weekly for 50 weeks (total dose: ~ 280 mg/kg)	life	20/20 liver 5/20 leukaemia	[102]
rat ♂ ♀	14	daily 8 mg/kg with the drinking water (total dose: ~ 1.3 g/kg)	t_{50} = 165 days	14/14 liver	[29]
	10	1 × weekly 5 mg/kg i.v. (total dose: ~ 290 mg/kg)	life	2/10 liver 1/10 nasal nerves	
	5	1 × weekly 10 mg/kg i.v. (total dose: ~ 500 mg/kg)	life	3/5 nasal cavity	

Species	Number of animals	Treatment	Duration of study	Animals with tumour(s) of the main target organs	Ref.
rat ♀	5	12 mg/kg/day with the drinking water (total dose: ∼ 1000 mg/kg)	195 days	5/5 liver	[103]
rat ♂	30	40 mg/l drinking water 5 × weekly (total dose: ∼ 420 mg/kg)	104 weeks	18/30 liver	[104]
rat ♂	48	150 mg/l drinking water (total dose: ∼ 2200 mg/kg)	40 weeks	36/48 liver	[105]
rat ♀	132	5 mg/kg diet (total dose: ∼ 260 mg/kg)	life	18/132 liver	[106]
	97	50 mg/kg diet (total dose: ∼ 2600 mg/kg)	life	87/97 liver	
rat ♂ ♀	58	120 mg/l drinking water for 7–14 weeks total dose: ∼ 100-200 mg/rat (total dose: ∼ 300-600 mg/kg)	∼ 2 years	40/58 kidney	[107]
	11	50 mg/l drinking water for 3 weeks total dose: ∼ 60-150 mg/rat (total dose: ∼ 180-450 mg/kg)	∼ 2 years	7/11 kidney	
mouse ♂	58	100 mg/l drinking water	352 days	respiratory tract liver kidney stomach (not specified in detail)	[108]
golden hamster ♂ ♀	60	10 mg/l drinking water (total dose: ∼ 400 mg/kg)	∼ 1 year	17/60 respiratory tract 4/60 liver	[109]
	60	50 mg/l drinking water (total dose: ∼ 1400 mg/kg)	∼ 1 year	42/60 respiratory tract 13/60 liver	
golden hamster ♂	20	26 mg/l drinking water for 26 weeks (total dose: ∼ 1000 mg/kg)	∼ 1 year	18/20 respiratory tract 1/20 liver	[110]
golden hamster ♂ ♀	10	1 × 50 mg/kg s.c.	life	2/10 respiratory tract	[111]
	10	1 × 100 mg/kg s.c.	life	3/10 respiratory tract	
	10	1 × 200 mg/kg s.c.	life	7/10 respiratory tract	
European hamster ♂ ♀	60	1 × ∼ 23 mg/kg/week s.c. (total dose: ∼ 620 mg/kg)	∼ 27 weeks	19/60 upper digestive tract and/or respiratory tract	[112]

Species	Number of animals	Treatment	Duration of study	Animals with tumour(s) of the main target organs	Ref.
Chinese hamster ♂♀	40	1 × 8 mg/kg/week s.c.	life	10/40 nasal cavity 2/40 brain 10/40 respiratory tract 40/40 upper digestive tract	[113]
zebra fish and guppy	50	75–320 mg/l water for 28 weeks	31 weeks	12/50 liver, intestine and connective tissue	[114]

N-Nitrosomorpholine is carcinogenic in all species tested to date (rat, mouse, golden hamster, Chinese hamster, European hamster, fish). The liver stands out as the main target organ; the respiratory tract and the kidneys are next in line. A total dose as small as 70 mg/kg is still very strongly carcinogenic in the rat.

N-Nitrosopiperidine

Structural formula   O=N−N⟨hexagon⟩   CAS number: 100-75-4

It has been stated (without any further details), that N-nitrosopiperidine has a clear carcinogenic effect in rodents at a concentration of 360 ppb in the drinking water (23 μg/kg/day; total dose) ∼ 21 mg/kg) [9].

Species	Number of animals	Treatment	Duration of study	Animals with tumour(s) of the main target organs	Ref.
rat ♂♀	78	daily 0.024 mg/kg with the drinking water (total dose: ∼ 20 mg/kg)	life	4% liver	[115]
	75	daily 0.12 mg/kg with the drinking water (total dose: ∼ 90 mg/kg)	life	7% liver 3% upper digestive tract	
	34	daily 0.6 mg/kg with the drinking water (total dose: ∼ 480 mg/kg)	life	47% liver 24% upper digestive tract	
	34	daily 3 mg/kg with the drinking water (total dose: ∼ 1200 mg/kg)	life	32% liver 71% upper digestive tract	

Species	Number of animals	Treatment	Duration of study	Animals with tumour(s) of the main target organs	Ref.
rat ♀	20	103 mg/l drinking water 5 × weekly for 28 weeks total dose: 280 mg/rat (total dose: ~ 800 mg/kg)	40 weeks	19/20 oesophagus 2/20 forestomach	[116]
rat ♂♀	10	daily 5 mg/kg with the drinking water (total dose: ~ 1400 mg/kg)	~ 280 days	8/10 oesophagus 3/10 liver	[29]
	15	2 × weekly 10 mg/kg i.v. (total dose: ~ 750 mg/kg)	~ 1 year	13/15 upper digestive tract	
	25	2 × weekly 10 mg/kg s.c. (total dose: ~ 850 mg/kg)	~ 1 year	22/25 nasal cavity 15/25 oesophagus	
rat ♂♀	30	100 mg/l drinking water 5 × weekly (total dose: ~ 2000 mg/kg)	50 weeks	10/30 liver 22/30 oesophagus 13/30 upper digestive tract 7/30 upper respiratory tract	[117]
mouse ♂	33	50 mg/kg diet for 1 year (total dose: ~ 3600 mg/kg)	life	20/33 upper digestive tract 11/33 liver 10/33 lung	[118]
	30	control		2/30 lung	
golden hamster ♂♀	60	60 mg/l drinking water (total dose: ~ 240 mg/kg)	life	10/60 respiratory tract 5/60 digestive tract 1/60 liver	[119]
golden hamster ♂♀	10 10 10	1 × 25 mg/kg s.c. 1 × 50 mg/kg s.c. 1 × 100 mg/kg s.c.	life life life	2/10 respiratory tract 3/10 respiratory tract 7/10 respiratory tract	[111]
golden hamster	20	1 × 100 mg/kg s.c. during pregnancy	life	tumour frequency in F_1 generation doubled (upper respiratory and digestive tracts)	[120]
European hamster ♂♀	60	1 × ~ 11 mg/kg/week s.c. (total dose: 540 mg/kg)	~ 48 weeks	17/60 upper digestive tract and/or respiratory tract	[112]

Species	Number of animals	Treatment	Duration of study	Animals with tumour(s) of the main target organs	Ref.
Chinese hamster ♂♀	40	1 × 5.7 mg/kg/week s.c. (total dose: ~ 395 mg/kg)	life	2/40 nasal cavity 18/40 lung 40/40 upper digestive tract 22/40 liver	[113]
guinea pig ♂♀	24–30	4.25 mg/kg, 6 × weekly with the drinking water	~ 1 year	2–4/24–30 digestive tract and/or lung	[121]
monkey		p.o. (no other details specified)		3 liver (malignant)	[122]

N-Nitrosopiperidine is a very potent carcinogen which was shown to be clearly carcinogenic in the rat and golden hamster even after a total dose of only ~ 20 mg/kg.

N-Nitrosopyrrolidine

Structural formula O=N-N⟨ ⟩   CAS number: 930-55-2

It has been stated (without any further details), that N-nitrosopyrrolidine has a clear carcinogenic effect in rodents at a concentration of 5000 ppb in the drinking water (290 µg/kg/day; total dose ~ 261 mg/kg) [9].

Species	Number of animals	Treatment	Duration of study	Animals with tumour(s) of the main target organs	Ref.
rat ♂♀	61	control	life	0/61 liver	[123]
	60	daily 0.3 mg/kg with the drinking water (total dose: ~ 200 mg/kg)	life	3/60 liver	
	62	daily 1 mg/kg with the drinking water (total dose: ~ 685 mg/kg)	life	17/62 liver	
	38	daily 3 mg/kg with the drinking water (total dose: ~ 1600 mg/kg)	life	31/38 liver	

Species	Number of animals	Treatment	Duration of study	Animals with tumour(s) of the main target organs	Ref.
rat ♂	80	1 mg/kg/day for 600 days with the drinking water (total dose: ~ 600 mg/kg)	life	53/80 liver	[117]
rat ♀	20	90 mg/l drinking water 5 × weekly for 50 weeks (total dose: ~ 1500 mg/kg)	life	20/20 liver 8/20 bile duct	[116]
rat ♂ ♀	25	5–20 mg/kg daily with the drinking water (total dose: ~ 4000 mg/kg)	~ 290–470 days	23/25 liver	[29]
golden hamster ♂ ♀	58	~ 2 mg/kg/week with the drinking water (total dose: ~ 100 mg/kg)	life	1/58 liver	[124]
	58	~ 8 mg/kg/week with the drinking water (total dose: ~ 400 mg/kg)	life	3/58 liver	
	59	~ 18 mg/kg/week with the drinking water (total dose: ~ 850 mg/kg)	life	13/59 liver	
golden hamster ♂	20	1.33 mg/hamster, 3 × weekly i.p. for 25 weeks (total dose: ~ 1000 mg/kg)	life	1/20 nasal cavity	[125]
	21	2.67 mg/hamster, 3 × weekly i.p. for 25 weeks (total dose: ~ 2000 mg/kg)	life	14/21 nasal cavity	

N-Nitrosopyrrolidine proved to be a very potent carcinogen in the rat. After a total dose of only ~ 200 mg/kg it still induced liver tumours in 3/60 rats and evidence for the induction of liver tumours was also obtained in the golden hamster after a total dose of ~ 100 mg/kg.

5 Manifesto (MAK value, classification)

Eleven of the twelve N-nitrosamines discussed here revealed strong carcinogenic effects in animal studies. The proof of carcinogenicity is missing only for N-nitrosoethylphenylamine because no long-term animal studies have been carried out with this compound. Structural analogy and the results of the available *in vitro* studies indicate that a strong carcinogenicity must be expected for N-nitrosoethylphenylamine as well.

The carcinogenic effects demonstrated in animal studies are clearly the main consideration in any toxicological assessment of the N-nitrosamines discussed here. Therefore, in addition to N-nitrosodimethylamine, which is already classified in Section III A 2) of the List of MAK Values, the following N-nitrosamines are also to be classified in Section III A 2):

N-nitrosodi-*n*-butylamine
N-nitrosodiethanolamine
N-nitrosodiethylamine
N-nitrosodi-*i*-propylamine
N-nitrosodi-*n*-propylamine
N-nitrosoethylphenylamine
N-nitrosomethylethylamine
N-nitrosomethylphenylamine
N-nitrosomorpholine
N-nitrosopiperidine
N-nitrosopyrrolidine

A MAK value cannot be established for any of the substances.

Because of the absence of relevant data, none of these substances can be classified into one of the groups of embryotoxic and/or foetotoxic substances. Any contact with these compounds should be avoided during pregnancy because of their strong carcinogenic effects.

6 References

1. Preussmann, R.: in Altmann, H.-W., F. Büchner, H. Cottier, E. Grundmann, G. Holle, E. Letterer, W. Masshoff, H. Meesen, F. Roulet, G. Seifert, G. Siebert (Eds.): *Handbuch der allgemeinen Pathologie*, Vol. 6, Part 6 – Geschwülste, p 421, Springer Verlag, Berlin-Heidelberg, 1975
2. Röper, H. in Preussman, R. (Ed.): *Das Nitrosamin-Problem*, p 189, Verlag Chemie, D-6940 Weinheim, 1983
3. Preussman, R., B. W. Stewart: in Searle, Ch. E. (Ed.): *Chemical Carcinogens*, Vol. 2, ACS Monograph 182, American Chemical Society, Washington DC, 1984
4. Berufsgenossenschaftliches Institut für Arbeitsschutz (BIA): Lecture presented at the Bundesanstalt für Arbeitsschutz, D-4600 Dortmund, on 24.3.1987
4a. Spiegelhalder, B., R. Preussman: *Carcinogenesis 4*, 1147 (1983)
5. Schmähl, D.: *Z. Krebsforsch. 74*, 457 (1970)
6. Michejda, C. J., M. B. Kroeger-Koepke, R. M. Kovatch: *Cancer Res. 46*, 2252 (1986)
7. Lijinsky, W., M. D. Reuber, C. W. Riggs: *Food chem. Toxicol. 21*, 601 (1983)
8. Reif, A. E.: *J. nat. Cancer Inst. 73*, 25 (1984)
9. Crampton, R. F.: *Oncology 37*, 251 (1980)
10. Keefer, L. K., W. Lijinsky, H. Garcia: *J. nat. Cancer Inst. 51*, 299 (1973)
11. Magee, P. N., J. M. Barnes: *J. Path Bact. 84*, 19 (1962)
12. Terracini, B., P. N. Magee, J. M. Barnes: *Brit. J. Cancer 21*, 559 (1967)
13. Moiseev, G. E., V. V. Benemanskij: *Vop. Onkol. 21*, 107 (1975)
14. Campbell, J. S., G. S. Wiberg, H. C. Grice, P. Lou: *Cancer Res. 34*, 2399 (1974)
15. Anderson, L. M., L. J. Priest, J. M. Budinger: *J. nat. Cancer Inst. 62*, 1553 (1979)
16. Toth, B., Ph. Shubik: *Cancer Res. 27*, 43 (1967)

17. Toth, B., P. N. Magee, P. H. Shubik: *Cancer Res. 24*, 1712 (1964)
18. Terracini, B., G. Palestro, M. R. Gigliardi, R. Montesano: *Brit. J. Cancer 20*, 871 (1966)
19. Ii, Y., A. Cardesa, K. Patil, J. Althoff, P. Pour: *Z. Krebsforsch. 86*, 165 (1976)
20. Clapp, N. K.: *Int. J. Cancer 12*, 728 (1973)
21. Vessilinovitch, S. D.: *Cancer Res. 29*, 1024 (1969)
22. Cardesa, A., P. Pour, J. Althoff, U. Mohr: *J. nat. Cancer Inst. 51*, 201 (1973)
23. Stenback, F., A. Ferrero, R. Montesano, Ph. Shubik: *Z. Krebsforsch. 79*, 31 (1973)
24. Reznik, G., U. Mohr, M. Kmoch: *Brit. J. Cancer 33*, 411 (1976)
25. Mohr, U., H. Haas, J. Hilfrich: *Brit. J. Cancer 29*, 359 (1974)
26. Haas, H., U. Mohr, F. W. Krüger: *J. nat. Cancer Inst. 51*, 1295 (1973)
27. Lijinsky, W., M. D. Reuber: *Cancer Res. 40*, 19 (1980)
28. Lijinsky, W., M. D. Reuber: *Cancer Lett. 14*, 297 (1981)
29. Druckrey, H., R. Preussmann, S. Ivankovic, D. Schmähl: *Z. Krebsforsch. 69*, 103 (1967)
30. Hofe, E. von, P. Kleihues: *J. Cancer Res. clin. Oncol. 112*, 205 (1986)
31. Schmähl, D., R. Preussmann: *Naturwissenschaften 47*, 8 (1960)
32. Argus, M. F., C. Hoch-Ligeti: *J. nat. Cancer Inst. 27*, 695 (1961)
33. Druckrey, H., D. Steinhoff, R. Preussmann, S. Ivankovic: *Z. Krebsforsch. 66*, 1 (1964)
34. Druckrey, H., A. Schildbach, D. Schmähl, R. Preussmann, S. Ivankovic: *Arzneimittel-Forsch. 13*, 841 (1963)
35. Schmähl, D., C. Thomas, K. König: *Z. Krebsforsch. 65*, 529 (1963)
36. Mohr, U., J. Hilfrich: *J. nat. Cancer Inst. 49*, 1729 (1972)
37. Schmähl, D., C. Thomas, K. König: *Naturwissenschaften 50*, 407 (1963)
38. Schmähl, D., C. Thomas: *Z. Krebsforsch. 66*, 533 (1965)
39. Clapp, N. K., A. W. Craig, R. E. Toya: *Int. J. Cancer 5*, 119 (1970)
40. Hoffmann, F., A. Graffi: *Acta biol. med. germ. 12*, 623 (1964)
41. Hoffmann, F., A. Graffi: *Arch. Geschwulstforsch. 23*, 274 (1964)
42. Kyriazis, A. P., M. Koka, S. D. Vessilinovitch: *Cancer Res. 34*, 2881 (1974)
43. Mohr, U., J. Althoff: *Z. Krebsforsch. 67*, 152 (1965)
44. Montesano, R., U. Saffiotti: *J. nat. Cancer Inst. 44*, 413 (1970)
45. Montesano, R., U. Saffiotti: *Cancer Res. 28*, 2197 (1968)
46. Mohr, U., O. Wieser, K. Pielsticker: *Naturwissenschaften 53*, 229 (1966)
47. Mohr, U., H. Reznik-Schüller, G. Reznik, J. Hilfrich: *J. nat. Cancer Inst. 55*, 681 (1975)
48. Mohr, U., J. Althoff, N. Page: *J. nat. Cancer Inst. 49*, 595 (1972)
49. Arcos, J. C., M. F. Argus, J. B. Mathison: *Experientia (Basel) 25*, 296 (1969)
50. Schmähl, D.: *Naturwissenschaften 51*, 466 (1964)
51. Hirao, K., K. Matsumura, A. Imagawa, Y. Enomoto, Y. Hosogi, T. Kani, K. Fujikawa, N. Ito: *Cancer Res. 34*, 1870 (1974)
52. Schmähl, D., M. Habs, S. Ivankovic: *Int. J. Cancer 22*, 552 (1978)
53. Graw, J. J., H. Berg, D. Schmähl: *J. nat. Cancer Inst. 53*, 589 (1974)
54. Schmähl, D., H. Oswald, K. Goerttler: *Z. Krebsforsch. 72*, 102 (1969)
55. Graw, J. J., H. Berg: *Z. Krebsforsch. 89*, 137 (1977)
56. Schmähl, D., C. Thomas: *Naturwissenschaften 52*, 165 (1965)
57. Rapp, H. J., J. H. Charleton, C. Crisler, E. M. Nadel: *J. nat. Cancer Inst. 34*, 453 (1965)
58. Schmähl, D., H. Oswald, C. Karsten: *Naturwissenschaften 53*, 437 (1966)
59. Haas, H., N. Kmoch, U. Mohr, A. Cardesa: *Z. Krebsforsch. 83*, 233 (1975)
60. Cardesa, A., P. Pour, H. Haas, J. Althoff, U. Mohr: *Cancer (Philad.) 37*, 346 (1976)
61. Pliss, G. B., V. V. Khudoley: *J. nat. Cancer Inst. 55*, 129 (1975)
62. Ishikawa, T., T. Shimamine, S. Takayama: *J. nat. Cancer Inst. 55*, 906 (1975)
63. Schmähl, D., H. R. Scherf: *Naturwissenschaften 70*, 94 (1983)
64. Kelly, M. G., R. W. O'Gara, R. H. Adamson, K. Gadekar, C. C. Botkin, W. H. Reese, W. T. Kerber: *J. nat. Cancer Inst. 36*, 323 (1966)
65. Adamson, R. H., P. Correa, D. W. Dalgard: *Toxicol. appl. Pharmacol. 29*, 93 (1974)
66. Dalgard, D. W., P. Correa, S. M. Sieber, R. H. Adamson: *Fed. Proc. 35*, 329 (1976)
67. Lijinsky, W., M. D. Reuber: *Cancer Lett. 19*, 207 (1983)
68. Lijinsky, W., H. W. Taylor: *J. nat. Cancer Inst. 62*, 407 (1979)
69. Reznik, G., U. Mohr, F. W. Krüger: *J. nat. Cancer Inst. 54*, 937 (1975)

70. Griciute, L., M. Castegnaro, J. C. Bereziat: *IARC Sci. Publ. No. 41*, 643 (1982)
71. Dickhaus, S., G. Reznik, U. Green, M. Ketkar: *Z. Krebsforsch. 90*, 253 (1977)
72. Pour, P., F. W. Krüger, A. Cardesa, J. Althoff, U. Mohr: *J. nat. Cancer Inst. 51*, 1019 (1973)
73. Althoff, J., C. Grandjean, P. Pour, B. Bertram: *Z. Krebsforsch. 90*, 141 (1977)
74. Althoff, J., P. Pour, C. Grandjean, S. Marsh: *Z. Krebsforsch. 90*, 79 (1977)
75. Akamatsu, Y.: *Proc. Amer. Ass. Cancer Res. 16*, 162 (1975)
76. Bertram, J. S., A. W. Craig: *Brit. J. Cancer 24*, 352 (1970)
77. Takayama, S., T. Imaizumi: *Gann 60*, 353 (1969)
78. Wood, M., A. Flaks, D. B. Clayson: *Europ. J. Cancer 6*, 433 (1970)
79. Fujii, K., S. Odashima, M. Okado: *Brit. J. Cancer 35*, 610 (1977)
80. Ivankovic, S., J. Bücheler: *Z. Krebsforsch. 71*, 183 (1968)
81. Althoff, J., P. Pour, A. Cardesa, U. Mohr: *Z. Krebsforsch. 79*, 85 (1973)
82. Althoff, J.: *Z. Krebsforsch. 82*, 153 (1974)
83. Althoff, J., P. Pour, C. Grandjean, M. Eagen: *Z. Krebsforsch. 86*, 69 (1976)
84. Mohr, U., J. Althoff, D. Schmähl, F. W. Krüger: *Z. Krebsforsch. 74*, 112 (1970)
85. Althoff, J., F. W. Krüger, U. Mohr, D. Schmähl: *Proc. Soc. exp. Biol. (N.Y.) 136*, 168 (1971)
86. Reznik, G., U. Mohr, N. Kmoch: *Cancer Lett. 1*, 183 (1976)
87. Althoff, J., U. Mohr, N. Page, G. Reznik: *J. nat. Cancer Inst. 53*, 795 (1974)
88. Preussmann, R., M. Habs, H. Habs, D. Schmähl: *Cancer Res. 42*, 5167 (1982)
89. Lijinsky, W., J. E. Saavedra, M. D. Reuber: *Carcinogenesis 5*, 167 (1984)
90. Lijinsky, W., R. M. Kovatch: *Carcinogenesis 6*, 1679 (1985)
91. Hilfrich, J., I. Schmeltz, D. Hoffmann: *Cancer Lett. 4*, 55 (1977)
92. Pour, P., L. Wallcave: *Cancer Lett. 14*, 23 (1981)
93. Hoffmann, D., K. D. Brunnemann, A. Rivenson, S. S. Hecht: *IARC Sci. Publ. No. 41*, 299 (1982)
94. Hoffmann, D., A. Rivenson, J. D. Adams, A. Juchatz, N. Vinchkoski, S. S. Hecht: *Cancer Res. 43*, 2521 (1983)
95. Schmähl, D.: *Cancer Lett. 1*, 215 (1976)
96. Goodall, C. M., W. Lijinsky, L. Tomatis, C. E. M. Wenyon: *Toxicol. appl. Pharmacol. 17*, 426 (1970)
97. Boyland, E., F. J. C. Roe, J. W. Gorrod, B. C. V. Mitchley: *Brit. J. Cancer 18*, 265 (1964)
98. Greenblatt, M., S. Mirvish, B. T. So: *J. nat. Cancer Inst. 46*, 1029 (1971)
99. Dunkel, V. C., R. J. Pienta, A. Sivak, K. A. Traul: *J. nat. Cancer Inst. 67*, 1303 (1981)
100. Alexandrov, V. A.: *IARC Sci. Publ. No. 4*, 112 (1973)
101. Lijinsky, W., H. W. Taylor, L. K. Keefer: *J. nat. Cancer Inst. 57*, 1311 (1976)
102. Lijinsky, W., M. D. Reuber: *Carcinogenesis 3*, 911 (1982)
103. Bannasch, P., H. A. Müller: *Arzneimittel-Forsch. 14*, 805 (1964)
104. Lijinsky, W., H. W. Taylor: *Cancer Res. 35*, 2123 (1975)
105. Mirvish, S. S., A. F. Pelfrene, H. Garcia, Ph. Shubik: *Cancer Lett. 2*, 101 (1976)
106. Newberne, P. M., R. C. Shank: *Food Cosmet. Toxicol. 11*, 819 (1973)
107. Bannasch, P., U. Schacht, E. Storch: *Z. Krebsforsch. 81*, 311 (1974)
108. Müller, H.-A.: *Z. Krebsforsch. 66*, 303 (1964)
109. Ketkar, M. B., J. Holste, R. Preussmann, J. Althoff: *Cancer Lett. 17*, 333 (1983)
110. Lijinsky, W., R. M. Kovatch, G. L. Knutsen: *Carcinogenesis 5*, 875 (1984)
111. Althoff, J., R. Wilson, A. Cardesa, P. Pour: *Z. Krebsforsch. 81*, 251 (1974)
112. Mohr, U., G. Reznik, H. Reznik-Schüller: *J. nat. Cancer Inst. 53*, 231 (1974)
113. Reznik, G., U. Mohr, N. Kmoch: *Z. Krebsforsch. 86*, 95 (1976)
114. Pliss, G. B., V. V. Khudoley: *J. nat. Cancer Inst. 55*, 129 (1975)
115. Eisenbrand, G., M. Habs, D. Schmähl, R. Preussmann: *IARC Sci. Publ. No. 31*, 657 (1980)
116. Lijinsky, W., M. D. Reuber: *Cancer Lett. 12*, 99 (1981)
117. Garcia, H., W. Lijinsky: *Z. Krebsforsch. 77*, 257 (1972)
118. Takayama, S.: *Naturwissenschaften 56*, 142 (1969)
119. Ketkar, M. B., R. Fuhst, R. Preussmann, U. Mohr: *Cancer Lett. 21*, 219 (1983)
120. Althoff, J., C. Grandjean, S. Marsh, P. Pour, M. Takahashi: *Z. Krebsforsch. 90*, 71 (1977)

121. Sharmanov., T. S., M. M. Aidjanov: *IARC Sci. Publ. No. 41*, 665 (1982)
122. O'Gara, R. W., R. H. Adamson, D. W. Dalgard: *Proc. Amer. Ass. Cancer Res. 11*, 60 (1970)
123. Preussmann, R., D. Schmähl, G. Eisenbrand: *Z. Krebsforsch. 90*, 161 (1977)
124. Ketkar, M. B., P. Schneider, R. Preussmann, Ch. Plass, U. Mohr: *J. Cancer Res. clin. Oncol. 104*, 75 (1982)
125. McCoy, G. D., S. S. Hecht, S. Katayama, E. L. Wynder: *Cancer Res. 41*, 2849 (1981)

completed 10. 9. 1987

Perchloromethylmercaptan

Classification/MAK value:	**not yet established** **see Section IIb)** **MAK List 1988**
Classification/MAK value dates from:	**1988**
Synonyms:	perchloromethyl mercaptan perchloro-methyl-mercaptan trichloromethanesulfenyl chloride trichloromethane sulfenyl chloride trichloromethylsulfenyl chloride PCM thiocarbonyl tetrachloride perchloromercaptan
Chemical name (CAS):	trichloromethanesulfenyl chloride
CAS number:	594-42-3
Structural formula:	$$Cl-\overset{\displaystyle Cl}{\underset{\displaystyle Cl}{C}}-S-Cl$$
Molecular formula:	$CSCl_4$
Molecular weight:	185.9
Melting point:	not specified
Boiling point:	147.5 – 149 °C (decomposes)
Vapour pressure at 20 °C:	~ 85 hPa

1 ml/m³ (ppm) = 7.70 mg/m³   **1 mg/m³ = 0.13 ml/m³ (ppm)**

1 Toxic Effects and Modes of Action

Perchloromethylmercaptan (PCM) is a yellow oily fluid with a very unpleasant odour. It is only sparely soluble in water but can be steam distilled [1, 2]. The concentration of a saturated solution is 18 g/m³ at 20 °C [3]. Formally, PCM is not a mercaptan because it has no -SH group.

PCM is an important intermediate e.g. in the production of insecticides, fungicides (Captan, Folpet), dyes, additives, mustard gas derivatives, thiophosgene as well as vulcanization accelerators in the rubber industry [2, 4, 5]. During the First World War it was used briefly as a war gas [6]. There are not yet many publications about its toxic effects. After being inhaled by man in even low concentrations, PCM irritates the mucous membranes of the eyes, nose, throat and lungs. It induces general nausea and vomiting as a result of its foetid odour [1, 2, 3]. High doses produce severe toxic irritation with respiratory distress, shooting pains in the chest and lung oedema as well as pains in the upper abdominal region [7].

In low doses the compound has sterilizing, herbicidal and fungicidal properties.

1.1 Pharmacokinetics

There are as yet no publications available as to distribution, metabolism or excretion of PCM.

The following possible biotransformation pathways have been suggested: hydrochloric acid is produced in the presence of hydroxyl or amino groups:

$$Cl_3C-S-Cl + H_2O \rightarrow Cl_3C-S-OH + HCl$$

$$Cl_3C-S-Cl + R-NH_2 \rightarrow Cl_3C-S-NH-R + HCl$$

or the substance is reduced to thiophosgene:

$$Cl_3C-S-Cl \rightarrow + 2e^- \rightarrow Cl_2C=S + 2Cl^- \quad [7].$$

The violent course of the intoxication and the multiplicity of the parenchymatous damage is put down to the effects of the hydrochloric and sulfenylic acids, the latter being an enzyme blocker [4].

2 Effects in Man

PCM induces irritation of the eyes and the respiratory tract as well as vomiting; the irritation threshold for the eyes is given as 10 mg/m^3. The limit of tolerance is said to be about 70 mg/m^3 (details not given) [3, 8]. Concentrations lower than those used by Flury and Zernik in animal studies (levels not specified) produced severe discomfort in the eyes, throat and chest of exposed men [9].

Although the substance is used in large quantities as starting material in the production of pesticides, before 1969 two important producers could report no cases of PCM intoxication [7]. Then in 1970 in the Federal Republic of Germany three industrial accidents took place within 2 months. One of them was lethal.

A 23 year old man was sprayed with PCM in the face and eyes while taking a sample from a tanker. He inhaled a small quantity (amount not specified). His eyes were rinsed immediately on site with a buffer solution. Severe bilateral blepharospasm and almost complete corneal erosion developed. A thorax X-ray after 7.5 hours revealed closely packed, sometimes confluent shadows in all sections of the lung and, together with the ausculatory findings, led to the diagnosis "lung oedema". Two days after the accident respiratory distress, coughing and livid discoloration of the skin and mucosa suddenly developed. The oxygen saturation was low, the partial pressure of oxygen markedly (by $\sim 1/3$) reduced. The patient recovered and was discharged healthy on the sixth day after the accident [7].

One morning a 24 year old employee at a chemical works inhaled PCM from a leaky pipe. The concentration of the gas and the duration of exposure were not determined. He was cyanotic, had shooting pains in the chest, respiratory distress and a severe cough. His oxygen saturation was reduced (85%); an X-ray revealed oedema in all parts of the lungs. In spite of intensive care (oxygen, medicines) his condition was still just as critical on the third day. The next day the shadows in his lung X-ray were smaller. He was transferred to a general ward without subjective symptoms seven days after the accident. He was discharged from there as healthy, but psychic damage remained in the form of asthma attacks [7].

A 15 year old trainee technician broke a 2.5 l glass bottle which contained about 200 ml PCM while attempting to take it out of a lift in a transportation bucket. The contents of the broken vessel poured onto the floor and onto the clothing of the young man. Bending down, he probably inhaled concentrated PCM vapour which arose not only from the atmosphere in the bottle but also by evaporation from a large surface area of the fluid. He was exposed for about 30 minutes from his contaminated clothing. About an hour later in hospital, after being undressed and washed intensively, his symptoms were mild cyanosis, respiratory distress, coughing and nausea. Moist, fine to medium bubbling rales, wheezing and humming noises were heard over the lungs. The blood picture and all other clinical laboratory results were still in the normal range. During the next hours the complete symptoms of a toxic lung oedema developed with increased rales and respiratory distress. Blood gas analysis revealed severe acidosis which did not respond to medication. Cardiac arrest occurred repeatedly, then breakdown of circulation and kidney failure. Death followed after about 36 hours [4, 7]. The macroscopic and microscopic autopsy findings were advanced vacuolization and degeneration of the central and medial segments of the liver lobes; focal lipoid deposits in the adrenal cortex; acute, almost total toxic nephrosis; acute diffuse oedema in the cerebrum, cerebellum, brain stem and spinal cord; partly haemorrhagic oedematization of the myocardial interstitial tissues and pronounced necroses in the walls of the coronary arteries [7].

3 Effects on Animals

3.1 Acute toxicity

Acutely toxic and acutely lethal doses of PCM are assembled in Table 1. The few available studies on short term inhalation of PCM (see Tables 1 and 2) revealed the typical symptoms of intoxication with an irritant gas (respiratory difficulties, lung oedema) which caused death more or less rapidly depending on the concentration.

There are no available long term studies with experimental animals.

Table 1. Acute toxic effects of perchloromethylmercaptan in animals

Species (sex)	Appl. route	Conc. or dose	Exposure period	Observations and symptoms	Ref.
mouse (n.s.)	i.v.	56 mg/kg		LD_{50}	[10]
mouse (n.s.)	inhal.	9 ml/m^3	3 h	LC_{50}	[11]
rat (n.s.)	oral	83 mg/kg		LD_{50}	[12]
rat (♀)	inhal.	10 ml/m^3	6 h	lethargy, respiratory difficulties; later 3/4 died histology: lung oedema	[13]
rat (♀)	inhal.	100 ml/m^3	1 h	severe respiratory difficulties; 4/4 died histology: lung oedema	[13]
rat (♂)	inhal.	11 (10–13) ml/m^3	1 h	LC_{50}	[14]
rat (♀)	inhal.	16 (13–22) ml/m^3	1 h	LC_{50}	[14]
mouse and cat (n.s.)	inhal.	45.5 ml/m^3	15 min	after 1–2 d: died (lung oedema)	[1]
rabbit (♀)	p.c.	1410 (360–5510) mg/kg	4 h	LD_{50}	[14]

n.s.: not specified
p.c.: *per cutem* (occlusive)

Table 2. Inhalation studies with repeated exposures

Species	Number ♂	Number ♀	Conc. ml/m^3	Exposure period	Symptoms	Ref.
rat		4	2	$20 \times 6h$	respiratory difficulties only initially autopsy: congested lungs	[13]
rat	4	4	0.5	$20 \times 6h$	no symptoms of intoxication, autopsy: organs normal	[13]

4 Genotoxicity

Results of Ames tests with PCM have not yet been published. The tests currently in progress at NTP with *Salmonella typhimurium* have not yet been finalized. There are, however, results obtained with biochemical systems which permit some comparisons.

Using isolated nuclei from bovine liver cells it was shown that PCM inhibits DNA polymerase [15]. In *Penicillium duponti* PCM reduces the activity of *p*-nitrophenylpropionate esterase [16].

These two studies show that PCM and Captan act very similarly. Captan has been shown to be mutagenic [16]. The results of the genotoxicity studies currently in progress must be awaited before the significance of this finding can be assessed.

5 Carcinogenicity and Teratogenicity Studies

Studies of the carcinogenicity or teratogenicity of PCM are currently unknown.

6 Manifesto (MAK value, classification)

The current MAK value was adopted from the TLV list in 1958. It is inadequately documented. The little published data from accidental exposure of persons and the scanty results of animal studies are insufficient either to confirm the MAK value or to provide the basis for establishing a new value. Therefore the substance will in future be listed in Section IIb) of the List of MAK Values. Mutagenicity studies have long been planned but have still not been completed. There are no carcinogenicity studies at all. Therefore perchloromethylmercaptan is to remain on the list of substances urgently requiring examination until the results of the mutagenicity studies are available. Consideration of analogous compounds suggests the possibility of a carcinogenic potential; until this can be clarified in detail a classification of the substance in one of the existing categories in the List of MAK Values is not possible.

7 References

1. Flury, F., F. Zernik: *Schädliche Gase*, p 362, Springer Verlag, Berlin, 1931
2. *Ullmanns Encyklopädie der technischen Chemie,* 3rd ed., Vol. 12, p 310, Urban u. Schwarzenberg, München, Berlin, 1960
3. Sartori, M.: *Die Chemie der Kampfstoffe*, p 222, Friedr. Vieweg und Sohn, Braunschweig, 1940
4. Althoff, H.: *Arch. Toxicol. 31*, 121 (1973)
5. Neumüller, O.-A. (Ed.): *Römpps Chemie-Lexikon*, 7th ed., p. 2550, Franckh'sche Verlagshandlung, D-7000 Stuttgart, 1974
6. Wachtel, C.: *Z. exp. Path. Ther. 21*, 1 (1920)
7. Guhl, C.: *Zur Intensivtherapie der gewerblichen Intoxikationen*, Thesis, D-5000 Köln, 1973
8. Meyer, J.: *Der Gaskampf und die chemischen Kampfstoffe*, p 310, S. Hirzel Verlag, Leipzig, 1938
9. American Conference of Governmental Industrial Hygienists Inc. (ACGIH): *Documentation of the Threshold Limit Values and Biological Exposure Indices*, 5th ed., p 466, Cincinnati, OH, USA, 1986
10. U.S. Army Armament Research & Development Command; cited in *Registry of Toxic Effects of Chemical Substances (RTECS)*, 1981–82 ed., Vol. 2, p 676, NIOSH, USDHHS, Cincinnati, OH, USA, 1983

11. Stauffer Chemical Company: Stauffer Chemical Bulletin (*Perchlormethylmercaptan*) No. 531, New York, USA, 1970
12. Marhold, J. V.: *Sbornik Vysledku Toxicologickeho Vysetreni Latek A Pripravku*, Institut Pro Vyčkowu Vedoucicu Prakovniku Chemickeho Prumyclu Praha, Czechoslovakia, p 13, 1972; cited in *Registry of Toxic Effects of Chemical Substances (RTECS)*, 1981–82 ed., Vol. 2, p 676, NIOSH, USDHHS, Cincinnati, OH, USA, 1983
13. Gage, I. C.: *Brit. J. industr. Med. 27*, 1 (1970)
14. Vernot, E. H., J. D. MacEwen, C. C. Haun, E. R. Kinkead: *Toxicol. appl. Pharmacol. 42*, 417 (1977)
15. Dillwith, J. W., R. A. Lewis: *Pesticide Biochem. Physiol. 14*, 208 (1980)
16. Neidert, K., L. VanEpps, W. Welch: *Pest. Biochem. Physiol. 23*, 221 (1985)

completed 11.4.1988

1,1,2,2-Tetrachloro-1,2-difluoroethane

Classification/MAK Value	**200 ml/m³ (ppm)** **1690 mg/m³**
Classification/MAK Value dates from:	**1989**
Synonyms:	R 112 FC 112 CFC 112 1,2-difluoro-1,1,2,2-tetrachloroethane
Chemical name (CAS):	1,1,2,2-tetrachloro-1,2-difluoroethane
CAS number:	76-12-0
Structural formula:	

$$\begin{array}{ccc} & Cl & Cl \\ & | & | \\ F-&C-&C-F \\ & | & | \\ & Cl & Cl \end{array}$$

Molecular formula:	$C_2Cl_4F_2$
Molecular weight:	203.83
Melting point:	25 °C
Boiling point:	93 °C
Vapour pressure at 20 °C:	55.9 hPa

1 ml/m³ (ppm) ≈ 8.46 mg/m³　　　　**1 mg/m³ ≈ 0.118 ml/m³ (ppm)**

Evidently a substance of very low toxicity, 1,1,2,2-tetrachloro-1,2-difluoroethane has been entered in the MAK list until now with a MAK value of 500 ml/m³.

1 Effects in Man

The literature contains no reports of effects of this substance on man.

2 Effects on Animals

Most of the available animal studies have investigated acute and sub-acute (sub-chronic) toxicity of 1,1,2,2-tetrachloro-1,2-difluoroethane.

Rats were given daily oral doses of 2 g/kg body weight for 23 to 33 days. The authors stated that there were no pathological findings in the organs at the end of the study [1]. Reports of brief exposures of rats to 10 000 ml/m^3 for 1½ to 2 hours described "slight signs of intoxication" without loss of reflexes. Concentrations between 20 000 and 30 000 ml/m^3 were lethal and caused severe pulmonary haemorrhage.

The same authors [1] exposed rats to 1000 ml/m^3 for 16 days (18 hours daily) and found no pathological changes in the liver, lungs or spleen, whereas the same exposure pattern with 5000 ml/m^3 resulted in unconsciousness and then death; here too pulmonary haemorrhage was observed.

In another study [2], a 4 hour exposure to 15 000 ml/m^3 proved to be lethal for rats. Occasional leukopenia and "liver changes" were found in rats after exposure to 1000 ml/m^3 for 31 days (6 hours per day).

Eight fluorocarbons as well as some other chlorinated hydrocarbons were compared for their induction of mortality and "CNS effect" in rats and for cardiac effects in dogs [3].

The LC$_{50}$ for rats after a single 15 minute inhalation exposure is given as 20 000 ml 1,1,2,2-tetrachloro-1,2-difluoroethane/m^3. Inhalation of the substance for 10 minutes caused tremor in the extremities in rats, an effect which was considered to reflect stimulation of the CNS. The mean EC$_{50}$ for this effect was 2400 ml/m^3.

Myocardial sensitization to adrenaline was investigated in dogs (for method see [4]). An EC$_{50}$ of 1200 ml/m^3 was obtained for a 15 minute inhalation exposure to 1,1,2,2-tetrachloro-1,2-difluoroethane.

Of all the halogenated hydrocarbons tested in the above-mentioned comparative study [3], 1,1,2,2-tetrachloro-1,2-difluoroethane was shown to be the substance with the most marked effects on all the measured biological parameters (see above).

3 Mutagenicity and Carcinogenicity

In an older carcinogenicity study [5], newborn mice (Swiss ICR/Ha) were administered solutions of 1,1,2,2-tetrachloro-1,2-difluoroethane (10%), piperonyl butoxide (5%) or a combination of the two substances subcutaneously for 51 weeks. The animals were given 0.1 ml of the solutions on days 1 and 7, 0.2 ml on days 14 and 21. At the end of the treatment period the combination had caused a high mortality (55% after one month); large numbers of tumours developed in animals which survived the 51 week combination treatment, namely, hepatomas (31% of male animals) and malignant lymphomas (8% of female animals). Administration of the single substances at the same concentrations in the same study did not produce tumours.

In a comparative study with a large number of other chemicals, doses of 200 and 1000 mg/kg 1,1,2,2-tetrachloro-1,2-difluoroethane were administered to mice for a dominant lethal test [6]. The results gave no indication of a mutagenic potential of the substance.

4 Manifesto (MAK value, classification)

The previous MAK value was 500 ml/m^3 and was based on the assumption that the potential effects of 1,1,2,2-tetrachloro-1,2-difluoroethane are minimal.

In a 31 day inhalation study on the rat (6 hours per day) a concentration as low as 1000 ml/m^3 was shown to have biological effects (leukopenia, liver changes) [2].

The EC$_{50}$ (15 minute inhalation) for the myocardial effect in the dog (sensitization to adrenaline) was 1200 ml/m^3. For this parameter, the effect on the CNS and the acute lethal effect (LC$_{50}$) 1,1,2,2-tetrachloro-1,2-difluoroethane proved to be more effective than other chlorinated fluorocarbons of related chemical structure [3]. Under these circumstances a MAK value of 500 ml/m^3 seems to be too high. In view of the still remaining uncertainty, the MAK value has been reduced to 200 ml/m^3. The substance is provisionally classified in the category II,2 for the limitation of concentration peaks.

These stipulations are provisional and will be revised if necessary when further toxicological data become available.

It is not possible to assess the carcinogenicity of the substance because adequate data are not available.

There are no studies on the reproduction toxicology of 1,1,2,2-tetrachloro-1,2-difluoroethane.

5 References

1. Greenberg, L. A., D. Lester: *Arch. industr. Hyg. 2*, 345 (1950)
2. Clayton, J. W., H. Sherman, S. D. Morrison: *Amer. industr. Hyg. Ass. J. 27*, 332 (1966)
3. Clark, D. G., D. J. Tinston: *Hum. Toxicol. 1*, 239 (1982)
4. Beck, P. S., D. G. Clark, D. J. Tinston: *Toxicol. appl. Pharmacol. 24*, 20 (1973)
5. Epstein, S. S., S. Joshi, J. Andrea, P. Clapp, H. Falk, N. Mantel: *Nature (Lond.) 214*, 526 (1967)
6. Epstein, S. S., E. Arnold, J. Andrea, W. Bass, V. Bishop: *Toxicol. appl. Pharmacol. 23*, 288 (1972)

completed 13. 12. 1988

Thiourea

Classification/MAK value:	**see Section III B**
	MAK List 1988
Classification/MAK value dates from:	**1988**
Synonyms:	thiocarbamide
	isothiourea
	pseudothiourea
	β-pseudothiourea
	sulfourea
	2-thiourea
Chemical name (CAS):	thiourea
CAS number:	62-56-6
Structural formula:	$H_2N-CS-NH_2$
Molecular formula:	CH_4N_2S
Molecular weight:	76.1
Melting point:	182 °C
Boiling point:	not specified

1 ml/m³ (ppm) = 3.15 mg/m³   **1 mg/m³ = 0.316 ml/m³ (ppm)**

1 Toxic Effects and Modes of Action

Thiourea is an antioxidant. After oral administration to man and animals, it is practically completely absorbed and is excreted largely unchanged via the kidneys. Thiourea inhibits the peroxidase in the thyroid gland and thus inhibits thyroxine production. The reduced synthesis of thyroid hormone causes an increased pituitary secretion of thyreotropic hormone and so hyperplasia of the thyroid which, on continuous stimulation in animals, can lead to tumour formation. In the 1940s thiourea was used as an anti-thyroid drug. The initial dose was 1–2 g and the maintenance dose 100–200 mg, occasionally 15 mg. This therapeutic use produced a multitude of reports of side-effects such as nausea, vomiting after the high initial dose, in more than 10% of cases immediate and delayed allergic reactions with high temperatures, rheumatic complaints, skin reactions and occasional disorders of the haematopoietic system. There are very few reports of adverse effects on health after occupational exposure. They describe stomach and intestinal disorders, reduced thyroid function, blood count changes and dermatoses with sensitivity to sunlight. In early animal studies high doses (0.25% in the diet) produced not only thyroid tumours but also tumours in other organs. A recent short-term study with rats produced no evidence for tumour initiating or promoting activity in the liver. Studies with isolated mammalian cells suggest a weak genotoxic effect, but it still remains to be clarified whether this may be put down to the specific conditions of the *in vitro* test system used.

2 Effects in Man

Most of our knowledge about the toxic effects of thiourea in man comes from its period of therapeutic use as a thyroid depressant. Exposure at work is described in only a few Russian publications. The authors [1, 2] describe, without details of exposure levels, thiourea-induced disorders in workers who were occupied, e.g., in the maintenance of machinery or in packing. The symptoms were typical of hypothyroidism with facial oedema, hypotonia, bradycardia, and ECG changes with reduced basal metabolism, constipation, flatulence, polyuria, granulocytopenia with lymphocytosis and monocytosis. The first changes in the blood count appeared after 5–6 months exposure. Most symptoms were observed in workers who had handled thiourea for 5–15 years [1]. Also described were cases of contact dermatitis which disappeared rapidly after the workers had been transferred to another workplace [2]. Contact dermatitis in persons who frequently used photocopiers was also related to thiourea exposure [3, 4].

The most comprehensive descriptions of the side-effects of thiourea therapy are given in the publications [5] and [6]. Mostly observations of individuals are described. Among 525 patients treated with thiourea 49, i.e. 9.3%, suffered from one or more of the following side-effects (the number of cases is given in brackets): agranulocytosis (1), leukopenia (4), raised temperature (24), erythema (9), urticaria (1), swollen lymph nodes (1), pains in muscles and joints (4), gastrointestinal disorders (17) and various other symptoms (90) [6]. The raised temperature occurred mostly shortly after treatment began and regressed on termination of the therapy. The attacks of feverishness which occur within 7 to 14 days after the start of the therapy are put down to sensitization, as are the skin reactions [5].

2.1 The dose-response relationship in therapeutic applications

The doses of thiourea recommended for the treatment of excessive thyroid gland activity vary considerably. Originally 2–3 g daily was used, especially as initial dose. This was later reduced because of the associated gastrointestinal disorders. Determination of the basal metabolic rate and the iodine bound to serum protein led to a recommended dose of 75–210 mg daily for the first 4–8 weeks of therapy [7]. An initial dose of 15–75 mg was not reliably effective [8]. A dose of 25–70 mg daily was recommended for the subsequent continuous therapy for which 10–15 mg were ineffective [8]. Thus 10 mg administered daily is said to be insufficient to depress thyroid activity.

3 Effects on Animals

3.1 Acute toxicity

The acute toxicity of thiourea varies with the species, strain, age and iodine content of the diet. The oral LD_{50} for the mouse is about 1 g/kg [9], for the rat 125–1830 mg/kg, depending on the strain [10], for the rabbit 10000 mg/kg [11]. The i.p. LD_{50} for the rat varies between 4 and 1340 mg/kg, depending on the strain [12, 13]. The animals die of lung oedema; pleural effusion is seen in the survivors. For this reason thiourea has been used in doses between 0.01 and 0.5 g/kg i.p. in experimental animals as a model substance for the production of lung oedema and pleural effusion [14–17], effects which are prevented by pretreatment of the animals with glutathione or cysteine. Glutathione reduces the irreversible binding of radioactivity to lung proteins after administration of ^{14}C-thiourea [18, 19]. In rats, toxic doses of thiourea also caused hyperglycaemia, glucosuria, polyuria and reduction of the glycogen level in the liver [17]. Young animals, less than 50 days old, were up to 50 times less sensitive to the effects of a 14 day treatment with thiourea than were older rats [20, 21].

3.2 Subacute and subchronic toxicity

The principal effect of repeated administration of thiourea to experimental animals is the inhibition of thyroid gland function. Accordingly, most effects of thiourea are prevented if thyroid hormone is given simultaneously.

Daily thiourea doses of 660 ± 60 mg/kg given for two weeks by gastric intubation to male rats which were 28 days old at the start of treatment led to a reduction in body weight gain of about 50% [22]. Daily ingestion of 131 mg/kg body weight by 21–30 day old female rats for 10 consecutive days resulted in hyperplasia of the thyroid, demonstrated both macroscopically and microscopically. In contrast, 12 mg/kg had no such effect [23]. A qualitatively and quantitatively similar dose-response relationship has been described for the reduction of the basal metabolic rate [20, 21]. Simultaneous administration of thyroxin prevented this effect. As little as 70 mg thiourea/kg, administered orally for 10 days, produces a reduction in the iodine level of the thyroid gland from 73 to 23 mg/100 g tissue [24] and 1% thiourea in the diet for 2 months reduced iodine uptake by the thyroid [25]. Associated with reduced thyroid activity, pituitary weights were increased and signs of pituitary overactivity were seen histologically and biochemically; the ovary, uterus and prostate weights were reduced [26–28]. Disorders of the haematopoietic system have also been described and could be accounted for in part by a haemolytic effect of thiourea. After administration of 16 to 50 daily doses of 1 ml of a 1% aqueous thiourea solution by gavage to rats, haemosiderosis was seen in the spleen, lymph nodes and intestinal villae. It could be prevented by thyroxin substitution therapy [29]. Repeated administration of high doses of thiourea in the diet, drinking water or by intraperitoneal injection resulted in reduced osmotic resistance of the erythrocytes, congestion, haemosiderosis and atrophy of the spleen, anaemia, leukocytopenia, granulocytopenia, increased erythropoiesis in the bone marrow, reduced clotting times and increased phospholipid levels in blood [29–34].

Mice seem to be less sensitive to thiourea because subcutaneous administration of 500 mg/kg daily for 10 days led only to a slight reduction in the colloid content of the thyroid [35] and 2.5 g/kg in the diet for 13 weeks had no effect on body weight [36].

3.3 Chronic toxicity

When the administration of thiourea to rats or other experimental animals is continued for months, the changes induced are similar to those found after subacute treatment. The available reports, however, are mostly from the 1940s with imprecise details of the doses administered so that dose-response relationships can only be estimated approximately. The thyroid gland plays the principal role in these studies but individual reports describe effects on the liver, the haematopoietic system, lungs, kidneys, bones and the endocrine system as well.

Daily administration of 1.72, 6.88 or 27.5 mg thiourea per kg body weight to mice in the drinking water for two years and to rats for their lifetimes or a maximum of 3 years caused reduced body weight gain and thyroid gland enlargement only in the rats of the highest dose group. No other changes were detected either macroscopically or microscopically [37, 38]. Administered in the drinking water, daily doses of 60 mg/kg body weight for 12 weeks also remained without any effects on the rat [11]. In another study [39] rats were given thiourea in the diet at concentrations between 0.01 and 1% corresponding to about 7 to 700 mg/kg body weight per day. A daily dose of about 175 mg/kg body weight caused reduced body weight gain in the first weeks, tumours in the liver and thyroid gland and 100% mortality within 17 months. In addition there were atrophy, congestion and haemosiderin deposits in the spleen, calcified tubular casts in the renal tubuli, reduced bone growth, hypoplasia in the bone marrow, reduction or cessation of spermatogenesis, slight generalized hypertrophy of hepatocytes with fatty deposits and bile duct proliferation. Doses of 35 mg/kg and less had no effects on the thyroid gland or the other organs. In contrast, 50 ppm thiourea in the diet (about 3.5 mg/kg body weight) resulted after 26 months in macroscopically and microscopically visible changes in the lungs and liver and occasionally in the spleen of rats [40]. Administration of 0.25% thiourea to rats in the drinking water for 65 to 122 days resulted in enlargement of the pituitary with structural changes in the pars intermedia, hyperplasia of the parathyroid gland and fibrotic inflammation of the bones [41].

4 Carcinogenicity

There are several older carcinogenicity studies which were carried out before the middle 1960s. Apart from the thyroid gland, numerous other tumour localizations can be recognized but the distribution varies from one study to the next. The results of these studies are assembled in Table 1. Most of the reports are highly unsatisfactory in that details of spontaneous tumour frequencies or of doses are missing or in

Table 1. Studies of the carcinogenicity of thiourea

Species (strain)	Number, sex, age	Dose, treatment period	Observations	Ref.
mouse 5 strains	4–65 ♂♀ per group controls: 4–51 ♂♀	2% in diet, up to 21 months	thyroid hyperplasia, no carcinomas	[42]
mouse (C3H)	21 ♀ controls: 25 ♀	0.25% in diet, 13 weeks; then 0.375%, 3–45 weeks; killed on appearance of tumours	thyroid hyperplasia, no tumours	[43]
mouse (C3H) +/− castration	25 ♂ + 25 ♀ controls: none	0.3% in diet, 7 months	thyroid hyperplasia	[44]
mouse (C3H)	49 ♀ controls: 33 ♀	0.1–0.2% in drinking water, 4–6 months	no thyroid hyperplasia (1/20 hypertrophy), mammary tumours in 54%, less in controls: 28%	[45]
mouse (R3) with high incidence of mammary tumours	11 ♀ controls: 7 ♀	0.2–0.5% in drinking water, av. 10 months	thyroid hyperplasia	[45]
mouse (ICR Swiss)	42 n.s. controls: 4 × 50, age: 24–72 h	1 × 2500 mg/kg s.c., killed after 6 months	incidence of lung adenomas: 5% controls: 2–14%	[46]
rat (*Rattus norw.*)	9 ♀	0.25% in drinking water, 12–23 months	thyroid: 4 carcinomas from month 20, 7 adenomas	[47]
rat (*Rattus norw.*)	8 ♀	0.25% in drinking water, 12–24 months	thyroid: 3 carcinomas from month 20, 8 adenomas	[47]
rat (Wistar)	8♀	0.25% in drinking water, 12–22 months	thyroid: 6 adenomas	[47]
rats from the above 3 groups	8 ♀ with adenomas	0.25%, 17–18 months, plus thyroid extract, thyroxine, injected from month 16	no thyroid gland tumours	[47]

Table 1 (continued)

Species (strain)	Number, sex, age	Dose, treatment period	Observations	Ref.
rat (albino)	19 ♂ controls: 12 ♂	0.2% in drinking water, 13–26 months	1 nasal tumour, 6 tumours in the ear, 6 orbital tumours; 5 animals with tumours in both of the latter localities	[48]
rat (Wistar)	9 ♂	0.2% in drinking water 12–23 weeks	squamous cell carcinoma of the Zymbal gland and/or meibomian glands in 8/9 animals	[49]
rat (Osborne-Mendel)	30 ♂ + 30 ♀ controls: 50 ♂ + 50 ♀	80 ppm in the diet, 24 months	no increased tumour frequencies	[50]
rat (Osborne-Mendel)	30 ♂ + 30 ♀ controls: 30 ♂ + 30 ♀	50 ppm in the diet, 26 months	21 tumours, 4 of them malignant; controls: 15 tumours not specified in detail	[40]
rat (albino)	18 ♂♀/group controls: 18 ♂♀	0.01–1% in the diet, 24 months	from 0.25%: thyroid hyperplasia, from 0.1%: liver adenomas in 14/29 survivors	[39]
rat (albino)	12 ♂♀	3–4 ml 10% soln i.p. 3 × /week, for 6 months, then 0.2% in drinking water to 15 months	6 animals died or killed after 6 weeks to 8 months: no effects after 1 year: 6 epidermoid carcinomas in ear and eye region, no hepatic tumours	[51]
rat (Sprague-Dawley)	5 ♂ + 5 ♀ 21 d old	3 × 200 mg/kg, p.o., after 1 week 2 × 10 mg PCB/kg weekly, 11 weeks	no increase in number or size of ATP-free islets in the liver	[52]
rat (Sprague-Dawley)	4 ♂ + 4 ♀ 21 d old	1 × 8 mg/kg di-ethylnitrosamine p.o., after 1 week 0.2% thiourea in the drinking water for 12 weeks	70%–90% reduction in the number and area of ATP-free islets in the liver	[52]

n.s.: not specified

that the administered doses were toxic, causing up to 100 % lethality. These studies do not meet present day standards and cannot contribute to an assessment of the carcinogenic effects of thiourea, apart from the effects on the thyroid gland. The only recent study [52], which investigated the initiating and promoting effect of thiourea on the liver, produced no evidence of such effects.

5 Pharmacokinetics, metabolism and mechanism of the effects on the thyroid gland and other organs

There are only few reports of the metabolism of thiourea in the experimental animal. Thiourea is mostly (more than 90 % of the dose) excreted unchanged via the kidney within 48 hours. About 10 % of the dose was found in urine as the sulfate [53, 54]. Most studies have investigated the metabolic pathways in the target organs, thyroid gland and lung, and are described in detail below.

5.1 Thyroid gland

In the presence of iodine or iodide and hydrogen peroxide, thiourea is oxidized by the thyroid gland peroxidase to formamidine disulfide, $NH_2(NH)CSSC(NH)NH_2$. Presumably, a thio-iodine complex is formed as an unstable intermediate [55]. Formamidine disulfide is also unstable: at pH values above 3.0 it decomposes forming cyanamide, elementary sulfur and thiourea. *In vitro*, cyanamide inhibits the peroxidation of iodide and the iodination of tyrosine. This explains the thyroid depressant action of thiourea.

Autoradiographic studies of the distribution of ^{35}S-labelled thiourea revealed a highly preferential and prolonged storage of the radioactivity in the thyroid gland [56]. Together with the main product, sulfate, protein-bound sulfur was detected [57].

Later studies with ^{35}S-thiourea demonstrated that, in the presence of NADPH or ascorbic acid, microsomal proteins from the thyroid are able to desulfurate thiourea. The products found included not only protein-bound sulfur but also thiosulfate and sulfate. This reaction did not take place with the corresponding protein fractions from liver or from kidney [58]. The point of attack in protein was seen to be the disulfide bonds. The disulfide produced in the protein by addition of thiourea (Figure 1) hydrolyses to a thiosulfenic acid and urea [59]. It must be assumed that such a reaction results in structural and functional changes in the protein involved. That these protein modifications could be relatively stable may be deduced from the finding that the protein-bound sulfur could only be dissociated after reaction with nucleophiles such as sulfite or thiocyanate.

5.2 Lung

Like a number of its derivatives, thiourea induces oedema and pleural effusion in the rat lung. The processes involved have been thoroughly studied. After intraperitoneal administration of ^{14}C-labelled thiourea the radioactivity was located preferentially

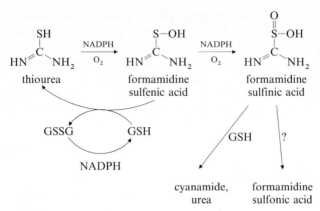

Figure 1. Metabolism of thiourea by the microsomal FAD dependent monoxygenase according to [60, 61]

in the lungs, less in the kidneys and less still in the liver. In the lung most of the radioactivity was bound to a low molecular weight protein in the $100\,000 \times g$ supernatant [62]. The extent of this protein binding correlated with the sensitivity of the animals to the toxic effects of thiourea on the lung: in young animals which are less sensitive to thiourea than older ones, the protein binding is less than in the older animals. Reduced protein binding was also observed in animals which had been treated once with thiourea and then reacted less sensitively to a second dose than did untreated animals. Micro-autoradiography revealed that the binding was mostly localized in the alveolar membrane. The formation of the protein-binding thiourea metabolite seems not to involve liver cytochrome P-450 because treatment of the animal with phenobarbital had no effect on the extent of binding [18].

The glutathione (GSH) level seems to play a critical role here. In rats treated with diethyl maleate, the glutathione level in the lung was reduced to 10% of the control value; after thiourea administration the amount of protein-bound thiourea metabolites in the pretreated animals was three times that in the controls. If GSH or cysteine were given as well the amount of thiourea metabolites bound *in vitro* was reduced and the lung oedema induced by thiourea *in vivo* was less severe [19]. One hour after treatment of the animals with thiourea on its own, the GSH content of the lung was reduced by more than 90%. The GSH level did not return to normal until 24 hours later [63].

The reduction of the GSH content after administration of thiourea was not stoichiometric, i.e., significantly more GSH disappeared than was expected for the thiourea dose [63]. This suggests that it is not only the formation of an addition product with thiourea which is responsible for the drop in GSH level but that an additional autocatalytic process involving GSH must be involved. It is conceivable that GSSG is formed by redox-cycling and that a thiourea radical functions as the electron carrier. That radicals can be intermediates in the oxidation of thiourea has been shown in studies of electrochemical oxidation and on the use of thiourea as a radical trap for oxygen radicals (see below). Thiyl radicals have been shown to be intermediates in GSH oxidation with horseradish peroxidase [64].

It is still unclear what role the reduced GSH level or the reactive, protein-binding metabolites of thiourea play in the lung toxicity. The oedema inducing effect of thiourea suggests that membrane damage is involved. It may be presumed that on reduction of the GSH level in the lung the concentration of reactive oxygen species rises and membrane damage caused by lipid peroxidation is the result.

The breaking of disulfide bonds in essential proteins by reaction with thiourea metabolites is particularly marked at low GSH levels and could contribute to lung toxicity.

5.3 Activation by isolated enzymes

Studies with isolated enzyme preparations have shown that thiourea can be metabolized by hepatic enzymes. Thiourea is a substrate for the microsomal flavoprotein-dependent aminoxidase from porcine liver [61]. This enzyme oxygenates lipophilic N-substituted thioureas via formamidine sulfenic acids, $NH_2(NR)CSOH$, to the corresponding sulfinic acids, $NH_2(NR)CSO_2H$, which can be converted by further oxidation to the sulfonic acids, $NH_2(NR)CSO_3H$. The sulfinic acids could be one of the metabolites responsible for the toxicity of thiourea because when these were administered alone they were more toxic than thiourea and produced the same symptoms [65]. Earlier in the chain of reactions, the sulfenic acid must also be considered to be a reactive species.

Thiourea reduces *in vivo* and *in vitro* the enzymatic activity and the amount of microsomal cytochrome P-450. This effect, however, was only seen at high doses and was only marked in animals treated with phenobarbital [66].

5.4 Reaction with oxygen radicals

Thiourea inhibits microsomal ethanol oxidation. The inhibitory effect has been put down to the ability of thiourea to act as a radical trap for OH radicals [67–69]. In the same way thiourea acts as a radical trap for oxygen radicals during the production of DNA single strand breaks with X-rays [70].

5.5 Non-enzymatic reactions

Thiourea reacts directly with hydrogen peroxide, forming formamidine sulfinic acid, $NH_2(NH)CSO_2H$, at neutral pH [71, 72]. Reaction of thiourea with iodine yields formamidine disulfide, $NH_2(NH)CSSC(NH)NH_2$.

The mechanisms of action may be summarized as follows: in addition to reductive activation which leads to breaking of disulfide bonds in protein, oxidation in the presence of iodine or with the flavoprotein-dependent aminoxidase is of importance. Thus at least three mechanisms which depend on metabolism may contribute to toxicity:

1. denaturation of functionally important proteins by breaking of disulfide bonds, forming thiosulfenic acids,

2. membrane damage as a result of reduction in the GSH level in the lung, and
3. metabolism to toxic sulfinic and sulfonic acids.

6 Genotoxicity

6.1 Mitogenic effects

Thiourea has mitogenic properties. Older studies [73, 74] with high doses of thiourea
$(1-14 \times 0.4$ g, i.p.) produced a high mitosis rate in the liver without hepatocellular
necrosis. Similar findings were the result of studies on partially hepatectomized rats
[75].

6.2 Mutagenicity

The effect of thiourea on *Salmonella typhimurium* in the standard Ames test in the
presence and absence of metabolizing liver cell fractions has been studied by several
research groups. With the exception of Yamaguchi [76], who reported a doubling of
the number of revertants in the strain TA100 with 150 µg thiourea/plate, all authors
reported negative results [77–82].

In the host-mediated assay with mice, thiourea $(1 \times 125$ mg/kg) increased the
mutation rate slightly, by a factor of 2 and 3.6 in the *S. typhimurium* strains TA1530
and TA1538, respectively, and by a factor of 1.7 in *Saccharomyces cerevisiae*
$(1 \times 1000$ mg thiourea/kg) [9].

In V79 Chinese hamster cells and in the absence of an added metabolic activation
system, thiourea (10–40 mM) induced a five-fold increase in the frequency of aza-
guanine resistant cells [83].

6.3 DNA repair in hepatocytes

Treatment of primary cultures of isolated rat hepatocytes with 5–25 mM thiourea
induced a linear, relatively slight increase in unscheduled DNA synthesis in the cells
[83]. Very similar results which, however, were interpreted as negative, presumably
erroneously (see [84]), had already been reported previously [85].

6.4 Induction of DNA strand breaks

Thiourea (30–300 mM) induces DNA single strand breaks in primary cultures of
isolated rat hepatocytes [86]. That thiourea is observed to inhibit DNA strand break
induction by various intercalating substances in mouse leukaemia cells [70] is perhaps a result of a change in chromatin structure which would alter the activity of a
topoisomerase responsible for the production of strand breaks under the influence
of intercalating substances.

6.5 Inhibition of DNA synthesis

Using the Friedman-Staub test [88], Seiler [87] found no inhibition of the incorporation of ^{3}H-thymidine into testicular DNA *in vivo*. In contrast, in the so-called "DNA synthesis inhibition test" [89] a concentration of 60 mM thiourea inhibited DNA synthesis in human fibroblasts. This was considered to be evidence for a genotoxic effect of the substance [90].

6.6 Current understanding of genotoxic effects

With one exception, research groups have found thiourea to be non-mutagenic in bacterial mutagenicity tests with and without S9 fraction. Presently there is no *in vitro* or *in vivo* finding which is indicative of adduct formation between thiourea metabolites and DNA. In an *in vivo* study of the production of preneoplastic liver foci in the rat, thiourea did not act as an initiator [52].

On the other hand, a weak mutagenic effect of thiourea has been found in the host-mediated assay [9], a mutagenic effect, the induction of unscheduled DNA synthesis, in V79 cells [83], and the induction of DNA single strand breaks in hepatocytes [86]. An explanation of this discrepancy is currently not possible.

It is conceivable, though, that as a result of a reduction in GSH levels during thiourea metabolism genotoxic reactive oxygen species could arise or a genotoxic metabolite could be produced by oxidation [61]. To what extent such an activation pathway is actually responsible for the genotoxicity demonstrated *in vitro* is not yet clear.

7 Reproductive and Developmental Toxicity

Studies with ^{35}S-thiourea in rats and mice demonstrate that the substance crosses the placenta and, depending on the stage of development of the thyroid gland, is stored in particular in this organ where it affects iodine metabolism [91, 92]. Accordingly, when the dams have been treated with 0.2% thiourea in the drinking water, thyroid hyperplasia is found in the rat foetuses and newborn animals [93]. Likewise, maternally toxic oral doses of 1000 mg/kg given to mice on day 10 or to rats on day 12 or day 14 of gestation were also embryotoxic. Absorption frequency was increased without malformations in the foetuses living on day 18 (mice) or 20 (rats) [94]. In foetuses whose dams had been treated with 0.2% thiourea in the drinking water from day 1 to day 14 of gestation, maturation defects were apparent on day 20 of gestation in the central and peripheral nervous system, the skeleton and the eyes [95]. These effects too can be put down to the thyroid depressant activity of thiourea. Therefore such effects are not to be expected at air levels which do not produce an inhibition of thyroid function.

8 Manifesto (MAK value, classification)

The experience gained from the extensive therapeutic use of thiourea as a thyroid depressant indicates that ingestion of 10 mg daily by adults does not inhibit thyroid function. That would be equivalent to a concentration in the workplace air of 0.5 mg/m^3, assuming that 20 m^3 air is inhaled in the course of a shift. Therefore 0.5 mg/m^3 could be established as the MAK value. The elimination half-life of thiourea in man is not known. From animal studies and experience of therapeutic use, however, it may be deduced that the substance does not accumulate and that the half-life is expected to be about as long as a shift. For the limitation of exposure peaks, therefore, thiourea would be classified in Category II,2.

High doses of thiourea produce thyroid carcinomas in animals. This effect is a result of the fact that the thyroid gland, inhibited in its function by the thiourea, in compensation is continually stimulated by thyreotropin. Via hypertrophy of the thyroid gland, this can lead to adenoma formation and finally to malignant degeneration. Thus, with respect to its effect on the thyroid, thiourea could be considered to be a typical indirect carcinogen for which a cancer risk only exists when the target organ is permanently stimulated. For this effect a threshold concentration could be given below which such an effect would not be expected. However, there are a number of older animal studies in which tumours were observed in other organs. The tumour localities were not uniform and the studies do not meet present day requirements. In addition, *in vitro* studies with mammalian cells did reveal a genotoxic effect of thiourea, although a weak one. The relevance of these findings can at present not be determined. Further studies must clarify the causes of these effects. Therefore thiourea is classified in Section III B of the List of MAK Values.

Teratogenic effects have only been observed with maternally toxic doses so that, provided the mean air concentration during the shift did not exceed 0.5 mg/m^3, the substance could be classified in pregnancy group C.

9 References

1. Zaslawska, A. G.: *Klin. Med. (Mosk.)* 42, 129 (1964)
2. Speranski, N. J., I. R. Zacharow, N. M. Taranucha: *Gig. Tr. prof. Zabol. No. 13*, 50 (1969)
3. Leun, J. C. Van der, E. J. de Kreek, M. M. Deenstra-van Leeuwen, H. van Weelden: *Arch. Derm.* 113, 1611 (1977)
4. Nurse, D. S.: *Contact Dermatitis 6*, 153 (1980)
5. Peters, J. P., E. B. Mann, D. M. Kidd, W. W. Enstrom, L. C. Waters: *Yale J. Biol. Med.* 22, 139 (1949)
6. Laan, W. P. Van der, V. M. Storrie: *Pharmacol. Rev. 7*, 301 (1955)
7. Danowski, T. S., E. B. Man, J. R. Elkinton, J. P. Peters, A. W. Winkler: *Amer. J. med. Sci.* 215, 123 (1948)
8. Winkler, A. W., E. B. Man, T. S. Danowski: *J. clin. Invest. 26*, 446 (1947)
9. Simmon, V. F., H. S. Rosenkranz, E. Zeiger, A. L. Poirier: *J. nat. Cancer Inst. 62*, 911 (1979)
10. Dieke, S. H.: *J. Pharmacol. exp. Ther. 90*, 260 (1947)
11. Flinn, F. B., J. M. Geary: *Contr. Boyce Thompson Inst. 11*, 241 (1940)
12. Dieke, S. H., C. P. Richter: *J. Pharmacol. exp. Ther. 83*, 195 (1945)
13. Landgrebe, F. W., T. N. Morgan: *Nature (Lond.) 157*, 22 (1946)
14. DuBois, K. P., R. G. Herrmann, W. F. Erway: *J. Pharmacol. exp. Ther. 89*, 186 (1947)

15. Henschler, D., W. Meyer: *Klin. Wschr. 40*, 264 (1962)
16. Giri, S. N., M. A. Hollinger, C. E. Cross: *Toxicology 2*, 211 (1974)
17. Cronin, S. R., S. N. Giri: *Proc. Soc. exp. Biol (N.Y.) 146*, 120 (1974); cited in Chem. Abstr. 81, 21973 (1974)
18. Hollinger, M. A., S. N. Giri, E. Budd: *Toxicol. appl. Pharmacol. 37*, 545 (1976)
19. Hollinger, M. A., S. N. Giri, F. Hwang: *Drug Metab. Dispos. 4*, 119 (1976)
20. MacKenzie, J. B., C. G. MacKenzie: *Proc. Soc. exp. Biol. (N.Y.) 54*, 34 (1943)
21. MacKenzie, C. G., J. B. MacKenzie: *Endocrinology 32*, 185 (1943)
22. Smith, C. C.: *J. Pharmacol. exp. Ther. 100*, 408 (1950)
23. Astwood, E. B.: *J. Pharmacol. exp. Ther. 78*, 79 (1943)
24. Astwood, E. B., A. Busswell, A.M. Hughes: *Endocrinology 37*, 456 (1945)
25. Keston, A. S., A. D. Goldsmith, A. S. Gordon: *J. biol. Chem. 152*, 241 (1944)
26. Leathem, J. H.: *Endocrinology 36*, 98 (1945)
27. Leathem, J. H.: *Endocrinology 37*, 482 (1945)
28. Huf, E., F. Auffarth: *Naunyn-Schmiedeberg's Arch. exp. Path. Pharmak. 206*, 394 (1949)
29. Arvy, L, M. Gabe: *C.R. Soc. Biol. (Paris) 144*, 486 (1950)
30. Arvy, L., M. Gabe: *C.R. Soc. Biol. (Paris) 140*, 945 (1946); cited in *Chem. Abstr. 41*, 5208b (1947)
31. Arvy, L., M. Gabe: *C.R. Soc. Biol. (Paris) 141*, 22 (1947); cited in *Chem. Abstr. 41*, 4853i (1947)
32. Arvy, L., M. Gabe: *C.R. Soc. Biol. (Paris) 143*, 1336 (1949); cited in *Chem. Abstr. 44*, 7434f (1950)
33. Daft, F. S., A. Kornberg, L. L. Ashburn, W. H. Sebreil: *Proc. Soc. exp. Biol. (N.Y.) 61*, 154 (1946)
34. Idris, R., K. Ahmad: *Biochem. Pharmacol. 24*, 2003 (1975); cited in *Chem. Abstr. 84*, 99 (1976)
35. Jones, R. P.: *J. Path. Bact. 58*, 483 (1946)
36. Morris, H. P., C. S. Dubnik (Jr.), A. Dalton: *J. nat. Cancer Inst. 7*, 159 (1946)
37. Hartzell, A.: *Contr. Boyce Thompson Inst. 12*, 471 (1942)
38. Hartzell, A.: *Contr. Boyce Thompson Inst. 13*, 501 (1945)
39. Fitzhugh, O. G., A. A., Nelson: *Science 108*, 626 (1948)
40. Deichmann, W. B., M. L. Keplinger, F. Sala, E. M. Glass: *Toxicol. appl. Pharmacol. 11*, 88 (1967)
41. Malcolm, J., W. E. Griesbach, F. Bielschowsky: *Brit. J. exp. Path. 30*, 17 (1949)
42. Gorbman, A.: *Cancer Res. 7*, 746 (1947)
43. Dalton, A. J., H. P. Morris, C. S. Dubnik: *J. nat. Cancer Inst. 9*, 201 (1948)
44. Casas, C. B., E. Koppisch: *Endocrinology 51*, 322 (1952)
45. Vasquez-Lopez, E.: *Brit. J. Cancer Res. 3*, 401 (1949)
46. Gargus, J. L., O. E. Paynter, W. H. Reese (Jr.): *Toxicol. appl. Pharmacol. 15*, 552 (1969)
47. Purves, H. D., W. E. Griesbach: *Brit. J. exp. Path. 28*, 46 (1947)
48. Rosin, A., H. Ungar: *Cancer Res. 17*, 302 (1957)
49. Ungar, H., A. Rosin: *Arch. De Vecchi Anat. pat. 31*, 419 (1960)
50. Radomski, J. L., W. B. Deichman, W. E. MacDonald, E. M. Glass: *Toxicol. appl. Pharmacol. 7*, 652 (1965)
51. Rosin, A., M. Rachmilewitz: *Cancer Res. 14*, 494 (1954)
52. Deml, E., D. Oesterle: *Cancer Lett. 41*, 245 (1988)
53. Schulman, J. (Jr.), R. P. Keating: *J. biol. Chem. 183*, 215 (1950)
54. Scheline, R. R., R. L. Smith, R. T. Williams: *J. med. pharm. Chem. 4*, 109 (1961)
55. Davidson, B., M. Soodak, H. V. Strout, J. T. Neary, C. Nakamura, F. Maloof: *Endocrinology 104*, 919 (1979)
56. Schulman, J. (Jr.): *J. biol. Chem. 186*, 717 (1950)
57. Maloof, F., M. Soodak: *Endocrinology 61*, 555 (1957)
58. Maloof, F., L. Spector: *J. biol. Chem. 234*, 949 (1959)
59. Maloof, F., M. Soodak: *J. biol. Chem. 236*, 1689 (1961)
60. Ziegler, D. M.: *Biochem. Soc. Trans. 6*, 94 (1978)
61. Poulsen, L. L., R. M. Hyslop, D. M. Ziegler: *Arch. Biochem. Biophys. 198*, 78 (1979)
62. Hollinger, M. A., S. N. Giri, M. Alley, E. R. Budd, F. Hwang: *Drug Metab. Dispos. 2*, 521 (1974)
63. Hollinger, M. A., S. N. Giri: *Res. Commun. chem. Path. Pharmacol. 26*, 609 (1979)

64. Harman, L. S., D. K. Carver, J. Schreiber, R. P. Mason: *J. biol. Chem. 261*, 1642 (1986)
65. Zhislin, L. E., N. M. Ovetskaya: *Gig. Tr. prof. Zabol. No. 16*, 52 (1972)
66. Hunter, A. L., R. A. Neal: *Biochem. Pharmacol. 24*, 2199 (1975)
67. Cederbaum, A. I., E. Dicker, E. Rubin, G. Cohen: *Biochem. biophys. Res. Commun. 78*, 1254 (1977)
68. Ohnishi, K., C. H. Lieber: *Arch. Biochem. Biophys. 191*, 798 (1978)
69. Cederbaum, A. I., E. Dicker, E. Rubin, G. Cohen: *Biochemistry 18*, 1187 (1979)
70. Pommier, Y., L. A. Zwelling, M. R. Mattern, L. C. Erickson, D. Kerrigan, R. Schwartz, K. W. Kohn: *Cancer Res. 43*, 5718 (1983)
71. Reid, E. E.: *Organic Chemistry of Bivalent Sulfur*, Vol. 5, p 38, Chemical Publ. Co., New York, 1963
72. Heikkila, R. E., B. Winston, G. Cohen, H. Barden: *Biochem. Pharmacol. 25*, 1085 (1976)
73. Rachmilewitz, M., A. Rosin, L. Doljanski: *Proc. Soc. exp. Med. 66*, 153 (1947)
74. Doljanski, F., Z. Eshkol, D. Givol, E. Kaufmann, E. Margoliash: *J. Endocr. 13*, 141 (1956)
75. Maini, M. M., H. F. Stich: *J. nat. Cancer Inst. 26*, 1413 (1961)
76. Yamaguchi, T.: *Agric. Biol. Chem. 44*, 3017 (1980)
77. McCann, J., E. Choi, E. Yamasaki, B. Ames: *Proc. nat. Acad. Sci. (Wash.) 72*, 5135 (1975)
78. McCann, J., B. N. Ames: *Proc. nat. Acad. Sci. (Wash.) 73*, 950 (1976)
79. Rosenkranz, H. S., L. A. Poirier: *J. nat. Cancer Inst. 62*, 873 (1979); cited in *Chem. Abstr. 91*, 14968 (1979)
80. Simmon, V. F.: *J. nat. Cancer Inst. 62*, 893 (1979)
81. Simmon, V. F.: *J. nat. Cancer Inst. 62*, 901 (1979)
82. Göggelmann, W.: *Überprüfung der Durchführbarkeit von Prüfungsvorschriften und der Aussagekraft der Grundprüfung des Chemikaliengesetzes*, p 204, GSF München, report prepared for the Umweltbundesamt, Berlin, 1981
83. Ziegler-Skylakakis, K., S. Rossberger, U. Andrae: *Arch. Toxicol. 58*, 5 (1985)
84. Rossberger, S., U. Andrae: *Tox. in vitro 1*, 215 (1987)
85. Lonati-Galligani, M., P. H. M. Lohman, F. Berends: *Mutat. Res. 113*, 145 (1983)
86. Sina, J. F., C. L. Bean, G. R. Dysart, V. I. Taylor, M. O. Bradley: *Mutat. Res. 113*, 357 (1983)
87. Seiler, J. P.: *Mutat. Res. 46*, 305 (1977)
88. Friedman, M. A., J. Staub: *Mutat. Res. 37*, 67 (1976)
89. Painter, R. B.: *Nature (Lond.) 265*, 650 (1977)
90. Yanigasawa, K., K. Nishio, S. Gotoh: *Mutat. Res. 183*, 89 (1987)
91. Shepard, T. M.: *Endocrinology 72*, 223 (1963)
92. Kertai, P., T. Remenar: *Acta med. Acad. Sci. hung. 32*, 271 (1975)
93. Balogh, R., P. Kertai: *Kisérl. Orvostud. 28*, 460 (1976)
94. Teramoto, S., M. Kaneda, H. Aoyama, Y. Shirasu: *Teratology 23*, 335 (1981)
95. Kern, M., Z. Tatar-Kiss, P. Kertei, I. Földes: *Acta morph. Acad. Sci. hung. 28*, 259 (1980)

completed 19. 5. 1988

Tri-n-butyltin compounds

(as TBTO)

Tributyltin compounds
  with the general formula:

$$CH_3-CH_2-CH_2-CH_2 \diagdown$$
$$CH_3-CH_2-CH_2-CH_2-Sn-x$$
$$CH_3-CH_2-CH_2-CH_2 \diagup$$

Classification/MAK value   **0.002 ml/m^3 (ppm)**
0.05 mg/m^3

Classification/MAK value dates from: 1989

Tri-n-butyltin	oxide	benzoate
Synonyms:	TBTO tributyltin oxide bis(tributyltin)oxide	TBTB tributyltin benzoate
Chemical name (CAS):	distannoxane, hexabutyl-	stannane, (benzoyloxy)tributyl-
CAS number:	56-35-9	4342-36-3
Structural formula:	$(C_4H_9)_3Sn-O-Sn(C_4H_9)_3$	$(C_4H_9)_3Sn-O-\overset{\overset{O}{\|\|}}{C}-C_6H_5$
Molecular formula:	$C_{24}H_{54}OSn_2$	$C_{19}H_{32}O_2Sn$
Molecular weight:	596	411
Melting point:	$< -45\,°C$	$20\,°C$
Boiling point:	$173\,°C$ at 1.3 hPa	ca. $135\,°C$ at 0.3 hPa
Vapour pressure at 20 °C:	$1.0 \cdot 10^{-5}$ hPa	$2 \cdot 10^{-6}$ hPa
1 ml/m^3 = × mg/m^3 1 mg/m^3 = × ml/m^3	24.73 0.040	17.05 0.058

Tri-n-butyltin	chloride	fluoride
Synonyms:	TBTCl tributyltin chloride	TBTF tributyltin fluoride
Chemical name (CAS):	stannane, tributylchloro-	stannane, tributylfluoro-
CAS number:	1461-22-9	1983-10-4
Strutural formula:	$(C_4H_9)_3Sn-Cl$	$(C_4H_9)_3Sn-F$

Molecular formula:	$C_{12}H_{27}ClSn$	$C_{12}H_{27}FSn$
Molecular weight:	325	309
Melting point:	$-16\,°C$	$240\,°C$
Boiling point:	140 °C at 13 hPa	$> 350\,°C$ (extrapolated)
Vapour pressure at 20°C:	not specified	not specified
$1\ ml/m^3 = \times\ mg/m^3$	13.48	12.82
$1\ mg/m^3 = \times\ ml/m^3$	0.074	0.078

Tri-n-butyltin	linoleate	methacrylate
Synonyms:	TBTL tributyltin linoleate	TBTM tributyltin methacrylate
Chemical name (CAS):	stannane, tributyl-(1-oxo- 9,12-octadecadi- enyl)oxy-(Z,Z)-	stannane, tributyl-(2-methyl- 1-oxo-2-propenyl)oxy-
CAS number:	24124-25-2	2155-70-6
Structural formula:	$(C_4H_9)_3Sn-O-\overset{\overset{\displaystyle O}{\|}}{C}-C_{17}H_{31}$	$(C_4H_9)_3Sn-O-\overset{\overset{\displaystyle O}{\|}}{C}-\overset{\overset{\displaystyle CH_3}{\|}}{C}=CH_2$
Molecular formula:	$C_{30}H_{58}O_2Sn$	$C_{16}H_{32}O_2Sn$
Molecular weight:	568.7	374.7
Melting point:	$< 0\,°C$	$16\,°C$
Boiling point:	ca. 140 °C at 0.5 hPa	$> 300\,°C$ (extrapolated)
Vapour pressure at 20°C:	$9 \cdot 10^{-4}$ hPa	$3 \cdot 10^{-4}$ hPa
$1\ ml/m^3 = \times\ mg/m^3$	23.59	15.54
$1\ mg/m^3 = +\ ml/m^3$	0.042	0.064

Tri-n-butyltin	naphthenate
Synonyms:	TBTN tributyltin naphthenate
Chemical name (CAS):	stannane, tributylmono(naphthenoyloxy)-derivatives

CAS number:	85409-17-2
Structural formula:	—
Molecular formula:	—
Molecular weight:	ca. 500
Melting point:	$< 0\,°C$
Boiling point:	ca. 125 °C at 0.5 hPa
Vapour pressure at 20°C:	$9 \cdot 10^{-7}$ hPa
1 ml/m³ = × mg/m³	~ 20.74
1 mg/m³ = × ml/m³	~ 0.048

The tri-n-butyltin compounds which are used in industry (TBTX, X = oxygen, halogen or carboxylate) do not differ substantially in the toxic effects they produce either after single or after repeated administration. Therefore a common MAK value may be established for these compounds. For this purpose bis(tri-n-butyltin) oxide (TBTO) is taken as representative of the group of TBT derivatives. This approach also makes sense for monitoring because the available analytical methods do not permit specific determination of the various TBT compounds when they are present together.

Apart from tributyltin fluoride, which is a solid, TBT derivatives are liquids under normal conditions.

1 Toxic Effects and Modes of Action

Tributyltin compounds are less toxic systemically after dermal application than after oral administration because they are absorbed more slowly by the dermal route. Because they are cytotoxic, tributyltin compounds have a strong irritant effect on skin and mucous membranes. Inhaled particles produce severe local irritation. Inhalation of vapour at room temperature, however, has no adverse effects on health.

The lymphatic organs are the main targets of the systemic toxicity (thymus atrophy) resulting from repeated oral administration (10 days to 2 years) to experimental animals. In addition, suppression of thymus-dependent immune responses and of nonspecific resistance has been demonstrated in rats. The discussed mechanism involves dibutyltin metabolites of the tributyltin compounds. Higher doses (≥ 80 ppm) damage the liver and bile ducts as well as producing microcytic anaemia and endocrine disorders. Unlike trimethyltin and triethyltin compounds, TBTO is not neurotoxic.

Inhalation of an atmosphere saturated with TBTO vapour at room temperature (0.16 mg/m³) for 4 hours daily during 4–5 weeks (5 days per week) produced neither local nor systemic toxic effects.

Mutagenicity tests of various kinds have mostly produced negative results. There is no good evidence that TBTO is genotoxic, in spite of a few doubtfully positive findings.

The highest dose of TBTO (50 ppm TBTO in the diet) used in a carcinogenicity study with rats induced an increase in benign tumours of the endocrine organs, probably by a non-genotoxic mechanism (suppression of immune response or disturbance of hormonal regulation).

In studies with mice, rats and rabbits, TBTO has no embryotoxic effects except at concentrations which are also toxic to the mother animals.

1.1 Toxicokinetics and metabolism

TBTO and various TBT carboxylates can be readily extracted as TBT chloride in essentially 100% yield from 1N hydrochloric acid [1]. This finding may be explained by dissociation of the TBT compound to form a hydrated TBT cation and the corresponding anion. Thus the same species, assumed to be TBTCl, is probably absorbed from the gastrointestinal tract after ingestion of various TBT compounds.

TBT compounds are readily absorbed after inhalation but incompletely after oral or dermal application. The proportion of TBTO absorbed from the gastrointestinal tract of the rat varied from 20%–55% depending on the vehicle used. In the monkey, about 10%–15% of a dose of undiluted TBTO was absorbed through the intact skin [2].

After administration of ^{113}Sn-TBTO to rats by gavage, the radioactivity was mostly excreted via the liver, biphasically with half-lives of about 12 hours and 3 days. The total activity was highest in the excretion organs, kidney and liver [2]. In rats who had been given TBTO for 4 weeks in the diet, the Sn concentrations were 5 to 10 times higher in the liver and kidneys than in the brain and fat tissue [3]. When mice were given ^{14}C-TBTO in the drinking water for 5–30 days, they excreted the radioactivity mostly in the faeces (little absorption). Kidney, liver, spleen and fat tissue contained the highest ^{14}C-activity. At the end of treatment the excretion was relatively rapid [4].

Hydroxylation of tributyltin compounds takes place mostly in the liver with subsequent dealkylation to yield dibutyltin and monobutyltin compounds and finally inorganic tin [5, 6]. Differential analysis of TBTO and its metabolites revealed that mostly unchanged substance was present in the lipophilic tissues of the rat (fat tissue, carcass) and that liver and kidney contained mostly metabolites.

Accumulation of TBTO and/or its metabolites was observed in the rat after repeated treatment by gavage. It is estimated that steady state conditions would be reached after about 3–4 weeks [2].

2 Effects in Man

2.1 Local effects

Undiluted tributyltin compounds applied to the back of the hand produced follicular inflammation in volunteers in about 2–3 hours and pustules from the second day after the application. Extensive, accidental skin contact also caused pain. The lesions were usually healed in 7–10 days [7]. Contact dermatitis of varying severity was observed in workers who had accidental contact with TBT compounds. Prompt cleaning of the affected skin areas prevented the irritation [8].

Tests were carried out to establish the local effects of model wood preservatives which contained 1% TBTO, 2% TBT naphthenate or 2% TBT linoleate in a white spirit vehicle with 10% binder. After exposures lasting from 30 minutes to 8 hours there was no remarkable difference between the effects of the preparations containing TBT and those without. The irritation after a 4 hour exposure was classified as slight to moderate [9].

Without any further details as to exposure it is reported that organotin workers suffered from sore throats, coughing and nausea several hours after inhalation of vapour or fumes [7]. In addition, the literature (see [10]) contains reports of irritation of the upper and lower respiratory tract as well as of the eyes of persons working with TBTO. The compound seems to have been present in the form of an aerosol (either because of spraying or binding to dust particles). In these cases the nature and extent of the exposure were only inadequately described.

2.2 Systemic effects

In the works of the large European organotin producers the employees are subjected to yearly medical examinations which include not only a general medical examination but also clinical laboratory parameters (alkaline phosphatase and transaminases in serum) and haematological tests (including differential blood count). In these examinations, but also in the special examinations carried out after more extensive accidental contact, there has still been no indication of adverse systemic effects of TBT compounds in spite of the presence of organotin in the urine [8, 11].

Recently the results of the yearly occupational medical examinations of the employees of an American organotin producer were published. There were no differences in clinical laboratory parameters, urine analysis, lung function tests, ECG (for employees over 45 years old) and lung X-rays between organotin workers and collectives of new employees or unexposed employees. The haematological parameters for the employees in organotin production were all within the normal range; however, workers from both inorganic and organic tin production had slightly but significantly lower values for erythrocyte count, haemoglobin and haematocrit than the above-mentioned control collectives. When only the data from the tributyltin production workers (only 14 in number) are compared with those from the office staff or maintenance workers there are practically no differences in the red cell parameters [12]. Therefore the existence of a TBT-related effect must be considered to be doubtful.

3 Effects on Animals

3.1 Acute toxicity

The LD_{50} values for TBT compounds for various administration routes in various species are assembled in Table 1.

The results obtained by various authors for the *oral* LD_{50} of TBTO in the rat (112–194 mg/kg) do not differ very much in spite of the fact that different formulations were used. There is also good agreement with the corresponding values for male (152 mg/kg) and female (92 mg/kg) mice [17]. Apathy and emaciation were the main toxic symptoms described. Autopsy of animals that died revealed in particular irritant effects in the gastrointestinal tract [13].

Table 1. Acute toxicity of TBTO

Species	Sex	Administration route	Form	LD_{50} mg/kg	LC_{50}/ other results	Ref.
Rat	♂, ♀	inhalation	undiluted		65 mg/m^3 (4 h LC_{50})	[13]
Rat	♂	oral	oil	148		[14]
	♂		aq. suspension	194		
Rat	n.s.	oral	isopropanol	112		[15]
Rat	n.s.	oral	oil	180		[16]
Rat	♂, ♀	oral	aq. emulsion	127		[13]
Mouse	♂	oral	oil	152		[17]
	♀		oil	92		
Rat	n.s.	dermal	isopropanol	605		[15]
Rat	♂, ♀	dermal	aq. emulsion		> 300 mg/kg*	[13]
Rabbit	n.s.	dermal	undiluted	11 700		[14]
Rabbit	n.s.	dermal	undiluted		900 mg/kg**	[16]
Mouse	n.s.	intravenous	suspension	6.0		[16]
Rat	♂, ♀	intraperitoneal	aq. emulsion	5.0		[18]
Rat	♀	intraperitoneal	oil	7.2		[19]
Rat	♂, ♀	intraperitoneal	oil	20		[17]
Mouse	♂, ♀	intraperitoneal	oil	16		[17]

  * highest tested dose, no mortality
** "absorbed dose"
n.s.: not specified

Table 2. Acute oral toxicity of some tri-n-butyltin compounds in the rat [13]

TBTX	LD_{50} (mg/kg)	LD_{50} (mmol TBT/kg)
– fluoride	94	0.30
– chloride	122	0.38
– oxide	127	0.42
– benzoate	99/203 [1]	0.24/0.49 [1]
– linoleate	190	0.34
– abietate	158	0.27
– naphthenate	224	0.37

[1] Results from two different experiments

The oral LD_{50} in the rat for a series of TBT compounds which were investigated at various times in one laboratory [13] are shown in Table 2. Because of the differing molecular weight of the anionic residue, X, the LD_{50} was also expressed as a molar TBT dose (in mmol/kg body weight). The then still apparent differences between the TBT derivatives are considered to be of no biological significance. There were also no marked differences in symptoms.

The *dermal* LD_{50} values for TBTO vary from 605 mg/kg for the rat [15] to 11 700 mg/kg for the rabbit [14]. This discrepancy may, at least in part, be put down to the different preparations used. The dermal LD_{50} of other TBT compounds is given as 505 mg/kg for the benzoate [15], 680 mg/kg for the fluoride [20] and 4600 mg/kg for the naphthenate [21]. These results demonstrate that the acute toxicity of TBT compounds is markedly less after dermal contact than after ingestion.

In studies of the acute inhalation toxicity in rats [13], *aerosols* of TBTO and TBT naphthenate (TBTN) were shown to be markedly toxic. The LC_{50} after 4 hours exposure was determined as 65 mg/m^3 (TBTO) and 152 mg/m^3 (TBTN) taking only those particles into account which are considered to be inspirable, diameter d < 10 µm. Irritation of the exposed surfaces (nasal discharge and, in animals that died, occasional lung oedema) was the principal symptom of the intoxication. In the guinea pig, deaths were observed after 1 hour exposure to 200 mg/m^3 TBTO (aerosol of a solution in olive oil) [22]. The results of these aerosol inhalation studies are in good agreement with the high toxicity observed after intraperitoneal or intravenous administration (see Table 1).

In "inhalation hazard tests" with tributyltin oxide, benzoate and naphthenate *vapour*, 7 hour exposures of rats to atmospheres which were as saturated as possible with the respective vapour caused only occasional slight nasal discharge. Mortalities were not observed [13].

3.2 Local effects

Undiluted technical TBTO was shown to be extremely irritating to the skin of rabbits [20] and of man [7]. Irritation of rabbit skin by an antifouling paint of unknown TBTO content, on the other hand, was described as moderate [20]. An emulsion containing 0.5% TBTO caused a severe intolerance reaction on 4 hour occlusive application to rabbit skin [13]. Solid tributyltin fluoride (TBTF) had only a slight irritant effect on rabbit skin but in a paint it was shown to cause severe irritation [20]. However, comparative studies of the local tolerance of a wood preservative containing 1 % TBTO in a white spirit vehicle showed that the skin of the rabbit is considerably more sensitive than that of man ([9], see also Section 2.1 – Local effects in man).

In the rabbit eye TBTO, TBTF (both substances applied undiluted and also in antifouling paint) and TBTCl caused severe irritation [20, 23]. Certain aqueous preparations containing 0.15 % – 2 % TBTO produced severe damage in the rabbit eye [24].

3.3 Toxicity after repeated administration

A review of the studies on toxicity caused by repeated administration of TBTO and other tributyltin compounds is to be found in the Proceedings of a workshop of the Organotin Environmental Programme Association [18], (see also [25]).

The principal data from studies of *oral* administration are assembled in Tables 3 and 4. Recent work indicates that the main targets of the toxicity of TBT compounds are the organs of the lymphatic system. When juvenile rats were given TBTO in the diet for 4 or 13 weeks, at a concentration of 100 ppm TBTO thymus weights were reduced [18]. Other authors [3] found the same effect after 4 weeks of treatment with as little as 20 ppm TBTO (only in male animals). A reduction in rat thymus weight was also observed after administration of TBTCl [30] and TBTN [31] in the diet. Histological studies revealed, although only after administration of higher concentrations, a reduction in the number of lymphocytes in the thymus cortex as well as in the thymus-dependent regions of the spleen and lymph nodes. In comparative studies in which TBTCl was administered to rats, mice and Japanese quails for 2 weeks in the diet, it was shown that rats are considerably more sensitive than the other two species with respect to thymus atrophy [29] (see Section 3.4 – Effects on the immune system – for details of the influence of TBT compounds on immune reactions).

It is also reported that administration of 5 ppm TBTO or more in the diet for 4 weeks caused the development of erythrocyte rosettes in the mesenteric lymph nodes and a reduction in the haemosiderin content of the spleen of rats [3]. The development of such rosettes in rats was also observed after administration of TBTCl (from 50 ppm) or TBTN (at 200 ppm) in the diet [30, 31]. They also arise spontaneously in this species [32]. The mechanism of their development and their biological significance are still unclear. In other studies the development of such rosettes was not observed in rats administered TBTO in the diet for 2 years although a reduction in the iron pigment of the spleen at 5 ppm (females) and 50 ppm was found after one year [33].

After oral administration of higher TBTO doses to rats (see Table 3), hepatocellular necroses and inflammatory lesions of the bile ducts were observed as well as microcytic anaemia and a reduction in the numbers of peripheral lymphocytes.

In studies of the effects on the endocrine system it was shown that, at concentrations of 20 and 80 ppm TBTO in the diet, the serum insulin concentration was

Table 3. Oral toxicity after repeated administration of TBTO

Species	Number/ group, sex	Admin. route	Dose	Duration	Principal findings	Ref.
Mouse, juvenile	10 ♂	diet	77 ppm	7 d	body weight gain ↓, spleen weight ↓	[26]
Mouse, adult	4 ♂		232 ppm 696 ppm	4 d	body weight ↓ leukocyte and lymphocyte number ↓	
Rat	10 ♂	diet	32 ppm 100 ppm 320 ppm	30 d	body weight gain ↓ body weight gain ↓ food intake ↓, mortality (6/10), no macroscopic findings	[14]
Rat, juvenile	5 ♂, 5 ♀	diet	4 ppm 20 ppm 100 ppm 500 ppm	4 wk (dose finding)	no substance-related findings no substance-related findings food intake and weight gain ↓, absolute thymus weight (♂) ↓ high mortality, apathy, emaciation, thymus and lymph node weight ↓, lymphocyte content of lymphatic organs ↓	[18]
Rat	10 ♂, 10 ♀ (10 ♂)*	diet	5 ppm 20 ppm 80 ppm 320 ppm	4 wk (6 wk)*	rosettes in the mesenteric lymph nodes, iron storage in the spleen ↓ thymus weight (♂) ↓, serum transferases ↑, food and water intake ↓, mikrocytic anaemia, lymphocyte content of lymphatic organs ↓, activity of the pituitary-thyroid system ↓, LH ↑ liver necroses, inflammation of the bile duct	[3]
Rat	20 ♂, 20 ♀	diet	4 ppm 20 ppm 100 ppm	13 wk	no substance-related findings clotting times (♂) ↑, food intake (♀) ↓ but weight normal food intake + body weight gain ↓, serum alkaline phosphatase ↑, albumin (♀) ↑ γ-globulin (♀) ↓, weights of thymus, lymph nodes and thyroid ↓, weight of adrenals (♂) ↑	[18]

Table 3 (continued)

Species	Number/ group, sex	Admin. route	Dose	Duration	Principal findings	Ref.
Rat	50 ♂, 50 ♀ (10 ♂, 10 ♀)**	diet	0.5 ppm	2 a (1 a)**	food intake (♂) ↑, flattening of the thyroid epithelium without changes in T$_4$, TSH	[27]
			5 ppm		food and water intake (♂) ↑, iron storage in the spleen ↓ (♀ only after 1 year!)	
			50 ppm		food intake ↑ (♂ inconsistently), weight gain ↓, mortality ↑, emaciation, apathy, ataxia, Hb + haematocrit + lymphocytes ↓, SGOT + SGPT + SAP ↑, nephrosis, benign tumors of the endocrine organs	
Rat	10 ♂, 10 ♀	gavage	1 mg/kg 25 mg/kg	10–11 d	no substance-related findings mortality (2 ♂, 2 ♀), microcytic anaemia, chronic inflammation of the bile duct, lymphotoxicity	[18]
Rat	5 ♀ and 5 ♂	gavage	3 mg/kg 6 mg/kg	26 wk 13 wk	thymus weight ↓, flattening of the thyroid epithelium, histological changes in the pituitary	[28]

ppm: mg/kg in the diet
  * additional study to examine the short-term effects on the endocrine system
** interim sacrifice

reduced in male rats while the glucose tolerance remained unchanged relative to the control group. In addition, reductions in the concentrations of thyroxine (T$_4$) and thyrotropin (TSH) in serum and an increase in the concentration of luteinizing hormone (LH) were seen at 80 ppm TBTO [3]. The concentrations of follicle-stimulating hormone (FSH) and corticosterone were unchanged. After stimulation with releasing hormones, the release of LH and FSH was increased at 80 ppm TBTO, that of TSH tended to be slightly reduced. Immunohistochemical studies revealed a dose-dependent reduction in number and staining intensity of the TSH-producing cells in the pituitary at 20 ppm or more as well as an increase in the number of LH-producing cells. Flattening of the epithelium of the thyroid was seen at 80 ppm TBTO. In a 2 year study with TBTO in the diet (see Table 3), however, administration of concentrations up to 50 ppm produced no marked changes in serum hormones (insulin, TSH, FSH, LH, T$_4$, and free T$_4$) [27].

Table 4. Oral toxicity after repeated administration of TBT compounds

Com-pound	Species	Number/ group, sex	Admin. route	Conc. in ppm	Dura-tion	Principal findings	Ref.
TBT chloride	mouse	10 ♂	diet	50 150	2 wk	no substance-related findings food intake and body weight ↓, weight of thymus and spleen ↓	[29]
TBT chloride	rat	10 ♂	diet	15 50 150	2 wk	no substance-related findings thymus and spleen weight ↓, lymphocytes in thymus cortex ↓, rosettes in mesenteric lymph nodes food intake and body weight ↓	[30]
TBT chloride	rat	6 ♂ (10 · 6 ♂)	diet	100 recovery	4 wk	thymus weight ↓, thymus weight after 1 wk normal	[30]
TBT naph-thenate	rat	10 ♂ and 10 ♀	diet	2 8 40 200	4 wk	no substance-related findings serum-Na$^+$ ↓ (not dose-related) weights of thymus, lymph nodes and kidney ↓, signs of thymolysis, TSH suspicion of ↓ food intake and body weight gain ↓, SGPT ↑, T_3 + LH suspicion of ↓, rosettes in mesenteric lymph nodes, haemosiderin in the spleen ↓	[31]

ppm: mg/kg diet

Concentrations of TBTO in the diet which are without adverse effects on the rat (no observed effect levels) are given as 4 ppm after 90 days [18] and 0.5 ppm after 2 years (taking into account the results of immune function tests, see Section 3.4 – Effects on the immune system).

In an *inhalation* study with TBTO, juvenile rats were exposed under "nose only" conditions 4 hours daily, apart from weekends, for 29–32 days [13]. With a total concentration of 2.8 mg/m^3 TBTO as *aerosol* there were marked toxic effects which included mortality. Histological investigation revealed inflammatory reactions in the whole of the respiratory tract and changes in the lymphatic organs like those occurring after ingestion of large doses.

After inhalation of TBTO *vapour* (0.03 or 0.16 mg/m^3) neither local nor systemic toxic effects could be demonstrated. The concentration, 0.16 mg/m^3 TBTO, corresponding approximately to the steady-state vapour pressure at room temperature can thus be taken as a no observed effect level for the rat.

3.4 Effects on the immune system

3.4.1 Suppression of immune reactions

The histological changes which are found in the lymphatic organs of juvenile rats after repeated administration of TBTO were described in the previous section. The function of the immune system was studied in newly weaned rats after administration of TBTO in the diet for 6 weeks [34]. Concentrations of 20 ppm and more produced a suppression of the thymus-dependent immune response and of parameters of non-specific resistance. Preliminary results of a 2 year study of the same species with TBTO in the diet [33, 35] indicate that 5 ppm (only in the infection model using *Trichinella spiralis*) and 50 ppm TBTO induce functional disorder of the immune system whereas 0.5 ppm is described as a no effect level. The validation of these test models is considered to be not yet complete.

3.4.2 Skin sensitization

No evidence for dermal sensitizing effects of TBTO [17] or TBTN [36] was obtained in the guinea pig maximization test. This result was confirmed in man in a study of two antifouling paints containing TBTO [37].

3.5 Neurotoxicity

Trimethyltin compounds cause neuronal damage in certain regions of the brain [38] whereas triethyltin compounds induce oedema of the white substance of the brain and spinal cord [39]. In the older literature [23, 40] there are also indications that tributyltin compounds could possibly damage the central nervous system. In more recent studies on the effects of TBTO, TBTCl and TBTN, reviewed in Section 3.3 – Toxicity after repeated administration, no morphological changes in the CNS were found even though this aspect was given particular attention in some studies. Similarly, none of the behavioural changes typical of the effects of the lower homologues were observed.

4 Genotoxicity

TBTO has been tested for mutagenic properties in numerous short-term tests *in vivo* and *in vitro*. The results of these studies are assembled in Table 5.

TBTO caused neither gene mutations in *Salmonella typhimurium* in the Ames test nor genetic changes (gene conversions) in the yeast *Saccharomyces cerevisiae* in the concentration range 0.0001 to 0.01 µl/plate [41]. However, in a study initiated by the WHO [42] with concentrations of 0.3–3 µg/ml TBTO in the fluctuation test, an increase in the number of revertants which was not dose-dependent arose in one strain of *S. typhimurium* (TA100) in the presence of rat liver S9 mix. It is questionable whether this finding is of biological significance. No evidence of point mutations or DNA damage was found in the other *in vitro* test systems with microbial or mammalian cells.

Name of test	in vitro	in vivo	End point				Result	Ref.
			Gene mutation	Chromosome mutation	Effects on DNA	other		
Standard Ames test (*Salmonella typhimurium*)	×		×				−	[41, 42]
Recombination assay (*Bacillus subtilis*)	×				×		−	[42]
Reverse mutation (*Klebsiella pneumoniae*)	×		×				−	[42]
Fluctuation test (*Salmonella typhimurium*)	×		×				+	[42]
Forward mutation (*Schizosaccharomyces pombe*)	×		×				−	[42]
Mitotic gene conversion (*Saccharomyces cerevisiae*)	×				×		−	[41, 42]
Recessive lethal mutations (*Drosophila melanogaster*)		×	×				−	[42]
HGPRT test (V79, Chinese hamster)	×		×				−	[42]
TK$^{+/-}$ and Na$^+$/K$^+$ ATPase test (L5178Y mouse lymphoma)	×		×				−	[42]
Sister chromatid exchange (CHO, Chinese hamster)	×				×		−	[42]
Chromosome aberrations								
– (CHO, Chinese hamster)	×			×			(+)	[42]
– (human lymphocytes)	×			×			−	[41]
Inhibition of metabolic cooperation (V79, Chinese hamster)	×					×	−	[42]
Micronucleus test (mouse)		×		×			(+)	[42]
		×		×			−	[41]

In ovary cells of Chinese hamster *in vitro* chromosome damage was observed at the highest concentration (5 µg/ml) in the presence of S9 mix [42]. A connection with the cytotoxicity which was also seen in this study may be surmised. In addition, the same authors report a positive result in the micronucleus test 48 hours after administering a single oral dose of 60 mg/kg to male mice. A subsequent evaluation of the bone marrow preparations from the WHO study produced no evidence of a mutagenic potential [43]. In their own studies too the authors [41] were unable to obtain evidence of chromosome mutations with TBTO, either in human lymphocytes *in vitro* (concentrations: 0.005–0.1 µg/ml without S9 mix; 0.01–1.0 µg/ml with S9 mix) or in the micronucleus test in the mouse, although the tested concentrations and doses extended into the distinctly cytotoxic range. In the last-mentioned micronucleus test 5000 polychromatic erythrocytes were scored instead of the usual 1000 cells. The highest administered dose, 125 mg/kg p.o., was about twice as high as that in the WHO study.

The results of the vast majority of tests with procaryotic or eucaryotic cells indicate that any potential of TBTO to induce point mutations may be disregarded. If one takes into account the critical remarks about the positive results of [42] as well as the convincingly negative result of the micronucleus test with a higher dose range and larger sample size [41], then the available data are not indicative of a clastogenic potential of TBTO.

In the Ames test, no evidence of mutagenic properties was found for six different TBT carboxylates. Similarly, in the micronucleus test in the mouse no evidence of damage to the chromosomes or spindle apparatus was found after oral administration of up to 500 mg/kg TBT naphthenate [41].

5 Carcinogenicity

In a two year carcinogenicity study, TBTO was added to the diet of groups of 50 male and 50 female Wistar rats in concentrations of 0, 0.5, 5 and 50 ppm [27]. The adverse effects on body weight gain in the second year indicate that 50 ppm was the maximally tolerated dose. Tumour incidences which differ from the control values are assembled in Table 6. In the highest dose group an increased number of benign pituitary tumours (prolactinoma) and tumours of the adrenal medulla (pheochromocytoma) were observed in both sexes. Towards the end of the study these resulted in increased mortality. The incidence of adenomas of the parathyroid gland was increased in male rats of the 50 ppm group and that of tumours of the adrenal cortex of male animals was reduced.

It is unlikely that TBTO has genotoxic effects (see Section 4 – Genotoxicity). Prolactinomas and pheochromocytomas had been observed in historical controls with a high and variable frequency (Table 7) [44–46]. Tumours of the adrenal medulla are often found in the rat together with multiple endocrine tumours [47]. Their frequency can be markedly influenced by environmental factors (e.g., nature and quantity of food ingested) and by endocrine disorders [48]. It was shown in short-term studies with the strain used here that TBTO at a concentration of 20 ppm or more in the diet has effects on hormonal regulation (see Section 3.3 – Toxicity

Table 6. Tumour incidences after administration of TBTO in the diet for 2 years to groups of 50 male and 50 female Wistar-Tox rats [27]

Conc. in ppm	Sex	Pituitary tumours		Adrenals total (malignant)				Parathyroid adenoma
		total	(lethal)	cortex		medulla, pheochromocytoma		
0	♂♂	34	(5)	13		16	(3)	0
0.5	♂♂	39	(11)	5		13	(2)	2
5	♂♂	29	(9)	11		14		1
50	♂♂	43	(17)	2		33	(6)	6
0	♀♀	22	(3)	8		3		0
0.5	♀♀	32	(5)	7		3		0
5	♀♀	22	(4)	8	(1)	3		0
50	♀♀	35	(11)	8		34	(4)	1

Table 7. Incidence of tumours (%) of the pituitary and the adrenal medulla of Wistar-Tox rats compared with the historical controls

Studies with	Duration	Pituitary tumours total (malignant)		Pheochromocytoma total (malignant)		Ref.
		♂	♀	♂	♀	
0 ppm TBTO	24 months	68	44	32 (6)	6	[27]
50 ppm TBTO		86	70	66 (12)	68 (8)	
historical	30 months	33 (8)	55 (8)	22 (2)	8 (1)	[44]
controls	24 months	70	34	44 (4)	10 (4)	[45]
	24 months	71 (5)	32 (5)	34 (3)	8 (2)	[46]

after repeated administration). TBTO (100 ppm) in the diet of male rats for 90 days caused an increase in the weight of the adrenal glands (without any changes in the light microscope picture) and this too indicates that TBTO has growth stimulating effects. A hormonal mechanism is also suggested by the opposite effects of TBTO in male animals on the tumour frequency in the adrenal medulla (increased) and adrenal cortex (decreased). In addition, TBTO at 20 ppm or more has toxic effects on the lymphatic organs and causes functional immune disorders which can result in weakened tumour resistance. Therefore, the increase in the incidence of the tumours described above is considered to be an epigenetic effect, probably a consequence of the described hormonal or immunotoxic effects of TBTO. Unless persons are exposed to such high doses for extended periods, an increased tumour risk is not to be expected.

6 Reproductive and Developmental Toxicity

In vitro, TBTO at concentrations of 0.03 µg/ml had adverse effects on the morphogenetic differentiation of the limb buds of the mouse embryo [49].

An increased frequency of cleft palates was observed in a study of embryotoxicity in the mouse after oral administration of doses of 11.7 mg/kg and more on days 6–15 of gestation. As these doses also had toxic effects on the dams (reduced body weight), the increased frequency of cleft palates can be attributed to unspecific effects [42]. The two highest doses, 23.5 mg/kg and 35 mg/kg, also caused reduced foetal weights and an increase in mild skeletal abnormalities and variations.

At 35 mg/kg the prenatal mortality was increased. Doses up to 6 mg/kg TBTO produced neither embryotoxic nor teratogenic effects nor toxic effects on the dams.

In a study with rats [50] a slight reduction in body weight gain in the dams (evidence of maternal toxic effects) and a slight delay in foetal ossification were observed after oral administration of 9 or 18 mg/kg TBTO on day 6 to day 19 of gestation. Embryolethal effects as well as a marked retardation of foetal development and teratogenic effects (mainly cleft palate) were reported only for the highest dose, 18 mg/kg, at which the body weight gain of the pregnant animals was markedly reduced. Doses of 5 mg/kg caused no adverse effects in dams or embryos.

When TBTO was administered to rabbits from day 6 to day 18 of gestation, the no effect level for toxic effects on dams, embryos and foetuses was 1.0 mg/kg [51]. At the highest dose tested, 2.5 mg/kg, there were toxic effects in the pregnant animals (body weight loss!) as well as increased numbers of abortions and a marginal retardation of foetal development without, however, any teratogenic effects.

In another study [52], oral doses of 0, 12 and 16 mg TBTO/kg body weight (dissolved in corn oil) given on day 6 to day 20 of gestation to groups of 18 Sprague-Dawley rats produced severe maternal toxicity. Therefore a second study was carried out with doses of 0, 2.5, 5 and 10 mg TBTO/kg given orally in corn oil to groups of 16 rats, also from day 6 to day 20 p.c.. The rats littered spontaneously. TBTO had adverse effects on the development of the pups only after maternally toxic doses of 10 mg/kg or more. Doses of 10 mg/kg or more markedly reduced the body weight gain of the dams. The litters and the pups were smaller and their viability was reduced. Number, weight and viability of the pups were not affected adversely by doses of 2.5 or 5 mg TBTO/kg. Malformations were not observed in the dosage groups up to and including 10 mg/kg. In the group given the maternally toxic dose of 12 mg/kg, two stillborn pups had cleft palates. In the dosage groups where no maternal toxicity was found, no persistent behavioural changes were observed.

7 Manifesto (MAK value, classification)

There is currently insufficient quantitative data from studies of persons at work for the establishment of a MAK value. Studies with TBT compounds in the diet of animals for up to 2 years have revealed mainly dose-dependent toxic effects on the lymphatic organs, in particular the thymus. They are, however, not suitable for the derivation of a MAK value. A 1 month inhalation study on rats, however, is suitable for this purpose. In this experiment, air which was practically saturated with TBTO vapour at 0.16 mg/m^3 at room temperature had no effect on the animals. Therefore a provisional MAK value of 0.05 mg/m^3, as TBTO (vapour), is established for TBT compounds. The available data indicate that adherence to this value will protect persons exposed at work from adverse effects on health and, in particular, from effects on the immune system because the rat inhales about 5–10 times higher doses, expressed in terms of the body weight, than does man. For the limitation of exposure peaks, TBT compounds are classified in category II,2 since local irritation is not to be expected at concentrations in the region of the MAK value. At places of work where mixed exposure to tributyltin and other organotin compounds occurs, the MAK value for organic tin compounds in general, 0.1 mg/m^3 as Sn, should still be observed.

In a long-term study with TBTO in the diet, an increased frequency of pituitary and adrenal tumours was found in rats at the highest concentration of 50 ppm TBTO, as well as an increase in adenomas of the parathyroid gland. It is very probable that they are a result of hormonal and immune disorders. Since such disorders are not to be expected in man at the suggested MAK value, there is no reason to expect an increased tumour risk from TBTO at work.

TBTO had no embryotoxic or foetotoxic effects in mice, rats and rabbits at concentrations which were not toxic to the dams (1, 5 and 6 mg/kg body weight). The no effect levels are so high – in terms of the exposures expected with a MAK value of 0.05 mg/m^3 – that embryotoxic and foetotoxic effects need not be expected if this limit value is observed. TBTO is therefore classified in group C.

8 References

1. Repenthin, W.: Bericht 58a/86, *Allgemeine Physikochemie*, Schering AG, D-1000 Berlin, 24.3.1987
2. Hümpel, M., G. Kühne, U. Täuber, P.E. Schulze: ORTEPA Workshop *Toxicology and Analytics of the Tributyltins – The Present Status*, p 122, Berlin, May 15–16, 1986, ORTEP Association, Vlissingen-Oost, NL, 1987
3. Krajnc, E. I., P. W. Wester, J. G. Loeber, F. X. R. van Leeuwen, J. G. Vos, H. A. M. G. Vaessen, C. A. van der Heijden: *Toxicol. appl. Pharmacol.* **75**, 363 (1984)
4. Evans, W. H., N. F. Cardarelli, D. J. Smith: *J. Toxicol. environm. Hlth* **5**, 871 (1979)
5. Kimmel, E. C., R. H. Fish, J. E. Casida: *J. Agric. Food Chem.* **25**, 1 (1977)
6. Wada, O., S. Manabe: ORTEPA Workshop *Toxicology and Analytics of the Tributyltins – The Present Status*, p 113, Berlin, May 15–16, 1986, ORTEP Association, Vlissingen-Oost, NL, 1987
7. Lyle, W. H.: *Brit. J. industr. Med.* **15**, 193 (1958)
8. Baaijens, P. A.: ORTEPA Workshop *Toxicology and Analytics of the Tributyltins – The Present Status*, p 191, Berlin, May 15–16, 1986, ORTEP Association, Vlissingen-Oost, NL, 1987
9. Schöbel, C., H. Wendt: ORTEPA Workshop *Toxicology and Analytics of the Tributyltins – The Present Status*, p 180, Berlin, May 15–16, 1986, ORTEP Association, Vlissingen-Oost, NL, 1987
10. National Institute for Occupational Safety and Health (NIOSH): *Criteria for a recommended standard...occupational exposure to Organotin Compounds*, p 33, Publ. No. 77–115, US Dept. of Health, Education and Welfare, Public Health Service, Washington, DC, USA, 1976
11. Balogh, R.: Personal communication, Schering AG, D-4619 Bergkamen, 1987

12. Meyer, C. R., C. R. Buncher, R. Gioscia, J. Dees: *Oceans '87 Proceedings, Vol. 4*, p 1432, International Organotin Symposium, Halifax, Nova Scotia, Canada, Sept. 28–Oct. 1, 1987, The IEEE Service Center, Piscataway, NJ, and The Marine Technology Society, Washington, DC, 1987
13. Schweinfurth, H.: *Tin and its Uses No. 143*, 9 (1985)
14. Elsea, J. R., O. E. Paynter: *Arch. industr. Hlth 18*, 214 (1958)
15. Klimmer, O. R.: *Arzneimittel-Forsch. 19*, 934 (1969)
16. Truhaut, R., Y. Chauvel, J.-P. Anger, N. Phu Lich, J. van den Driessche, L. R. Guesnier, N. Morin: *Europ. J. Toxicol. 9*, 31 (1976)
17. Poitou, P., B. Marignac, C. Certin, D. Gradiski: *Ann. pharm. franc. 36*, 569 (1978)
18. Schweinfurth, H.: ORTEPA Workshop *Toxicology and Analytics of the Tributyltins – The Present Status*, p 14, Berlin, May 15–16, 1986, ORTEP Association, Vlissingen-Oost, NL, 1987
19. Robinson, I. M.: *Food Cosmet. Toxicol. 7*, 47 (1969)
20. Sheldon, A. W.: *J. Paint. Technol. 47*, 54 (1975)
21. Scantox Biologisk Laboratorium, DK-4623 L1. Skensved, *Dermal LD_{50} determination of tributyltennaphthenat*, Report, 29th July 1978
22. Anger, J.-P., F. Anger, Y. Cano, Y. Chauvel, M. Louvet, J. van den Driessche, N. Morin: *Europ. J. Toxicol. 9*, 339 (1976)
23. Gohlke, R., E. Lewa, A. Strachovsky, R. Köhler: *Z. ges. Hyg. 15*, 97 (1969)
24. Pelikan, Z.: *Brit. J. industr. Med. 26*, 165 (1969)
25. Schweinfurth, H. A, P. Günzel: *Oceans '87 Proceedings, Vol. 4*, p 1421, International Organotin Symposium, Halifax, Nova Scotia, Canada, Sept. 28–Oct. 1, 1987, The IEEE Service Center, Piscataway, NJ, and The Marine Technology Society, Washington, DC, 1987
26. Ishaaya, I., J. L. Engel, J. E. Casida: *Pest. Biochem. Physiol. 6*, 270 (1976)
27. Wester, P. W., E. I. Krajnc, F. X. R. van Leeuwen, J. G. Loeber, C. A. van der Heijden, H. M. G. Vaessen, P. W. Hellemann: *Two-Year Feeding Study in Rats with Bis(tri-n-butyltin)oxide (TBTO)*, National Institute of Public Health and Environmental Hygiene, Report No. 658112 002, Bilthoven, NL, Feb. 1988
28. Funahashi, N., I. Iwasaki, G. Ide: *Acta path. jap. 30*, 955 (1980)
29. Snoeij, N. J., A. H. Penninks, W. Seinen: in Snoeij, N. J. (Ed.): *Triorganotin compounds in immunotoxicology and biochemistry*, p 55, Thesis, Univ. of Utrecht, NL, 1987
30. Snoeij, N. J., A. A. J. van Iersel, A. H. Penninks, W. Seinen: *Toxicol. appl. Pharmacol. 81*, 274 (1985)
31. Schweinfurth, H.: Schering AG, Bericht Nr. IC 35/88, Berlin, 11.11.1988
32. van der Heijden, C. A., E. I. Kraijnc: ORTEPA Workshop *Toxicology and Analytics of the Tributyltins – The Present Status*, p 49, Berlin, May 15–16, 1986, ORTEP Association, Vlissingen-Oost, NL, 1987
33. Wester, P. W., E. I. Krajnc, C. A. van der Heijden: ORTEPA Workshop *Toxicology and Analytics of the Tributyltins – The Present Status*, p 54, Berlin, May 15–16, 1986, ORTEP Association, Vlissingen-Oost, NL, 1987
34. Vos, J. G., A. De Klerk, E. L. Krajnc, W. Kruizinga, B. van Ommen, J. Rozing: *Toxicol. appl. Pharmacol. 75*, 387 (1984)
35. Krajnc, E. I., J. G. Vos, P. W. Wester, J. G. Loeber, C. A. van der Heijden: ORTEPA Workshop *Toxicology and Analytics of the Tributyltins – The Present Status*, p 35, Berlin, May 15–16, 1986, ORTEP Association, Vlissingen-Oost, NL, 1987
36. Scantox Biologisk Laboratorium, DK-4623 L1. Skensvad, *Test for delayed contact hypersensitivity in the albino guinea-pig of tributyltennaphthenat*, Report, 31st July 1978
37. Gammeltoft, M.: *Contact Dermatitis 4*, 238 (1978)
38. Brown, A. W., R. D. Verschoyle, B. W. Street, W. N. Aldridge: *J. appl. Toxicol. 4*, 12 (1984)
39. Watanabe, I.: in Spencer, P. S., H. H. Schaumburg (Eds.): *Experimental and Clinical Neurotoxicology*, p 545, Williams and Wilkins, Baltimore, London, 1980
40. Barnes, J. M., H. B. Stoner: *Brit. J. industr. Med. 15*, 15 (1958)
41. Reimann, R., R. Lang: ORTEPA Workshop *Toxicology and Analytics of the Tributyltins – The Present Status*, p 66, Berlin, May 15–16, 1986, ORTEP Association, Vlissingen-Oost, NL, 1987
42. Davis, A., R. Barale, G. Brun, R. Forster, T. Günther, H. Hautefeuille, C. A. van der Heijden, A. G. A. C. Knaap, R. Krowke, T. Kuroki, N. Loprieno, C. Malaveille, H. J. Merker, M.

Monaco, P. Mosesso, D. Neubert, H. Norppa, M. Sorsa, E. Vogel, C. E. Voogd, M. Umeda, H. Bartsch: *Mutat. Res. 188*, 65 (1987)
43. Lang, R.: Pharma Research Report IC 7/86, Schering AG, D-1000 Berlin, 21.11.1986
44. Kroes, R., J. M. Garbis-Berkvens, T. de Vries, J. H. van Nesselrooij: *J. Gerontol. 36*, 259 (1981)
45. Wester, P. W., C. A. van der Heijden, A. Bisschop, G. J. van Esch: *Toxicology 36*, 325 (1985)
46. Wester, P. W., C. A. van der Heijden, A. Bisschop, G. J. van Esch, R. C. Wegmann, T. de Vries: *Sci. Tot. Environm. 47*, 427 (1985)
47. Hollander, C. F., K. C. Snell: *IARC Sci. Publ. No. 6*, 273 (1976)
48. Roe, F. J. C., A. Bär: *Hum. Toxicol. 4*, 27 (1985)
49. Krowke, R., U. Bluth, D. Neubert: *Arch. Toxicol 58*, 125 (1986)
50. Sheldon, A. W.: ORTEPA Workshop *Toxicology and Analytics of the Tributyltins – The Present Status*, p 101, Berlin, May 15–16, 1986, ORTEP Association, Vlissingen-Oost, NL, 1987
51. Nemec, M. D.: *A Teratology Study in Rabbits with TBTO. Final Report*, Project No. WIL-B0002, WIL Research Laboratories Inc., Ashland, OH, March 27, 1987, Property of Sherex Chemical Co. Inc., Schering AG, M + T Chemicals Inc. and Aceto Corp.
52. Crofton, K. M., K. F. Dean, V. M. Boncek, M. B. Rosen, L. P. Sheets, N. Chernoff, L. W. Reiter: *Toxicol. appl. Pharmacol. 7*, 113 (1989)

completed 29. 5. 1989

Trichlorofluoromethane

Classification/MAK value:	**1000 ml/m³ (ppm)**
	5600 mg/m³
Classification/MAK value dates from:	**1958**
Synonyms:	fluorocarbon 11 (FC 11)
	refrigerant 11 (R 11)
	fluorotrichloromethane
	trichloromonofluoromethane
	fluorochloroform
Chemical name (CAS):	trichlorofluoromethane
CAS number:	75-69-4
Structural formula:	

$$\begin{array}{c} Cl \\ | \\ F-C-Cl \\ | \\ Cl \end{array}$$

Molecular formula:	CCl_3F
Molecular weight:	137.37
Melting point:	$-111\,°C$
Boiling point:	$23.7\,°C$
Vapour pressure at 20 °C:	889 hPa

1 ml/m³ (ppm) = 5.709 mg/m³   **1 mg/m³ = 0.175 ml/m³ (ppm)**

1 Toxic Effects and Modes of Action

Trichlorofluoromethane (FC 11) is a very weak narcotic. It is hardly metabolized at all [1–11]. High concentrations ($> 1\%$ in inhaled air) can sensitize the heart to sympathetic stimuli and induce typical arrhythmia. FC 11 has neither mutagenic nor carcinogenic activity.

Pharmacokinetic studies reveal that effective blood concentrations increase and decrease rapidly in both animals and man [6, 12–16]. The half-lives for the two elimination phases which can be distinguished are 7–11 minutes for phase 1 and 1–1.8 hours for phase 2 [3].

1.1 Pharmacokinetics and metabolism

Because of its use as a propellant in aerosols, numerous studies on the intake, distribution and excretion of FC 11 have been carried out in experimental animals, volunteers and patients. Their only relevance for the occupational situation is in the rapid excretion after the end of exposure. An equilibrium between the central and peripheral compartments is achieved within 3 hours after inhaling FC 11 for several hours. Elimination from the central compartment, the blood, is very rapid whereas the diffusion back into the blood from the peripheral compartment, namely tissue and fat, proceeds more slowly and is therefore the rate limiting step in the elimination process [5, 17].

For a long time it was thought that FC 11 cannot be metabolized at all. Recently, however, a very low level of oxidative metabolic chlorine elimination has been demonstrated for one specific set of conditions: in *in vitro* studies with hepatic microsomal fractions from mice, rats, rabbits and hamsters dichlorofluoromethane was produced under anaerobic conditions at a rate of 0.04–0.055 nmol/min/mg protein. This FC 11 metabolism was increased by pretreatment of the animals with phenobarbital but inhibited by air or oxygen [18].

2 Effects in Man

There are no reports of long term exposures in industry. The tolerance limit for FC 11 in man is said to be 50000 ppm [1]. Even this concentration, however, is said to produce irritation of the eyes accompanied by nervous symptoms (vertigo). The symptoms vanish immediately in fresh air [7]. 28 white men and 18 white women between 18 and 46 years old were exposed to concentrations of FC 11 of 250, 500 or 1000 ml/m^3 for 1–8 hours. There was no evidence of effects on heart, lungs or general condition of the persons and no neurological deficits were produced [19].

10 healthy men (20–24 years old) inhaled 9.5% FC 11 for 15–60 seconds. Vital capacity measured during the period that followed sank twice, the first time after only a few minutes and the second time 10–20 minutes later. The reduction was between 6.4% and 9.9%, the second peak being more marked. After the 15 second inhalation the ECG revealed respiratory sinus arrhythmias in most subjects, and in 2 persons after the 60 second inhalation transient tachycardia and negative T-waves [20].

A mixture of equal parts of FC 11 and FC 12 (dichlorodifluoromethane) was sprayed from a distance of 30 cm once for 20 seconds onto the hair of 5 healthy quietly breathing persons; the tracheal mucous velocity and the lung function remained unchanged [21].

20 white women between 32 and 65 years old made use of 13 different sprays daily for 4 weeks. They included a hair-spray with 25% FC 11 (2 seconds daily) and a frying pan spray with 62% FC 11 (6–10 seconds daily). At the end of the study no changes in the blood count or the clinical laboratory blood parameters were found; the general state of health of the volunteers was also unchanged [22].

Also for 4 weeks, 28 men and 18 women, 18-46 years old, inhaled 1000 ml FC 11/m^3 air for 8 hours daily. Apart from a slight reduction in perceptiveness in 8 of the men, examination of heart, lungs and general state of health during the subsequent year revealed no deviations from the norm [19].

There are no epidemiological studies of the effect of pure FC 11 on fertility and gravidity.

3 Effects on Animals

3.1 Acute toxicity

The LD$_{50}$ and LC$_{50}$ values for FC 11 in various animal species are presented in Table 1.

The results of studies in which non-anaesthetized experimental animals inhaled FC 11 for short periods are assembled in Table 2 and reveal that the principal effects – though only after high concentrations – are changes in heart and lung function.

The results obtained with non-anaesthetized animals have been confirmed by numerous studies on anaesthetized experimental animals (mouse [37, 38], rat [39–41], hamster [31], dog [42–46] and rhesus monkey [47]) as well as with isolated rat hearts [39]. In these studies FC 11 caused reduction in blood pressure, heart arrhythmias, changes in heart rate and atrioventricular block (AV block).

With isolated rat hearts [39] it was shown that the AV block was not caused by O$_2$ deficiency as had initially been surmised from the results of the animal studies because of the high doses used (see Table 2).

In a study using isolated heart-lung preparations from dogs which were ventilated with 2.5% or 5% FC 11, adverse effects on heart action were established – reduced contraction force and ejection volume as well as increased pressure in the left atrium [48].

The effect of FC 11 on the lungs was also confirmed with anaesthetized animals (mouse [38], rat [40], dog [42, 45] and rhesus monkey [49]). In particular, changes in

Table 1. LD$_{50}$ and LC$_{50}$ values for trichlorofluoromethane

Species; sex (if specified)	Application route	Application period	LD$_{50}$ mg/kg	LC$_{50}$ ml/m^3	Ref.
mouse ♂	i.p.	once	1743		[23]
♀	i.p.	once	1871		[23]
mouse	inhalation	30 min		100000	[24]
mouse	inhalation	30 min		100000	[7]
rat ♂, ♀	inhalation	15 min		130000	[25]
rat	inhalation	30 min		150000	[24]
guinea pig	inhalation	30 min		250000	[24]
rabbit	inhalation	30 min		250000	[24]

Table 2. Acute inhalation toxicity of trichlorofluoromethane in animal studies

Species sex (strain)	Number	Concen- tration ml/m³	Exposure period	Observations	Ref.
mouse	6	10 000	24 h	no clinical findings histology: unspecific lung changes	[26]
rat ♂ (Wistar)	5 5 5	25 000 50 000 100 000	5 min 5 min 5 min	arrhythmia in 1/5, increased heart rate (23.1%) arrhythmia in 2/5, increased heart rate (27.6%) arrhythmia in 4/5, increased heart rate (34.4%)	[27]
the same rats anaes- thetized	4 4 4	25 000 50 000 100 000	5 min 5 min 5 min	arrhythmia in 0/4, heart rate unchanged arrhythmia in 1/4, heart rate unchanged arrhythmia in 4/4, heart rate unchanged	[27]
rat ♂, ♀ (Alderley Park)	6	35 000	10 min	3 animals with CNS effects (tremor in the extremities, cramps)	[25]
rat ♂ (albino, ChR-CD)	6 6 6 6 6 6 6	5 100 7 700 9 600 24 900 30 000 31 700 35 300	4 h 4 h 4 h 4 h 4 h 4 h 4 h	– slight hyperactivity in 1st and 2nd h, rapid respiration, occasional slight weight loss for 1 d after exposure 3/6 died – during the whole exposure: slight 5/6 died hyperactivity, then tremor, inactivity 3/6 died and irregular respiration; slight to 6/6 died moderate weight loss for 1 d	[28]
rat	1	50 000	30 min	no toxic effects	[29]
rat guinea pig	4 2	50 000	up to 2 h	slight narcosis	[30]
rat	1	60 000– 70 000	30 min	loss of the postural reflex	[29]
rat	1	80 000	30 min	loss of the righting reflex	[29]
rat	1	90 000	30 min	deep narcosis	[29]
rat guinea pig	4 2	100 000	50 min	deep narcosis	[30]
rat	1	100 000	20–30 min	lethal dose	[29]
rat	1	150 000	8 min	lethal dose	[29]
rat	1	200 000– 300 000	4 min	lethal dose	[29]
rat	1	500 000	1 min	lethal dose	[29]

Table 2 (continued)

Species sex (strain)	Number	Concen-tration ml/m³	Exposure period	Observations	Ref.
hamster, n.s. (random bred)	4 4 4	20 000 75 000 100 000	4 h 4 h 4 h	0/4 died, no other details given 0/4 died, no other details given 2/4 died, no other details given	[31]
hamster, n.s. (random bred)	4 4 4 4	25 000 50 000 75 000 100 000	5 min 5 min 5 min 5 min	no arrhythmia no arrhythmia no arrhythmia after 60-240 s: tachycardia and altered ventricular depolarization (ECG) in all animals	[31]
guinea pig	n.s.	9 000– 12 000	2 h	slight irritation, no narcosis	[32]
guinea pig	n.s.	22 000– 25 000	up to 2 h	occasional tremor, chewing movements, irregular respiration, rapid recovery	[32]
guinea pig	n.s.	45 000– 51 000	2 h	irritation, initially trembling, slow and irregular respiration; then stupor, incoordination; rapid recovery at end of exposure	[32]
guinea pig	n.s.	100 000– 106 000	2 h	unconsciousness, tremor, cramp-like movements. recovery slow. histology: lung haemorrhage	[32]
rabbit ♂ (New Zea-land White)	4 4	50 000 150 000	4 min 4 min	after 2 min: increased heart rate; drop in median arterial blood pressure; arrhythmia (premature ventricle contraction) in one animal after 4 min: no further arrhythmia after 2 min: increased heart rate and further drop in median arterial blood pressure after 4 min: no arrhythmia	[33]
dog, n.s. (beagle)	4 4 4	12 500 20 000 40 000	5 min 5 min 3 min	no signs of toxicity, no ECG changes slight trembling of the extremities and slight tachycardia after 2 min, animals disturbed above symptoms more marked	[34]
dog, n.s. (beagle)	4–7	12 500 + 5 µg/kg bw adrenaline i.v.	5 min	50% of animals sensitized for arrhythmia-induction by adrenaline	[35]
dog ♂ (beagle)	1 1 1 1	10 010 15 510 15 850 17 783	5 min 4 min 5 min 5 min	irregular respiration irregular respiration, lacrimation, stiffening of the body and jerking movements, pale eyes irregular respiration, lacrimation, yelping irregular respiration	[11]

Table 2 (continued)

Species sex (strain)	Number	Concentration ml/m³	Exposure period	Observations	Ref.
dog ♂ (beagle)	1	18 957	5 min	irregular respiration, lacrimation, stiffening of the body and jerking movements, yelping	[11]
	1	29 527	4 min	all the above symptoms, salivation and incoordination after end of exposure.	
monkey, n.s. (stumptailed) and	n.s.	4 000	10 min	changes in respiratory volume and minute volume, increase blood pressure; various arrhythmias (ECG)	[36]
guinea pig, n.s.		40 000	10 min	above symptoms more marked	
		400 000	10 min	all animals died	

n.s.: not specified
bw: body weight

lung resistance and elasticity as well as reduction in the respiration rate and the respiratory volume were seen.

In a study of the effect of 5% FC 11 on metabolic functions of anaesthetized rabbits and dogs, a transient significant increase in blood glucose and lactate was found [50].

In the isolated rat lung, inhalation of FC 11 was seen to cause dose-dependent inhibition of 5-hydroxy-tryptamine uptake by the lung [51].

FC 11 in the medium led to total inhibition of the basal tonus and the spontaneous contraction of isolated rat uteruses (at a concentration of 50%) and a rabbit duodenum (concentration 20%) [52].

6 female albino rats were given a single oral dose of 0.5 ml FC 11 (in paraffin 1:1) per 100 g body weight. Neither 3 hours nor 24 hours later could changes in the serum ß-glucuronidase level be detected. The NADP and NADPH$_2$ levels were also unchanged after 1 hour. Histological examination after 3 and 24 hours revealed no liver necrosis [53].

Male mice (not better specified) received single oral doses of 13.6, 54.5 or 217.9 mg FC 11/kg body weight; female mice were given 14.6, 58.5 or 233.9 mg/kg body weight. One month later no changes were observed apart from vacuolation of the hepatocytes in one animal from the highest dose group and a slight decrease in food utilization [23].

0.1 ml of a 15% or 40% solution of FC 11 in dimethyl phthalate or a 15% solution in propylene glycol was applied to the eyes of 6 albino rabbits. The cornea and iris remained unchanged by this treatment. There was a slight inflammation of the conjunctiva in almost all animals but this could be put down to the solvent [54].

FC 11 was also applied to the eyes of 6 rabbits by spraying from a distance of about 5 cm. The cornea and iris remained completely unaffected. After about 1 hour the conjunctiva was slightly reddened in one of the animals; slight lacrimation was seen in 2 animals after 1 and 4 hours [55].

3.2 Subchronic and chronic toxicity

3.2.1 Inhalation

10 anaesthetized male Wistar rats and 5 anaesthetized rabbits inhaled 2.5% or 5% FC 11 for 15 days, twice daily for 1 hour. At the concentration of 2.5% no effects on metabolism were detected. At 5% FC 11, oxygen consumption was reduced (rats by 44%, rabbits by 25%) and the respiratory quotient was increased (above 1); the levels of blood glucose and lactate, liver glycogen and free fatty acids in blood increased slightly, the blood urea level decreased a little [50].

Rats, guinea pigs, dogs and monkeys were exposed continuously for 90 days to a concentration of about 1000 ppm. In a second experiment the same species were exposed to a concentration of 10250 ppm for 8 hours daily, 5 days per week with a total of 30 exposures in 6 weeks. During the studies and at the end of exposure there were no differences between the control and the exposed animals in any of the parameters tested (body weight gain, blood count, enzymes) [56].

Rats, mice, guinea pigs and rabbits were exposed to 4000 ppm for 28 days, 6 hours per day and then allowed to recover for 15 days. No signs of a toxic effect were observed [57].

12000 ppm for 10 days, 4 hours daily, permitted normal body weight gain in rats. Clinically, their breathing was deeper and more rapid. Histological studies revealed lung emphysema, vacuolation in the liver, increased haematopoiesis in the spleen, and in the brain neuronal oedema with neuroglial vacuolation [58]. 12500 ppm, on the other hand, produced no toxic effects in dogs (exposed for 20 days, 3.5 hours daily) nor did 25000 ppm have toxic effects in rats, guinea pigs or rabbits under the same experimental conditions [30].

20 male and 20 female rats (Sprague-Dawley) inhaled 10000 ml/m^3 FC 11 6 hours daily for 90 days without any recognizable adverse effects on behaviour, clinical laboratory blood parameters or histology [59].

Three male and three female beagles inhaled 5000 ml FC 11/m^3 6 hours daily, also for 90 days. In this species too there were no changes in behaviour, clinical laboratory blood parameters or histology [59].

Inhalation (8 hours daily for 30 consecutive days) of a mixture of equal parts of FC 11 and FC 12 (dichlorodifluoromethane) induced no changes in mice at 2000 ppm. Under the same conditions the mixture caused "alveolar irritation" in rats without any signs of lung oedema. At 1000 ppm a shift to the right in the blood picture was described and 500 ppm was tolerated without reaction [60].

Inhalation of a mixture of FC 11 and FC 12 in the proportions 50:50 or 10:90 for 100 days (2 hours daily) produced no indications of a narcotic effect in mice, rats or guinea pigs at concentrations of 5000, 15000 or 50000 ppm. Body weight gain and blood count were normal [61].

3.2.2 Ingestion

Groups of 20 male and 20 female rats (ChR-CD) received daily oral doses of FC 11 in corn oil (250–450 mg/kg body weight) for 90 days. Minimal increases in fluoride level, which followed no consistent pattern during the course of the study, were found in the urine of the highest dose group (450 mg/kg body weight); the relevance of this finding is unclear. The other urine and blood parameters remained unchanged during the treatment and for 1 day afterwards and there were no clinical signs of an intoxication [62].

Groups of 8 male and 8 female dogs were given single daily oral doses of 40 to 350 mg/kg body weight FC 11 in corn oil for 90 days. Toxic effects were seen in none of the animals during the treatment or one day later nor were biochemical changes detectable [62].

3.2.3 Effects on skin and mucous membranes

Undiluted FC 11 was sprayed for 10 seconds onto the shaved ventral skin of 3 young and 3 older male rats twice daily, 5 days per week for 6 weeks. Erythema, swelling of the skin (like a grade 1 chilblain) and delayed regrowth of the fur was seen. Histological study revealed oedematous swelling of both the hypodermis and deeper levels, with effects on the fur in one of the three young animals. In the three older animals (about 4 months old) there was destruction of the epidermis, haematoma and a slight penetration of the connective tissue around the blood vessels by leukocytes [63].

Applied by spraying into the mouth for 6 weeks (twice daily, 5 days/week, no further details given) FC 11 is said to have no adverse effects on the tongue and soft palate nor indirectly on the auditory canal apart from occasional congestion of blood in the tongue, mostly in weaker animals and considered by the authors to represent slight inflammation (no more details given) [63].

In the rabbit eye, 0.1 ml FC 11 applied 9 times in 11 days into the conjunctival sac produced no damage [10].

FC 11 was sprayed for 5 seconds into the eyes of 6 male rabbits once daily (5 days/week for 4 weeks) from a distance of 20 cm. The eyes became red during the spraying and then watered for several hours. At the end of the study a slight inflammation was found on the eyelid but histologically there were no changes [63].

When open wounds on 3 rats were sprayed with FC 11 for 5 seconds per day until a scab formed, erythema was more severe and the wound healed more slowly than in controls. The healing of burns (grade 2) on 3 rats was also delayed by spraying them once daily (5 days/week, 4 weeks) with FC 11 [63].

The skin of rats (no other details given) was painted with undiluted FC 11 three times daily, 6 days per week for 2 months. The epidermis remained completely intact; there was no irritation [64].

An aerosol containing 40% v/v FC 11 and 60% v/v sesame oil is well tolerated when sprayed onto the rabbit flank 12 times within 16 hours. It produces neither skin irritation nor damage [10].

4 Reproductive and Developmental Toxicity

Charles River rats (25 females per group) were exposed to atmospheres containing 36000, 10000 or 1000 ml/m^3 FC 11 for 6 hours daily from day 6 to day 15 of gravidity. 36000 ml/m^3 caused marked symptoms of intoxication in the dams and disturbed the intrauterine development of the foetuses. This took the form of a significant increase in embryo mortality, delayed body weight gain and increased frequency of malformations (particularly anomalies of the heart and aortic arch). After the 10000 or 1000 ml/m^3 exposures neither maternally toxic nor embryotoxic nor teratogenic effects were seen [65].

New Zealand White rabbits (15 females per group) were exposed to FC 11 concentrations of 36000, 10000 or 1000 ml/m^3 for 6 hours daily from day 6 to day 18 of gestation. After inhalation of 36000 ml/m^3 there were marked symptoms of intolerance in the dams and frequent intrauterine embryonic death. There was delayed body weight gain and development of extra thoracolumbar ribs in 81.6% of the foetuses. 10000 ml/m^3 caused weight loss in the dams during the first two days of exposure. In addition 66.7% of the foetuses had extra ribs compared with 45.5% in the control group. Otherwise there was no increased occurrence of malformations, anomalies or variations in the progeny of the group exposed to FC 11. The exposure to 1000 ml/m^3 revealed no evidence of embryotoxic or foetotoxic effects. Since adverse effects on intrauterine development were only seen in the 36000 ml/m^3 group and at this concentration marked intolerance was shown by the dams, FC 11 is unlikely to have selective or specific embryotoxic effects in the rabbit [66].

5 Genotoxicity

FC 11 was bactericidal for 5 different species of bacteria (*Escherichia coli, Staphylococcus aureus, Serratia marcescens, Bacillus subtilis* and *Salmonella typhimurium*): none of the species of bacteria survived 100% FC 11 in air, 10% FC 11 was survived by 38–106% of the colonies (*S. typhimurium* 106%), 1% by 54–103% of the colonies, depending on the species of bacteria (*S. typhimurium* 98%) [67].

The Ames test with the *S. typhimurium* strains TA1535, TA100, TA1537, TA98 and TA1538 and FC 11 (up to 15%) with or without activating rat liver homogenate (S9 mix) remained negative [68–72].

Another test for point mutations in Chinese hamster ovary (CHO) cells with and without an activating system also revealed no mutagenic effects of FC 11 [73].

In a transformation test with baby hamster kidney cells (BHK 21) in the presence of S9 mix, no transformation could be induced with FC 11 [70].

6 Carcinogenicity

In a carcinogenicity study a total of 120 male and 120 female mice (Swiss, 8 weeks old at the start) inhaled 1000 or 5000 ppm FC 11 for 78 weeks, 4 hours daily, 5 days per week. Neither mortality nor tumour frequency were increased.

120 male and 120 female 9 week old rats (Sprague-Dawley) and 60 male and 60 female 13 week old rats also inhaled 1000 or 5000 ppm FC 11 for 4 hours daily, 5 days/week but for 104 weeks. Here too neither increased mortality nor increased tumour frequency were observed [74].

52 male and 52 female newborn mice (Swiss, ICR/HA) were given 0.1 ml of a 10% FC 11 solution in tricaprylin by subcutaneous injection in the neck when 1 and 7 days old and 0.2 ml on day 14 and 21. The animals were observed for up to one year. No carcinogenic effect of FC 11 could be demonstrated [75].

In a carcinogenicity study lasting two years, 200 rats (Osborne-Mendel) and 200 mice (B6C3F$_1$) were given various doses of FC 11 in corn oil by gastric intubation. Thus 50 male rats each received 425–500 or 850–1000 mg/kg body weight, 50 female rats each 750–500 or 1500–1000 mg/kg body weight and 100 mice (50 male and 50 female) each 1580–2000 or 3160–4000 mg/kg body weight. The substance was administered on 5 days a week for 78 weeks; the rats were then observed for 33 weeks, the mice for 13. No increase in tumour incidence was seen in the mice; the treated animals were in no way different from the controls. For the rats no conclusion as to the carcinogenic effect of FC 11 was possible in this study because too many animals died during the first year. Among those who survived at least 52 weeks, no increase in tumour incidence could be seen [76].

7 Manifesto (MAK value, classification)

The available data indicate that the MAK value of 1000 ml/m^3 is not a toxicity threshold. Only few studies of the toxicity of FC 11 at concentrations in the range of this MAK value have been carried out. In these studies no adverse effects on health were detected. Toxic effects on the heart and lungs could be demonstrated in animals only with extremely high concentrations.

Studies with rats and inhalation of concentrations up to 10000 ml/m^3 have revealed no embryotoxic or foetotoxic effects. In the rabbit the no effect level for a foetotoxic effect is at 1000 ml/m^3 inhaled FC 11. In the rat malformations developed only with concentrations which were highly toxic to both dams and foetuses. The results of these two studies indicate that, given adherence to the MAK and BAT values, an embryotoxic or foetotoxic effect of FC 11 is very unlikely. The substance is therefore classified in pregnancy group C.

FC 11 yielded negative results in all tests for mutagenicity and carcinogenicity.

The MAK value is set at 1000 ml/m^3 since higher values are not to be expected in practice and higher levels of inhaled impurities are considered deleterious to health in general. Thus FC 11 is classified in category IV for the limitation of exposure peaks.

8 References

1. Mergner, G. W., D. A. Blake, M. Helrich: *Anesthesiology 42*, 345 (1975)
2. Morgan, A., A. Black, M. Walsh, D. R. Belcher: *Int. J. appl. Radiat. 23*, 285 (1972)

3. Heinrich, R., B. Schröder, J. Angerer: in Konietzko, H., F. Schuckmann (Eds.): *Verhandlungen der Deutschen Gesellschaft für Arbeitsmedizin e.V.*, 24th Annual Meeting in D-6500 Mainz, May 2–5 1984, Gentner Verlag, Stuttgart
4. Paulet, G., J. Lanoë, A. Thos, P. Toulouse, J. Dassonville: *Toxicol. appl. Pharmacol. 34*, 204 (1975)
5. Williams, F. M., G. H. Draffan, C. T. Dollery: *Thorax 29*, 99 (1974)
6. Blake, D. A., G. W. Mergner: *Toxicol. appl. Pharmacol. 30*, 396 (1974)
7. Paulet, G.: *Aerosol Report 8*, 612 (1969)
8. Paulet, G., R. Chevrier: *Arch. Mal. prof. 30*, 251 (1969)
9. Paulet, G., R. Chevrier, J. Paulet, M. Duchêne, J. Chappet: *Arch. Mal. prof. 30*, 101 (1969)
10. Cox, P. J., J. King, D. V. Parke: *Biochem. J. 130*, 13 (1972)
11. Sarver, J. W., D. A. Snee: *"Wash-out Time" of Freon® 11*, Haskell Laboratory Report No. 349–70, DuPont Co., Wilmington, DE, USA, 1970
12. Angerer, J., B. Schröder, R. Heinrich: *Int. Arch. occup. environm. Hlth 56*, 67 (1985)
13. Azar, A., H. J. Trochimowicz, J. B. Terrill, L. S. Mullin: *Amer. industr. Hyg. Ass. J. 34*, 102 (1973)
14. Shargel, L., R. Koss: *J. pharm. Sci. 61*, 1445 (1972)
15. Chiou, W. L., S. Niazi: *Res. Commun. chem. Path. Pharmacol. 6*, 481 (1973)
16. Niazi, S., W. L. Chiou: *J. pharm. Sci. 64*, 763 (1975)
17. Adir, J., D. A. Blake, G. M. Mergner: *J. clin. Pharmacol. 15*, 760 (1975)
18. Wolf, C. R., L. J. King, D. V. Parke: *Chem.-Biol. Interact. 21*, 277 (1978)
19. Stewart, R. D., P. E. Newton, E. D. Baretta, A. A. Herrmann, H. V. Forster, R. J. Soto: *Environm. Hlth Perspect. 26*, 275 (1978)
20. Valić, F., Z. Skurić, Z. Bantić, M. Rudar, M. Hećej: *Brit. J. industr. Med. 34*, 130 (1977)
21. Friedman, M., R. Dougherty, S. R. Nelson, R. P. White, M. A. Sackner, A. Wanner: *Amer. Rev. resp. Dis. 116*, 281 (1977)
22. Marier, G. G., H. MacFarland, P. Dussault: *Household & Personal Products Industry 10*, 68 (1973)
23. Kudo, K., S. Toida, S. Matsunra, T. Sasaki, H. Kawamura: *J. med. Soc. Toho Univ. 18*, 363 (1971)
24. Paulet, G.: *Europ. J. Toxicol. 9*, 385 (1976)
25. Clark, D. G., D. J. Tinston: *Hum. Toxicol. 1*, 239 (1982)
26. Quevauviller, A., M. Chaigneau, M. Schrenzel: *Ann. pharm. franç. 21*, 727 (1963)
27. Watanabe, T., D. M. Aviado: *Toxicology 3*, 225 (1975)
28. Barras, C. E.: *Acute Inhalation Test*, Haskell Laboratory Report No. 648–74, DuPont Co., Wilmington, DE, USA, 1974
29. Lester, D., L. A. Greenberg: *Arch. industr. Hyg. 2*, 335 (1950)
30. Scholz, J.: *Fortschritte der biologischen Aerosol-Forschung*, F.K. Schattauer-Verlag, Stuttgart, 1961
31. Taylor, G. J., R. T. Drew: *Toxicol. appl. Pharmacol. 32*, 177 (1975)
32. Nuckolls, A. H.: *Underwriters' Lab. Rep. Misc. Hazards 2375* (1933), cited in v. Oettingen, W. F.: *The halogenated hydrocarbons*, p 112, Public Health Service, Publ. No. 414 (1955)
33. Taylor, G. J.: *Arch. environm. Hlth 30*, 349 (1975)
34. Clark, D. G., D. J. Tinston: *Ann. Allergy 30*, 536 (1972)
35. Clark, D. G., D. J. Tinston: *Brit. J. Pharmacol. 49*, 355 (1973)
36. Swann, H. E. (Jr.), S. Carson, J. Scheimberg, O. P. McShane: *Toxicol. appl. Pharmacol. 22*, 307 (1972)
37. Aviado, D. M., M. A. Belej: *Toxicology 2*, 31 (1974)
38. Brody, R. S., T. Watanabe, D. M. Aviado: *Toxicology 2*, 173 (1974)
39. Wibowo, A. A. E.: *Toxicity of Pressurized Isoprenalin Inhalers, an Experimental Study*, Thesis, Univ. of Utrecht, NL, 1975
40. Friedman, S. A., M. Cammarato, D. M. Aviado: *Toxicology 1*, 345 (1973)
41. Doherty, R. E., D. M. Aviado: *Toxicology 3*, 213 (1975)
42. Simaan, J. A., D. M. Aviado: *Toxicology 5*, 127 (1975)
43. McClure, D. A.: *Toxicol. appl. Pharmacol. 22*, 221 (1972)
44. Flowers, N. C., R. C. Hand, L. G. Horan: *Arch. environm. Hlth 30*, 353 (1975)

45. Belej, M. A., D. M. Aviado: *J. clin. Pharmacol. 15*, 105 (1975)
46. Hand, R. C., N. C. Flowers, L. G. Horan: *Circulation, Suppl. III, 49*, 147 (1974)
47. Belej, M. A., D. G. Smith, D. M. Aviado: *Toxicology 2*, 381 (1974)
48. Aviado, D. M., M. A. Belej: *Toxicology 3*, 79 (1975)
49. Aviado, D. M., D. G. Smith: *Toxicology 3*, 241 (1975)
50. Paulet, G., G. Roncin, E. Vidal, P. Toulouse, J. Dassonville: *Toxicol. appl. Pharmacol. 34*, 197 (1975)
51. Hede, A. R., L. Andersson, C. Post: *Acta pharmacol. (Kbh.) 57*, 291 (1985)
52. Paulet, G., Y. Lessard: *Soc. Biol. Rennes 169*, 665 (1975)
53. Slater, T. F.: *Biochem. Pharmacol. 14*, 178 (1965)
54. Eddy, C. W.: *Eye Irritation Test in Rabbits*, Haskell Laboratory Report No. 423–70, DuPont Co., Wilmington, DE, USA, 1970
55. Hood, D. B.: *Eye Irritation Tests*, Haskell Laboratory Report No. 107–64, DuPont Co., Wilmington, DE, USA, 1964
56. Jenkins, L. J., Jr., R. A. Jones, R. A. Coon, J. Siegel: *Toxicol. appl. Pharmacol. 16*, 133 (1970)
57. Unpublished Haskell Laboratory Report, cited in Clayton, J.F., Jr.: *Handbuch der experimentellen Pharmakologie* Vol. 20, Part 1, p 474, Springer, Berlin, 1966
58. Haskell Laboratory Report, cited in Clayton, J.F., Jr.: *Handbuch der experimentellen Pharmakologie*, Vol. 20, Part 1, p 474, Springer, Berlin, 1966
59. Leuschner, F., B. W. Neumann, F. Hübscher: *Arzneimittel-Forsch. 33*, 1475 (1983)
60. Paulet, G., S. Desbrousses, J. Sorais: *Arch. Mal. prof. 28*, 464 (1967)
61. Kübler, H.: *J. Soc. Cosmet. Chem. 14*, 341 (1963), cited in Clayton, J.F., Jr.: *Handbuch der experimentellen Pharmakologie* Vol. 20, Part 1, p 474, Springer, Berlin, 1966
62. Sherman, H.: *Ninety-day Feeding Study in Rats and Dogs with Trichlorofluoromethane [Freon® 11]*, Haskell Laboratory Report No. 63–72, DuPont Co., Wilmington, DE, USA, 1972
63. Quevauviller, A., M. Schrenzel, V. N. Huyen: *Thérapie 19*, 247 (1964)
64. Quevauviller, A.: *Parfumerie Cosmétique Savons 3*, 228 (1960)
65. Palmer, A. K., N. M. Leeming, R. Clark, G. C. Clark, G. Jackson: *Effect of trichlorofluoromethane on pregnancy of the rat*, unpublished report by Imperial Chemical Industries, Huntington Research Center, GB, 29.O3.1979
66. Palmer, A. K., N. M. Leeming, R. Clark, G. C. Clark, G. Jackson: *Effect of trichlorofluoromethane on pregnancy of the New Zealand White Rabbit*, unpublished report by Imperial Chemical Industries, Huntington Research Center, GB, 20.03.1979
67. Van Auken, O. W., J. Healy, A. J. Kaufmann: *Canad. J. Microbiol. 21*, 221 (1975)
68. Koops, A.: *Mutagenic Activity of Methane, Trichlorofluoro- in the Salmonella/Microsome Assay*, Haskell Laboratory Report No. 568–77, DuPont Co., Wilmington, DE, USA, 1977
69. Zeiger, E., B. Anderson, S. Haworth, T. Lawlor, K. Mortelmans, W. Speck: *Environm. Mutag. 9*, 1 (1987)
70. Longstaff, E., M. Robinson, C. Bradbrook, J. A. Styles, I. F. H. Purchase: *Toxicol. appl. Pharmacol. 72*, 15 (1984)
71. Uehleke, H., T. Werner, H. Greim, M. Krämer: *Xenobiotica 7*, 393 (1977)
72. Speck, W.: *NTP Techn. Bull. 9*, 5 (1983)
73. Krahn, D. F., F. C. Barsky, K. T. McCooey: in Tice, R. R., D. L. Costa, K. M. Schaich (Eds.): *Genotoxic Effects of Airborne Agents*, p 91, Plenum Press, New York, 1980
74. Maltoni, C.: *Final Report on the Long-Term Carcinogenicity Bioassays of Fluorocarbons, F 11 and F 12, Administered by Inhalation to Sprague-Dawley Rats and Swiss Mice*, Institute of Oncology, Bologna, Italy, 1983
75. Epstein, S. S., S. Joshi, J. Andrea, P. Clapp, H. Falk, N. Mantel: *Nature (Lond.) 214*, 526 (1967)
76. National Cancer Institute (NCI): *Bioassay of Trichlorofluoromethane for Possible Carcinogenicity*, CG-TR-106, Bethesda, MD, USA, 1978

completed 29. 5. 1989

2,2,4-Trimethylpentane

Classification/MAK value	**not yet established see Section IIb)**
	MAK List 1989
Synonyms:	isooctane
	isobutyltrimethylmethane
Chemical name (CAS):	2,2,4-trimethylpentane
CAS number:	540-84-1
Structural formula:	

Molecular formula:	C_8H_{18}
Molecular weight:	114.23
Melting point:	$-107\,^\circ C$
Boiling point:	$99.2\,^\circ C$
Vapour pressure at 20 $^\circ C$:	52.94 hPa

1 ml/m³ (ppm) = 4.74 mg/m³   **1 mg/m³ = 0.21 ml/m³ (ppm)**

1 Toxic Effects and Modes of Action

2,2,4-Trimethylpentane (2,2,4-TMP), a volatile, colourless, inflammable liquid, is a principle constituent of alkylate and polymerization gasolines (ca. 10% in unleaded gasoline).

2,2,4-TMP is a mild narcotic. In the male postpubertal rat its main effects are characteristic kidney changes: deposition of hyaline droplets, cell necrosis, desquamation of tubulus epithelium leading to blockage of the urine canaliculi with consequent secondary effects. These changes are caused by accumulation of a protein ($\alpha_{2\mu}$-globulin) which is synthesized in the liver under the influence of testosterone. Above a certain concentration, the requirement for oxidative degradation of $\alpha_{2\mu}$-globulin exceeds the detoxication capacity of the cell. The accumulated protein causes degeneration and necrosis of the tubulus cells in the renal cortex. This pathogenetic chain reaction is also activated after exposure to p-dichlorobenzene, decalin, limonene and numerous other compounds; other species (mouse, guinea pig, monkey, dog) are not affected. The process has not been demonstrated to occur in man. It has, however, not (yet) been adequately studied.

Long-term exposure of male rats to inhaled motor gasolines containing 2,2,4-TMP results in the development of renal adenocarcinomas. The mechanism is considered to be a secondary effect of the process described above.

2,2,4-TMP is not mutagenic in any of the test systems used to date; the mutagenic properties of its metabolites have not yet been tested.

Inhalation of 2,2,4-TMP vapour produces marked irritation of the mucous membranes of the respiratory tract.

Studies with monkeys have demonstrated that isooctane is considerably less well absorbed through the skin than is benzene.

1.1 Pharmacokinetics

2,2,4-TMP is rapidly and completely absorbed from the gastrointestinal tract. Whole body autoradiography of rats 72 hours after administration of 500 mg/kg 2,2,4-[^{14}C-5]-TMP as a single oral dose revealed that the majority of radioactivity in the male rat was localized in the kidney. Kidney levels displayed a pronounced sex

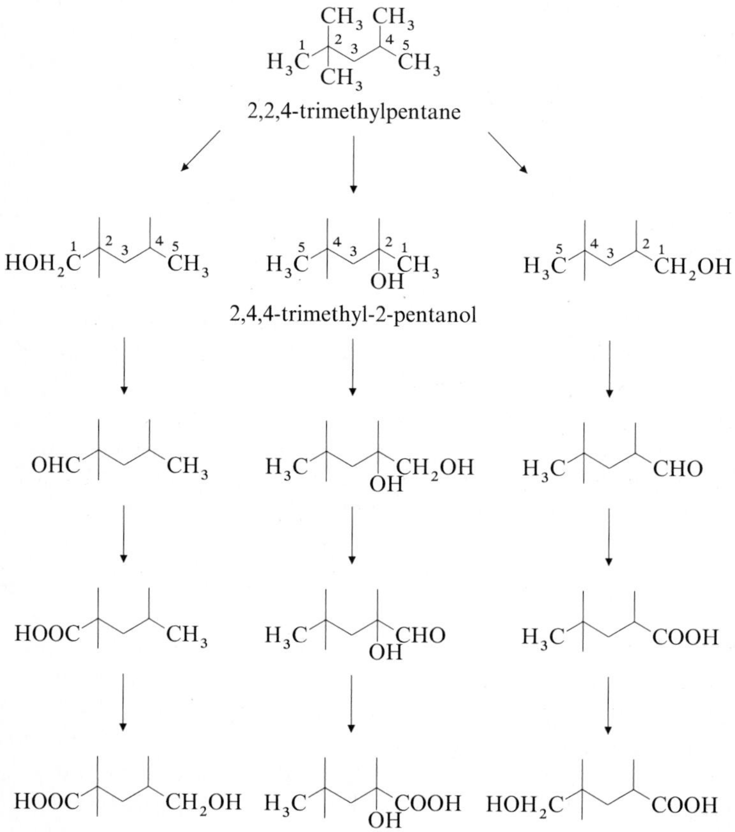

Figure 1. Probable metabolic pathways for 2,2,4-TMP in the rat [2, 3]

difference, with males having about ten times more radioactivity than females. Moderate enrichment of radioactivity was found in the liver and fat tissue without sex-specific differences [1]. Concentrations of radioactivity in kidneys and urine which increase with time are indicative of lively metabolism. The metabolic pathways which have been demonstrated to date in the rat are shown in Figure 1. The main pathway seems to involve oxidative attack at C2; the secondary alcohol is excreted as the conjugate. The terminal methyl groups can also be oxidized, as demonstrated by the detection of alcohols, aldehydes and carboxylic acids. There seems to be a slight difference between the sexes in the kinds and proportions of oxidative metabolites [2, 3].

After subcutaneous injection, radioactively labelled isooctane (no further details specified) was excreted in the urine both in the subsequent 24 hours and in the three weeks that followed much more slowly and less completely than was benzene. The total amount of radioactive material excreted made up only 6−7% of the administered dose [4].

Comparative studies in which isomeric trimethylpentanes were administered daily by oral intubation to male rats demonstrated that 2,3,4-TMP yields a much higher proportion of pentanoic acid derivatives than does 2,2,4-TMP. The larger amount of acid is said to produce greater tubulus damage. 2,3,4-TMP is indeed markedly more nephrotoxic than 2,2,4-TMP [5]. In another comparative study using similar experimental conditions 2,3,3-TMP was less nephrotoxic than 2,2,4-TMP or 2,3,4-TMP [6, 7].

2 Effects in Man

There are no reports available as to acute or chronic toxicity of 2,2,4-TMP to man.

A correlation between Goodpasture syndrome (glomerulonephritis with haemorrhagic oedema of the lungs) and exposure to hydrocarbons has often been reported [e.g., 8−13, reviewed in 14]. Studies of refinery workers, varnishers, aeroplane mechanics, etc. did not differentiate between the individual components of the complex mixtures (mineral oil, gasolines, varnish vapours) to which the workers were exposed. The lesions found in the glomeruli are pathogenetically distinct from the tubulus damage characteristic of the rat nephropathy [5].

3 Effects on Animals

Since the recognition of the species and sex specific, severely nephrotoxic effects of 2,2,4-TMP in male rats [16] a series of studies have investigated the mechanism by which the renal tubulus lesion is produced. The results are given in Table 1.

The first symptom is an increase in kidney weight. This is a result of the formation in the tubulus epithelium of hyaline droplets which can already be demonstrated histologically a few hours after oral administration of the substance. The number of hyaline droplets increases for 2−3 days and then slowly decreases again within a

Table 1. Acute and subchronic administration of 2,2,4-trimethylpentane by oral intubation and inhalation

Species (strain)	Number ♂	♀	Appl. route	Dose mg/kg bw or concentration	Exposure duration	Observations	Ref.
rat (SPF Alderley Park)	4	—	gavage	1370	once	♂♂ (only postpubertal): hyaline droplet formation, 7 × more $\alpha_{2\mu}$-globulin in the kidneys than in controls or prepubertal ♂♂, progressive increase in the first 48 h after 7 d: slow decrease in $\alpha_{2\mu}$-globulin, still above normal value	[17]
	4	4	gavage	2740	once	♂♂ (only postpubertal): hyaline droplet formation ♂♂ and ♀♀: increase in the total protein level in the renal cortex and decreased blood urea concentrations	
rat (Wistar albino)	3	—	gavage	1380	1×/d for 2 d	liver and kidney weights increased reduced feed and water consumption after dose 1, urine parameters: increase in N-acetyl-β-D-glucosaminidase activity and alkaline phosphatase activity after dose 2	[18]
	3	—	gavage	1380	1×/d for 3 d	creatinine in plasma and urine reduced body weight reduced by 9.3 %	
	3	—	gavage	1380	1×/d for 4 d	increase in aspartate transaminase activity body weight reduced by 6.3 %	
rat (Fischer 344)	6	—	gavage	100	1×/d for 11 d	increase in DNA concentration in the liver	[19]
rat (Alderley Park)	5	5	gavage	1370	1×/d for 10 d	♂ + ♀: enlargement of liver and kidney, activation of lipid metabolism ♂ : increase in $\alpha_{2\mu}$-globulin in the kidney ♀ : increase in cytochrome P-450 and cytochrome b_5 in the liver, but not in the kidney	[20]

Table 1 (continued)

Species (strain)	Number ♂	Number ♀	Appl. route	Dose mg/kg bw or concentration	Exposure duration	Observations	Ref.
rat (Fischer 344)	5	–	gavage	50	1 × /d for 21 d	generally: non dose-dependent kidney damage ("protein droplets", tubular degeneration and necrosis), no liver damage from 100 mg/kg: number of dilated tubuli with cell debris significantly increased	[21]
	5	–	gavage	100			
	5	–	gavage	200			
	5	–	gavage	500			
rat (Fischer 344)	2	–	gavage	0.2	1 × /d 5 d/week for 3 weeks	no substance-related findings no substance-related findings from 2.0 mg/kg: dose-dependent increase in hyaline droplets, number of granular deposits and foci of regeneration slightly increased but only significant for 50 mg dose	[22]
	3	–	gavage	0.5			
	3	–	gavage	2.0			
	3	–	gavage	5.0			
	3	–	gavage	20.0			
	3	–	gavage	50.0			
mouse (Swiss)	4*		inhal.	1 000 ppm	5 min	from 1000–8000 ppm: no narcotic effects but marked irritant effects (no details given)	[23]
	4*		inhal.	2 000 ppm	5 min		
	4*		inhal.	4 000 ppm	5 min		
	4*		inhal.	8 000 ppm	5 min		
	4*		inhal.	16 000 ppm	5 min	sensory (no details given) and motoric irritation (sporadic movements), 1/4: sudden respiratory arrest after 5.50 min	
	4*		inhal.	32 000 ppm	5 min	4/4: death by respiratory arrest during expiration after 3–4 min	

* sex not specified
bw: body weight

period of several days to a few weeks. After prolonged application of the substance or very high single doses the process is no longer completely reversible and results in cell necrosis and desquamation which, depending on the dose, can be so extensive that it leads to blockage of the tubuli and marked cell proliferation in the repair process. In mice, guinea pigs, dogs and monkeys these effects are not seen. In man $\alpha_{2\mu}$-globulin could not be demonstrated after two dimensional gel electrophoresis [24]. $\alpha_{2\mu}$-Globulin is a protein of 20,000 dalton molecular weight which is produced under the influence of testosterone in the liver and either excreted in the urine or – also under the influence of testosterone – taken up by the renal epithelia; 2,2,4-TMP increases the uptake and the retention in the cells [25, 26]. A specific transport mechanism involving formation of an adduct of 2,2,4-TMP with $\alpha_{2\mu}$-globulin was ruled out [27]. On the other hand, the formation of an adduct between the principal metabolite of 2,2,4-TMP, 2,2,4-trimethyl-2-pentanol, and $\alpha_{2\mu}$-globulin has recently been demonstrated; it is assumed that this complex is poorly degradable and accumulates in the form of hyaline droplets in the proximal tubulus cells [28].

^{14}C-isooctane (no further details specified) was absorbed through the skin markedly less readily than was benzene. This was shown in studies in which the substance was applied occlusively to monkeys for 10, 15 and 30 minutes [4].

4 Genotoxicity

The results of studies carried out to date on the genotoxicity of 2,2,4-TMP are listed in Table 2 and demonstrate no genotoxic effects.

5 Carcinogenicity

Carcinogenicity studies with pure 2,2,4-TMP are currently not available. There is, however, a 2 year inhalation study with unleaded gasoline containing 2,2,4-TMP. The results are shown in Table 3 and reveal the following pattern: in male rats, as well as symptoms of dose-dependent nephrotoxicity (see Section 3 – Effects on Animals), there were increased numbers of adenomas and adenocarcinomas in the kidney; in female mice, on the other hand, there were increased hepatic adenomas and carcinomas, some of which metastasized to the lung [31]. The liver tumours found in female mice were of two kinds: (a) hepatocellular adenomas, usually small and less than 1 cm in diameter, spherical, without distinct sinusoids or portal areas and composed of hepatocytes that were usually larger than those of the surrounding parenchyma. The juncture of the tumour with the adjacent tissue was distinct and there was evidence of compression of the surrounding hepatocytes. (b) The hepatocellular carcinomas were characterized by great variability of cell size, some containing large nuclei. The border of the tumour with the surrounding hepatocytes was indistinct with evidence of invasion of the adjacent parenchyma. The pattern of growth varied and included trabecular and solid patterns with areas of necrosis or haemorrhage.

Table 2. Short-term tests for genotoxic effects of 2,2,4-trimethylpentane

Test	Test organism	No.	Appl. route and duration	2,2,4-TMP dose or concentration	Observations and findings	Ref.
in vitro						
UDS test	hepatocytes from ♂ Fischer 344 rats	–	in medium for 18 h	saturated solution	negative	[19]
TK6 mutation	TK6 human lymphoblasts	–	in medium for 3 h	saturated or ½ saturated solution	negative with or without S9 mix	[29]
sister chromatid-exchange	TK6 human lymphoblasts	–	in medium for 3 h	saturated or ½ saturated solution	negative with or without S9 mix	[29]
in vivo						
UDS test	B6C3F₁/CrlBR mice	6 ♂ 6 ♀	gavage once gavage once	500 mg/kg bw 500 mg/kg bw	negative ♂ and ♀: increase in replicative DNA synthesis in hepatocytes 24 h after application	[30]
UDS test	Fischer 344-rats	4 × 3 ♂	gavage once	500 mg/kg bw	negative maximal accumulation of hyaline droplets in the kidney after 2, 12, 24 or 48 h; only after 24 h: number of hepatocytes in the S phase increased	[19]

Table 3. Chronic inhalation toxicity of unleaded gasoline (16.7% trimethylpentane isomers: 2,2,3-TMP; 2,2,4-TMP; 2,2,5-TMP; 2,3,3-TMP and 2,3,4-TMP) (100 animals per dose and sex) [31]

Species (strain)	Conc. ppm	Exposure duration	Tumours ♂	Tumours ♀	Other findings ♂	Other findings ♀
mouse (B6C3F₁)	0	107–113 weeks	no substance-related findings	14% hepatocellular adenomas and carcinomas	no substance-related findings	no substance-related findings
	67	6 h/d 5 d/week 103–113 weeks	no substance-related findings	19% hepatocellular adenomas and carcinomas	no substance-related findings	no substance-related findings
	292	6 h/d 5 d/week 103–113 weeks	no substance-related findings	21% hepatocellular adenomas and carcinomas	no substance-related findings	no substance-related findings
	2056	6 h/d 5 d/week 107–113 weeks	no substance-related findings	48% hepatocellular adenomas and carcinomas from week 40, some metastasizing in the lungs, 2 renal tumours (1 adenoma, 1 adenosarcoma)	reduced body weight increase from week 66	increase in liver nodules

Table 3 (continued)

Species (strain)	Conc. ppm	Exposure duration	Tumours ♂	Tumours ♀	Otherfindings ♂	Otherfindings ♀
rat (Fischer 344)	0	107–109 weeks	no substance-related findings	no substance-related findings	27% protein casts	no substance-related findings
	67	6 h/d 5 d/week 107–109 weeks	1 carcinoma in the kidney	no substance-related findings	40% tubular baso-philia, 5% mineralization in renal pelvis	no substance-related findings
	292	6 h/d 5 d/week 107–109 weeks	2 carcinomas, 2 adenomas and 1 sarcoma in the kidney	1 sarcoma in the kidney	kidney and testis weights increased, 100% tubular baso-philia, 80% protein casts, 20% chron. interstit. inflammation, 63% mineralization in renal pelvis	kidney and ovary weights increased
	2056	6 h/d 5 d/week 107–109 weeks	6 carcinomas and 1 adenoma in the kidney	no substance-related findings	reduced body weight gain from week 13, kidney weights increased, 100% tubular baso-philia, 100% protein casts, 70% chron. interstit. inflammation, 91% mineralization in renal pelvis	reduced body weight gain from week 26, kidney weights increased

In addition there is a study in which petrolatum was applied dermally to mice as a 15% solution in isooctane. Twice weekly application of 60 µl isooctane (the solvent control) for 70 weeks produced 2 skin tumours, one of which was a carcinoma, in 2 of 50 male Swiss mice. The results were similar after application of the petrolatum solution: one female mouse with 2 tumours, one of which was a papilloma on the eyelid, and two males with 3 tumours, one a papilloma under the chin [32].

6 Manifesto (MAK value, classification)

There is very little information available as to the toxicity of 2,2,4-TMP. Effects on man, especially dose-response relationships, are not known. Studies on reproduction and teratogenesis are also not available.

2,2,4-TMP was not mutagenic in the test systems applied to date.

In animal experiments, inhaled 2,2,4-TMP caused irritation of the mucous membranes of the respiratory tract.

The only available carcinogenesis study is of inhalation of gasoline containing 2,2,4-TMP which led to the development of renal adenomas and carcinomas in male rats as well as liver adenomas and carcinomas in female mice.

Trimethylpentane is one of the group of substances which induce nephropathological changes (hyaline droplets, degeneration of the tubulus epithelium, cell necrosis) in postpubertal male rats. These changes are dependent on the accumulation of $\alpha_{2\mu}$-globulin. The occurrence of this or a similar protein in man is currently the subject of controversy (see also Limonene, this volume).

Until this question has been clarified and because of the inadequate data base 2,2,4-TMP is to be classified provisionally in Section IIb of the List of MAK Values.

7 References

1. Kloss, M. W., M. G. Cox, R. M. Norton, J. Swenberg, J. S. Bus: in Bach, P. H., E. A. Lock (Eds.): *Renal Heterogeneity and Target Cell Toxicity*, p 489, John Wiley, New York, 1985
2. Charbonneau, M., E. A. Lock, J. Strasser, M. G. Cox, M. J. Turner, J. S. Bus: *Toxicol. appl. Pharmacol. 91*, 171 (1987)
3. Olson, C. T., K. O. Yu, D. W. Hobson, M. P. Serve: *Biochem. biophys. Res. Commun. 130*, 313 (1985)
4. Franz, T. J.: *US Environmental Protection Agency, No. FYI-AX-1284-0185*, Washington, DC, USA, 1984
5. Olson, C. T., D. W. Hobson, K. O. Yu, M. P. Serve: *Toxicol. Lett. 37*, 199 (1987)
6. D'Addario, A. P., D. W. Hobson, D. E. Uddin, E. R. Kinkead: *The Toxicologist 5*, 58 (1985)
7. Yu, K. O., C. T. Olson, D. W. Hobson, M. P. Serve: *Biomed. environm. Mass Spectrom. 14*, 639 (1987)
8. Churchill, D. N., A. Fine, M. H. Gault: *Nephron 33*, 169 (1983)
9. Bell, G. M., A. C. H. Gordon, P. Lee, A. Doig, M. K. MacDonald, D. Thomson, J. L. Anderton, J. S. Robson: *Nephron 40*, 161 (1985)
10. Ravnskov, U., B. Forsberg, S. Skerfving: *Acta med. scand. 205*, 575 (1979)
11. Ehrenreich, T., S. L. Yunis, J. Churg: *Environm. Res. 14*, 35 (1977)
12. Beirne, G. J., J. T. Brennan: *Arch. environm. Hlth 25*, 365 (1972)
13. Klavis, G., W. Drommer: *Arch. Toxicol. 26*, 40 (1970)

14. Phillips, S. C., R. L. Petrone, G. P. Hemstreet: *Occupational Medicine – State of the Art Reviews 3* (3), 495 (1988)
15. Swenberg, J. A., B. G. Short, S. Borghoff, J. Strasser, M. Charbonneau: *Toxicol. appl. Pharmacol. 97*, 35 (1989)
16. Carpenter, C. P., E. R. Kinkead, D. L. Geary, L. J. Sullivan, J. M. King: *Toxicol. appl. Pharmacol. 32*, 282 (1975)
17. Stonard, M. D., P. G. N. Phillips, J. R. Foster, M. G. Simpson, E. A. Lock: *Toxicology 41*, 161 (1986)
18. Fowlie, A. J., P. Grasso, J. W. Bridges: *J. appl. Toxicol. 7*, 335 (1987)
19. Loury, D. J., T. Smith-Oliver, S. Strom, R. Jirtle, G. Michalopoulos, B. E. Butterworth: *Toxicol. appl. Pharmacol. 85*, 11 (1986)
20. Lock, E. A., M. D. Stonard, C. R. Elcombe: *Xenobiotica 17*, 513 (1987)
21. Short, B. G, V. L. Burnett, J. A. Swenberg: *Toxicol. Path. 14*, 194 (1986)
22. Short, B. G, V. L. Burnett, M. G. Cox, J. S. Bus, J. A. Swenberg: *Lab. Invest. 57*, 564 (1987)
23. Swann, H. E., B. K. Kwon, G. K. Hogan, W. M. Snellings: *Amer. industr. Hyg. Ass. J. 35*, 511 (1974)
24. Alden, C. L.: *Toxicol. Path. 14*, 109 (1986)
25. Roy, A. K., O. W. Neuhaus: *Biochim. biophys. Acta (Amst.) 127*, 82 (1966)
26. Carruthers, L., K. Reeves, M. Paul, A. Searle: *Biochem. Pharmacol. 36*, 2577 (1987)
27. Loury, D. J., T. Smith-Oliver, B. E. Butterworth: *Toxicol. appl. Pharmacol. 88*, 44 (1987)
28. Lock, E. A., M. Charbonneau, J. Strasser, J. A. Swenberg, J. S. Bus: *Toxicol. appl. Pharmacol. 91*, 182 (1987)
29. Richardson, K. A., J. L. Wilmer, D. Smith-Simpson, T. R. Skopek: *Toxicol. appl. Pharmacol. 82*, 316 (1986)
30. Loury, D. J., T. Smith-Oliver, B. E. Butterworth: *Environm. Mutag. 7*, 70 (1985)
31. MacFarland, H. N., C. E. Ulrich, C. E. Holdsworth, D. N. Kitchen, W. H. Halliwell, S. C. Blum: *J. Amer. Coll. Toxicol. 3*, 231 (1984)
32. Lijinsky, W., U. Saffiotti, P. Shubik: *Toxicol. appl. Pharmacol. 8*, 113 (1966)

completed 29. 5. 1989

2,4,6-Trinitrotoluene   H
(and isomers in technical mixtures)

Classification/MAK value:	**0.01 ml/m³ (ppm)**
	0.1 mg/m³
	see Section IIIB
	MAK List 1988
Classification/MAK value dates from:	**1988**
Synonyms:	2,4,6-TNT
	TNT
	sym-trinitrotoluene
	tritol
	triton
	trotyl
	tolite
	1-methyl-2,4,6-trinitrobenzene
Chemical name (CAS):	2-methyl-1,3,5-trinitro-benzene
CAS number:	118-96-7

Structural formula:

Molecular formula:	$C_7H_5N_3O_6$
Molecular weight:	227.1
Melting point:	81 °C
Boiling point:	240 °C (explodes)

1 ml/m³ (ppm) = 9.42 mg/m³   **1 mg/m³ = 0.106 ml/m³ (ppm)**

1 Characterization of the individual trinitrotoluenes and the technical mixture

Trinitrotoluene (TNT) has six isomers whose physical properties are shown in Figure 1. Commercial or technical grade trinitrotoluene (t-TNT) as prepared by stepwise nitration of toluene is a mixture of $\sim 95\%$ 2,4,6-TNT, $\sim 2.9\%$ 2,4,5-TNT,

	Formula [CAS-number]	Form	Melting point °C	Detonation temperature °C	Vapour pressure
2,4,6-TNT	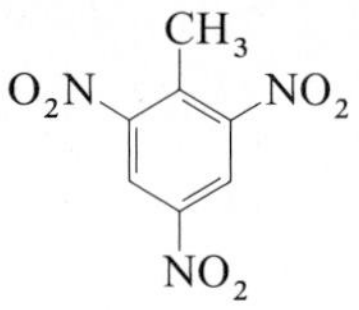 [118-96-7]	monoclinic colourless prisms	82	240	0.046 mm Hg (82 °C)
2,3,4-TNT	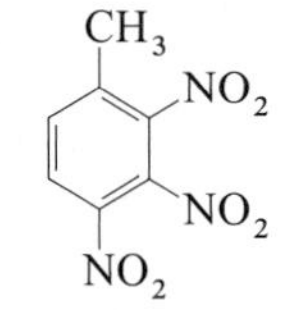 [602-29-9]	crystals	112	290–310	n.s.
2,4,5-TNT	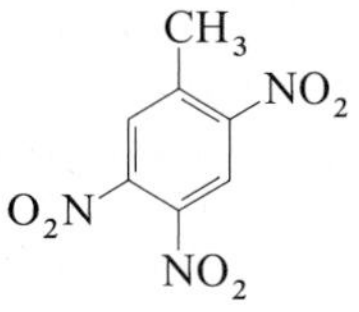 [610-25-3]	pale yellow prisms	104	288–293	n.s.
2,3,5-TNT	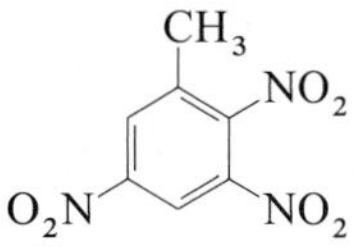 [609-74-5]	yellow rhombic crystals	97	333–337	n.s.
2,3,6-TNT	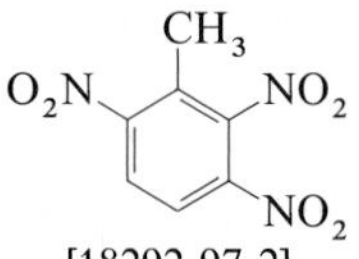 [18292-97-2]	monoclinic needles	111	327–335	n.s.
3,4,5-TNT	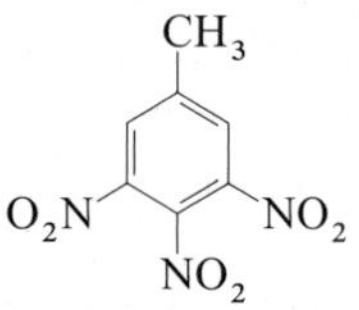 [603-15-6]	yellowish green prisms or needles	132	305–318	n.s.

n.s.: not specified

Figure 1. Physical properties of the isomers of trinitrotoluene [1]

~ 1.3% 2,3,4-TNT and 0.3% 2,3,6-TNT. Traces of trinitrocresols, trinitrobenzoic acid and trinitrobenzene [2], dinitrotoluene and tetranitromethane have also been detected [3].

All trinitrotoluenes are very stable to heat. 2,4,6-TNT does not decompose on melting; gaseous decomposition products are only formed above 160 °C [2]. During melting of t-TNT 0.005–0.009% evaporates in 5–10 hours [4]. Pure 2,4,6-TNT explodes at 240 °C [1], the mixture of isomers at 300 °C [2].

Trinitrotoluenes, on their own or mixed with other explosives, are poured or pressed into moulds to make commercial or military explosive charges [2].

2 Toxic Effects and Modes of Action

Trinitrotoluenes are taken up readily via the skin, lungs and gastrointestinal tract [5–8].

The toxic symptoms described in man include cyanosis, damage to the bone marrow, spleen and liver. Cataracts can develop after chronic exposure to t-TNT. Milder symptoms include irritation of eyes and nose, yellowish coloration of the skin, skin rashes, pallor and gastrointestinal complaints (nausea, vomiting, diarrhoea). Severe intoxications are relatively rare in industry although deaths do occur (aplastic anaemia, toxic hepatitis, massive deterioration of the blood count).

In animals formation of methaemoglobin and Heinz bodies has been demonstrated. Subchronic and chronic exposures damage particularly the liver, spleen and blood.

All the isomers are mutagenic in the Ames test, particularly 2,3,6-TNT, 2,4,5-TNT and 3,4,5-TNT.

Teratogenicity studies are not known to date. There are no long-term or carcinogenicity studies which meet currently accepted standards.

2,4,6-TNT and t-TNT are equally toxic in animals [9–12]. 2,4,6-TNT is said to be less toxic than 2,3,4-TNT or 2,4,5-TNT in acute intoxications but more effective in subacute intoxications [13].

2.1 Pharmacokinetics

Trinitrotoluenes are readily absorbed through the skin and can then cause systemic toxicity (see Section 3.3 – Subchronic and chronic toxicity) [8, 14, 15]. About 3.80 µg/cm^2 (leg) or 2.62 µg/cm^2 (chest) are absorbed through human skin in eight hours [16].

t-TNT is also rapidly taken up through the human lung and gastrointestinal tract [17]. 60–90% of orally administered ^{14}C-labelled 2,4,6-TNT was absorbed within 24 hours (rat). It was detected in liver and kidney; other tissues contained only negligible amounts while in exhaled air none could be detected at all [18].

^{14}C-labelled 2,4,6-TNT (0.2–4 mg/kg body weight) applied to rats i.v., i.p. or dermally was distributed uniformly in the animal tissues. The half-life in rats was 6.3 hours. Repeated i.p. doses revealed no depot effect [19].

Using rats with cannulated bile ducts it was shown that 2,4,6-TNT, or its metabolites, appears in the bile [18]; excretion, however, takes place largely in the urine [20].

Unmodified 2,4,6-TNT has been found in faeces (e.g. rabbit [4], munitions work-ers [4, 12, 21]) and rarely in urine; most investigators have not detected it. Excretion of metabolites in urine has been studied in rabbits. 47% of the dose was found as glucuronides, 30% as 2,6-dinitro-4-aminotoluene and the corresponding dinitro-aminobenzyl alcohol conjugated with glucuronic acid together with trinitrobenzyl glucuronide [22].

2,4,6-TNT (6–13 µg) and the metabolites, 2-amino-4,6-dinitrotoluene (20–46 µg), 2,6-dinitro-4-aminotoluene (16–57 µg) and 2,4-diamino-6-nitrotoluene (0.26–0.54 µg) were detected by mass spectrometry in the urine of rats (200–250 g) during the 48 hours after a dose of 20 mg 2,4,6-TNT. Most excretion of metabolites took place during the first 12 hours. Unmodified 2,4,6-TNT could only be detected during the first 24 hours [20]. 2,6-Dinitro-4-aminotoluene is the main metabolite (one group of workers excreted 0.96–2.09 mg 2,6-dinitro-4-aminotoluene in 24 hours [23] and another group excreted $10^{-4} - 10^{-3}$ g 2,6-dinitro-4-aminotoluene per litre urine [24]; in neither study were exposure levels given). Since other dinitroaminotoluenes and 4-hydroxyamino-2,6-dinitrotoluene are excreted as well, it seems likely that metabolism involves predominantly reductive processes [4, 17, 20, 22, 25–30]. This has been confirmed in studies with the blood of rabbits dosed with 2,4,6-TNT. Apart from unmodified 2,4,6-TNT only 2-amino-4,6-dinitrotoluene and 2,6-dinitro-4-aminotoluene were found [20].

After 8 hours incubation with mouse liver microsomes, 90% of the 2,4,6-TNT had been converted to 2,6-dinitro-4-aminotoluene [31]. Extracts of liver and of other tissues from pig and rat reduced 2,4,6-TNT in a stepwise manner (see Figure 2) [32].

Oxidative metabolites such as 2,4,6-trinitrobenzyl alcohol, 2,4,6-trinitrobenzalde-hyde and 2,4,6-trinitrobenzoic acid were not detected in the urine of dogs after 50 mg 2,4,6-TNT/kg body weight [30]. Yinon [33] also found only reductive metabolites in animal urine. Lemberg alone [29] claims to have detected 5-nitro-*m*-phenylenedi-amine in rat urine.

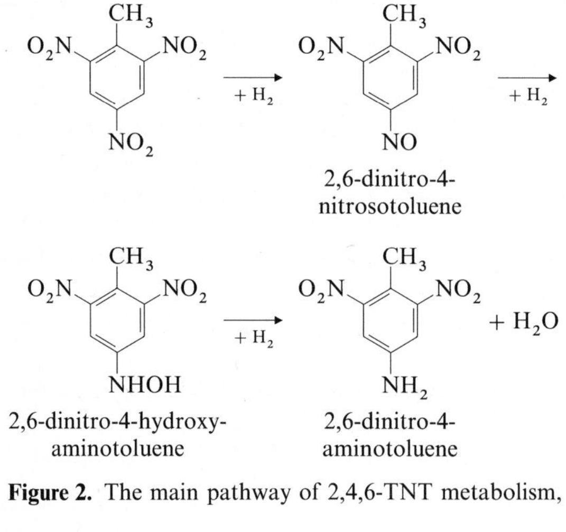

Figure 2. The main pathway of 2,4,6-TNT metabolism, stepwise reduction

Volunteers who had been given a single oral dose of 10–30 mg 2,4,6-TNT excreted on average 44% of the dose in the form of metabolites with diazotizable amino groups. Whereas after a dose of 20 mg 2,4,6-TNT the excretion of diazotizable amines diminished after 48 hours, it remained high after a dose of 30 mg [29]. The highest levels of t-TNT metabolites (2,4-dinitroaminotoluene and 2,6-dinitroaminotoluene) in the urine of workers exposed occupationally to 0.22–0.71 mg/m^3 t-TNT (measured using active charcoal tubes) were found within the few hours after the end of the shift (up to 21 mg/l urine). Samples taken the next morning revealed that levels up to 3.2 mg/l urine were still detectable in two thirds of cases. Even 17 days after the last exposure traces of TNT metabolites could be detected by gas chromatography in urine from 8 of 9 workers; the concentrations were, however, only one tenth of those found after a weekend (on Monday morning) [17].

Added to mitochondrial or microsomal suspensions, 2,4,6-TNT increases the formation of adrenochrome from adrenaline. The adrenochrome production suggests that during cyclic reduction of 2,4,6-TNT by nitroreductases the formation of superoxide anions could occur [34], and they can induce lipid peroxidation and thus cause membrane damage under aerobic conditions [35].

3 Effects in Man

Before and during the First World War the armaments industries of England, Germany and the USA processed large amounts of t-TNT, which was considered to be non-toxic [36]. In 1917 pure, recrystallized trinitrotoluene was still considered not to be poisonous [37] and its toxic effects were blamed on a wide variety of impurities. The first descriptions of t-TNT intoxications came from England where, in the years 1911–1915, there were 279 deaths (101 ♂♂, 178 ♀♀) in munitions factories which could be put down to the effects of t-TNT [38]. This number is a relatively small percentage of the whole munitions work force. As usual, exact occupational exposure was not determined but only the job or conditions of work described – e.g., the t-TNT level during melting was 6 mg/m^3 air. That gave a calculated uptake of at least 16 mg t-TNT in 7.5 hours. The floor was swept three times a day which brought an extra inhaled dose of 9.1 mg t-TNT per day. Workers employed in blowing out the booster cavities of bombs and mines with compressed air took up 2–3 mg t-TNT with each breath [9]. Later measurements of air concentrations at workers' nose height during loading of the melting kettle revealed 10.7 mg t-TNT per m^3 air [39].

In wartime the first signs of intoxication were not taken seriously enough, as can be seen in a study in which subjective symptoms (fatigue, pallor, cyanosis) were recorded for 72% of munitions factory workers but were not considered to be genuine [25].

Observations from the years before 1921 of at least 1800 persons who had worked for one month to three years in munitions factories and were exposed to variously high levels of t-TNT may be summarized as shown in the list below [9, 12, 13, 21, 38, 40–46].

Symptoms of irritation

of the respiratory tract: nose bleeding, nasal discharge, burning eyes, headache, chest
   tightness, dry cough;

of the gastrointestinal tract: bitter taste in the mouth, increased or reduced appetite,
   nausea, vomiting, abdominal pain (in the area of the liver, stomach and di-
   aphragm), constipation, later diarrhoea, (polyuria, only [45]);

of the skin: dermatitis on contact areas, itching rash (erythema with tiny red spots),
   weals, blisters, yellow coloration of the skin (hands, feet and face).

Symptoms of toxicity

of the gastrointestinal tract: anorexia, biliary colic, gastritis, epigastric pain, toxic
   hepatitis;

of the blood: methaemoglobin formation and its consequences (pallor, cyanosis,
   respiratory distress), anaemia, anaplastic anaemia, altered blood count (reduced
   erythrocyte number, damaged erythrocytes, leukopenia, leukocytosis, lymphocytosis, fragmented cells), subcutaneous bleeding;

of the circulation: bradycardia, palpitations; swollen hands and feet;

of the nervous system: somnolence, depression, apathy (peripheral neuritis, only
   [40]);

others: irregular weak menstruation, dark urine, increased perspiration.

In studies of munitions factory workers, individual predisposition is often mentioned [15, 47, 48]. Experience in England showed that workers who had tolerated
t-TNT for 5–6 months without symptoms had no more reason to fear serious
consequences and were considered to have developed a kind of immunity [48, 49].

It has been claimed in numerous studies [15, 37, 38, 50, 51] that sensitivity to
t-TNT varies, e.g., with sex and race. On the other hand, Morton [52] found no
differences between men, women, blacks, Caucasians or various age groups. McGee
[5] also confirmed the uniform distribution of toxic symptoms in men of various age
groups.

Intoxications – even fatal ones – were more frequent during night shifts from May
to September during warm weather [4]. "Eine bedeutende Wendung zum Besseren"
(a marked change for the better) was also reported by Teisinger [53] for medical
examinations in October in comparison to those during a hot August (see also
Section 3.2 – Dermal toxicity). Alcohol also increases the toxic effects [53, 54].

3.1 Acute toxicity

The main symptom was usually the altered blood parameters. This was expected
particularly in workers with glucose-6-phosphate dehydrogenase deficiency [55] and
also found in such [56].

In three men (18, 23 and 35 years old) who suffered from glucose-6-phosphate
dehydrogenase deficiency, a haemolytic crisis was seen after 2–3 days of relatively
high level t-TNT exposure (1.8–2.95 mg/m^3) – haemoglobin: 40–82 g/l (normal
value $\male$: 140–180 g/l), haematocrit: 17–24% (normal value $\male$: 40–54%), reticulo-

cytes (% of red blood cells): 10–26.2%. All three recovered rapidly when they changed their jobs [56].

Altered liver parameters were seen after exposures below the then valid TLV value of 1.5 mg/m³. At 0.8 mg/m³ the activities of SGOT (serum glutamate oxaloacetate transaminase) and LDH (lactate dehydrogenase) were significantly increased [52]. These observations led to a reduction in the TLV value to 0.5 mg/m³.

The acute lethal dose for man is said to be 1–2 g 2,4,6-TNT [57]. 1100 regularly monitored workers were exposed to t-TNT either by inhalation or by skin contact (hands). 1% of the group exposed by inhalation and 10% of the group exposed by direct skin contact became ill [11]. Greasy hands favoured the absorption – severe symptoms were observed in 17% of workers with greasy hands against 11% of those with dry hands [42]. Perspiration also intensified the effects and that explains the increased number of cases, particularly of dermatitis, during the warm seasons of the year [4, 37, 45, 58].

3.2 Dermal Toxicity

Itching, burning skin inflammation, usually papular [59], sometimes with blisters or weals [36] counts as one of the first (after 5 days or more [60]) symptoms of an intoxication [47].

Yellow coloration of the skin and orange coloration of the hair are often described as evidence of TNT contamination [4, 6, 8, 12, 53, 60, etc.]. It developed after contact of uncovered skin areas (hands, forearms, face) with t-TNT sometimes even during the first month [23] but usually after about two months [61]. "Trotylkrätze" (TNT itch) [62], as the dermatitis used to be called in explosives factories in Germany, developed particularly frequently when the t-TNT was mixed with ammonium nitrate, which is hygroscopic. High temperatures and perspiration intensified the effects [54].

Workers who were involved with charging or unloading t-TNT or with filling melted t-TNT into hollow forms (bombs, mines, grenades) had a particularly high risk of developing allergies and dermatitis [5, 63] or mild forms of dermatosis which remained restricted to the hands [48]. Dermatitis was observed in some workers (?/43) even at a mean daily level of only 0.35 mg 2,4,6-TNT/m³ air [52].

Of 52 students (44 female, 8 male, on average 20 years old), temporary workers in the filling room (0.3–0.6 mg/m³) of a munitions factory, 18 developed mild, 5 moderate and 4 severe dermatitis on the hands. On the other hand, not one of the 10 male students who worked in the melt room (0.3–1.3 mg/m³) developed a skin rash [64].

Of 495 cases of mild t-TNT intoxication (examined within one year) 181 had cyanosis, 107 gastritis and 207 dermatitis [15].

3.3 Subchronic and chronic toxicity

The symptoms most frequently observed in exposed workers were mild anaemia (hypochromic, normochromic or hyperchromic), dermatitis venenata, hepatitis and toxic polyneuritis. This follows, as shown below, from a study of men (18–65 years old) working in several munitions factories (exposure duration and level not specified) [5].

	Frequency per 1000 workers per year
pain or paraesthesia in the extremities	58
headache	52
weakness, lassitude	49
lack of appetite, nausea, vomiting	49
vertigo	37
upper abdominal discomfort	36
impairment of the sense of taste	31
anaemia	52
dermatitis	51
hepatitis	32
cyanosis	13

In another study of 150 workers (90% of whom were less than 40 years old), 89% had been in contact with t-TNT for longer than 5 years. As well as toxic hepatitis, changes in the peripheral blood and cataract, 18% complained of palpitations. In the resulting examinations, myocardial dystrophy was demonstrated in 70% of the workers [65]. "Labile heart action" was also found in 44/100 workers suffering from t-TNT intoxication [54].

The results of an occupational medical study are shown in Table 1. The examinations were carried out in a munitions factory on a section of the work force (total number not specified) which operated in three areas – sieving and transport of the t-TNT (considerable skin contact), melting and filling t-TNT (mainly inhalation exposure) and finishing the bombs and mines (skin contact and inhalation). Air concentrations were neither measured nor estimated. In all areas the workers were expected to wear gas masks and gloves. Later the wearing of gloves was no longer recommended as they promoted skin absorption of the compound.

3.4 Blood and liver changes after t-TNT exposure

Since the First World War many case descriptions involving blood or liver changes have appeared. However, only those later than 1941 are included in Table 2. The results are summarized below.

Cyanotic discoloration appears first on the lips and ears and can be very pronounced (blue to lilac). Methaemoglobin levels are only slightly (2–2.2%) or, after higher level exposures, also markedly increased. Heinz bodies occur only rarely [23, 54, 64, 68] (see also Table 2).

In very severe intoxications, aplastic anaemia is concomitant with toxic purpura [7]. All parts of the haematopoietic system are damaged [68].

Table 1. Results of a study on a representative group of 353 munitions workers and 105 control persons who were not exposed [23]

	Workers		Controls	
number:	250 ♂	103 ♀	55 ♂	50 ♀
mean period of employment:	7.8 months (1 week- 14 months)	3.04 months (1 week- 7.5 months)	(10–12 months as watchmen)	(12 months as medical personnel)
mean age:	35.8 years	32.8 years	34.9 years	26.7 years
Observations and symptoms				
weight loss	10 ♂ (mean: 6.5 kg)	5 ♀ (mean: 6.1 kg)	0	5 ♀ (mean: 3.3 kg)
weakness, sleepiness, indisposition	43.6%	20%	16%	20%
dizziness	21%	18%	11%	6%
headaches	23%	13%	16%	10%
nausea, vomiting	28%	18%	11%	6%
abdominal pain	27%	21%	14%	14%
dyspnoea (respiratory distress)	22%	9%	11%	6%
nocturia or polyuria	20%	10%	0	0
menstruation changes	–	19%	–	2%
cyanosis (lips, mucosa, finger nails)	17%	12%	1.8%	0
lilac cyanotic areas	51%	25%	3.6%	2%
yellowish brown-red discoloration of the hair	8%	64% (they wore head coverings less often)	n.s.	n.s.
dermatitis (at any time during the first months)	43%	38%	n.s.	n.s.
abdomen sensitive to pressure	14%	14%	9%	8%

n.s.: not specified

The bone marrow [7] reacts to the cell loss with increased erythropoiesis and leukopoiesis [48, 64]. The sternal marrow is severely underdeveloped and contains large areas which are occupied only by fat cells, numerous sinusoids and capillaries [48].

Changes in the blood parameters were seen in workers exposed to concentrations between 0.05 and 7.5 mg/m^3 for one to 20 years even after the lowest level exposures and increasing in severity with the concentration. Erythrocyte number and Hb

Table 2. Cases of blood and liver damage after t-TNT exposure

Persons examined (♂, ♀; mean age)	t-TNT-Exposure			Observations and symptoms	Number of deaths: causes of death	Ref.
	job description	t-TNT concentration	exposure time			
7 (1 ♂, 6 ♀; n.s.)	t-TNT filler	n.s.	3 weeks–6 months	nausea, anorexia, upper abdominal pain, cyanosis, hepatitis	2: acute liver atrophy (1), aplastic anaemia (1)	[49]
7 (all ♂; 27.8 a)	n.s.	n.s.	n.s.	730000 erythrocytes/mm^3, liver necrosis, damage to the bone marrow and the vascular endothelium	7: toxic hepatitis (4), aplastic anaemia (2), acute toxic purpura (1)	[59]
510 (166 ♂, 344 ♀; n.s.)	mixing explosives, grinding (dust); melting (vapour); filling mines (solid and molten t-TNT); poor industrial hygiene	n.s	12 months	495 (165 ♂,330 ♀) mild intoxications: cyanosis, gastritis, dermatitis; 15 (1 ♂,14 ♀) severe intoxications: toxic hepatitis (12), aplastic anaemia (3)	6: toxic hepatitis (3), aplastic anaemia (3)	[15]
3 (2 ♂; 54.5 a, and 1 ♀; 22 a)	charging mines, cleaning changing room; nurse exposed indirectly via contaminated clothing of workers and by eating (2× daily) in air-raid shelter	n.s. / n.s.	2.5–6 months / 7 months	all 3: toxic liver necrosis, upper abdominal pain, vomiting, weight loss, hepatitis, blood parameters normal	0	[66]

Table 2 (continued)

Persons examined (♂, ♀; mean age)	t-TNT-Exposure job description	t-TNT concentration	exposure time	Observations and symptoms	Number of deaths: causes of death	Ref.
17 (n.s.;n.s.)	charging the melt kettle with t-TNT, melting, pouring into moulds	0.5–2.0 mg/m³	2–4 months	initially transient leukocytosis and moderate eosinophilia, no other changes in blood parameters	0	[47]
3 (all ♂; 47.0 a)	cleaning jobs in munitions factory (1), loading room (1), cooling off room (1)	⊘ 1.5 mg/m³ (1–3.5 mg/m³)	2 months-several months	hepatitis, vomiting, soft enlarged liver, gastrointestinal haemorrhage, abdominal pain, ⊘ 2800 less leukocytes/mm³, MetHb not detected	3: toxic hepatitis (1), aplastic anaemia (2)	[48]
62 (18 ♂, 44 ♀; 20 a)	filling room melting room	0.3–0.6 mg/m³ (filling room) 0.3–1.3 mg/m³ (melt room)	1–2.7 months	reduced haemoglobin (∼11%) and erythrocytes (∼8,6%) in 85% of persons; bone marrow: increased erythropoiesis, increased number of reticulocytes MetHb determined in 9 persons: 0–3% (5), 3–6% (4) the haemolytic effects were more marked in men than in women and were more frequent at higher room temperatures (melt room)	0	[64]

Table 2 (continued)

Persons examined (♂, ♀; mean age)	t-TNT-Exposure job description description	t-TNT concentration	exposure time	Observations and symptoms	Number of deaths: causes of death	Ref.
22 (17 ♂, 5 ♀; 39.9 a)	munitions factory	up to 1.5 mg/m^3 for 1/3	∅ 6.5 months (39–720 d)	rapidly increasing icterus index, acute jaundice, weakness, decreased erythrocytes and Hb, petechia bone marrow: aplastic or hypoplastic	22: toxic hepatitis (8), aplastic anaemia (13), combined hepatitis and anaemia (1)	[67]
27 (n.s.; n.s.)	munitions factory	n.s.	1 month- > 2 a	pallor, tiredness, vertigo, haemorrhage, cyanosis (6), functional liver disorder, Hb reduced to: 12–70% erythrocytes: 630000 – 3.5 × 10^6/mm^3 leukocytes: 300–4800 (including 8 × < 2000)/mm^3	15: haemorrhage (5), purpura thrombocytopenica (3), agranulocytosis (3), anaemia (1), cerebral haemorrhage (2), pulmonary embolism (1)	[7]

a: years
n.s.: not specified

values were decreased even at 0.48 mg/m^3, reticulocytes and Heinz bodies were increased. There was no correlation between blood changes and period of employment [69].

Blood tests carried out during an occupational medical study of 353 persons (see Table 1) revealed no changes in leukocyte numbers, questionable effects on the lymphocytes and only a slight decrease in erythrocyte number in men but not in women. A 9.1% reduced Hb value was also found in men whereas in women no significant deviations from the control values were seen.

Two young men who were exposed to t-TNT during recycling of old mines (ages and duration not specified) developed haemolytic anaemia and, in one case, also toxic hepatitis. Both were later shown to have a glucose-6-phosphate dehydrogenase deficiency [70].

3.5 Eye damage after t-TNT exposure – "TNT-cataract"

A worker (48 years old) had filled grenades with explosive (pure 2,4,6-TNT and 2,4,6-TNT mixed with ammonium nitrate) for 4 years. Deterioration of his sight led him to have a thorough medical examination. There was an absolutely central scotoma in each eye, caused by chronic retrobulbar neuritis and described as a toxic impairment of vision. Specific neurological examination revealed no indications of other organic disease [62]. Later, damage of the eye and especially of the lens (see Table 3) after t-TNT exposure was studied particularly in eastern Europe [71–74]. The typical "TNT-cataract" has the form of an irregular ring of greyish-white, spicular or bow-shaped cataracts in the region of the lens equator. Since this marginal opacity does not result in visus deterioration it is an effect of t-TNT exposure which is difficult to detect. This is especially true for the early form of "TNT-cataract", so-called suspect cataract. This is characterized by larger opalescent forms which occur equatorially in the lens as points or cloud-shaped cataracts but which do not form a continuous ring [73].

Even in young persons and in those whose health was not otherwise affected "TNT-cataract" was observed after exposure for more than 6 years [73]. Later investigators [77, 79], on the other hand, found eye lesions after exposure for only one or more years (see Table 3). The development of a cataract is said to be determined by the amount of TNT taken up [8, 71]. 0.011 µg 2,4,6-TNT was determined in a lens which had been removed operatively from a patient with cataract. Cataract development could, therefore, be caused by TNT which penetrates the lens of the eye from the vascular system [71].

4 Effects on Animals

4.1 Acute and subacute toxicity

We know of no recent inhalation studies. An early paper comes to the conclusion that inhalation studies are difficult because condensation of the sublimate on the

Table 3. Cataract ("TNT-cataract") in workers from explosives and munitions factories and mines

Number of workers	Mean age (range)	Exposure concentration mg/m³	Exposure time in years (range)	Cases of "TNT-cataract" (%)	Observations	Ref.
221 miners	(86.4% under 40)	0 in air samples skin (hand): 0.0016–0.8 mg/cm²*	~3	n.s. (81.9%)	normal cataract: 22.1%, ring-shaped cataract: 18.5% ("TNT-cataract"), other forms of cataract: 11.8%	[72]
61	42.1 (26–57)	see below**	6.4 (1 month–15a)	26 (42.6%)	also cataract developing in 8 (13.1%) "suspect cataract"	[73]
360	n.s. (29–52)	n.s.	5	163 (45.3%)		[74–76]
of these:						
163	(29–50)	n.s.	(5–15 a)	106 (59%)		[74]
54	48.7 (40–59)	1.52	13.9	47 (87%)		[76]
12	39.5 (31–48)	0.14–0.58	6.8 ± 4.7	6 (50%)	mean age of the persons with cataract (∅ 43.8) higher than of those without (∅ 35.2)	[77]
46	47 (n.s.)	n.s.	~20	20 (43.4%)	cataract mostly in initial stadium	[78]
9	40.4 (21–58)	0.10–0.35	14 (1–27 a)	7 (77.7%)	cataract variously pronounced; blood tests: reduced activities of δ-aminolaevulinate synthetase and haem synthetase	[79]

* The cartridges of explosive were packed in paraffin cases. TNT dissolved in the paraffin (10-13 mg TNT detected in 1 g paraffin) and was taken up from there through the skin of the hands [72].

** Of 42 air samples – taken in this factory in 10 years – 22 (52.4%) did not exceed the maximal permitted value of 1 µg/l air, 15 (35.7%) were in excess of 5.5 µg/l air. A further 5 samples (11.9%) exceeded this value under intentionally altered conditions, e.g. the exhaust system was shut down. The persons examined worked alternately at the various t-TNT concentrations. The total TNT-exposure time was determined by anamnesis.

n.s.: not specified   a: years

walls of the apparatus as well as exhalation by the animals prevents attainment of the nominal dose. Nevertheless four dogs which inhaled for 10 days a dose of 50 or 100 mg 2,4,6-TNT/kg body weight (calculated) as vapour through an operatively fitted tube showed initially no signs of toxic effects and then, towards the end of the exposure, occasional vomiting, diarrhoea and incoordination of the rear extremities. Two dogs lost weight. The blood count and histopathological studies revealed no changes [28].

The results of studies of acute toxicity after oral and subcutaneous administration are shown in Tables 4–6. Dogs and cats are seen to be more sensitive than rabbits, guinea pigs and rats. Differences between strains have been described as well – e.g., Fischer 344 rats are more sensitive than Alderley Park rats (see Table 6).

In animals too 2,4,6-TNT affects principally blood and the CNS. Formation of MetHb and Heinz bodies is also described (see Table 6) although rarely in early publications (see Table 5).

A single intraperitoneal injection of 100 mg 2,4,6-TNT/kg body weight increased the concentration of reduced glutathione in brain, liver and kidneys of Wistar rats. In the kidney the levels were already increased 4 hours after the injection, in brain and liver only after 20 hours. Slight morphological changes were seen in the liver. In the epithelial cells of the renal proximal tubules the lipid level increased markedly.

Table 4. Lethal effects of 2,4,6-TNT in experimental animals

Purity of 2,4,6-TNT	Species (strain)	Application route	LD_{50} mg/kg ♂	LD_{50} mg/kg ♀	LD_{low} mg/kg	Ref.
> 99%	mouse (Swiss-Webster)	oral	660 (524–831)	660 (574–758)		[80]
n.s.	mouse (n.s.)	oral	1009			[81]
n.s.	rat (n.s.)	oral	1837.8	1663.8		[82]
> 99%	rat (Sprague-Dawley)	oral	1320 (955–1824)	795 (602–1047)		[80]
n.s.	rat (n.s)	oral	820			[83]
n.s.	rabbit (n.s.)	oral s.c.			500 500	[84]
n.s.	cat (n.s.)	oral s.c.			1850 200	[84]

n.s.: not specified
LD_{low}: lowest published lethal dose

Table 5. Acute and subacute toxicity of trinitrotoluenes in animals

Substance (purity)	Species (strain) weight	Number	Appl. route	Dose	Exposure time	Symptoms	Ref.
unspecified TNT (n.s.)	rat ♂ (Wistar)	10	i.p.	100 mg/kg bw	once	reduced urine volume, porphyrin excretion and δ-aminolaevulinate synthetase	[85]
2,4,6-TNT (n.s.)	rabbit (n.s.)	1	gavage	400 mg	once	d2: red-brown urine d3: appetite normal again d8: no substance-related findings	[4]
2,4,6-TNT (n.s.)	rabbit (n.s.)	2	gavage	500 mg	once	d1–d4: red-brown urine, soft faeces d6: no substance-related findings	[4]
2,4,6-TNT (n.s.)	rabbit (n.s.)	1	gavage	900 mg	once	d2: brown urine, normal appetite d3: general weakness, no appetite d4: died histology: lungs pale yellow, heart blood brown, MetHb not detectable, blood in the urine	[4]
2,4,6-TNT (pure)	rabbit (n.s.) 3 kg	1	gavage	3000 mg	once	no substance-related findings MetHb not detectable	[37]
TNT (impure)*	rabbit (n.s.) 3 kg	1	gavage	3000 mg	once	no substance-related findings MetHb not detectable	[37]
2,4,6-TNT (pure)	rabbit (n.s.) 2.4 kg	1	gavage	2 × 1200 mg	2 d	d3: died	[37]

Table 5 (continued)

Substance (purity)	Species (strain) weight	Number	Appl. route	Dose	Exposure time	Symptoms	Ref.
TNT (impure)*	rabbit (n.s.) 2.8 kg	1	gavage	4 × 1400 mg	6 d	d7: died	[37]
2,4,6-TNT (n.s.)	rabbit (n.s.)	1	gavage	d1: 500 mg d3: 500 mg d4: 200 mg	4 d	d1: red-brown urine free of blood d2: soft faeces d6: animal unable to raise itself d7: died histology: brown urine, MetHb not detectable	[4]
2,4,6-TNT (n.s.)	rabbit (n.s.)	1	gavage	3 × 500 mg on d1, d4, d6	6 d	d1: brown urine d3: diarrhoea d4: brown urine free of blood d19: died histology: brown discoloration of all internal organs	[4]
2,4,6-TNT (n.s.)	rabbit (n.s.)	1	gavage	d1: 500 mg d2: 1000 mg	2 d	d5: brown urine, no appetite d7: venous blood brown, MetHb not detectable d8: died histology: brown discoloration of all internal organs	[4]
2,4,6-TNT (n.s.)	rabbit (n.s.)	1	gavage	4 × 500 mg on d1, d2, d4, d5 d6: 600 mg	6 d	d1: red-brown urine d7: died histology: small intestine yellowish brown, MetHb not detectable	[4]

Table 5 (continued)

Substance (purity)	Species (strain) weight	Number	Appl. route	Dose	Exposure time	Symptoms	Ref.
TNT (impure)*	rabbit (n.s.) 2.5 kg	1	gavage	3 × 2500 mg	3 d	d4: died	[37]
2,4,6-TNT (pure)	rabbit (n.s.) 2.3 kg	1	gavage	4 × 2300 mg	4 d	d5: died	[37]
2,4,6-TNT (n.s.)	cat (n.s.)	13	s.c.	20 mg/kg bw/d	6 d/week 4 – ~ 15 doses	13/13 died before the 15th dose mild fatty degeneration of the liver: 41%, marked weight loss, marked reduction in haemoglobin: 2.5 g/100 ml	[86]
2,4,6-TNT (n.s.)	cat (n.s.)	14	s.c.	20 mg/kg bw/d + 200 mg ascorbic acid/kg bw/d	6 d/week 11–19 doses	5/14 survived 15 or 19 doses, survival better than in the group without ascorbic acid, mild fatty degeneration of the liver: 45%, marked weight loss, less reduction in haemoglobin: 1.2 g/100 ml	[86]
unspecified TNT (n.s.)	cat (n.s.)	5	s.c.	4–6 × 50 mg/kg bw/d	4–9 d	d9: all died histology: mild to moderate fatty degeneration of the liver, centrolobular congestion and atrophy of "cell cords", haemosiderosis of Kupffer's cells, spleen: myelosis, haemosiderosis	[87]

* : not recrystallized

n.s.: not specified

Table 6. Blood parameters after administration of TNT to animals

Substance (purity)	Species (strain) sex	Number	Appl. route	Dose mg/kg	Exposure time	% MetHb	Other observations	Ref.
2,4,6-TNT (> 99%)	rat (Fischer 344) ♂	6 9 3 5	oral oral oral oral	200 500 750 1000	once once once once	∼ 9 ∼ 19 ∼ 20 ∼ 22		[88]
2,4,6-TNT (> 99%)	rat (Alderley Park) ♂	2 2 1	oral oral oral	100 200 500	once once once	∼ 3 ∼ 4 ∼ 11		[88]
TNT (n.s.)	dog (n.s.) n.s.	1	oral	50	11 d 6 ×/week	15–25	Heinz body formation, reduction of total Hb from 15.3 to 9.3 g/100 ml	[28]
TNT (n.s.)	dog (n.s.) n.s.	1	oral	50	9 month 6 ×/week	∼ 25	Heinz body formation, reduction of total Hb from 16 to 13 g/100 ml	[28]

n.s. : not specified

Table 7. Effects of trinitrotoluene (isomer and purity not specified) after topical application to animals

Species	Number ♂♀ (weight in g)	Dose in mg	Skin area treated cm²	Observation period	Observations	Autopsy findings	Ref.
rabbit	1 ♀ (950)	1000	250 occlusive (fine TNT powder rubbed into unshaved skin, closed with silver foil, cloth and bandage	12 h died	initially very restless, then still, after 7–8 h stopped eating, hung its head, died in the night	mucosa bluish, heart normal, blood vessels not full; marked hypostasis in the lungs, liver normal, urinary bladder contained only 3 ml thick urine	[90]
rabbit	1 ♂ (900)	1000	250 occlusive (as above)	ca. 48 h died	no obvious signs of illness but died in the night	10 h after death: no substance-related findings blood and urine normal	[90]
rabbit	1 ♂ (1850)	1000	250 occlusive (as above)	50 h	no substance-related findings	–	[90]
rabbit	1 ♂ (1890)	2000	250 occlusive (as above)	50 h	no substance-related findings	–	[90]
pig (shoats)	2	2000 on moist gauze	n.s.	5 d	no skin irritation, excretion of a little 2,6-DN-4-A and 2,4-DA-6-N	–	[28]
pig (shoats)	2	2000 in glycerine	n.s.	9 d	no skin irritation, excretion of a little 2,6-DN-4-A and 2,4-DA-6-N	–	[28]

2,6-DN-4-A: 2,6-dinitro-4-aminotoluene
2,4-DA-6-N: 2,4-diamino-6-nitrotoluene
n.s.: not specified

The chromatin was frequently aggregated and the mitochondria swollen. Autopsy of rats killed after 48 hours revealed slight swelling of the brain and marked aggregation of chromatin in the nuclei of the neurons [35].

4.2 Dermal toxicity

2,4,6-TNT can penetrate the intact skin (guinea pig) and does so in proportion to the applied dose, almost linearly with increasing exposure time [89].

Table 7 – largely older literature – shows the effects of dermally applied TNT on animals.

4.3 Subchronic and chronic toxicity

The main targets of subchronic and chronic TNT-poisoning are liver, spleen, testis and blood (see Table 8).

Coloration of the urine, which is free of blood, by a red pigment is often described [22] – orange coloration in dog urine after high TNT doses and red in rat urine on day 2, persisting until the end of the study. At low doses (7 mg/kg body weight, rat) the red colour did not appear until day 50. During recovery phases the colour disappeared. Mouse urine also became colored red – at the highest doses within a week. The colour disappeared 8-10 days after the end of the experiment [81].

Intensification of the red colour with an increasing proportion of fat in the diet was observed in rats [10].

The results of studies in which various diets were tested for their effects on the toxicity of TNT are assembled in Table 8.

5 Genotoxicity

In the Ames test the trinitrotoluenes are far more mutagenic than the dinitrotoluenes [92–95].

Trinitrotoluenes cause mainly frameshift mutations, whereby the highest activity is found in *Salmonella typhimurium* TA100, but also to some extent base pair substitutions (*S. typhimurium* TA1535) [92–96]. The mutagenic activity of the trinitrotoluenes in various *S. typhimurium* strains is shown in Table 9.

Comparison of the activities of the individual isomers reveals a marked influence of the structure on the reactivity of the substance. The isomers 2,3,6-TNT, 2,4,5-TNT and 3,4,5-TNT were stronger mutagens than 2,4,6-TNT [95].

Mutagenic isomers were active without enzymatic activation. The mutagenicity of 2,4,6-TNT and 2,3,4-TNT was enormously reduced in nitroreductase-deficient strains of *S. typhimurium* [92–95].

The mutagenic activity of all isomers was reduced by the addition of rat liver homogenate [93, 95].

Urine samples from 14 workers who were exposed to 2,4,6-TNT in a chemical works were shown to be mutagenic without metabolic activation in both *S. ty-*

Table 8. Subchronic and chronic toxicity of trinitrotoluene in experimental animals

Abbreviations:

tr.:	treatment
ery:	erythrocytes
Hb:	haemoglobin
hct:	haematocrit
leu:	leukocytes
ly:	lymphocytes
MCHC:	mean corpuscular haemoglobin concentration
MCV:	mean corpuscular volume
+/- obs.:	with or without 4 weeks observation
obs.:	observation period
PMC:	polymorphonuclear cells
TNT*:	commercially available mixture of the 3 isomers 2,4,6-TNT; 2,3,4-TNT and 2,4,5-TNT

Species (strain)	Number ♂♂ + ♀♀	Substance (purity)	Application route	Dose/d (♂, ♀ mg/kg bw)	Exposure time	Observations	Ref.
mouse (Swiss-Webster)	20 + 20	2,4,6-TNT (> 99%)	diet	0.001% (1.56, 1.57 mg/kg bw)	4 or 13 weeks +/- obs.	no substance-related findings	[80]
mouse Swiss-Webster	20 + 20	2,4,6-TNT (> 99%)	diet	0.005% (7.46, 8.06 mg/kg bw)	4 or 13 weeks +/- obs.	no substance-related findings	[80]
mouse (Swiss-Webster)	20 + 20	2,4,6-TNT (> 99%)	diet	0.025% (35.7, 37.8 mg/kg bw)	4 or 13 weeks +/- obs.	13 weeks tr. + obs.: haemosiderosis in the spleen in 4/5 ♀ + 1/5 ♂	[80]
mouse (Swiss-Webster)	20 + 20	2,4,6-TNT (> 99%)	diet	0.125% (193, 188 mg/kg bw)	4 or 13 weeks +/- obs.	4 weeks tr.-obs.: in all ♀♀ + all ♂♂ decrease in ery, hct, ly, increase in PMC; 13 weeks tr.-obs.: in 3/5 ♂ + all ♀♀ haemosiderosis in the spleen, all ♂♂ decrease in ly and increase in PMC; 13 weeks tr. + obs.: all ♂♂ liver enlargement and 2/5 ♂ liver necrosis; +/- obs.: all ♂♂ + all ♀♀ splenomegaly	[80]

Table 8 (continued)

Species (strain)	Number ♂♂ + ♀♀	Substance (purity)	Application route	Dose/d (♂, ♀ mg/kg bw)	Exposure time	Observations	Ref.
rat (Sprague-Dawley)	20 + 20	2,4,6-TNT (> 99 %)	diet	0.002 % (1.40, 1.45 mg/kg bw)	4 or 13 weeks +/− obs.	no substance-related findings	[80]
rat (Sprague-Dawley)	20 + 20	2,4,6-TNT (> 99 %)	diet	0.01 % (6.97, 7.41 mg/kg bw)	4 or 13 weeks +/− obs.	13 weeks tr.-obs.: from d50 red urine (all); 3 weeks tr. + obs.: red urine disappeared after ca. 2 weeks	[80]
rat Sprague-Dawley	20 + 20	2,4,6-TNT (> 99 %)	diet	0.05 % (34.7, 36.4 mg/kg bw)	4 or 13 weeks +/− obs.	from d2: red urine (all); 13 weeks tr.-obs.: ♂♂ splenomegaly	[80]
rat (Sprague-Dawley)	20 + 20	2,4,6-TNT (> 99 %)	diet	0.25 % (160, 164 mg/kg bw)	4 or 13 weeks +/− obs.	from d2: red urine (all); 4 weeks tr.-obs.: weight loss especially in ♂♂, haemosiderosis of the spleen and splenomegaly in all ♀♀ + all ♂♂; 13 weeks tr.-obs.: weight loss especially in ♂♂ and in all animals haemosiderosis of the spleen, splenomegaly, decrease in ery, Hb, hct, increase in MCV, all ♂♂: decrease in testis weight	[80]
rat (Fischer 344)	10 + 10	2,4,6-TNT (99.1 ± 0.4 %)	diet	1 mg/kg bw	13 weeks	no substance-related findings	[91]
rat (Fischer 344)	10 + 10	2,4,6-TNT (99.1 ± 0.4 %)	diet	5 mg/kg bw	13 weeks	no substance-related findings	[91]
rat (Fischer 344)	10 + 10	2,4,6-TNT (99.1 ± 0.4 %)	diet	25 mg/kg bw	13 weeks	slight increase in cholesterol level	[91]

Table 8 (continued)

Species (strain)	Number ♂♂ + ♀♀	Substance (purity)	Application route	Dose/d (♂, ♀ mg/kg bw)	Exposure time	Observations	Ref.
rat (Fischer 344)	10 + 10	2,4,6-TNT (99.1 ± 0.4 %)	diet	125 mg/kg bw	13 weeks	red urine, weight loss, ataxia, splenomegaly hepatomegaly; increase: cholesterol; 6/10 ♂: hyperplasia of interstitial cells and degeneration of epithelium of seminiferous tubules in the testis	[91]
rat (Fischer 344)	10 + 10	2,4,6-TNT (99.1 ± 0.4 %)	diet	300 mg/kg bw	13 weeks	red urine, weight loss, ataxia, splenomegaly, hepatomegaly; increase: MetHb, cholesterol, ery; all ♂♂: testis damage as with 125 mg/kg bw	[91]
rat (Wistar)	6	TNT^x	diet	150 mg/kg bw in protein diet	70 d	no disturbance of normal bw gain	[10]
rat (Wistar)	6	TNT^x	diet	150 mg/kg bw in carbohydrate diet	50 d	reduction in normal bw gain of 27%	[10]
rat (Wistar)	6	TNT^x	diet	150 mg/kg bw in fat diet	50 d 100 d	rapid loss of weight; 30 min: red urine; 1–2 weeks: weakness, anaemia, liver damage; from 3 weeks: hair loss	[10]
rat (Wistar)	16	TNT (n.s.)	diet	0.3 %, 5 % or 37 % in casein diet	60 d or 70 d	weight loss or only slight bw gain; liver: mild to moderate fatty degeneration depending on the casein diet in 70 % or 28 % of animals	[86]
rat (Wistar)	10	TNT (n.s.)	diet	0.3 % in casein diet	200 d	average bw gain 59 g; liver: mild to moderate fatty degeneration in 20 % of animals	[86]

Table 8 (contained)

Species (strain)	Number ♂♂ + ♀♀	Substance (purity)	Application route	Dose/d (♂, ♀ mg/kg bw)	Exposure time	Observations	Ref.
guinea pig (n.s.)	40	TNT (n.s.)	gavage	16 × 200 and 26 × 400 mg/kg bw with 100 mg/d or 20 mg/kg bw/week ascorbic acid (s.c.)	6 d/weeks 42 ×	30–35% of animals survived 42 doses; mild to moderate centrolobular fatty degeneration of the liver: 88%, no cases of anaemia	[86]
rabbit (n.s.)	24	TNT (n.s.)	s.c.	every 2 d 200 mg/kg bw +/− 200 mg/kg bw/d ascorbic acid (s.c.)	8 weeks 20–24 ×	54% of animals survived all 24 doses; fatty degeneration of the liver: 27%	[86]
dog (Beagle)	5 + 5	2,4,6-TNT (> 99%)	gelatine capsules (oral)	0.2 mg/kg bw/d	4 or 13 weeks +/− obs.	no substance-related findings	[80]
dog (Beagle)	5 + 5	2,4,6-TNT (> 99%)	gelatine capsules (oral)	2.0 mg/kg bw/d	4 or 13 weeks +/− obs.	9 weeks: slight weight loss (all)	[80]
dog (Beagle)	5 + 5	2,4,6-TNT (> 99%)	gelatine capsules (oral)	20 mg/kg bw/d	4 or 13 weeks +/− obs.	4 weeks tr. (♀ + ♂) and 4 weeks tr. + obs. (♀): congested spleen and/or spleen haemosiderosis; 4 weeks/13 weeks tr.: moderate anaemia and reduction in ery, Hb, hct, leu, MCHC with increase in MCV, PMC in all animals; 13 weeks tr. + obs.: ♂ slight anaemia, leukocytosis, many PMC, haemosiderosis in the liver; ♀ weight loss, many PMC, granulocytosis, haemosiderosis in the spleen	[80]

Table 9. Mutagenicity of trinitrotoluenes in *Salmonella typhimurium* [95]

Isomer	Conc. (µg/ plate)	TA1535 S9 + −	TA1537 S9 + −	TA1538 S9 + −	TA98 S9 + −	TA100 S9 + −	TA100 NR3* S9 + −	Revertants/µg in TA100 without S9 mix
2,3,4-TNT	50–100	− −	− −	− −	− −	+ +	− −	5
2,4,6-TNT	10–5000	− −	+ +	+ +	+ +	+ +	− −	6
2,3,6-TNT	10–100	− −	− −	+ +	+ +	+ +	+ +	15
3,4,5-TNT	0.5–20	− −	− +	− +	− +	+ +	+ +	44
2,4,5-TNT	10–1000	+ +	+ +	+ +	+ +	+ +	+ +	57

* nitroreductase-deficient strain

phimurium TA98 and *Escherichia coli* WP2 uvrA, but not mutagenic after the addition of liver microsomes. The mutagenic potency was correlated with the concentration of TNT in the workplace air (maximal air concentration 0.29 mg/m^3, exposure times not specified). Urine samples taken from the same workers after a holiday served as controls [97, 98].

Other studies of genotoxic effects of TNT using short term tests are currently not available.

6 Carcinogenicity

In a carcinogenicity study in which the development of only lung tumours in groups of 20 mice, rat and guinea pigs (strains not specified) was investigated, intratracheal injection of TNT during 12 months (dose and frequency not specified) induced no tumours [99].

Further, after administration of 2,4,6-TNT to rats (0.15 g/kg body weight and day, p.o. for 120 days) [10], guinea pigs (1, 2, 4 or 10 ml/kg, s.c. for 9–12 months) [100] and dogs (5–100 mg, diet or inhalation for 4-17 weeks) [28], no tumours were observed [101].

Carcinogenicity studies at a currently acceptable standard have not yet been carried out with TNT.

7 Manifesto (MAK value, classification)

The MAK value of 1.5 mg/m^3, which has been valid until now, was adopted from the TLV list in 1958. In 1978 the TLV value was reduced to 0.5 mg/m^3 because of the liver parameter changes observed after 0.8 mg/m^3 exposures [102]. In view of the frequency of dermatitis after exposures between 0.3 and 0.6 mg/m^3 and the reduced erythrocyte numbers at 0.48 mg/m^3, this value also seems to be too high. Cataract formation has been observed after prolonged exposure to 0.1–0.35 mg/m^3. The

actual amount absorbed (internal exposure) may have been higher than expected
from the concentration in the workplace air, because of direct contact and uptake
through the skin. Until biological monitoring data become available, the MAK
value will be provisionally reduced to 0.1 mg/m³.

All TNT isomers are mutagenic in the Ames test. Mutagenic activity has been
demonstrated in the urine of exposed workers. For this reason and because TNT in
man causes MetHb formation, which requires the reduction of nitro groups, and the
principle urinary metabolites are the products of reductive metabolism, TNT must
be assumed to have genotoxic effects in man too. The structural analogy to other
nitroaromatics justifies the suspicion of a carcinogenic risk. 2,4,6-TNT and its isomers in technical mixtures are therefore classified in Section III B of the List of MAK
Values. Further studies are urgently required. The designation H is necessary because of the danger of skin absorption.

8 References

1. Beard, R. R., J. T. Noe: in Clayton, G. D., F. E. Clayton (Eds.): *Patty's Industrial Hygiene and Toxicology, 3rd rev. ed., Vol. 2A*, p 2479, John Wiley & Sons, New York, Chichester, Brisbane, Toronto, 1981
2. *Ullmanns Encyklopädie der technischen Chemie, 3rd ed., Vol. 12*, p 781 und Vol. 16, p 77, Urban u. Schwarzenberg, München, Berlin, 1960 und 1965
3. N. N.: *Amer. industr. Hyg. Ass. J. 25*, 516 (1964)
4. Lewin, L.: *Naunyn-Schmiedeberg's Arch. exp. Path. Pharmak. 89*, 340 (1921)
5. McGee, L. C., A. McCausland, J. F. Preston, L. A. Houff: *Gastroenterology 4*, 72 (1945)
6. Goodwin, J. W.: *Amer. industr. Hyg. Ass. J. 33*, 41 (1972)
7. Crawford, D.: *Brit. med. J. 2*, 430 (1954)
8. Hassman, P.: *Pracov. Lék. 23*, 285 (1971)
9. Voegtlin, C., C. W. Hooper, J. M. Johnson: *J. industr. Hyg. 28*, 280 (1921)
10. Himsworth, H. P., L. E. Glynn: *Clin. Sci. 4*, 421 (1942)
11. Moore, B.: *Spec. Rep. Ser. med. Res. Comm. (Lond.) No. 11* (1917); cited in [37 und 105]
12. N. N.: *Lancet II*, 1026 (1916)
13. Panton, P. N.: *Spec. Rep. Ser. med. Res. Coun. (Lond.) No. 58*, 72 (1921); cited in [9 und 105]
14. Hathaway, J. A.: in Rickert, D. E. (Ed.): *Toxicity of Nitroaromatic Compounds*, Chemical Industry Institute of Toxicology Series, p 255, Hemisphere Publishing Co., Washington DC, USA, 1985
15. Swanston, C.: cited in [103]
16. Gong, Z., B. Yu, Y. Wang, C. Sun: *Zhonghua Laodong Weiheng Zhiyebing Zazhi 3*, 332 (1985)
17. Woollen, B. H., M. G. Hall, R. Craig, G. T. Steel: *Brit. J. industr. Med. 43*, 465 (1986)
18. Hodgson, J. R., S. W. Hwang, J. C. Dacre, C. C. Lee: *Fed. Proc. 36*, 996 (1977)
19. Dymova, E. G., M. R. Zeltser, E. P. Shedova: *Gig. Tr. prof. Zabol. No. 9*, 26 (1984)
20. Yinon, J., D. G. Hwang: *Toxicol. Lett. 26*, 205 (1985)
21. Koelsch, F.: *Zbl. Gewerbehyg. 6*, 15 und 53 (1918)
22. Channon, H. J., G. T. Mills, R. T. Williams: *Biochem. J. 38*, 70 (1944)
23. Sievers, R. F., A. H. Lawton, F. Skoog, P. A. Neal, W. F. von Oettingen: *Publ. Hlth Bull. (Wash.) 291*, 1 (1945)
24. Almog, J., S. Kraus, A. Basch: *Arch. Toxicol. 6*, 351 (1983)
25. Voegtlin, C., C. W. Hooper, J. M. Johnson: *Hyg. Lab. Wash. Bull. No. 126* (1920)
26. Westfall, B. B., M. I. Smith: *Proc. Soc. exp. Biol. (N.Y.) 51*, 122 (1942)
27. Westfall, B. B: *J. Pharmacol. exp. Ther. 78*, 386 (1943)
28. Oettingen, W. F. von, D. D. Donahue, R. K. Snyder, B. L. Horecker, A. R. Monaco, A. H. Lawton, T. R. Sweeney, P. A. Neal: *Publ. Hlth Bull. (Wash.) 285*, 17 (1944)

29. Lemberg, R. J., J. P. Callaghan: *Aust. J. exp. Biol. med. Sci. 23*, 1 (1945)
30. Snyder, R. K.: *J. industr. Hyg. 28*, 59 (1946)
31. Naumova, R. P., E. N. Ofitserov, T. O. Belousova, S. Y. Selivanovskaya, L. F. Khisamutdino-va: *Izv. Akad. Nauk S.S.R., Ser. Biol. 3*, 448 (1986)
32. Bueding, E., N. Jolliffe: *J. Pharmacol. exp. Ther. 88*, 3 (1946)
33. Yinon, J., D. G. Hwang: *J. Chromatogr. 375*, 154 (1986)
34. Köchli, H. W., B. Wermuth, J. P. von Wartburg: *Biochim. biophys. Acta (Amst.) 616*, 133 (1980)
35. Zitting, A., G. Szumanska, J. Nickels, H. Savolainen: *Arch. Toxicol. 51*, 53 (1982)
36. Flury, F., F. Zernik: *Schädliche Gase*, p 431, Springer Verlag Berlin, 1931
37. Koelsch, F.: *Zbl. Gewerbehyg. 5*, 98 (1917)
38. O'Donovan, W. J.: *Proc. roy. Soc. Med. 10*, 73 (1917)
39. Hart, W. L.: *Industr. Med. 13*, 896 (1944)
40. Livingstone-Learmouth, A., B. M. Cunningham: *Lancet II,* 261 (1916)
41. White, R. P.: *Lancet I,* 400 (1916); cited in [21]
42. Barnes, J. A. P.: *Proc. roy. Soc. Med. 10*, 84 (1916/17)
43. Stewart, M. J.: *Lancet I,* 153 (1917)
44. Curschmann, F.: *Zbl. Gewerbehyg. 6*, 166 (1918)
45. Putnam, T. J., W. Herman: *J. industr. Hyg. 1*, 238 (1919)
46. Minot, G. R.: *J. industr. Hyg. 1*, 301 (1919)
47. Cone, T. E.: *J. industr. Hyg. 26*, 95 (1944)
48. Eddy, J. H.: *J. Amer. med. Ass. 125*, 1169 (1944)
49. Evans, R. M.: *Lancet II,* 552 (1941)
50. Taeger, H.: *Die Klinik der entschädigungspflichtigen Berufskrankheiten*, p 158, Springer Verlag, Berlin, 1941
51. Fairhall, L. T.: *Industrial Toxicology, 2nd ed.*, p 352, Williams & Wilkins Co., Baltimore, 1957
52. Morton, A. R., M. V. Ranadive, J. A. Hathaway: *Amer. industr. Hyg. Ass. J. 37*, 56 (1976)
53. Teisinger, J.: *Arch. Gewerbepath. Gewerbehyg. 4*, 491 (1933)
54. Schwarz, L.: *Zbl. Arbeitsmed. 8*, 104 (1958)
55. Stokinger, H. E., J. T. Mountain: *J. occup. Med. 9*, 537 (1967)
56. Djerassi, L. S., L. Vitany: *Brit. J. industr. Med. 32*, 54 (1975)
57. Dreisbach, R. H.: *Handbook of Poisoning: Diagnostic Treatment*, Lange Medical Publications, Los Altos, CA, USA, 1961; cited in [3]
58. McNally, W. D.: *Industr. Med. 13*, 491 (1944)
59. Davie, T. B.: cited in [103]
60. Schwartz, L.: *J. Amer. med. Ass. 125*, 186 (1944)
61. Eddy, J. H.: *Amer. J. med. Sci. 210*, 374 (1945)
62. Reis, W.: *Z. Augenheilk. 47*, 199 (1922)
63. Goh, C. L.: *Contact Dermatitis 10*, 108 (1984)
64. Stewart, A., L. J. Witts, G. Higgins, J. R. P. O'Brien: *Brit. J. industr. Med. 2*, 74 (1945)
65. Soboleva, L. P.: *Gig. Tr. prof. Zabol. No. 11*, 47 (1969)
66. Palmer, W. L., G. S. McShane, W.H. Lipman: *J. Amer. med. Ass. 123*, 1025 (1943)
67. McConnell, W. J., R. H. Flinn: *J. industr. Hyg. 28*, 76 (1946)
68. Lane, R. E.: cited in [103]
69. Gribova, I. A., R. A. Gabulgalimova, E. G. Dymova, T. B. Popova: *Gig. Tr. prof. Zabol. No. 9*, 24 (1983)
70. Fenakel, G.: *Harefuah 109*, 188 (1985)
71. Gleserow, S. J.: *Vestn. Oftal. 32*, 21 (1953)
72. Penkow, M. A.: *Vestn. Oftal. 78*, 82 (1965)
73. Hassman, P., J. Juran: *Int. Arch. Gewerbepath. Gewerbehyg. 24*, 310 (1968)
74. Manoilova, J. K.: *Vestn. Oftal. No. 4*, 76 (1968)
75. Zacharova, A. K., I. K. Manoilova: *Gig. Tr. prof. Zabol. No. 12*, 28 (1971)
76. Hassman, P.: *Coll. Sci. Commun. Charles Univ. Fac. Med. 22*, 1 (1979)
77. Härkönen, H., M. Kärki, A. Lahti, H. Savolainen: *Amer. J. Ophthal. 95*, 807 (1983)
78. Gombosi, K., A. Medgyaszay: *Munkavédelem 29*, 221 (1983)
79. Savolainen, H., R. Tenhunen, H. Härkönen: *Brit. J. industr. Med. 42*, 354 (1985)

80. Dilley, J. V., C. A. Tyson, R. J. Spanggord, D. P. Sasmore, G. W. Newell, J.C. Dacre: *J. Toxicol. environm. Hlth 9*, 565 (1982)
81. NTIS AD-A080-146, Nat. Tech. Inform. Serv., Springfield, VA 22161, USA; cited in [104]
82. Wang, T., C. Guo, H. Nan, G. Li, S. Heng: *Shanxi Yiyao Zazhi 15*, 67 (1986)
83. NTIS AD-B011-150, Nat. Tech. Inform. Serv., Springfield, VA 22161, USA; cited in [104]
84. *Spec. Rep. Ser. med. Res. Coun. (Lond.) 58*, 32 (1921); cited in [104]
85. Tenhunen, R., A. Zitting, J. Nickels, H. Savolainen: *Exp. molec. Path. 40*, 362 (1984)
86. Smith, M. I., B. B. Westfall, E. F. Stohlmann: *J. industr. Hyg. Toxicol. 25*, 391 (1943)
87. Lillie, R. D.: *Publ. Hlth Rep. (Wash.) 58*, 1436 (1943)
88. Ashby, J., B. Burlinson, P. A. Lefevre, J. Topham: *Arch. Toxicol. 58*, 14 (1985)
89. Yu, B., Z. Gong, Y. Wang, C. Sun: *Zhonghua Yufangyixue Zazhi 20*, 202 (1986)
90. Dambleff, J.: *Beiträge zur Kenntnis der giftigen Wirkung nitrierter Benzole und Toluole insbesondere von der Haut aus*, Thesis, Würzburg, 1908
91. Levine, B. S., E. M. Furedi, D. E. Gordon: *Toxicology 32*, 253 (1984)
92. Whong, W. Z., N. D. Speciner, G. S. Edwards: *Proc. Amer. Ass. Cancer Res. 21*, 195 (1980)
93. Whong, W. Z., G. S. Edwards: *Mutat. Res. 136*, 209 (1984)
94. Sundvall, A., H. Marklund, U. Rannug: *Mutat. Res. 137*, 71 (1984)
95. Spanggord, R. J., K. E. Mortelmans, A. F. Griffin, V. F. Simmon: *Environm. Mutag. 4*, 163 (1982)
96. Won, W. D., L. H. DiSalvo, J. Ng: *Appl. environm. Microbiol. 31*, 576 (1976)
97. Einistö, P., G. Ahlborg, B. Bergström, K. Falck, C. Hogstedt, M. Sorsa: *Mutat. Res. 130*, 262 (1984)
98. Ahlborg, G., B. Bergström, C. Hogstedt, P. Einistö, M. Sorsa: *Brit. J. industr. Med. 42*, 691 (1985)
99. Schepers, G. W. H.: *Industr. Med. 40*, 48 (1971)
100. Velling, E. J.: *Farmakol. i Toksikol. 6*, 61 (1943); cited in [101]
101. Hartwell, J. L.: *Survey of compounds which have been tested for carcinogenic activity*, National Cancer Institute, National Institutes of Health, Bethesda, MD, USA, Publ. Hlth Serv., Publ. No. 149, 91 (1951)
102. American Conference of Governmental Industrial Hygienists Inc. (ACGIH): *Documentation of the Threshold Limit Values and Biological Exposure Indices*, 5th ed., p 610, Cincinnati, OH, USA, 1986
103. Lawrence, R. D.: *Proc. roy. Soc. Med. 35*, 553 (1942)
104. National Institute for Occupational Safety and Health (NIOSH): *Registry of Toxic Effects of Chemical Substances (RTECS)*, 1981–82 ed., Vol. 3, p 776, USDHHS, Cincinnati, OH, USA, 1983
105. Oettingen, W. F. von: *Publ. Hlth Bull. (Wash.) 271*, 111 (1941)

completed 19. 5. 1988

4-Vinyl-1-cyclohexene dioxide

Classification/MAK value	**see Section III A 2)** **MAK List 1987**
Classification/MAK value dates from:	**1987**

Synonyms:	4-vinyl-1,2-cyclohexene diepoxide
	1,2-epoxy-4-(epoxyethyl)cyclohexane
	1-(epoxyethyl)-3,4-epoxycyclohexane
	3-(epoxyethyl)-7-oxabicyclo(4.1.0)-
	   heptane
	4-(epoxyethyl)-7-oxabicyclo(4.1.0)-
	   heptane
	3-(1,2-epoxyethyl)-7-oxabicyclo-
	   (4.1.0)heptane
	4-(1,2-epoxyethyl)-7-oxabicyclo-
	   (4.1.0)heptane
	vinyl cyclohexene diepoxide
	4-vinylcyclohexene diepoxide
	4-vinyl-1-cyclohexene diepoxide
	vinylcyclohexene dioxide
	4-vinylcyclohexene dioxide
	1-vinyl-3-cyclohexene dioxide
	4-vinyl-1-cyclohexene dioxide
	1-ethyleneoxy-3,4-epoxycyclohexane

Chemical name (CAS):	3-oxiranyl-7-oxabicyclo[4.1.0]- heptane
CAS number:	106-87-6
Structural formula:	
Molecular formula:	$C_8H_{12}O_2$
Molecular weight:	140.2
Melting point:	$-55\,°C$
Boiling point:	$227\,°C$
Vapour pressure at $20\,°C$:	0.13 hPa

1 ml/m³ (ppm) ≈ 5.82 mg/m³   **1 mg/m³ ≈ 0.172 ml/m³ (ppm)**

1 Toxic Effects and Modes of Action

4-Vinyl-1-cyclohexene dioxide (VCD) is chemically reactive and is therefore an irritant of skin and mucous membranes, is mutagenic without metabolic activation in *in vitro* test systems and induces local and systemic tumours after dermal or intraperitoneal application.

In addition to its use in the manufacture of epoxide resins in polymer production, VCD also finds application as a polar dehydrating agent in the preparation of samples for electron microscopy. Employees can be exposed both by skin contact and by inhalation of the volatile substance [1, 2].

2 Effects in Man

There are no publications which describe adverse effects on the health of exposed persons. However, a producer [3] has reported that VCD causes mild to severe skin irritation and that a worker who wore shoes contaminated with the substance developed blisters on his feet.

3 Effects on Animals

The oral LD_{50} in the rat is 2.83 g/kg, the dermal LD_{50} in the rabbit 0.62 ml/kg [4]. After inhalation for 4 hours the LC_{50} in the rat was 4580 mg/m^3 (800 ml/m^3) with irritation of the respiratory tract and pulmonary congestion [5].

Focal thymus necrosis, 60 % reduction in leukocyte number and diminution of the size of the spleen, thymus and testes were found in Long Evans rats on day 12 after an intramuscular injection of 400 mg/kg [6].

4 Metabolism

In analogy to the metabolism of cyclohexane it has been postulated that VCD is metabolized by dihydrodiol formation on the ring with subsequent glucuronidation, and hydroxylation of the ring C-3 as well as reduction of the epoxide residue on the side chain, also followed by glucuronidation [1]. The postulate that dihydrodiol formation takes place both on the ring and the vinyl residue arose from studies of the metabolism and mutagenicity of the reaction products of 4-vinylcyclohexane [7]. Whereas the substance itself was a mutagen, none of its metabolites could be shown to be mutagenic. As early as 1976 the two dihydrodiols had been detected after metabolism of VCD with rat liver microsomes [8].

5 Mutagenicity

The alkylating and mutagenic potency of the metabolites of 4-vinylcyclohexane and epoxides of similar structure have been compared [9]. In the 4-(*p*-nitrobenzyl)pyridine binding test, VCD was more reactive than 1,2-epoxycyclohexane, 4-vinyl-1,2-epoxycyclohexane and 4-epoxyethyl-1,2-dihydrocyclohexane. Only styrol oxide was more reactive. Similar differences between the substances were found when their mutagenicity was determined in *S. typhimurium* TA100 and in fibroblast cultures (CHO cells) without the addition of a metabolizing cell fraction. The largest increase in mutation rate, however, was achieved with 1,2-epoxycyclohexane.

The results available from *in vitro* mutagenicity tests indicate that VCD is directly mutagenic but only within a narrow concentration range since higher concentrations are cytotoxic. The weak mutagenic effects which were initially described for VCD may be explained by its high vapour pressure which, in the absence of special measures such as exposure in a dessicator, allowed a considerable proportion of the substance to evaporate from the incubation mixtures during the experiments. The increased mutation rates found particularly in *S. typhimurium* TA1535 and TA100 suggest that base pair substitution is the mechanism of the genotoxic action. Increased mutation rates in the absence of a metabolizing system have been found in the following organisms: *Salmonella typhimurium* TA100 and TA98 [10], TA100 [11], in TA1535 and TA100 more than in TA98 [12], in TA1535 and TA100 but not in TA1537 or TA98 [13], TA1535 and TA100 [14], in TA1535 and TA100 but not in TA1537, TA1538 or TA98 [2], in TA1535 and TA100 more than in TA1537 and TA98 [15] as well as in *Klebsiella pneumoniae* [16]. VCD induced point mutations in V79 fibroblast cultures [9] and mitotic gene conversions, back mutations and mitotic crossing over in *Saccharomyces cerevisiae* [17]. In these tests the addition of a metabolizing cell fraction did not change the mutation rates.

These findings, which demonstrate a genotoxic effect independent of metabolic activation, have been confirmed recently by studies carried out as part of the National Toxicology Program with *S. typhimurium* TA98, TA100 and TA1535, mouse lymphoma cells (point mutations) and CHO cells (chromosome aberrations) [15, 18].

6 Carcinogenicity

By 1976 five carcinogenicity studies has been carried out on rats and mice, four with dermal application and one with intraperitoneal administration. All of these studies are inadequately documented. They did, however, induce the IARC to classify the substance as carcinogenic in mice by skin application [19].

Recently two more studies with dermal application of VCD to B6C3F$_1$ mice and F344/N rats were completed as part of the National Toxicology Program [18].

Dermal application

Doses of about 16 mg VCD dissolved in acetone and containing one water-insoluble impurity were applied five times a week for 12 months to the dorsal skin of male albino mice [20]. In 11 of the 20 treated animals local skin tumours developed, 9 of which were squamous epithelial carcinomas (in one case with metastases in the lungs) or sarcomas of which 3 had penetrated into the subcutaneous tissue. In addition, it is reported that 1 skin tumour and 4 malignant lymphomas developed in 16 survivors of a group of initially 20 C57B1 mice which had been treated with a total of 70 mg VCD [21].

Local tumours including one carcinoma were found in 4 of 18 C3H mice which had been treated with a total of 78 mg VCD (10% in acetone), however, with markedly reduced survival times [4].

In another study, ca. 10 mg VCD was applied to the dorsal skin of 30 male Swiss ICR/ha mice three times a week as a 10% solution in benzene. This treatment induced extensive skin lesions which were not described more specifically. Skin tumours, of which 9 were squamous epithelial carcinomas, developed in 14 animals [22].

Table 1. Results of a 2 year carcinogenicity study with dermal application of VCD in acetone on 5 days per week [18]

F344/N Rats (0, 15 or 30 mg/rat)		B6C3F₁ Mice (0, 2.5, 5 or 10 mg/mouse)	
♂♂	♀♀	♂♂	♀♀
Body weight gain			
highest dose group less than controls	highest dose group less than controls	medium and highest dose group less than controls	highest dose group less than controls
Survival in week 85			
7/50, 8/50, 4/50	27/50, 23/50, 15/50	38/50, 35/50, 4/50, 0/50	30/50, 31/50, 15/50, 10/50
Non-neoplastic skin changes			
acanthosis and hypertrophy of the sebaceous glands	acanthosis and hypertrophy of the sebaceous glands	acanthosis, hyperkeratosis and necrotising inflammation	acanthosis, hyperkeratosis and necrotising inflammation
Neoplastic changes			
Skin:	*Skin*:	*Skin*:	*Skin*:
basal cells: 2/50, 4/50, 8/50 squamous epithelium: 0/50, 33/50, 36/50	basal cells: 2/50, 5/50, 5/50 squamous epithelium: 0/50, 16/50, 34/50	squamous epithelium: 0/50, 14/50, 40/50, 43/50	squamous epithelium: 0/50, 6/50, 37/50, 43/50
			Ovaries: granulosa cells, benign tumours of mixed type or luteomas: 1/50, 0/49, 17/49, 18/50
			Lungs: bronchiolar/alveolar adenomas or carcinomas: 4/50, 9/50, 11/50, 7/50

The results of the carcinogenicity study carried out recently as part of the National Toxicology Program with dermal application to rats and mice [18] are shown in Table 1. In all treated groups VCD caused a dose-dependent increase in the frequency of variously differentiated squamous epithelial skin carcinomas. Rats were more sensitive than mice. In addition, benign and malignant ovarian tumours developed in the female mice of the medium and high dose groups but not in the female rats. Bronchiolar alveolar adenomas and carcinomas occurred in 22% and 16% of the female mice from the medium and high dose groups, respectively. In the corresponding control group the incidence was 8%; the historical incidence in controls was 6%.

The ovarian tumours in the female mice are particularly noteworthy because 4-vinylcyclohexene, of which 0.001% is metabolized to VCD [7, 11, 23], has also been shown to induce ovarian tumours in female mice [24] and in a long-term inhalation study with 1,3-butadiene, which dimerizes to yield 4-vinylcyclohexene [25], ovarian tumours developed at high frequency in mice [26]. The authors discuss the possibility of an effect of these substances on hormonal regulation.

In the preliminary experiments for the NTP study, groups of 10 male and 10 female rats and mice were given 0, 62.5, 125, 500 or 1000 mg/kg VCD in corn oil by oral intubation on 5 days a week for 13 weeks. Body weight gain was severely inhibited. In week 83 all male animals from the highest dose group had died. In keeping with its local effectiveness at the site of application, VCD doses of 250 mg/kg or more produced a high incidence of hyperplasia and hyperkeratosis of the squamous epithelium of the forestomach in all treated groups as well as ovarian atrophy in the female mice [18].

Intraperitoneal administration

10 male and 4 female albino rats were given intraperitoneal injections of 250 mg/kg VCD twice a week for 10 weeks. 7 months after the first injection a disseminated sarcoma had developed in the abdominal cavity of one of the animals and metastases in the lungs. No tumours were found in the remaining animals by the end of the observation period, 21 months after the start of treatment [21].

7 Manifesto (MAK value, classification)

VCD is an alkylating diepoxide and thus a direct mutagen in *in vitro* test systems. After dermal application to animals it induces local carcinomas but also tumours in the ovaries and lungs in female mice. 4-Vinyl-1-cyclohexene dioxide is therefore classified in Section III A 2) of the List of MAK Values. A safe level of VCD cannot be determined because of its genotoxicity.

8 References

1. Stratton, C. J.: *Tissue and Cell 8*, 729 (1976)
2. Ringo, D. L., E. F. Brennan, E. H. Cota-Robles: *J. Ultrastruct. Res. 80*, 280 (1982)
3. Union Carbide Corp.: ERL-4206 ("UNOX" EPOXIDE 206), *Vinylcyclohexene Dioxide, Toxicology Studies*, Chemicals and Plastics Div., New York (June 8, 1965); cited in American

Conference of Governmental Industrial Hygienists Inc. (ACGIH): *Documentation of the Threshold Limit Values and Biological Exposure Indices*, 5th ed., p 627, Cincinnati, OH, USA, 1986

4. Weil, C. S., N. Condra, C. Haun, J. A. Striegel: *Amer. industr. Hyg. Ass. J. 24*, 305 (1963)
5. Hine, C. H., V. K. Rowe in Patty, F. A. (Ed.): *Industrial Hygiene and Toxicology*, 2nd rev. ed., Vol. II, p 1651, Interscience Publishers, Wiley & Sons, New York, London, 1963
6. Kodama, J. K., R. J. Guzman, M. K. Dunlap, G. S. Loquvam, R. Lima, C. H. Hine: *Arch. environm. Hlth 2*, 50 (1961)
7. Gervasi, P. G., A. Abbondandolo, L. Citti, G. Turchi: in Gut, J., M. Cikrt, G. L. Plaa (Eds.): *Industrial and Environmental Xenobiotics Metabolism and Pharmacokinetics of Organic Chemicals and Metals*, p 205, Springer Verlag, Berlin, Heidelberg, New York, 1981
8. Watabe, T., T. Sawahata: *Biochem. Pharmacol. 25*, 601 (1976)
9. Turchi, G., S. Bonatti, L. Citti, P. G. Gervasi, A. Abbondandolo: *Mutat. Res. 83*, 419 (1981)
10. Wade, M. J., J. W. Moyer, C. H. Hine: *Mutat. Res. 66*, 367 (1979)
11. Watabe, T., A. Hiratsuka, M. Isobe, N. Ozawa: *Biochem. Pharmacol. 29*, 1068 (1980)
12. Simmon, V., J. M. Baden: *Mutat. Res. 78*, 227 (1980)
13. El-Tantawy, M. A., B. D. Hammock: *Mutat. Res. 79*, 59 (1980)
14. Frantz, S. W., J. E. Sinsheimer: *Mutat. Res. 90*, 67 (1981)
15. Mortelmans, K., S. Haworth, T. Lawlor, W. Speck, B. Tainer, E. Zeiger: *Environm. Mutag. 8*, Suppl. 7, 1 (1986)
16. Voogd, C. E., J. J. van der Steel, J. J. J. A. A. Jacobs: *Mutat. Res. 89*, 269 (1981)
17. Bronzetti, G., C. Bauer, C. Corsi, C. Leporini, R. Nieri: *Boll. Soc. ital. Biol. sper. 56*, 1803 (1980)
18. National Toxicology Program (NTP): *Techn. Rep. Ser. No. 362*, USDHHS, NIH Publication, Research Triangle Park, NC 27709, USA, 1989
19. International Agency for Research on Cancer (IARC): *IARC Monographs on the Evaluation of the Carcinogenic Risk of Chemicals to Man*, Vol. 11, p 141, Lyon, France, 1976
20. Hendry, J. A., F. Homer, F. L. Rose: *Brit. J. Pharmacol. 6*, 235 (1951)
21. Kotin, P., H. L. Falk: *Radiat. Res., Suppl. 3*, 193 (1963)
22. Van Duuren, B. L., N. Nelson, L. Orris, E. D. Palmes, F. L. Schmitt: *J. nat. Cancer Inst. 31*, 41 (1963)
23. Watabe, T., A. Hiratsuka, N. Ozawa, M. Isobe: *Xenobiotica 11*, 333 (1981)
24. National Toxicology Program (NTP): Techn. Rep. Ser. No. 303, USDHHS, NIH Publication No. 86-2559, Research Triangle Park, NC 27709, USA, 1986
25. International Agency for Research on Cancer (IARC): *IARC Monographs on the Evaluation of the Carcinogenic Risk of Chemicals to Humans*, Vol. 39, p 183, Lyon, France, 1986
26. Huff, J., R. Melnick, H. Solleveld, J. Haseman, M. Powers: *Science 227*, 548 (1985)

completed 2. 8. 1989

Index for Volume 1